Cape Creek Bridge on the Oregon Coast, U. S. Highway 101. (Courtesy of Oregon State Highway Commission.)

Statically Indeterminate Structural Analysis

R. L. SANKS

PROFESSOR AND CHAIRMAN,
DEPARTMENT OF CIVIL ENGINEERING
GONZAGA UNIVERSITY

THE RONALD PRESS COMPANY · NEW YORK

Library of Congress Catalog Card Number: 61–6785

Dedicated to the memory of my father

JOHN B. SANKS

A self-taught civil engineer

PREFACE

After extensive experimentation in teaching structural analysis the author has found several advantages in approaching the subject by method (e.g., virtual work) rather than by problem type (e.g., truss deflection). In studying by problem type, the student usually meets several different methods of analysis in quick succession; this is confusing, since each method has its own peculiarities. After learning to compute deflections, he then superimposes deflections (method of consistent deflections) to find redundant forces.

In this volume a single method is treated thoroughly in several chapters before a new method is introduced. Therefore, the theory can be developed more deliberately and more rigorously. A normal progression from simple to complex problems is directed not so much toward mere solutions as toward the exposition of the method—the correlation of theory and application. This leads to a more fundamental understanding of indeterminate structural analysis. It is advantageous for the student, because he meets new concepts less frequently, and the chance for confusion is reduced. In order to find redundant forces, the *loads* (including the redundant ones) are superimposed rather than *deflections*. This is, perhaps, a more scientific approach, because loads can always be superimposed, whereas the superposition of deflections is limited to structures in which deflections are not only elastic—but small. Throughout the text, emphasis is placed upon deflections, structural visualization, and the interrelationships between the various methods.

The author has found the approach herein to be so successful that students are likely to have less difficulty with the "indeterminate" phase of analysis than with the application of the principles of equilibrium—a subject in which they are supposed to be thoroughly trained. To assist students in mastering the principles of equilibrium, free body diagrams are extensively shown in the example problems and often explained in the text. Students should be admonished to study the figures meticulously because they contain the very essence of the theory and its application. If confusion persists in spite of repeated readings of the text, the student is advised to copy the related figure, since the deliberation required to do so will usually provide the key to understanding.

This book is primarily a textbook for undergraduate courses. Enough material and advanced topics are included, however, to make it suitable for graduate courses and for reference. It is divided into six parts. Following Part I, Parts II, III, IV, and the first two chapters in Part VI are mutually independent. This permits maximum flexibility in coverage and assignments. Unusually complete explanation is offered in both text and figures to permit serious students to progress on their own.

The author expresses his gratitude to the following: to Professor Emeritus Bruce Jameyson, who developed the formulas for areas and centroids of M/EI diagrams for non-prismatic members, to Professors David Pirtz and Milos Polivka for their approach to the Williot-Mohr diagram, to Professor Emeritus Raymond E. Davis and the University of California for permission to include parts of *Tests on Structural Models of Proposed San Francisco-Oakland Suspension Bridge*, to the Portland Cement Association for the tabular data in Appendix A, to D. L. Sargent for material on influence lines for complex structures, to Dr. Kenneth Bush, to Dr. Egor Popov, to Gregorio Fuentes, and to the Rev. Charles Keenan, S.J., for assistance with the manuscript, to the U. S. Forest Service for plans of the Big Horn Trail bridge, to Professor W. J. Eney, the U. S. Bureau of Reclamation, the California Division of Highways, and the Oregon State Highway Commission for photographs. A special debt is owed to Professors Howard D. Eberhart and Harmer E. Davis for basic training in thinking and writing.

The author is deeply indebted to Mary Sanks for critical review, proof-reading, and typing.

R. L. SANKS

Spokane, Washington
    January, 1961

CONTENTS

PART I

Review of Fundamentals

PART II

Moment Area

PART III

Virtual Work

PART IV

Moment Distribution

CONTENTS

PART V
Other Methods

PART VI
Models

Appendix

Part I

REVIEW OF FUNDAMENTALS

The objective of the structural engineer is the construction of a functional, safe, and economical structure that is beautiful or at least pleasing. His tools are creativity, judgment, elements of design, analysis, communication, and finally experience—personal, vicarious, and historical. It would be difficult to compare the relative importance of each tool, but it is self-evident that the lack of any one could hamper or even hamstring his best efforts.

This book treats one phase of analysis—the analysis of structures too complex to be solved only by equations of static equilibrium. Nevertheless, the principles of static equilibrium are inextricably interwoven with the solution of the more complex structures, so that the book also deals with the principles of static equilibrium—sometimes in considerable detail.

In spite of the singularity of the subject matter, the reader should remember that analysis is only a tool, not an end in itself. The literature is replete with methods of analysis, each proclaimed to be superior by its adherents. Dilettantes are constantly inventing new methods. This is as it should be, for out of these efforts come better ways of doing things. But one should keep his perspective. A method of analysis is of value only if it is ultimately useful to the practicing structural engineer. Since the structural engineer spends more time on communication and on the details of design than he does on analysis, his methods of analysis ought to be simple and universal; he cannot afford to clutter his mind with special methods of limited application just because they may have a slight advantage in speed for a few selected problem types. It is better to know three, or two, or even one method well than to be superficially acquainted with many.

Even before he developed any considerable theoretical knowledge of analysis, man used the other tools of the structural engineer to build some remarkable structures, for example, the Parthenon, the arches in Roman aqueducts and bridges, St. Peter's in Vatican City, the Taj Mahal, and the great cathedrals in France and England. Although a working knowledge of structural behavior can be traced to the ancient Egyptians and Babylonians, Archimedes[1] (287–212 B.C.) was the first to state even the simplest principles

[1] Ernst Mach, *Science of Mathematics*, trans. T. J. McCormack (2d ed; Chicago: Open Court Publishing Co., 1902), pp. 8–19.

1

of the lever. These principles were generalized by da Vinci (1452–1519), who explained the fundamentals of statical moments. Even as late as the time of Galileo (1564–1642), the principles of equilibrium were apparently not generally recognized. In 1678 Hook stated that deformations are proportional to loads. In a paper dated 1776, Coulomb[2] assumed fiber stress in rectangular beams to be proportional to strain and determined correctly the position of the neutral axis and the moment of the internal forces.

The analysis of statically indeterminate structures was made possible in 1825 by Navier,[3,4] who found deflections of beams by double integration and showed that statically indeterminate structures can be solved by considerations of elasticity. In 1857 Clapeyron[5] gave us a more rapid solution for continuous beams with the theorem of three moments. Ten years earlier, Whipple[6] made the first correct analysis of a pin-connected truss, and in 1863 Ritter[7] published the "method of sections" (still the best analytical method) for the analysis of forces in trusses. In 1864 Maxwell[8] invented the stress diagram for the solution of forces in trusses, and in 1877 Williot[9] introduced a graphical method for determining the deflections of a truss. Maxwell[10] also announced, in 1864, the theorem of reciprocal deflections. Mohr[11] in 1874 confirmed the theorem by means of virtual work, and Müller-Breslau[12] extended it to show that certain elastic curves are also influence lines. Since 1924, Beggs,[13] Eney,[14] and others have invented devices which can be used

[2] Augustin Coulomb, "Essai sur une application des règles de maximus et minimus à quelques problèmes de statique, relatifs à l'architecture," *Memoirs de Mathématique et de Physique* (1776), pp. 343–382.

[3] C. L. M. H. Navier, "Sur des questions de statique dans lesquelles on considère un corps pesant supporté par un nombre de points d'appui surpassant trois," *Paris Soc. Philom. Bull.* (1825), pp. 35–37.

[4] Navier, *Résumé des leçons données à l'école des ponts et chaussées sur l'application de la mécanique à l'établissement des constructions et des machines* (Paris: Carilian-Goeury, 1833).

[5] B. P. E. Clapeyron, "Comptes Rendus," *Paris, l'Academie des Sciences*, 45: 1076–1080, 1858.

[6] Squire Whipple, *Elementary and Practical Treatise on Bridge Building* (New York: D. Van Nostrand Co., Inc., 1872).

[7] August Ritter, *Elementare Theorie und Berechnung eiserner Dach- und Brücken-konstruktionen* (Hannover: C. Rumpler, 1870).

[8] James Clerk Maxwell, "On Reciprocal Figures and Diagrams of Forces," *Philosophical Magazine* 27(4): 250–261, 1864.

[9] Williot, "Notations practiques sur la statique graphique," *Annales Génie Civil*, 6: 601–621, 713–727, 1877.

[10] Maxwell, "On the Calculation of the Equilibrium and Stiffness of Frames," *op. cit.*, pp. 294–299.

[11] Otto Mohr, *Abhandlungen aus dem Gebiete der technischen Mechanik* (2d ed; Berlin: Ernst und Sohn, 1914), pp. 390–479.

[12] H. F. B. Müller-Breslau, *Die neuren Methoden der Festigkeitslehre und der Statik der Baukonstruktionen* (Leipzig: Baumgartner, 1893).

[13] George E. Beggs, "An Accurate Mechanical Solution of Statically Indeterminate Structures by Use of Paper Models and Special Gages," *Proc. ACI*, 18: 58–82, 1922.

[14] William J. Eney, "A Large Displacement Deformeter Apparatus for Stress Analysis with Elastic Models," *Eng. News-Record*, 122(7): 221, February 16, 1939.

to construct influence lines mechanically. In 1930 Cross[15] presented moment
distribution, a method that (when applicable) has largely supplanted all
others because of its speed and convenience.[16]

Before the early part of the twentieth century, most bridges and buildings
were designed to be statically determinate, or simple, structures. At the turn
of the century, reinforced concrete came into use, and since it is a material
readily used in continuous (statically indeterminate) structures but poorly
adapted to simple structures, the need for methods of statically indeterminate
structural analysis increased enormously. Another impetus to the use of such
analysis resulted from the growing importance of arc welding, which makes
continuous steel frameworks feasible and economical. Nowadays, most
structures must be studied—at least to some extent—by methods of indeterminate analysis.

A thorough understanding of the principles of static equilibrium is of
paramount importance in indeterminate analysis. Therefore, Part I is a
restatement and a review of those principles that are widely applied to
indeterminate methods.

[15] Hardy Cross, "Analysis of Continuous Frames by Distributing Fixed-End
Moments," *Proc. ASCE*, May, 1930. *Op. cit.* with discussions, *Trans. ASCE*, 96: 1–156,
1932.
[16] These historical notes are by no means complete. See: H. M. Westergaard, "One
Hundred Fifty Years Advance in Structural Analysis," *Trans. ASCE*, 94: 226–240,
1930; J. I. Parcel and G. A. Maney, *An Elementary Treatise on Statically Indeterminate
Stresses* (2d ed; New York: John Wiley & Sons, Inc., 1936), pp. 413–420; and J. Sterling
Kinney, *Indeterminate Structural Analysis* (Reading, Mass: Addison-Wesley Publishing
Co., Inc., 1957), pp. 1–16.

1

EQUILIBRIUM

1–1. Symbols and Conventions. Certain symbols and conventions are almost universally used in order to save time. It is worth while to review them here because often they are not meant to be accepted at face value.

Individual members in figures are represented by heavy solid lines which are actually the centerlines of the real members. The depth or width of such members is usually—though not always—ignored in sketching, and loads are projected to the centerline along their lines of action.

SUPPORTS. Rigid supports are shown in Fig. 1–1A. As supports for simple cantilever beams they are considered truly immovable. However, that interpretation applied to a beam fixed at both ends would result in six reaction components—shear, thrust (i.e., tension), and moment at each end. A beam truly fixed at both ends would stretch as it bends, creating a tensile force within the beam which would result in appreciable horizontal reactions. Practically, it is not possible to build supports to withstand such loads without movement, so it is usually assumed that deflection does not cause thrust. This is equivalent to considering one of the fixed reactions to be a guided reaction—able to resist rotation and vertical forces but free to move horizontally. When fixed reactions are shown at both ends of the beam, all the horizontal loads are assumed to be resisted by only one of the

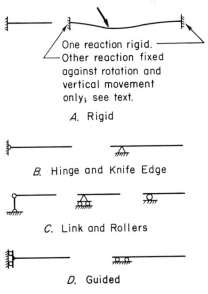

One reaction rigid.
Other reaction fixed against rotation and vertical movement only; see text.

A. Rigid

B. Hinge and Knife Edge

C. Link and Rollers

D. Guided

Fig. 1–1. Supports.

supports, or sometimes the horizontal loads are considered to be equally divided between the two supports.

Knife-edge or hinge supports are represented by the symbols shown in Fig. 1–1B. These two supports indicate the same conditions and are assumed to prevent all movement except rotation. Thus a knife edge can supply a

5

downward reaction as well as an upward one. The beam cannot slide on a knife edge. Either a knife edge or a hinge would be used, for example, to represent a seat angle supporting a beam and bolted to it; the angle resists loads acting down and the bolts resist uplift and sliding. It would also be used to represent the flexible connections shown in Fig. 1–3*A*.

Links and rollers are indicated by the symbols of Fig. 1–1*C*. These symbols are interchangeable; all indicate freedom of horizontal movement and rotation but restraint against any vertical movement—either up or down.

Guided reactions are met occasionally. Two are shown in Fig. 1–1*D*. The left one obviously indicates freedom of vertical movement but restraint against rotation or horizontal movement; the right one provides restraint only against rotation and vertical movement. The kind of restraint of other guided reactions can be drawn similarly.

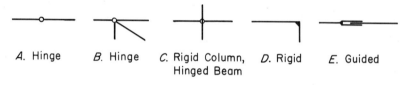

| *A*. Hinge | *B*. Hinge | *C*. Rigid Column, Hinged Beam | *D*. Rigid | *E*. Guided |

Fig. I–2. Joints.

JOINTS. Joints or connections are generally assumed to be rigid except in trusses, where they are ordinarily pin-connected. The joints of Figs. 1–2*A* and 1–2*B* are unmistakably pinned. The joint shown in Fig. 1–2*C* indicates that the column (vertical member) is continuous, but the beam is pin-connected to it. On the other hand, the joint of Fig. 1–2*D* is unmistakably rigid. The guided joint of Fig. 1–2*E* provides freedom of axial movement but restraint against shear and moment. The type of problem usually indicates whether the joints are to be considered pin-connected or rigid, so unless there are some unusual conditions these symbols are customarily omitted.

LOADS. Loads are usually given in kips. The word "kip" is an abbreviation of "kilo-pound," which is 1000 pounds. A uniform load of 2000 pounds per foot is written 2 kips/ft. Moments are usually given in terms of kips times feet, abbreviated kip-ft.

I–2. Equations of Static Equilibrium. This article should contain nothing new to the reader. Nevertheless, a restatement is not amiss because, in general, most student difficulties stem from a weakness in statics.

The principles of static equilibrium are basic to the solution of both statically determinate and statically indeterminate structures. As applied to plane structures (whose members and loads lie in a single plane), these principles can be expressed by three equations of static equilibrium:

$$\Sigma M = 0 \qquad (1–1)$$
$$\Sigma H = 0 \qquad (1–2)$$
$$\Sigma V = 0 \qquad (1–3)$$

where M is a moment (force $\times$ distance), H is the horizontal component of a force, and V is the vertical component of a force. In three-dimensional problems (space structures), there are three additional equations which can be expressed as:

$$\Sigma M_{XZ} = 0 \qquad\qquad\qquad (1\text{–}4)$$
$$\Sigma M_{YZ} = 0 \qquad\qquad\qquad (1\text{–}5)$$
$$\Sigma Z = 0 \qquad\qquad\qquad (1\text{–}6)$$

where M_{XZ} is a moment in the XZ plane, M_{YZ} is a moment in the YZ plane, and Z represents a force component perpendicular to the plane in which H and V act. In Eq. 1–1, M is a moment in the XY plane.

Most structural engineering problems can be resolved into plane-stress problems, and as the scope of this text is limited to plane problems, no further use is made of Eqs. 1–4, 1–5, and 1–6.

FREE BODIES. Equations 1–1, 1–2, and 1–3 are always used to evaluate forces acting upon a free body. A free body may be either an entire structure or a portion of a structure. The free body must always be accompanied by *all* the forces acting upon it. If the free body is the entire structure, the forces must include all the loads and all the reactions. If the free body is only a portion of the structure—made by cutting away the unwanted portions—the real stresses in the cut members must be replaced by equivalent forces.

Consider the beam of Fig. 1–3A acted upon by any loads such as P_1, P_2, and P_3. In actual practice, the beam would be isolated from the rest of the structure and idealized by assuming the clip angle connections to be replaced with a knife-edge support at the centerline of the left support (column) and a roller at the right (or vice versa), and the beam itself would usually be assumed to have no depth. Hence, the beam can be represented by a single, heavy line, as shown in Fig. 1–3B. Of course, these assumptions violate the actual conditions to some degree, and the analysis will be in error to that same degree.

A free body of the entire beam can be made by passing a cutting line between the beam and its supports, and the supports must be replaced with equivalent forces, as shown in Fig. 1–3C. Note that the equivalent forces are circumscribed by the assumptions made in idealizing the beam and its connections. The clip angle at the right is certainly capable of resisting some of the horizontal load, but, since the assumptions included a roller at the right end, a free body of the beam based on those assumptions can show no horizontal force at the right end. Thus, there are three unknown forces: H_A, V_A, and V_B. Since there are three equations of equilibrium as well, the three unknown reaction components may be found by making use of Eqs. 1–1, 1–2, and 1–3 in turn.

Forces at any point in the beam can be found by passing a cutting line through the point. Since it is possible for any member to contain shear or transverse force, thrust or axial force, and moment or bending (unless assumptions or special conditions decree otherwise), the cut-away material must be replaced with these three forces, as illustrated in Fig. 1–3D. All the other forces are known in magnitude (H_A and V_A have been found according to the preceding paragraph); so V_O, H_O, and M_O can be determined by the equations of equilibrium just as the reactions were.

It is always necessary to know the position and orientation of the line of action of an unknown force, but it is never necessary to know in which

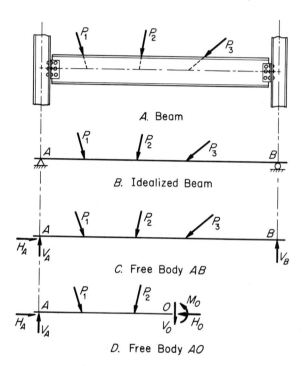

A. Beam

B. Idealized Beam

C. Free Body *AB*

D. Free Body *AO*

Fig. 1–3. Free bodies of a beam.

direction (sense) the force acts. A direction may always be assumed. If the solution shows a plus force, the assumed direction is correct. If the solution yields a minus force, the force acts opposite to the direction assumed.

Reactions for a truss are found in the same way as those for a beam. Forces in the members are found by passing a cutting line through the members whose forces are wanted. A typical roof truss is shown in Fig. 1–4A. It is idealized and shown with its loads in Fig. 1–4B, and a free body is shown in Fig. 1–4C. According to a previous statement, each cut member may contain shear, thrust, and moment, resulting in the nine unknowns shown in Fig. 1–4C. But if the usual assumptions are employed, the members are considered to be pin-connected. Therefore, moments at the ends of each member are zero, shears (transverse) forces are zero, and the only forces remaining are those that are axial. Thus the number of unknowns is reduced

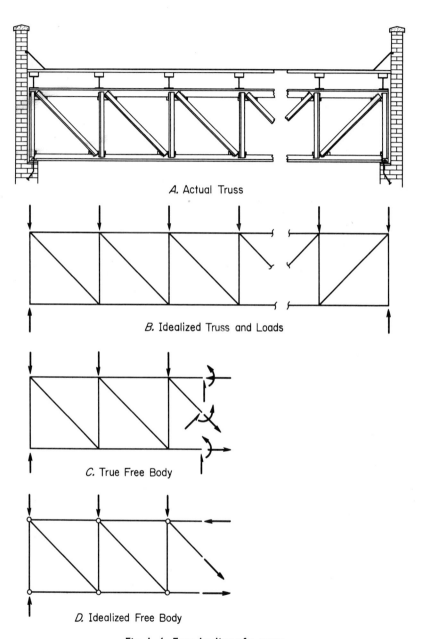

A. Actual Truss

B. Idealized Truss and Loads

C. True Free Body

D. Idealized Free Body

Fig. I–4. Free bodies of a truss.

to the three unknown axial forces shown in Fig. 1–4*D*. Since there are only three unknowns, the three equations of equilibrium are sufficient for a solution.

These principles, briefly illustrated here, are always applicable to every structure and to every portion of every structure. That is to say, every free body must be in equilibrium under the action of all of the forces acting on that free body—otherwise the structure will move until its forces *are* in equilibrium. Think of every free body as a physical entity—a real structure—suspended and motionless under the action of *all* forces applied to it.

1–3. Definition of Indeterminate. A structure is indeterminate (or more properly, its forces are indeterminate) when the equations of equilibrium alone are insufficient for obtaining a solution. If the reactions cannot be found from equations of equilibrium, it is externally indeterminate; if the reactions are known but the forces in any or all the members cannot be so determined, it is internally indeterminate.

Indeterminate forces, whether internal or external, must be found by consideration of the deformation within the structure. For most structures, the deformation caused by design loads is essentially elastic. Some inelastic deformation is nearly always present (particularly near fastenings such as rivets or welds), but it is usually localized and does not appreciably affect the primary forces in the members even though localized strains may be very high. Inelastic deformation is, therefore, commonly ignored.[1] If inelastic deformation is appreciable, it cannot, of course, be ignored. Regardless of the kind of deformation, the effect must be evaluated in some way to solve the indeterminate forces.

1–4. Stability and Indeterminacy. Structures are unstable, stable, determinate, or indeterminate depending on the comparison of the number of unknown reactions and the number of equations of equilibrium and condition.

If there are more equations of equilibrium and condition than there are reaction components, the structure is unstable and would collapse under a generalized loading condition. If the number of reaction components equals the number of equations of equilibrium and condition, the structure is stable and determinate. If the reaction components outnumber the equations, the structure is indeterminate. The degree of indeterminacy depends upon the deficit in equations. If there are, say, four equations and six unknown reaction components, the structure is indeterminate to

$$6 - 4 = 2 \text{ degrees}$$

[1] "Limit," "plastic," or "ultimate" strength design theory is based on assumptions of inelastic strains. However, these methods are often more concerned with design than with analysis, and are sometimes based—at least in part—upon elastic analysis. Even when the analysis is based primarily on inelastic deformation, a knowledge of elastic theory is still necessary.

Therefore two equations of elasticity must be added before a solution can be obtained.

EQUATIONS OF EQUILIBRIUM. There are *always* three equations of equilibrium. They are Eqs. 1–1, 1–2, and 1–3.

EQUATIONS OF CONDITION. Special features within a structure may lead to equations of condition. A hinge within a structure is the most common special condition; it insures that the moment at that point is zero. Thus it adds one equation to the three equations of equilibrium, making a total of four. Two hinges would add two additional equations, etc.

Any special type of construction that produces a definite value of shear, thrust, or moment adds one equation of condition for each value so determined. Thus a link in a cantilever bridge that reduces moment and thrust to zero but does transmit shear produces two equations of condition.

INSTABILITY. If all the reactive forces are parallel or if all are concurrent (meet at a single point), the structure is always unstable.

Special loads can be applied to an unstable structure without necessarily causing collapse. In such cases, the structures are said to be in a state of unstable equilibrium.

Example 1–4. The application of the above statements will now be tested on the structures shown in Fig. 1–5.

A. One possible reaction component, a vertical force at the roller; three available equations of equilibrium. The structure is unstable.

B. Two reaction components at the knife edge; three equations of equilibrium. The structure is unstable.

C. Three reaction components and three equations of equilibrium. However, all reactions are parallel, so according to a previous statement, the structure is unstable.

D. Three reaction components are concurrent, so the structure is unstable.

E. Three reaction components and three equations of equilibrium. The structure is stable and determinate.

F. Three reaction components—two at the hinge and one at the roller. Do not be misled into thinking that there are two unknowns at the roller just because it may have two reaction components (vertical and horizontal). The relation between the two components is fixed by the slope; if one is known, the other is automatically determined. There is only one unknown at the roller. The structure is stable and determinate.

G. Three unknown reactions and three equations of equilibrium. The structure is stable and determinate. If you like, you can consider that there are nine unknowns—three reaction components (shear, thrust, and moment) at the base of each of the three supports. Then six hinges furnish six equations of condition, and there are three equations of equilibrium, so there is a total of nine equations to solve the nine unknowns. The structure is stable and determinate by this method of reasoning also.

H. Six unknowns and three equations. Indetermniate to the third degree.

I. Six unknowns; three equations of equilibrium plus two equations (one for each hinge) of condition. Indeterminate to the first degree.

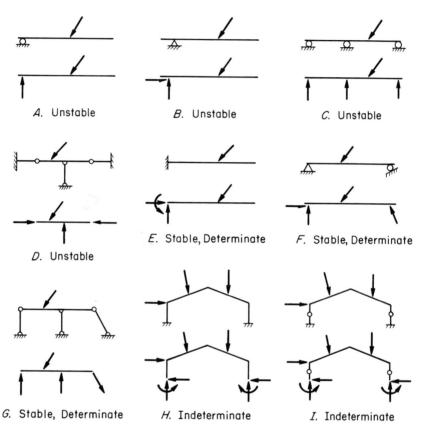

Fig. 1–5. Unstable to indeterminate beams and frames.

These principles are applicable to any structure, including the trusses shown in Fig. 1–6.

A. Externally determinate. Only one inclined web member per panel is required for stability. Since there are three extra members not required for stability (called redundant members), it is internally indeterminate to the third degree. Another, less direct, way to figure the indeterminacy is to consider free bodies made by cutting vertically through each of the three panels in turn. Every such free body contains four unknowns, and for each there are three equations of equilibrium, leaving a deficit of one equation for each of the three panels.

B. It may look indeterminate or even unstable, but it is, on the contrary, both stable and determinate. In some of the panels a vertical section cuts only three members; there being three equations of equilibrium, forces in these

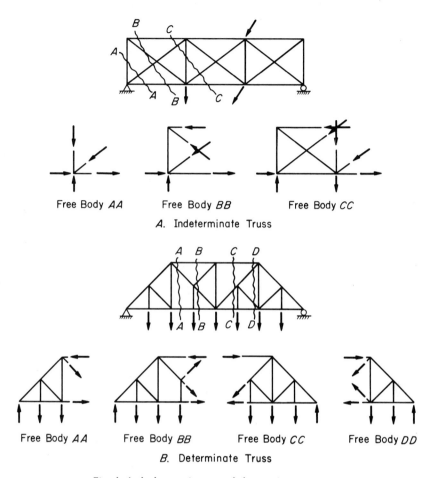

Fig. I-6. Indeterminate and determinate trusses.

members are determinate. Thus the forces in the upper chord are known. Now no other vertical section can possibly cut more than three unknowns, and these also can be solved. By proceeding thus in the proper order, forces in all members can be computed.

2

MOMENT DIAGRAMS

2–1. Load, Shear, and Moment. Certain definite relationships exist between diagrams of load, shear, and moment. These relationships are often helpful in drawing moment diagrams.

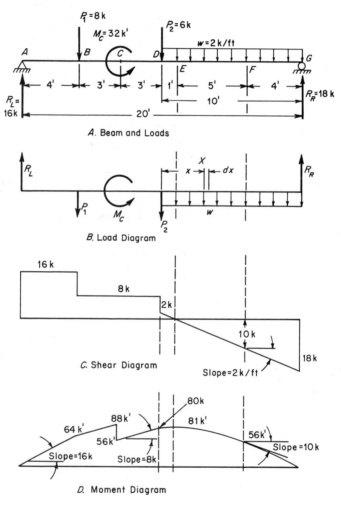

Fig. 2–1. Load, shear, and moment diagrams.

Several kinds of loads—enough to demonstrate all the principles—are shown acting upon the beam of Fig. 2–1*A*. It is common practice to show the loads *pushing* against the beam and, since that practice is the one most widely used, it is followed here.

The load diagram in Fig. 2–1*B* shows the loads *pulling* on the beam. The load diagram is helpful for visualizing the relationships between load, shear, and moment and is indispensable for preserving a consistent convention for signs.

Shear at a section or point is defined as the sum of all transverse forces to the left of the section. When the sum of the forces to the left acts upward, the shear is always considered positive. Since the sum of all forces must—from the equations of equilibrium—be zero, it follows that the forces to the left must equal the forces to the right. Thus shear is also defined as the sum of all transverse forces to the right, and when those forces act down, the shear is positive. The shear diagram in Fig. 2–1*C* is simply a plot of the shear at every point in the beam.

Bending moment (or simply "moment") is defined as the sum of the moments of all forces to the left. Since moments of all forces must be zero (again from the equation of equilibrium), it follows that bending moment can also be defined as the sum of the moments of all forces to the right. Bending moment is considered positive when the uppermost fibers in the beam are in compression. The bending-moment diagram in Fig. 2–1*D* is a plot of bending moment at every point in the beam. Because of the sign convention assumed, the bending-moment diagrams are always plotted on the side of compression in the beam.[1]

ORDINATES. The ordinate of any diagram is equal in magnitude and sign to the slope of the diagram below. Ordinates above the base are positive; those below are negative. Slope is positive up and to the right ($/$), and it is negative down and to the right ($\backslash$).

Between A and B in Fig. 2–1*B*, the ordinate of the load diagram is zero; the slope of the diagram below (shear diagram, Fig. 2–1*C*) is also zero. At F, for example, the ordinate of the load diagram is -2 kips/ft; the slope of the shear diagram is also -2 kips/ft.

Between A and B, the ordinate of the shear diagram is 16 kips; the slope of the moment diagram equals

$$64 \text{ kip-ft}/4 \text{ ft} = 16 \text{ kip-ft/ft} = 16 \text{ kips}$$

At F, for example, the ordinate of the shear diagram is -10 kips, and so the slope of the moment diagram is also -10 kips.

---

[1] Some writers use the reverse of this convention—moment is positive when the uppermost fibers are in tension. Then the moment diagrams are plotted on the side of tension. It does not matter at all which convention is used, but the one stated above is more common and, for that reason, is preferred herein.

In summary: ordinate of load equals slope of shear, and ordinate of shear equals slope of moment. The only exception occurs at an applied moment such as M_C. The shear at this point is only 8 kips, but the slope of the moment diagram is infinite. The slope of the moment diagram is always infinite at an applied moment.

AREAS. Between any two points, the area of a diagram is equal in magnitude and sign to the change of ordinate in the diagram below it. Areas above the base are positive, and distances to the right are positive. Areas below the base are negative, and distances to the left are negative.

For example, between A and B in Fig. 2–1, the area of the load diagram is zero and so is the change of ordinate in the shear diagram below. Between F and G, the area of the load diagram is

$$(-2 \text{ kips/ft})(+4 \text{ ft}) = -8 \text{ kips}$$

which is equal in sign and magnitude to the change in ordinate of the shear diagram from F to G. The rule works from right to left just as well. Then the area of the load diagram is

$$(-2 \text{ kips/ft})(-4 \text{ ft}) = +8 \text{ kips}$$

which is equal in sign and magnitude to the change in ordinate of the shear diagram from G to F.

Between A and B, the area of the shear diagram is

$$(+16 \text{ kips})(+4 \text{ ft}) = +64 \text{ kip-ft}$$

which is equal to the change of moment from A to B. Between E and F, the area of the shear diagram is

$$\tfrac{1}{2}(-10 \text{ kips})(+5 \text{ ft}) = -25 \text{ kip-ft}$$

which is the change in the ordinate of the moment diagram from E to F. Again, the rule works just as well from right to left. From G to F, the area of the shear diagram is

$$\left(\frac{-18 \text{ kips} - 10 \text{ kips}}{2}\right)(-4 \text{ ft}) = +56 \text{ kip-ft}$$

which is the change of moment from G to F.

The only exception to this rule occurs at the point of application of an external moment such as at C where M_C is applied. At such points the moment diagram always changes abruptly, even though the shear be constant. The rule works everywhere else, however, as can be verified by computing the shear diagram area between A and C (it equals 88 kip-ft) and again by computing the shear diagram area between G and C (it equals 56 kip-ft).

In summary: area of load diagram equals change of shear, and area of shear diagram equals change of moment.

MAXIMUM MOMENT. Recall that the shear equals the slope of the moment diagram. It gives rise to a useful relationship. When the shear is zero, the slope of the moment diagram must be zero, and in real structures this nearly always indicates a point of maximum or minimum moment. To locate a point of maximum moment, locate the point of zero shear. The rule is not infallible, however, as inspection of Fig. 2–1D will show. There is a maximum moment at E, the point of zero shear, but there is another, greater maximum moment at C. The shear diagram, then, is not an indicator of maximum moment at the point of application of an applied external moment.

PROOF. The numerical value of each critical point on the shear and moment diagrams can be computed directly according to the definition of shear and moment. These values correspond exactly with those obtained by using the rules stated herein. This is evidence of the validity of the rules, although it cannot be called "proof."

A more rigorous proof can be established as follows. In Fig. 2–1B, let X be a point at the distance x to the right of D; let dx be an infinitesimal distance to the right of point X; let V and M be shear and moment respectively at X, and V' and M' be shear and moment, respectively, dx to the right of X. According to the definition of shear,

$$V = R_L - P_1 - P_2 - wx$$

and

$$V' = R_L - P_1 - P_2 - w(x + dx)$$

Subtracting,

$$V' - V = -w\, dx$$

but

$$V' - V = dV, \text{ the change in shear}$$

so

$$dV = -w\, dx \tag{2-1}$$

That is, change of shear equals area of load diagram. Dividing,

$$\frac{dV}{dx} = -w \tag{2-2}$$

That is, slope of shear diagram equals ordinate of load diagram. According to the definition of moment,

$$M = R_L(\overline{AD} + x) - P_1(\overline{BD} + x) - M_C - P_2 x - \frac{wx^2}{2}$$

and

$$M' = R_L(\overline{AD} + x + dx) - P_1(\overline{BD} + x + dx) - M_C - P_2(x + dx)$$
$$- \frac{w(x + dx)^2}{2}$$

Subtracting,

$$M' - M = R_L\, dx - P_1\, dx - P_2\, dx - wx\, dx - \frac{w(dx)^2}{2}$$

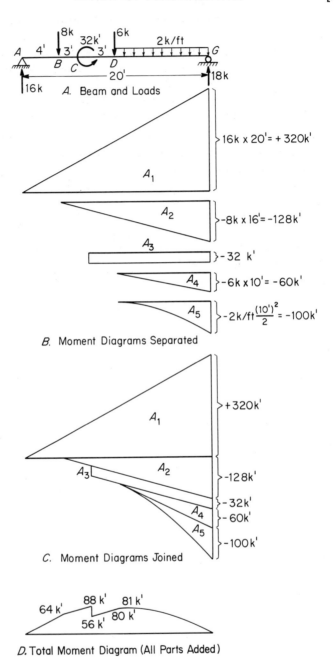

A. Beam and Loads

$16k \times 20' = +320k'$

A_1

A_2

$-8k \times 16' = -128k'$

A_3

$-32 \ k'$

A_4

$-6k \times 10' = -60k'$

A_5

$-2k/ft \dfrac{(10')^2}{2} = -100k'$

B. Moment Diagrams Separated

$+320k'$

A_1

A_3

A_2

$-128k'$

$-32k'$

A_4

$-60k'$

A_5

$-100k'$

C. Moment Diagrams Joined

64 k'   88 k'   81 k'

56 k'   80 k'

D. Total Moment Diagram (All Parts Added)

Fig. 2-2. Moment diagrams. Cantilever parts from left.

But

$$M' - M = dM, \text{ the change in moment}$$

and second-order differentials may be dropped, so

$$dM = R_L\, dx - P_1\, dx - P_2\, dx - wx\, dx = (R_L - P_1 - P_2 - wx)\, dx$$

Substituting,

$$V = R_L - P_1 - P_2 - wx$$

$$dM = V\, dx \tag{2–3}$$

That is, change of moment equals area of shear diagram. Dividing,

$$\frac{dM}{dx} = V \tag{2–4}$$

That is, slope of moment diagram equals ordinate of shear diagram (or, simply, "shear").

2–2. Moment Diagrams in Cantilever Parts. Indeterminate analysis of continuous beams and rigid frames constantly deals with the areas and centroids of moment diagrams. The shape of a total moment diagram is usually much too complicated to deal with as a whole, so it is necessary to break it into several simple parts that can be handled more easily. There are two rational systems: one is to draw moment diagrams in cantilever parts and the other (Art. 2–5) is to draw them in simple beam parts. It is not sufficient to know just one, for each has advantages and limitations.

SIMPLE BEAMS. Moment diagrams in cantilever parts are drawn for each separate force to the left (or to the right) of any section. This is equivalent[2] to assuming a fixed support at the right (or left) and treating all real supports as loads.

Moment diagrams in cantilever parts from the left are shown in Fig. 2–2. The beam is identical to that of Fig. 2–1. Starting at the left, the moment diagram for each force, in turn, is plotted individually, as shown in Fig. 2–2B. According to our sign convention (Art. 2–1), the moment diagrams are plotted on the compressive side. Thus the left reaction, considered alone, would cause compression along the upper fibers; the moment diagram is therefore positive and plotted above the base. All the other moment diagrams are negative by the same reasoning and are plotted below the base. It is a waste of space and often inconvenient to separate the diagrams this way, so they are usually joined, as shown in Fig. 2–2C, with each succeeding moment diagram stacked upon the last. The two figures (Figs. 2–2B and 2–2C) are identical. If all the parts of Fig. 2–2B or Fig. 2–2C are added, the total

---

[2] Equivalent only with respect to moment diagrams. The assumption of a fixed support is not truly equivalent with respect to deflection. The system described is simply a convenient way to break up the total moment diagram into several easy-to-handle parts.

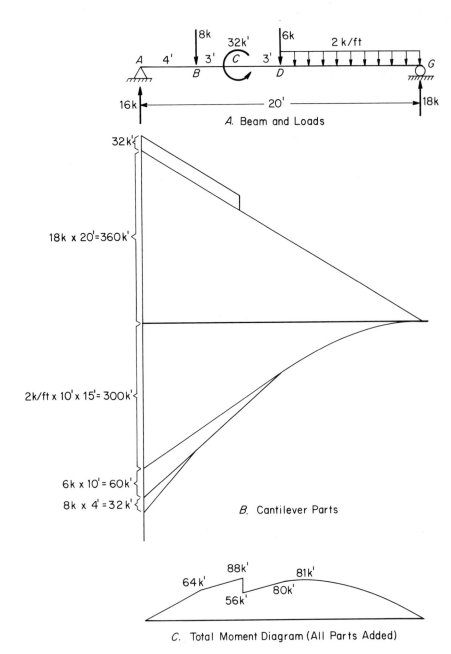

A. Beam and Loads

B. Cantilever Parts

C. Total Moment Diagram (All Parts Added)

Fig. 2–3. Moment diagrams. Cantilever parts from right.

moment diagram of Fig. 2–2D is obtained. It is identical to Fig. 2–1D, a fact which demonstrates the validity of the construction of moment diagrams in cantilever parts.

Moment diagrams in cantilever parts from the right are shown in Fig. 2–3. The construction is similar, but we start from the right. Again, the parts add to the same total moment diagram of Figs. 2–1 and 2–2.

CONTINUOUS BEAMS AND FRAMES. The drawing of moment diagrams in cantilever parts for a portion of a rigid frame is illustrated in Fig. 2–4. The principles and the details are the same as for simple beams. Moment diagrams for the member CD are drawn considering separately V, M, and H (which cause compression in the upper fibers and are therefore positive) and then the uniform load (which causes compression on the bottom and is therefore negative).

The moment diagram for the uniform load is a parabola with its vertex at point B. Areas and centroids of parabolas can be found by simple formulas,[3] but formulas for segments of parabolas are less simple. The moment diagram from C to D can be transformed into a parabola instead of a parabolic segment by the construction of Figs. 2–4C and 2–4D. On a free body of CD there is, acting at C, a moment of $[(3 \text{ kips/ft})(6 \text{ ft})^2]/2 = 54$ kip-ft and a shear of $(3 \text{ kips/ft})(6 \text{ ft}) = 18$ kips caused by the uniform load from B to C. There is also the uniform load along the full length of the free body as well as the effects of M, V, and H. Moment diagrams for the 54-kip-ft moment, the 18-kip shear, and the uniform load are shown in Fig. 2–4D. The curved portion is a parabola. Thus a parabolic segment can be divided into a rectangle, a triangle, and a parabola.

2–3. Signs of Moments. Occasionally there is some uncertainty about the direction of a moment in a rigid frame, that is, doubt about which side is in compression. There is no guesswork or magic involved, and straightforward mechanics will always indicate the sign beyond doubt.

The frame of Fig. 2–5A furnishes a good example. To determine the sign of the bending moment at section XX caused by any load, say M, ignore all other loads on the frame and then draw free body AX (Fig. 2–5B). To satisfy equilibrium, a counterclockwise moment must act at section XX to balance the clockwise moment at A. Now consider a short free body of the frame above section XX as in Fig. 2–5C. The moment at the bottom is counterclockwise, as we have seen; the moment at the top must be equal and opposite to satisfy equilibrium. Thus the short section bends concave to the right, and the fibers in compression are on the right. Can there be any doubt about it? If there is, apply similar moments to a short, flexible spline held in your hands.

Or consider the sign of the moment caused by H. Again, load the frame with force H only and draw free body AX with all its forces and reactions,

[3] See Art. 3–1.

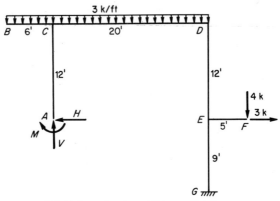

A. Rigid Frame, Loads, and Unknown Reactions

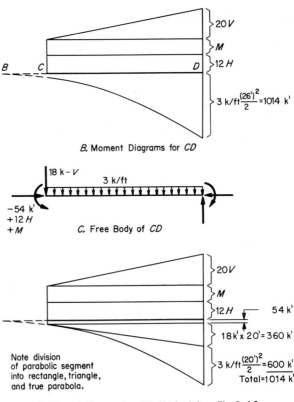

B. Moment Diagrams for *CD*

C. Free Body of *CD*

Note division
of parabolic segment
into rectangle, triangle,
and true parabola.

D. Moment Diagram for *CD* Obtained from Fig. 2-4C

Fig. 2–4. Moment diagrams in cantilever parts for member
CD of rigid frame.

as in Fig. 2–5D. The force H applied at point A acts clockwise[4] at section XX, so there must be a balancing, counterclockwise moment at section XX. As we have seen in Fig. 2–5C, such a counterclockwise balancing moment causes compression on the right.

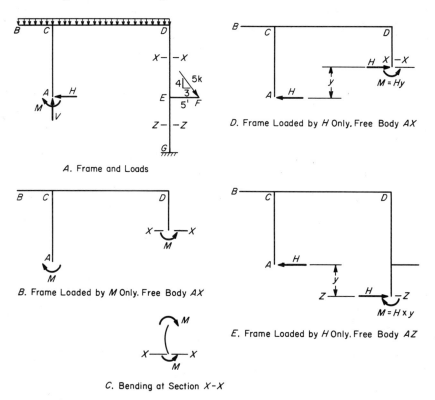

A. Frame and Loads

B. Frame Loaded by M Only. Free Body AX

C. Bending at Section X-X

D. Frame Loaded by H Only. Free Body AX

E. Frame Loaded by H Only. Free Body AZ

Fig. 2–5. Direction of bending moments.

In Fig. 2–5E, on the other hand, H applied at point A acts counterclockwise[5] at section ZZ, so that the balancing moment at section ZZ is clockwise. Such a moment, opposite to that shown in Fig. 2–5C, would cause compression on the left.

This line of reasoning takes a little time and requires a few freehand sketches and, perhaps, some paper models. But it is always a dependable method.

---

[4] Prove it by copying this figure on a sheet of paper. Stick a pin through the member at section XX into a drawing board, so that the paper can rotate about the pin. Apply a horizontal force with a long wire hooked through point A. (A straightened paper clip will do.) The paper will rotate clockwise.

[5] Try the pin, paper, and paper clip on this one too. The paper will rotate counterclockwise.

2–4. Moment Equations. Sometimes it is necessary to express the moment diagrams in terms of equations to permit a solution by calculus. The moment equation is merely an algebraic expression for the moment diagram in cantilever parts. Each term of the moment equation represents one of the cantilever parts. There is one unfortunate characteristic of a moment equation; one equation cannot be written for the full length of the beam if there are load changes or concentrated loads on the beam. That is, the equation must be changed at each load. The following example will clarify this statement.

Example 2–4A. Let us write moment equations for the beam of Fig. 2–1. Let x be any variable distance from the left reaction. Then the moment from A to B is

$$M_{A\text{-}B} = +16 \text{ kips} \times x = +16x$$

And that is all. The signs follow the convention previously stated. This one is plus because it causes compression in the top fibers. From B to C, the lever arm to the reaction is x according to the definition above, but the lever arm to the concentrated load of 8 kips is $x - 4$ ft; so the moment is

$$M_{B\text{-}C} = +16 \text{ kips} \times x - 8 \text{ kips} (x - 4 \text{ ft}) = +8x + 32$$

When x increases enough to reach point C, a new moment of -32 kip-ft is suddenly introduced, so between C and D the moment is

$$M_{C\text{-}D} = +16 \text{ kips} \times x - 8 \text{ kips} (x - 4 \text{ ft}) - 32 \text{ kip-ft} = +8x$$

Between D and G, the moment[6] can be expressed,

$$M_{D\text{-}G} = +16 \text{ kips} \times x - 8 \text{ kips} (x - 4 \text{ ft}) - 32 \text{ kip-ft} - 6 \text{ kips} (x - 10 \text{ ft})$$

$$- (2 \text{ kips/ft}) \frac{(x - 10 \text{ ft})^2}{2}$$

$$M_{D\text{-}G} = -40 + 22x - x^2$$

Example 2–4B. For another example, let us write the moment equation for member CD of Fig. 2–4. We must account for the loads H, M, and V at point A, and for the uniform load from B to D. One way to account for the uniform load is to resolve the load from B to C into a shear and a moment, as shown in Fig. 2–4C. Letting x be any variable distance from C, the expression for moment is

$$M_{C\text{-}D} = 12H + M + Vx - 18 \text{ kips} \times x - 54 \text{ kip-ft} - (3 \text{ kips/ft}) \frac{x^2}{2}$$

$$M_{C\text{-}D} = 12H + M + (V - 18)x - 54 - \frac{3x^2}{2}$$

[6] See Table 3–1 for the expression of moment for uniform loads.

Another way to account for the uniform load is to express the moment due to the uniform load in terms of the full distance from B. Then letting x be a variable distance measured (as before) from C, we have

$$M_{\text{due uniform load}} = (3 \text{ kips/ft}) \frac{(x + 6 \text{ ft})^2}{2}$$

Then the expression for total moment is

$$M_{C\text{-}D} = 12H + M + Vx - (3 \text{ kips/ft}) \frac{(x + 6 \text{ ft})^2}{2}$$

When the terms are expanded and collected, there results

$$M_{C\text{-}D} = 12H + M + (V - 18)x - 54 - \frac{3x^2}{2}$$

exactly as before.

Example 2–4C. Still another way to write moments is to let x be any variable distance from point B. Then

$$M_{C\text{-}D} = 12H + M + V(x - 6 \text{ ft}) - (3 \text{ kips/ft}) \frac{x^2}{2}$$

So there are scores of ways to write expressions for moments, but all follow the same principle: write the expression "force × distance" for each force separately in terms of a variable distance, and supply that expression with the proper sign.

2–5. Moment Diagrams in Simple Beam Parts. Drawing moment diagrams in simple beam parts is preferred at interior spans of continuous structures, particularly when there are many loads in the exterior spans. Simple beam parts are ideal for solutions by moment distribution.

Except for the reactions, which are always assumed to be a knife-edge support at one end and a roller support at the other, moment diagrams are drawn for each load or set of loads. Thus we conceive of several beams, each simply supported at the ends, with one load acting on each beam which must be in equilibrium under the action of that load and the two supports. This is illustrated in Fig. 2–6.

Example 2–5A. Each load shown in Fig. 2–6A is separately applied to a simply supported beam, as shown in Fig. 2–6B. The reactions are not considered as loads. Each beam must be in equilibrium. Then the moment diagram for each beam is drawn as shown in Fig. 2–6C. If all these are added, the total moment diagram (Fig. 2–6D) is identical to the one obtained by cantilever parts (Figs. 2–2D and 2–3C). If the left reactions of the simple beams of Fig. 2–6B are added, the result is 16 kips, the same value that is found in Fig. 2–6A.

Example 2–5B. Rigid Frame. Moments in the rigid frame of Fig. 2–7A are solved by moment distribution, as shown in Figs. 14–2 to 14–5. The signs of these moments indicate whether the moments act clockwise (plus) or

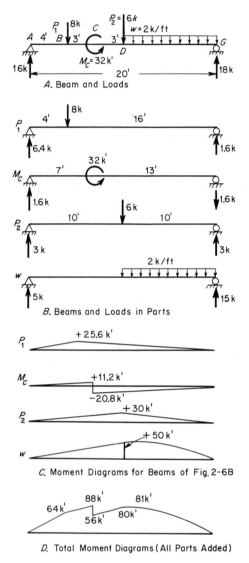

counterclockwise (minus) on a free body of the member. The moment at the left end of CD is given as -18 kip-ft, so it acts counterclockwise on CD, as shown in Fig. 2–7B. The other forces[7] acting on the free body CD are found from free bodies of portions of the frame by using the moments given in Fig. 2–7A.

The beam is assumed to be simply supported (by a knife edge and a roller), and each load, in turn, is applied to the beam, as shown in Fig. 2–7C. These loads are: the uniform load, the moment of 18 kip-ft at the left, and the moment of 52 kip-ft at the right. The shears at each end are not considered as *loads*; they are considered as *reactions*, and each beam (marked w, M_C, and M_D) must be in equilibrium under the action of its load and its reactions. The sum of the left reactions is 10.3 kips, which is the true shear on the free body at C.

Moment diagrams drawn for each of the beams are shown in Fig. 2–7D. For the uniform load, the moment diagram is the typical symmetrical parabola whose maximum value is

$$\frac{wL^2}{8} = 60 \text{ kip-ft}$$

A. Beam and Loads

B. Beams and Loads in Parts

C. Moment Diagrams for Beams of Fig. 2-6B

D. Total Moment Diagrams (All Parts Added)

Fig. 2–6. Moment diagrams. Simple beam parts.

The moment diagram for M_C is a triangle with a maximum value at the left of -18 kip-ft, and for M_D, a triangle with a maximum value at the right of

---

[7] The mechanics of finding these forces is explained in detail in Arts. 13–4 and 14–2.

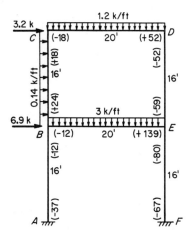

Note: Figures in ( ) are total moments in k'; plus indicates clockwise moment.

A. Frame, Loads, and Moments

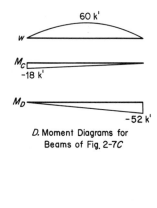

D. Moment Diagrams for Beams of Fig. 2-7C

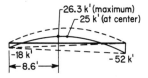

E. Total Moment Diagram. Sum of Parts in Fig. 2-7D

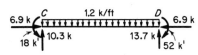

B. Free Body CD

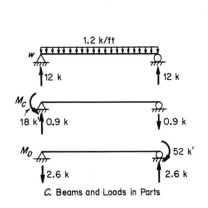

C. Beams and Loads in Parts

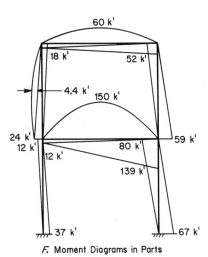

F. Moment Diagrams in Parts

Fig. 2–7. Moment diagrams for rigid frame. Simple beam parts.

—52 kip-ft. The shapes and the signs of these moment diagrams can be verified by applying the definition of moment to the beams marked M_C and M_D in Fig. 2–7C; that is, moment equals the sum of *all* moments—including moments of reactions—to the left (or to the right).

In simple beam parts the moment diagram for any end moment is therefore always a triangle.[8] Remember it.

If all the moment diagrams in Fig. 2–7D are added together, the total moment diagram of Fig. 2–7E is obtained. The dotted lines in Fig. 2–7E show the partial moment diagrams of Fig. 2–7D all plotted on the same base. The moment diagrams plotted in simple beam parts are shown for the entire frame in Fig. 2–7F.

[8] There seems to be an overwhelming fixation on the part of some students to think the moment diagram to be a rectangle, as for moment diagrams in cantilever parts. But it must be remembered that the moment diagram of M_C in Fig. 2–7D is *not* for just the moment, M_C, alone, but for the moment and for the supports as well. The moment diagram for M_C can be constructed in cantilever parts from the left, say, as follows: draw the moment diagram for only the 18-kip-ft moment. This is a rectangle. Then draw the moment diagram for the upward force of 0.9 kip. This is a triangle increasing from zero at the left to +18 kip-ft at the right. Add the two diagrams together and you obtain a "total" diagram exactly like that shown in Fig. 2–7D.

3

AREAS AND CENTROIDS

3–1. Simple Moment Diagrams. We do so much work with areas and centroids of moment diagrams that it is desirable to remember a few simple formulas to save time. Table 3–1 gives shear and moment diagrams, moment equations, and areas and centroids for a few regular types of load. The formulas are easy to remember because they, as well as the shear and moment diagrams and the moment equations, fit a regular progression.

Example 3–1*A*. Areas and centroids for moment diagrams for other beams or other loads can usually be obtained by combining the areas and centroids of Table 3–1 with a little ingenuity. For example, no formula for area or centroid of moment diagram is given for the load of Fig. 3–1*A*, but the area and centroid can be easily found by a combination of equivalent loads W_1 and W_2, shown in Fig. 3–1*B*. Areas and centroids of moment diagrams for these loads can be found in Table 3–1, so the net area can be found by subtraction:

$$A = A_1 - A_2 = \frac{1}{3}Lh_1 - \frac{1}{4}Lh_2 = wL^3\left(\frac{1}{6} - \frac{1}{24}\right) = \frac{wL^3}{8}$$

The centroid can be found from the principle of moments of areas, which states that the moment (area × distance to centroid) of an area about any axis equals the sum of the moments of its parts (about the same axis), or, algebraically

$$\Sigma A\bar{x} = A_1\bar{x}_1 + A_2\bar{x}_2 + A_3\bar{x}_3 + \cdots \tag{3-1}$$

But in our example

$$A\bar{x} = A_1\bar{x}_1 - A_2\bar{x}_2$$

in which the minus sign is required because the moment diagrams are opposite in sign. Substituting for area A as found above, and substituting for A_1, A_2, $\bar{x}_1$, and $\bar{x}_2$ from Table 3–1, results in

$$\frac{wL^3}{8}\bar{x} = \frac{wL^3}{6} \times \frac{3L}{4} - \frac{wL^3}{24} \times \frac{4L}{5}$$

$$\bar{x} = \tfrac{11}{15}L$$

Example 3–1*B*. A very common problem involves finding the area and the centroid of one-half of the moment diagram for a simply supported, uniformly loaded beam. Such a beam is shown in Fig. 3–2*A*, and the area A_2 is shown

29

TABLE 3–1
Areas and Centroids of Moment Diagrams

Beam and Loads	Shear Diagram	Moment Diagram	Moment Equation	Area of Moment Diagram, A_{MD}	Centroid, $\bar{x}$ From Free End
			$M_x = -M_A$	$Lh = LM_A$	$\bar{x} = \frac{1}{2}L$
			$M_x = -Px$	$\frac{1}{2}Lh = \frac{PL^2}{2}$	$\bar{x} = \frac{2}{3}L$
		Parabola	$M_x = -\frac{wx^2}{2}$	$\frac{1}{3}Lh = \frac{wL^3}{6}$	$\bar{x} = \frac{3}{4}L$
	Parabola	Cubic parabola	$M_x = -\frac{wx^3}{6L}$	$\frac{1}{4}Lh = \frac{wL^3}{24}$	$\bar{x} = \frac{4}{5}L$
Parabola	Cubic parabola	Quartic parabola	$M_x = -\frac{wx^4}{12L^2}$	$\frac{1}{5}Lh = \frac{wL^3}{60}$	$\bar{x} = \frac{5}{6}L$
Cubic parabola	Quartic parabola	Quintic parabola	$M_x = -\frac{wx^5}{20L^3}$	$\frac{1}{6}Lh = \frac{wL^3}{120}$	$\bar{x} = \frac{6}{7}L$

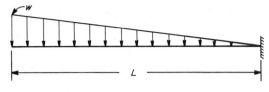

A. Beam and Loads

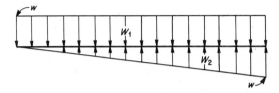

B. Equivalent Loads

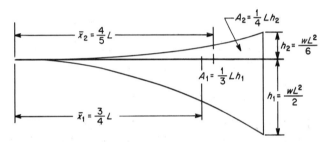

C. Areas of Equivalent Moment Diagrams

Fig. 3–1. Areas and centroids for complex moment diagrams.

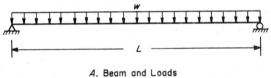

A. Beam and Loads

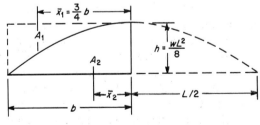

B. Moment Diagram

Fig. 3–2. Area and centroid of half of a moment diagram.

in Fig. 3–2B. The area of the rectangle (shown by dashed lines in Fig. 3–2B) enclosing the left half of the moment diagram equals altitude × base, and the area of the parabolic portion (outside the moment diagram) labeled A_1 equals one-third of the altitude × base. Therefore the area of the left half of the moment diagram equals the difference, which is two-thirds of the altitude × base. Since the base equals $L/2$, the area A_2 is

$$A_2 = \frac{2}{3}\,\text{altitude} \times \text{base} = \frac{2}{3}\frac{wL^2}{8} \times \frac{L}{2} = \frac{wL^3}{24}$$

The centroid of A_2 can be found as explained before. Letting A be the area of the rectangle, $\bar{x}$ the distance from the center of the beam to the centroid of the rectangle, and b the base (which is $L/2$), we obtain

$$A\bar{x} = A_1\bar{x}_1 + A_2\bar{x}_2$$

$$h \times b \times \tfrac{1}{2}b = \tfrac{1}{3}h \times b \times \tfrac{3}{4}b + \tfrac{2}{3}h \times b\bar{x}_2$$

$$h \times \frac{L}{2} \times \frac{1}{2} \times \frac{L}{2} = \frac{1}{3}h \times \frac{L}{2} \times \frac{3}{4} \times \frac{L}{2} + \frac{2}{3}h \times \frac{L}{2}\bar{x}_2$$

from which

$$\bar{x}_2 = \tfrac{3}{16}L \qquad \text{from the center}$$

3–2. Segments of Parabolic Moment Diagrams. Quite often, we must compute deflections at points other than the end or center of a beam. In the process we must find areas and centroids of segments of moment diagrams. Now, the most common loads are concentrated loads or uniformly distributed loads. Moment diagrams for concentrated loads are triangular or trapezoidal, and segments of such moment diagrams can be divided into triangles or into a combination of rectangles and triangles. There is no problem in finding areas and centroids of such simple figures. Moment diagrams for uniformly distributed loads are parabolic. Areas and centroids of parabolic segments are also easy to compute by the following method. Of course, it is always possible to compute areas and centroids of any curve by means of the calculus, but such computations are laborious.

PROPERTIES OF A PARABOLA. The properties of a parabola that provide the basis for this method are illustrated in Figs. 3–3A and B. The upper curve is a parabola, symmetrical about axis yy and tangent at its vertex to axis xx. It is required to find the area and the centroid of any segment such as AOB. The segment may include the vertex as shown here, or it may be so far off center that the vertex is not included. This makes no difference in the development or conclusions. The area of the parabolic segment AOB equals two-thirds of the height (defined as CD, the vertical bisector of AB) times the horizontal projection of the base AB. The centroid of the segment AOB lies on line CD.

PROOF. In Fig. 3–3A, draw EF parallel to AB and tangent to the parabola at point C. Draw a vertical line through point C intersecting AB at D. Let GH be any ordinate b at any given abscissa a from the yy axis. At the same distance a from line CD, draw the vertical line JKL.

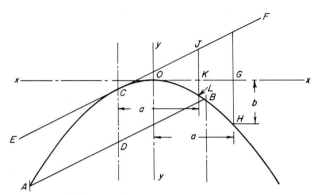

A. Parabola Symmetrical About Axis yy

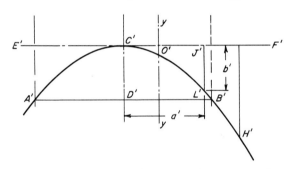

B. Ordinates from EF in Fig. 3–3A Make Identical
Parabola Symmetrical About Axis $C'D'$

Fig. 3–3. Properties of parabolas.

In Fig. 3–3B construct $A'B'$, the horizontal projection of AB. Draw $C'D'$ equal to and collinear with line CD. Also draw $J'L'$ equal to and collinear with JL. So a equals a'.

By means of algebra it can be proved[1] that JL equals GH. Thus

$$JL = GH = b$$

and

$$J'L' = b'$$

Since $J'L'$ was constructed equal to JL

$$b = b'$$

---

[1] Mathematically minded students may wish to do so.

And by construction

$$a = a'$$

Therefore curve $A'C'B'$ is a parabola with its vertex at C'. Furthermore, $C'D'$ is the bisector of $A'B'$, therefore CD must be the bisector of AB. The area of segment ACB equals the area of parabola $A'C'B'$ which is two-thirds the base (which is the horizontal projection of AB) times the altitude (which is the vertical distance from the mid-point of the base to the curve).

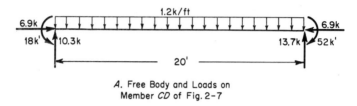

A. Free Body and Loads on
Member CD of Fig. 2–7

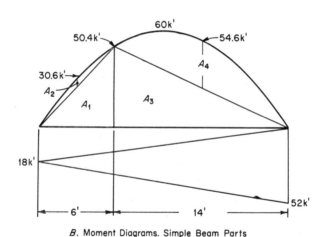

B. Moment Diagrams. Simple Beam Parts

Fig. 3–4. Use of parabolic segments.

Example 3–2. The free body shown in Fig. 3–4A could represent one full span of a continuous beam or frame or it could represent only a portion of a complete span. The moment diagrams are shown in Fig. 3–4B. Any portion of the negative moment diagrams can be handled by dividing the portion into triangles or into a triangle and a rectangle. Any portion of the positive parabolic moment diagram can be handled by dividing the portion into a triangle and a parabolic segment.

Suppose the area and the centroid of the left 6-ft segment of the parabola are required. Divide the parabolic segment into the areas marked A_1 and A_2. Compute the moments in the beam at the end of the segment (50.4 kip-ft) and at the middle of the segment (30.6 kip-ft). These moments, along with others which will be needed later, are shown in Fig. 3–4B. The mid-height of A_1 is 50.4/2 or 25.2, so the height at the middle of the parabolic area A_2 is 30.6 − 25.2, or 5.4 kip-ft. The area of the 6-ft segment of the positive moment diagram is then,

$$A_1 = \tfrac{1}{2}hb = \tfrac{1}{2} \times 50.4 \times 6 = 151.20$$
$$A_2 = \tfrac{2}{3}hb = \tfrac{2}{3} \times 5.4 \times 6 = \underline{21.60}$$
$$\text{Total area} = 172.80$$

The centroid can be found by taking moments about any convenient point— the left end, for example. The centroid of the triangle is 4 ft from the left end; that of the parabolic segment is at the mid-point, 3 ft from the left end.

$$\Sigma A\bar{x} = A_1\bar{x}_1 + A_2\bar{x}_2 \tag{3–1}$$
$$172.80\bar{x} = 151.20 \times 4 + 21.60 \times 3$$

So

$$\bar{x} = 3.88 \text{ ft}$$

The area of the entire parabola should equal the sum of the areas A_1, A_2, A_3, and A_4. The height at the center of the parabolic area A_4 is found in precisely the same manner as that for area A_2. It equals, then, 54.6 − 50.4/2 or 29.4 kip-ft. Adding all these areas, we have

$$A_1 + A_2 \text{ (from above)} = 172.80$$
$$A_3 = \tfrac{1}{2}hb = \tfrac{1}{2} \times 50.4 \times 14 = 352.80$$
$$A_4 = \tfrac{2}{3}hb = \tfrac{2}{3} \times 29.4 \times 14 = \underline{274.40}$$
$$\text{Total area} = 800.00 \quad \text{(This value is exact.)}$$

The validity of this procedure can be checked by comparing the total area as found above with the answer below.

$$A = \tfrac{2}{3}hb = \tfrac{2}{3} \times 60 \times 20 = 800.00$$

SLOPING BASES. When moment diagrams are stacked on top of one another (as in Fig. 2–2C or Fig. 2–3B), the bases of some are often sloping. The preceding discussion shows that it is the projection of the base (upon the centerline of the beam) that is used to compute areas of parabolas. Areas of other configurations are also computed by using the length of base as projected on the centerline of the beam.

Actually, the base or length of a moment diagram cannot slope with respect to the member. They appear to do so in Fig. 2–2C because of the way they are drawn, but actually the length of a moment diagram must, by definition, be measured along the centerline of the member. If the moment diagrams of Fig. 2–2C are drawn as shown in Fig. 2–2B, there is no question that the lengths of the diagrams are measured parallel to the axis of the member.

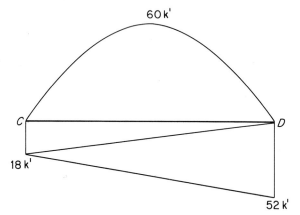

A. Moment Diagrams. Simple Beam Parts

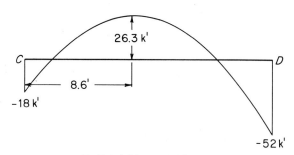

B. Total Moment Diagram

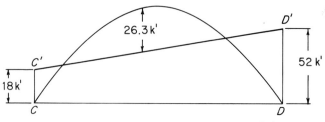

C. Total Moment Diagram. Base is *C'D'*

Fig. 3–5. Graphical addition of moment diagrams.

Any uncertainty should be immediately clarified by replotting the parts as in Fig. 2–2 B. There is no uncertainty about the length of diagram A_4 in this figure.

3–3. Graphical Addition of Moment Diagrams.

The moment diagrams of Fig. 3–4 B represent the most convenient style for computation of deflections or for checking solutions by moment distribution, but they are not convenient for the design of members. Only *total* moment diagrams are convenient for design.

One way to obtain a total moment diagram from moment diagrams plotted in simple beam parts is by the algebraic addition of ordinates at several points and the subsequent replotting of the moment curve. This is illustrated in Fig. 3–5 B, which is a plot of the algebraic sum of ordinates at several points taken from Fig. 3–5 A.

It is an inconvenient method because it requires replotting a curve. An easier and, for that reason, better method is to replot the moment diagrams for end moments *above* the line CD. These moment diagrams consist of straight lines and are, therefore, quickly drawn. Let the line $C'D'$ become the new base line. Then the vertical ordinates between the parabola and the base line $C'D'$ are exactly the same as those of Fig. 3–5 B. The unchanged parabola is, then, a *total* moment diagram when referred to base $C'D'$. Such moment diagrams can be used to locate points of inflection, points where steel reinforcing bars can be bent, and the total bending moment at any point can be graphically determined very rapidly by means of a scale. The accuracy that can be obtained even with small-scale plots is sufficient for usual design purposes.

Plotting a parabola (which is by far the most common moment curve) is a waste of time. It is much better to cut a small piece of plastic into a template from which a parabola can be traced. Since the moment curve so drawn may not fit any standard scale, it is usually necessary to employ an odd scale (for example, 1 in. = 76 kip-ft), but this is easy to do with the help of a slide rule set to the proper proportionality figure.

3–4. Units and Dimensions.

Values of moments of inertia are usually given in tables in (inches)^4, written in.^{4}, and modulus of elasticity is usually considered in pounds per square inch (psi). Calculations must be consistent in units; if some figures are in pound-inch (lb-in.) dimensions, all other figures must also be in pound-inch dimensions. Now, lengths of members vary widely, of course, but an average length for members in building frames might be, say, 20 ft. If the length were expressed in inches and the load in pounds, calculations of deflections would involve astronomical figures. To avoid such cumbersome numbers, it is desirable to use dimensions of kips and feet for all units. Hence, the modulus of elasticity must be converted from pounds per square inch to kips per square foot, and the moment of inertia from (inches)^4 to (feet)^4.

To convert any figure from one set of dimensions to another, multiply the figure by fractions whose values are unity. Such operations do not change the true value of the figure. By cleverly choosing the proper fractions, the unwanted dimensions can be canceled and replaced with desirable dimensions. For example, one useful fraction whose value is unity is

$$\frac{12 \text{ in.}}{1 \text{ ft}}$$

Used as a multiplier it cannot change the intrinsic value of any quantity; it can only change the dimensions.

To convert the modulus of elasticity, multiply it by unit fractions and cancel as follows:

$$E \frac{\text{pounds}}{(\text{inch})^2} \times \frac{12 \text{ inches}}{1 \text{ foot}} \times \frac{12 \text{ inches}}{1 \text{ foot}} \times \frac{1 \text{ kip}}{1000 \text{ pounds}} = E \times \frac{144}{1000} \frac{\text{kip}}{(\text{foot})^2}$$

That is, E in pounds per square inch multiplied by 0.144 is E in kips per square foot.

To convert the moment of inertia, multiply and cancel as follows:

$$I \text{ (inches)}^4 \times \left(\frac{1 \text{ foot}}{12 \text{ inches}}\right)^4 = I \text{ (inches)}^4 \times \frac{1 \text{ (foot)}^4}{20{,}736 \text{ (inches)}^4} = \frac{I \text{ (foot)}^4}{20{,}736}$$

That is, I in (inches)^4 divided by 20,736 equals I in (feet)^4.

Or to convert EI from pound-(inches)^2 to kip-(feet)^2, multiply by

$$\frac{144}{1000 \times 20{,}736} = \frac{1}{144{,}000}$$

3–5. Accuracy. Do not be hypnotized by a fine show of mathematical precision in an answer to a structural problem. Although an answer may indicate great precision, it is rarely accurate to more than two significant figures. Many factors contribute to the uncertainty of computations. Certain liberties are taken with the analysis itself: shearing and axial distortions (except in trusses) are usually very small and are neglected; in flexural computations it is assumed that plane sections remain plane; the beam is prismatic; the material is homogeneous, isotropic, and elastic; etc. These are justifiable assumptions, but it can be shown that errors of 10 percent or more can occur under quite ordinary circumstances.

The numerical values of Young's modulus E and moment of inertia I cannot be known exactly. For steel, Young's modulus is assumed to be 29,000,000 or 30,000,000 psi, but it can vary as much as 3 percent. Young's modulus for concrete is assumed to be 1000 times the ultimate strength, but actually it varies erratically and, in the final analysis, concrete is not really elastic anyway. Even in steel sections—our most accurately controlled building material—manufacturing tolerances may well account for a variation of ±3 percent in moment of inertia. Various methods of computing moment of inertia in reinforced concrete members have been suggested. Some engineers use the transformed section; others, the gross concrete section, neglecting the steel; and still others use the gross section plus the transformed steel area. Naturally, these different assumptions would result in different answers. Fortunately, only small variations in moments and forces result from large variations in modulus and moment of inertia.

These uncertainties are dwarfed by the uncertainties of loads and the actual structural action. Dead loads can be computed within an accuracy of, perhaps, 5 or 6 percent, but live loads are usually stipulated by a building code. It is not likely that such loads would apply with great accuracy to a specific structure. For example, the live load specified in most codes for stairs and corridors is 100 psf; yet such a loading is impossible except in a crush of tall people. Or consider highway bridges: for many years they were designed for an H-20 loading (20 tons on one axle). Some of today's bridges are being designed for an ultimate loading of H-60. All other sources of inaccuracy combined are probably not as important as this.

Actual structural action is often quite different from the assumed action. The main structural framework is assumed to carry all primary loads. Curtain walls, bracing, roofing, etc., are rarely assumed to carry any primary loads, but yet they do. Bridges have been known to carry their own dead weight plus pedestrian traffic when the lower chords had completely rusted away at several points; the lower horizontal bracing acted as the lower chord in defiance of the usual assumptions. Is it any wonder that measured strains often differ from computed strains by 20 percent or more?

All of this does not indicate that we should abandon stress calculations in discouragement, nor that we should overlook any stress-influencing factors as being unimportant in the face of so many uncertainties. Some of the uncertainties can be minimized by making fewer sweeping assumptions. The uncertainties may be on the unsafe as well as on the safe side, so computations should be as accurate as the circumstances justify. But put the emphasis on accuracy where it belongs—on the assumptions of structural action, the amount and frequency of the loads, the desirable safety factor, the strength of the building materials, and on the elimination of blunders.

SLIDE RULE. The slide rule furnishes sufficient accuracy for most computations, and most of the examples in this text have been worked with the slide rule. Although answers to these examples are rarely accurate to more than two places, more significant figures may be shown for the purpose of comparison. (A number between 1 and 2, such as 1.742, can be obtained to four places on the slide rule.) When more than three (four between 1 and 2) places are shown, the computations were made with a calculator. The solution of simultaneous equations (or any other problem where large numbers are subtracted to yield small residuals) usually requires five- or six-place accuracy to obtain an answer correct to two or three places.

The utmost care must be used at all times to prevent blunders. Decimal points are particularly troublesome because some of the calculations involve very large numbers. Two suitable means for locating the decimal point are the exponent, or powers-of-ten, method and the logarithm characteristic method. Combined with a quick mental calculation, either provides a check on the manipulation of the slide rule as well as on the location of the decimal point. Methods which depend on counting the number of manipulations of the slide are not suitable because they are not always applicable to every scale and because they do not provide a check upon the manipulation itself.

Example 3–5. To illustrate the exponent method of decimal-point location, let it be required to compute the deflection of a steel 16 W⁻ 36 beam (a beam 16 in. deep weighing 36 lb/ft) carrying a total uniform load of 8 kips on a span of 40 ft. The formula[2] for deflection is

$$\Delta = \frac{5}{384} \frac{wL^4}{EI}$$

in which w is load in pounds per inch (16.7 lb/in.), L is span length in inches (40 × 12), E is 29,000,000 psi, and I from the Steel Construction Manual[3] is 446.3 (inches)[4].

$$\Delta = \frac{5}{384} \times \frac{16.7(40 \times 12)^4}{29,000,000 \times 446.3}$$

This can be rewritten,

$$\Delta = \frac{5}{3.84 \times 10^2} \times \frac{1.67 \times 10(4.0 \times 1.2 \times 10^2)^4}{2.9 \times 10^7 \times 4.463 \times 10^2}$$

Note that only one digit precedes each decimal point. Collecting the powers of ten and noting that $(10^2)^4$ is 10^8, we have

$$\Delta = \frac{5 \times 1.67(4.0 \times 1.2)^4}{3.84 \times 2.9 \times 4.463} \times \frac{10^9}{10^{11}}$$

By mental arithmetic this is a little less than[4]

$$\Delta = \frac{5 \times 2(5)^4}{4 \times 3 \times 4} \times 10^{-2} \cong 120 \times 10^{-2}$$

The answer found by slide rule is

$$\Delta = 89 \times 10^{-2} = 0.89 \text{ in.}$$

If the comparison between mental and slide-rule answers were much poorer, the work would be rechecked.

---

[2] *Steel Construction Manual of the American Institute of Steel Construction* (New York).
[3] *Ibid.*
[4] The symbol $\cong$ means approximately equal.

In practice, tens and their powers need not actually be written. Simply mark temporary decimals with a small, faint x. Figure the answer with the slide rule, check by mental arithmetic locating the temporary decimal point in the answer, and finally count the powers of ten and locate the actual decimal point. The complete calculation takes the following form:

$$\Delta = \frac{5 \times 1_x6.7(4_x0 \times 1_x2)^4}{3_x84 \times 2_x9,000,000 \times 4_x46.3} = 0.89_x$$

In general, if answers are wanted correct to two significant figures, the calculations must be made with three significant figures.

3–6. Methods for Indeterminate Analysis. There is a certain romance in indeterminate analysis that is not to be denied. Hence it is not strange that many ingenious methods have been invented for solving indeterminate problems. There are, in fact, so many that no one could be sure of naming all of them. Some of the better known ones are: double integration, three-moment theorem, moment area, virtual work, Castigliano's theorem, conjugate beam, Maxwell's law (and the Müller-Breslau principle), slope deflection, moment distribution, neutral point, column analogy, and the "fundamental" or "general" method. Some of these methods are known by other names as well.

To those who insist on classifying everything, each of the above is a separate and distinct method, and some of these methods are more "general" or more "fundamental" than others. To the author this seems a myopic viewpoint. Every method is founded upon the elastic curve, and each method is only a device for handling the mathematics necessary to describe a point on the elastic curve. One method yields the equation of the elastic curve directly, others can be made to do so indirectly. Some methods are easier than others; some, like moment distribution, permit one to observe the development of the elastic curve as the calculations progress; some are quite limited in application, whereas at least two are suited to a very wide variety of problem types; but none can be considered more fundamental than any other. Indeed, so closely related are these methods that the primary equation for a specific problem will often be exactly the same, even when derived from two apparently completely "different" methods. So it might be more accurate to call them "procedures" or "avenues of thought" rather than "methods."

Competence in structural analysis depends not upon the acquisition of a great number of methods but upon an intimate understanding of a very few. The methods to be explained in detail are moment area, virtual work, moment distribution, and models. There are sound reasons for selecting these. Moment area is one of the simplest methods in its conception. Its relationship with the elastic curve is direct and not subverted by a mathematical manipulation, nor obscured as an analogy, nor buried under a heap of formulas. Moment area is not the easiest of methods because one cannot substitute routine procedure for clear reasoning, and therefore it is unparalleled for teaching structural mechanics. Furthermore, it is perhaps the best of all methods for checking solutions obtained by moment distribution. Virtual work is the most powerful tool of all—capable of analyzing trusses, beams, frames, arches, or problems involving torsion. Its connection with the elastic curve is not so apparent as with moment area, but it is more foolproof. Moment distribution, although limited essentially to the solution of continuous beams and frames, is so much faster than any other method that it has revolutionized structural analysis. Models are included partly because of their importance and partly because they are unparalleled as devices for learning to anticipate structural action. Any problem that can be solved by any other method can be solved as quickly and as effectively by one of these four. Mastery of these four is, then, more to be desired than an acquaintance with many.

Several other methods are explained in Part V. Some, such as double integration, are included because of their historical significance; others, such as the Williot-Mohr diagrams, are included because they are better or faster for a special purpose than any other method; and still others, such as conjugate beam and least work, are included because some portion of the literature requires an understanding of their basic principles.

The advent of the electronic computer makes it possible to solve some problems much faster and more cheaply than by any other means. But it is practical only when there are prepared programs readily available or when there are a great many problems of the same type to be solved. The method of analysis chosen must be one that is adapted to the requirements of the computer, and these methods are not always those that are best for pencil and paper. Although the computer will find increasing use in engineering work, there will still be a need for manual methods, just as the invention of the automatic welding machine resulted in an increase—not a decrease—of hand welding.

Part II

MOMENT AREA

The moment area method was developed by Professor Charles E. Greene about 1873. A parallel development by Professor Otto Mohr, called the method of elastic weights, or the conjugate beam,[1] although different in concept leads to identical equations.

Moment area is one of the most useful methods for finding deflections of beams, frames, and arches, and for solving statically indeterminate structures. In the literature, moment area and certain minor variations of it are called by several other names such as the arch method, graphical arch method, and curved beam theory. It forms the basis for several variations such as the neutral point method and the column analogy. Some of the variations are interesting and have an advantage over moment area in that many loading conditions can be solved with less labor, but moment area is easier to understand and is more rapid for the solution of a single loading condition. Indeed, there are some problems which can be solved more rapidly by moment area than by any other method. It is, in short, a universal method that will do anything the more complicated methods will do, sometimes will do it faster, and is easier to use and to understand.

[1] See Chapter 20.

4

STATICALLY DETERMINATE BEAMS

4–1. Basic Moment Area Equations. The moment area method consists of writing equations for deflection caused by angle changes. In beams, rigid frames, and arches subject to flexure, the angle changes are caused by bending and, thus, are functions of the area of the moment diagrams—hence the name "moment area." In trusses, angle changes are functions of the axial strain in the various elements, and are assumed to be finite values occurring only at the joints.

The three basic moment area equations are actually equations of the geometry of small angle changes.[1] To develop the equations, consider the line diagram ABC of Fig. 4–1A to be fixed in position at C and subject to a small angle change, θ_B, at any point B. The angle change causes point A to move to A_1. Coordinate axes xx and yy are passed through point A, and the position of any and all points is always referred to these coordinate axes. The vertical and horizontal components of the movement of point A are ΔY_A and ΔX_A, respectively, and the change of slope at A is $\Delta\theta_A$. Construct a straight line of length r from B to A and from B to A_1.

By definition of a radian, the arc AA_1 equals $r\theta_B$ (if θ_B is expressed in radians). But if θ_B is small, the arc AA_1 approaches a straight line, and the figure AA_1E approaches a triangle that is similar to triangle ABD because all sides are mutually perpendicular. Since triangle $AA_1E \approx$ triangle ABD,

$$\angle BAD = \angle A_1AE = \beta$$

By the definition of a sine

$$\Delta X_A = EA_1 = AA_1 \sin\beta = r\theta_B \sin\beta$$

But from the triangle ABD,

$$\sin\beta = \frac{BD}{AB} = \frac{y_B}{r}$$

Therefore

$$\Delta X_A = r\theta_B \sin\beta = r\theta_B \frac{y_B}{r} = y_B\theta_B$$

---

[1] *Angle change* is used to distinguish a *change* from an *angle*. An angle of itself cannot cause deflection but, if bending occurs, the *change in angle* due to the bending does cause deflection.

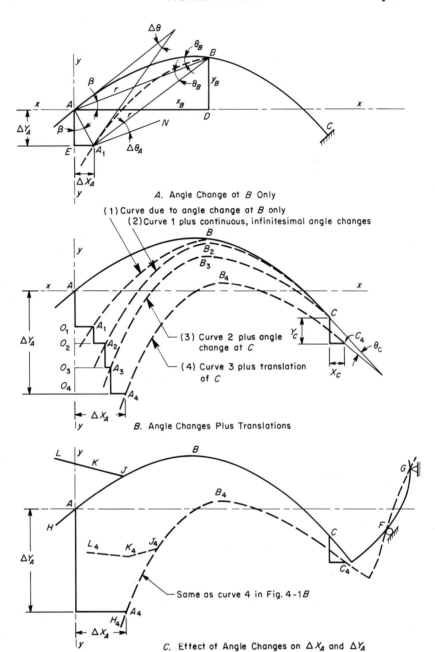

A. Angle Change at B Only

(1) Curve due to angle change at B only
(2) Curve 1 plus continuous, infinitesimal angle changes

(3) Curve 2 plus angle change at C

(4) Curve 3 plus translation of C

B. Angle Changes Plus Translations

Same as curve 4 in Fig. 4-1B

C. Effect of Angle Changes on ΔX_A and ΔY_A

Fig. 4–1. Construction for the development of basic moment
area equations.

so that for any general angle change θ at any ordinate y, the horizontal movement of point A is

$$\Delta X_A = y\theta \tag{4–1}$$

Similarly,

$$\Delta Y_A = AA_1 \cos \beta = r\theta_B \frac{x_B}{r} = x_B\theta_B$$

or for any general angle change θ at any abscissa x, the vertical movement of point A is

$$\Delta Y_A = x\theta \tag{4–2}$$

The angle change (or change of slope) at point A is found by constructing a line $A_1 N$ through point A_1 parallel to line AB, as shown in Fig. 4–1A. From principles of geometry,

$$\angle BA_1 N = \angle ABA_1$$

Therefore the change of slope at A is

$$\Delta\theta_A = \theta_B$$

and for any general angle change occurring at any point between A and C

$$\Delta\theta_A = \theta \tag{4–3}$$

Now suppose that there were several finite angle changes between A and C, called $\theta_1, \theta_2, \theta_3, \cdots, \theta_n$. The y deflection due to θ_1 would be $x_1\theta_1$ (in which x_1 is the x coordinate at angle change θ_1); the vertical deflection due to θ_2 would be $x_2\theta_2$, etc., so that the total vertical deflection would be

$$\Delta Y_A = x_1\theta_1 + x_2\theta_2 + \cdots + x_n\theta_n = \sum_A^C x\theta \tag{4–4}$$

By the same reasoning, the total horizontal deflection at A due to several finite angle changes would be:

$$\Delta X_A = y_1\theta_1 + y_2\theta_2 + \cdots + y_n\theta_n = \sum_A^C y\theta \tag{4–5}$$

and the total change of slope at point A would be:

$$\Delta\theta_A = \theta_1 + \theta_2 + \cdots + \theta_n = \sum_A^C \theta \tag{4–6}$$

Suppose, in addition to the finite angle changes which led to Eqs. 4–4, 4–5, and 4–6, there are infinitesimal angle changes occurring continuously along some portion between A and C. The effect of these also must be added. Calling each infinitesimal angle change $d\theta$, we obtain the following equations from elementary calculus:

$$\Delta Y_A = \int_A^C x\, d\theta + \sum_A^C x\theta \tag{4–7}$$

$$\Delta X_A = \int_A^C y\, d\theta + \sum_A^C y\theta \tag{4–8}$$

$$\Delta\theta_A = \int_A^C d\theta + \sum_A^C \theta \tag{4–9}$$

Later on, it will be shown that there is frequently no fixed point (such as point C, Fig. 4–1A) in a structure. To be perfectly general, the above equations must be expanded to provide for this possibility. Suppose point C moves and rotates to point C_4, as shown in Fig. 4–1B. The horizontal movement of point C is X_C, the vertical movement of point C is Y_C, and the angular rotation at point C is θ_C. By the construction in Fig. 4–1B, it should be noted that

$$AO_1 = x_B\theta_B \qquad \text{for an angle change at point } B \text{ only}$$

$$O_1O_2 = \int_A^C x\, d\theta \qquad \text{for continuous, infinitesimal angle changes}$$

$$O_2O_3 = x_C\theta_C \qquad \text{for an angle change at point } C$$

$$O_3O_4 = Y_C \qquad \text{for the vertical movement of point } C$$

The total deflection is

$$\Delta Y_A = AO_1 + O_1O_2 + O_2O_3 + O_3O_4$$

or

$$\Delta Y_A = x_B\theta_B + \int_A^C x\, d\theta + x_C\theta_C + Y_C \qquad (4\text{–}10)$$

Rewriting Eq. 4–10 in general form, we have

$$\Delta Y = \int x\, d\theta + \sum x\theta + Y \qquad (4\text{–}11)$$

In a similar manner,

$$\Delta X = \int y\, d\theta + \sum y\theta + X \qquad (4\text{–}12)$$

$$\Delta\theta = \int d\theta + \sum \theta \qquad (4\text{–}13)$$

These three are the basic equations of moment area.[2]

4–2. Review of Basic Moment Area Equations. To emphasize the significance of the equations, it should be noted that:

1. All values of x and y must be referred to coordinate axes which pass through the original position of the point whose deflection is wanted.

2. Only those angle changes occurring along a single centerline between the point of deflection (e.g., point A, Fig. 4–1B) and the end point of summation (e.g., point C, Fig. 4–1B) are considered. All other angle changes must be omitted.

[2] As originally proposed by Greene, all except the integral terms were dropped. The resulting deflection or rotation then becomes deflection or rotation from a tangent. Such equations are just as easy for an experienced structural engineer to use, but they are tricky and somewhat confusing for the beginner, particularly in complex problems. The approach used here is universally applicable, is more straightforward, and promotes quicker understanding and appreciation of structural action than does Greene's original approach.

To illustrate the last statement, compare Figs. 4–1B and 4–1C. Curve $A_4B_4C_4$ in Fig. 4–1B is identical with curve $A_4B_4C_4$ in Fig. 4–1C. If Eq. 4–10 yields the absolute vertical deflection of point A in Fig. 4–1B, then it must do likewise in Fig. 4–1C, since the two curves and, therefore, deflections and angle changes are identical. But, if Eq. 4–10 gives the true value of ΔY_A in Fig. 4–1C, it must be concluded that angle changes between H and A and between C and G must be omitted, because *these angle changes do not appear in Eq.* 4–10.

Again, suppose JKL is a part of the structure in Fig. 4–1C, and assume that an angle change occurs at K. This angle change also must be omitted because it can have no effect on the curve $A_4B_4C_4$. Furthermore, it does not appear in Eq. 4–10—the equation that gives the true vertical deflection of point A.

It is important to remember, then, that only those angle changes that occur on a single centerline (or elastic curve) between the point of deflection and the end point of summation of angle changes are to be written into the general moment area equations. All other angle changes *must* be omitted.

The only assumption made thus far is that the angle changes are small; that is, the sine and tangent are assumed to be numerically equal to the angle in radians. Equations 4–11, 4–12, and 4–13 are equations of geometry only, and no structural engineering is as yet involved.

4–3. Use of Basic Equations. The basic equations are of limited usefulness, but they can be used for the analysis of structures subjected to finite angle changes as illustrated in the following example.

Example 4–3. Imagine one bay of a series of continuous rigid frames being constructed first by tack-welding each member in place (as shown by the solid lines in Fig. 4–2), after which the joints are welded rigidly. The joints are likely to distort somewhat because of thermal stresses caused by the welding. Let us determine the movement of point A, assuming that member DE remains fixed in position and assuming that the angular distortions listed in Table 4–1 occur in the joints so that the angles become more acute.

TABLE 4–I
Direction of Angle Changes Shown in Fig. 4–2

Joint	Angle	θ (Angle Change Due to Distortion)	
		Bevel* (Inches of Rise)	Radians
B	ABC	$\frac{1}{32}$	0.0026
C	BCD	$\frac{1}{16}$	0.0052
D	CDE	$\frac{3}{64}$	0.0039
D	FDE	$\frac{1}{32}$	0.0026

* In structural fabricating shops, an angle is expressed as a bevel, which indicates (in inches and fractions) the *rise* or height of a right triangle whose base length is 12 in.

To find the vertical (component of) deflection of point A, the coordinate axes must be passed through point A, and all distances must be measured from these coordinate axes. Equation 4–11,

$$\Delta Y = \int x\, d\theta + \sum x\theta + Y \qquad (4\text{–}11)$$

reduces to

$$\Delta Y_A = 0 + \sum_A^E x\theta + 0$$

The first term (on the right side) of Eq. 4–11 is zero because there are no infinitesimal angle changes—only finite changes at the joints. The third

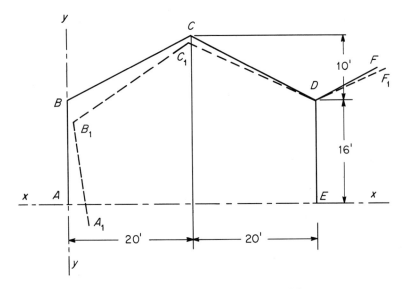

Fig. 4–2. Welding deformations in a rigid frame.

term is also zero if we sum angle changes from A to E, because E—the end point of summation—is a point that does not move. Substituting the angle changes from Table 4–1 and the proper distances from Fig. 4–2 into Eq. 4–11,

$$\Delta Y_A = \sum_A^E x\theta = 0\theta_B + 20\theta_C + 40\theta_D$$

$$= 0 \times 0.0026 + 20 \times 0.0052 + 40 \times 0.0039$$

$$= 0.26 \text{ ft} = 3.1 \text{ in. down}$$

The effects of each $x\theta$ term are additive, and the deflection is downward.

This can be determined[3] by visualizing the distorted shape of the structure or by drawing a sketch of the distorted shape, as shown by the broken line in Fig. 4–2. If you experience difficulty in this visualization because of the number of effects, consider each angle change separately. Make several sketches of the frame, showing one angle change on each, as shown in Fig. 6–3. Another excellent way to use a sketch is to stick a pin through a point which undergoes an angle change. Rotate the sketch about the pin point in the direction that would be caused by the angle change. This enables you to see the direction of deflection without guessing.

To find the horizontal deflection of point A, write Eq. 4–12

$$\Delta X = \int y \, d\theta + \sum y\theta + X \tag{4–12}$$

which, for this problem, becomes

$$\Delta X_A = 0 + \sum_A^E y\theta + 0$$

The first and last terms are zero for the same reasons that were indicated in this example for Eq. 4–11. Substituting values from Table 4–1 and Fig. 4–2 into the second term gives

$$\Delta X_A = \sum_A^E y\theta = 16\theta_B + 26\theta_C + 16\theta_D$$
$$= 16 \times 0.0026 + 26 \times 0.0052 + 16 \times 0.0039$$
$$= 0.24 \text{ ft} = 2.9 \text{ in. right}$$

Again the direction of deflection due to each angle change can be determined from sketches of the frame, as explained above.

The total deflection can be obtained by adding ΔY_A and ΔX_A vectorially:

$$\Delta Y_A \mapsto \Delta X_A = \sqrt{(3.1)^2 + (2.9)^2} = 4.2 \text{ in. down and to the right}$$

In actual practice, this deflection would be minimized by welding one joint at a time and adjusting succeeding members to compensate for the distortion.

This problem was chosen to emphasize the fact that moment area equations are basically equations of geometry. To use moment area intelligently, the geometry of the angle changes must always be kept in mind. For example, the angle change F_1DF was omitted in the solution. Why? Because, even though it is an angle change occurring at point D, it has no effect on the deflection of point A, as can be seen from Fig. 4–2. Blindly including all angle changes in Eqs. 4–11 and 4–12 without considering the effect of each angle change would have produced a wrong answer. From a pedagogical

---

[3] The direction of a deflection can be determined by establishing a set of rules, but then the rules are usually substituted for reasoning and for structural visualization which are so very important. Such rules are therefore to be avoided wherever it is practical to do so. Part II avoids such rules entirely.

standpoint this is one of the finest qualities of moment area. Blind substitution and failure to use fundamental reasoning usually result in wrong answers.

4–4. Integral Moment Area Equations. Except in trusses, deflections in structures usually result from flexure which produces continuous infinitesimal angle changes—the $d\theta$ of Eqs. 4–11, 4–12, and 4–13. By expressing $d\theta$ in terms of bending moment M, Young's modulus of elasticity E, and moment of inertia I, the equations can be altered to a form more suitable for most structural analyses. The relation[4] between $d\theta$, M, E, and I is

$$d\theta = \frac{M\,ds}{EI} \tag{B–4}$$

where ds is an infinitesimal distance along the neutral axis of the beam, that is, the length over which $d\theta$ occurs. Substituting Eq. B–4 into Eqs. 4–11, 4–12, and 4–13 produces

$$\Delta Y = \int \frac{Mx\,ds}{EI} + \sum x\theta + Y \tag{4–14}$$

$$\Delta X = \int \frac{My\,ds}{EI} + \sum y\theta + X \tag{4–15}$$

$$\Delta \theta = \int \frac{M\,ds}{EI} + \sum \theta \tag{4–16}$$

These are called the "integral moment area" equations. The terms

$$\int \frac{Mx\,ds}{EI} \qquad \int \frac{My\,ds}{EI} \qquad \text{and} \qquad \int \frac{M\,ds}{EI}$$

account for the effects of the curvature of the elastic curve. The terms $\sum x\theta$, $\sum y\theta$, and $\sum \theta$ account for the effects of finite angle changes which may be caused by inelastic slip in a riveted joint, rotation of a footing, or by the *change of slope* of the elastic curve at the upper limit of integration. The terms X and Y account for horizontal and vertical movements caused by foundation settlement, temperature variations, or just by the *deflection of the elastic curve* at the upper limit of integration.

The terms can be explained in other words, as follows. Imagine that we intend to compute ΔY at some point P in some structure, and that we wish to integrate between the limits of P and any general point Q. Now imagine a line constructed *tangent to the elastic curve* at point Q. The term $\int (Mx/EI)\,ds$ accounts for the deflection of the elastic curve *from this tangent*. The term $\sum x\theta$ accounts for the deflection due to the *rotation* (or *change of slope*) *of this tangent*. And the term Y accounts for the *deflection of the point of tangency*.

---

[4] See Appendix B for the development of equations of flexure.

4–5. Deflection of a Cantilever Beam. To illustrate the use of the integral moment area equations, let us compute deflections of a cantilever beam subjected to a uniform load as shown in Fig. 4–3.

Example 4–5A. Maximum Deflection. To find the maximum deflection (which occurs at the free end of the beam), first pass the coordinate axes

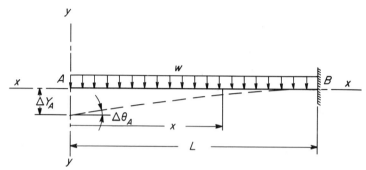

A. Integrating from *A* to *B*

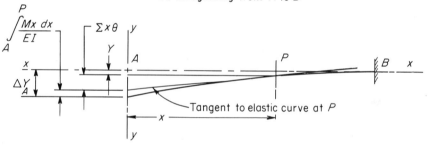

B. Integrating from *A* to *P*

Fig. 4–3. Slope and deflection at end of cantilever beam.

through point A, the free end. Any distance, such as x, must be measured from these coordinate axes. The deflection is given by Eq. 4–14,

$$\Delta Y = \int \frac{Mx\,ds}{EI} + \sum x\theta + Y \qquad (4\text{–}14)$$

which reduces to

$$\Delta Y_A = \int_0^L \frac{Mx\,dx}{EI} + 0 + 0$$

Because ds is measured along the centerline of the beam, it becomes dx. If the effects of the infinitesimal angle changes $[(Mx/EI)\,dx]$ are added over the full length of the beam by integrating from $x = 0$ to $x = L$, the second and third terms (of the right side of the equation) are each equal to zero. That is because at the upper limit of integration (where $x = L$), the beam is fixed and there is neither finite angle change nor deflection. The bending moment

M is not a constant and must therefore be expressed in terms of x. From Table 3–1, the moment at any point x distance from point A is

$$M = \frac{-wx^2}{2}$$

Substituting in Eq. 4–14, we have

$$\Delta Y_A = \int_0^L \frac{-wx^2}{2} \frac{x}{EI}\, dx = \left[-\frac{wx^4}{8EI}\right]_0^L = -\frac{wL^4}{8EI}$$

The minus sign comes from Table 3–1, in which moments that cause compression in the lower fibers are arbitrarily termed minus in accordance with custom. However, the direction of deflection ought to be determined, not by an arbitrary sign but, instead, by considering the effects of the angle changes. In this example, it is easy to do, and obviously a beam bends down when it is pushed down.

However, suppose we had wished to integrate between points A and P. Then the term

$$\int_A^P (Mx/EI)\, dx$$

represents only the infinitesimal angle changes from A to P. Geometrically it represents the deflection of the elastic curve from a *tangent to the elastic curve at P*, and is so shown in Fig. 4–3B. The next term $\sum x\theta$ represents that portion of the deflection due to the slope of the tangent, and it, too, is so marked in the figure. The last term Y represents the deflection of the point of tangency, and it, too, is shown in Fig. 4–3B. The sum of all three terms gives the total deflection. The effect of omitting any term is easy to see when the equation is applied to beams, but it is less apparent when the equation is applied to rigid frames. Total deflection is always easily visualized, and that is why the equations are used in the form presented herein.

Example 4–5B. Maximum Slope. The slope at the end of the beam can be found from Eq. 4–16,

$$\Delta\theta = \int \frac{M\, ds}{EI} + \sum \theta \tag{4–16}$$

which reduces to

$$\Delta\theta_A = \int_0^L \frac{M\, dx}{EI} + 0$$

Substituting for M as before gives

$$\Delta\theta_A = \int_0^L \frac{-wx^2\, dx}{2EI} = \left[-\frac{wx^3}{6EI}\right]_0^L = -\frac{wL^3}{6EI}$$

Again, the minus sign as used here stems from a customary but arbitrary rule that moments causing compression in lower fibers are "minus." The minus does not indicate the direction of rotation. The beam slopes upward to the right. This fact is determined by common sense and not by the application of arbitrary rules.

Example 4–5C. Deflection at Any Point. Suppose we wish to find the deflection at some other point, for example, at the mid-span, point C. The

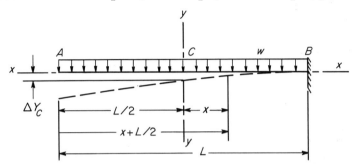

A. Beam and Loads

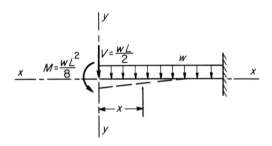

B. Free Body CB

Fig. 4–4. Deflection at center of cantilever beam.

coordinate axes must be passed through point C, as shown in Fig. 4–4A. The deflection is given by Eq. 4–14,

$$\Delta Y = \int \frac{Mx\,ds}{EI} + \sum x\theta + Y \qquad (4\text{–}14)$$

which reduces to

$$\Delta Y_C = \int_0^{L/2} \frac{Mx\,dx}{EI} + 0 + 0$$

The second and third terms each equal zero for the same reasons that were indicated at the beginning of this article. The deflection is caused only by the angle changes[5] between points C and B; therefore the integral is evaluated

---

[5] Angle changes between points A and C affect the end deflection but not the deflection at point C. Of course the *loads* between points A and C have a decided effect on the deflection at point C and therefore the effect of the loads cannot be disregarded. The effect of those loads on the deflection of point C must be included in the expression for the moment M.

only between the limits $x = 0$ and $x = L/2$. The expression for the moment must include the effects of the load between A and C as well as between C and B and, furthermore, the moment must be written in terms of a variable distance x from point C. The expression for moment in a uniformly loaded cantilever beam (see Table 3–1) is

$$M = \frac{wx^2}{2}$$

where x is the distance from the free end. But in this problem, x must be the distance to point C, so the distance to the free end is, then, $x + L/2$. Substituting $x + L/2$ for x in the above expression, we have

$$M = \frac{w(x + L/2)^2}{2}$$

Substituting in Eq. 4–14 and solving gives the deflection

$$\Delta Y_C = \int_0^{L/2} \frac{w(x + L/2)^2}{2EI} x\, dx = \frac{17wL^4}{384EI}$$

Another way to develop an expression for the moment is to draw a free body of only that portion of the beam between points C and B as shown in Fig. 4–4B. At point C there must be a shear and a moment to replace the loads between points A and C. The shear is $w(L/2)$ and the moment is $w(L/2)(L/4)$ or $wL^2/8$. Then the moment at any point between C and B due to the shear is

$$M_V = \frac{wLx}{2}$$

The moment due to the applied moment is

$$M_M = \frac{wL^2}{8}$$

and the moment due to the uniform load is

$$M_L = \frac{wx^2}{2}$$

The total moment is

$$M = M_V + M_M + M_L = \frac{wLx}{2} + \frac{wL^2}{8} + \frac{wx^2}{2}$$

Substituting these terms for M in Eq. 4–14 and solving gives the deflection

$$\Delta Y_C = \frac{1}{EI} \int_0^{L/2} \left(\frac{wLx}{2} + \frac{wL^2}{8} + \frac{wx^2}{2} \right) x\, dx = \frac{17wL^4}{384EI}$$

as before.

4–6. Deflection of a Simple Beam. The simply supported beam shown in Fig. 4–5 is uniformly loaded over half of its span.

Example 4–6. *Center Deflection.* First, place the coordinate axes at the center, at the point at which the deflection is to be calculated. The deflection is given by Eq. 4–14 as

$$\Delta Y = \int \frac{Mx\,ds}{EI} + \sum x\theta + Y \tag{4–14}$$

If angle changes are integrated between the center and one end of the beam (end B, for example), the limits on the integral sign are $x = 0$ and $x = L/2$. But now the second term ($\sum x\theta$) in the equation is *not* equal to zero; there is, instead, a very large finite angle change[6] of θ_B at B. If there were no other angle changes at all, the rotation of the beam at point B would cause deflections as shown by the straight line $A_1 B$ in Fig. 4–5C. (Of course, the beam could not deflect as shown by $A_1 B$ because of the support at A, but the line $A_1 B$ is a *part* of the angle changes and must be included in equations of deflection. The other angle changes, which are infinitesimal and are expressed in the first term of Eq. 4–14, result in the curved, dashed line AB of Fig. 4–5C, and these *together with the angle change at B* produce the elastic curve of the beam.) Thus the second term of Eq. 4–14 becomes $x_B \theta_B$ and, since $x_B = L/2$, the term can be expressed $\theta_B L/2$. The third term Y is zero because the deflection at point B is zero. Equation 4–14 becomes then

$$\Delta Y_C = \int_0^{L/2} \frac{Mx\,dx}{EI} + \frac{\theta_B L}{2} + 0$$

But the deflection cannot be solved directly because the term θ_B is as yet unknown. It must be determined before any deflections can be found. To do so, first consider the quantities which pertain to moment area equations:

1. There are finite angle changes at A and B. (This fact is of no help because we do not know the value of either one.)
2. The deflections at both A and B are zero.

The second fact provides the key to the solution because Eq. 4–14 written for the deflection of point A contains only one unknown θ_B. Placing the coordinate axes through point A as in Fig. 4–5D and writing Eq. 4–14, we have

$$\Delta Y = \int \frac{Mx\,ds}{EI} + \sum x\theta + Y \tag{4–14}$$

which becomes, for deflection at point A,

$$0 = \int_0^L \frac{Mx\,dx}{EI} + x_B \theta_B + 0$$

---

[6] The situation is similar to the rotation at point C in Fig. 4–1B, where the rotation causes a deflection, specifically the deflection $O_2 O_3$ as explained in Art. 4–1.

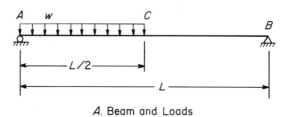

A. Beam and Loads

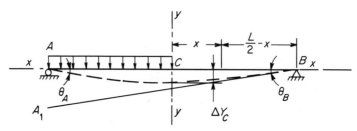

B. Load Diagram

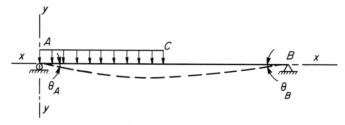

C. Position of Axes for ΔY_C

D. Position of Axes for ΔY_A

Fig. 4–5. Deflection of simple beam.

In the second term, $x_B = L$. In the first term, the moment from $x = 0$ to $x = L/2$ is

$$M = \frac{3wL}{8} x - \frac{wx^2}{2}$$

and the moment from $x = L/2$ to $x = L$ is

$$M = \frac{3wL}{8} x - \frac{wL}{2}\left(x - \frac{L}{4}\right) = \frac{wL^2}{8} - \frac{wLx}{8}$$

Because there are two different expressions for moment, the first term must be broken into two parts and each part integrated separately, giving

$$0 = \int_0^{L/2} \left(\frac{3wL}{8} x - \frac{wx^2}{2}\right) \frac{x\,dx}{EI} + \int_{L/2}^{L} \left(\frac{wL^2}{8} - \frac{wLx}{8}\right) \frac{x\,dx}{EI} + L\theta_B$$

from which

$$\theta_B = \frac{-7wL^3}{384EI}$$

The minus sign indicates that the angle change is opposite in sign to the infinitesimal angle changes which were considered positive; that is, angle changes concave upward (the infinitesimal changes) were considered positive and therefore θ_B, being minus, must be considered as an angle change concave downward.

Now the equation for deflection at the center can be solved. It was

$$\Delta Y_C = \int_0^{L/2} \frac{Mx\,dx}{EI} + \frac{\theta_B L}{2}$$

Referring to Fig. 4-5C, we find that the moment can be expressed as

$$M = \frac{wL}{8}\left(\frac{L}{2} - x\right)$$

Substituting this value for M and $-7wL^3/384EI$ for θ_B and solving, we have

$$\Delta Y_C = \int_0^{L/2} \left(\frac{wL^2}{16} - \frac{wLx}{8}\right) \frac{x\,dx}{EI} - \frac{7wL^3}{384EI}\frac{L}{2}$$

$$\Delta Y_C = \frac{2wL^4}{768EI} - \frac{7wL^4}{768EI} = \frac{-5wL^4}{768EI}$$

The minus sign indicates that, if angle changes concave upward are considered positive, a deflection downward must be considered negative,[7] *but for this problem only.* Fundamentally, we note that the effect of the minus

---

[7] This is not a general rule. The significance of signs in moment area must be determined separately for each problem by fundamental reasoning, not by applying rules.

sign in the second term (for θ_B) is greater than the effect of the plus sign in the first term. Referring to Fig. 4–5C, note that θ_B causes downward deflections. Therefore, since the term for θ_B is minus, it follows that a minus sign indicates downward deflection. Figure 4–5C also shows that the effect of the infinitesimal angle changes (the first term, which is plus in the above equation) is to *decrease* the downward deflection.

4–7. Graphical Moment Area Equations. A disadvantage of the preceding equations (4–14, 4–15, and 4–16) is that the first term (of the right

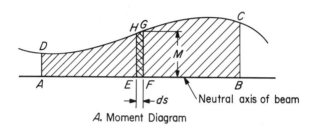

A. Moment Diagram

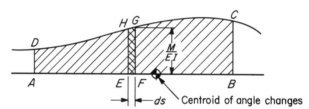

B. Moment Diagram Divided by *EI, MD/EI*

Fig. 4–6. Graphical integration of $\int (M/EI)\, ds$.

side of the equation) must be integrated, and this usually involves writing several moment equations, integrating, substituting limits, and collecting terms. Since the moment equations and the limits often involve two or more terms, the entire solution requires a great many individual computations. This disadvantage is serious for multi-span beams or for rigid frames.

Fortunately, the first term (on the right side) of Eqs. 4–14, 4–15, and 4–16 can quickly and easily be integrated semi-graphically by multiplying the distance to the centroid of the moment diagram by the area of the moment diagram divided by EI. To prove and to clarify this statement, consider the construction in Fig. 4–6. Let each ordinate of the moment diagram in Fig. 4–6A be divided by EI to produce the M/EI diagram of Fig. 4–6B. From this construction

$$\frac{M}{EI}\, ds = \text{area } EFGH$$

From Eq. B–4

$$d\theta = \frac{M\,ds}{EI} \qquad (B\text{–}4)$$

$$d\theta = \text{area } EFGH$$

That is, area $EFGH$ equals the infinitesimal angle change between points E and F. If all the angle changes are added between points A and B, we have

$$\int_A^B d\theta = \int_A^B \frac{M\,ds}{EI} = \text{area } ABCD = \sum_A^B A_{MD/EI} \qquad (4\text{–}17)$$

in which the term $\sum_A^B A_{MD/EI}$ means "area of the M/EI diagram between points A and B."

To evaluate the integral $\int (Mx/EI)\,ds$, let

$$y = \frac{M}{EI}$$

Then

$$\int \frac{Mx\,ds}{EI} = \int yx\,ds$$

But from calculus

$$\int y\,ds = \text{area} = A$$

and

$$\int yx\,ds = \text{first moment of area} = \bar{x}A$$

in which the area A is, of course, the area of the M/EI diagram, $A_{MD/EI}$, and $\bar{x}$ is the distance to the centroid of the M/EI diagram. The M/EI diagram is usually (like the moment diagram) drawn in parts and, since the parts themselves must be added to produce the whole, the integral term is expressed for generality as

$$\int \frac{Mx\,ds}{EI} = \sum \bar{x}A_{MD/EI} \qquad (4\text{–}18)$$

and in a similar manner,

$$\int \frac{My\,ds}{EI} = \sum \bar{y}A_{MD/EI} \qquad (4\text{–}19)$$

Thus Eqs. 4–14, 4–15, and 4–16 can be rewritten

$$\Delta Y = \sum \bar{x}A_{MD/EI} + \sum x\theta + Y \qquad (4\text{–}20)$$

$$\Delta X = \sum \bar{y}A_{MD/EI} + \sum y\theta + X \qquad (4\text{–}21)$$

$$\Delta\theta = \sum A_{MD/EI} + \sum \theta \qquad (4\text{–}22)$$

But it must be remembered that, basically, we are dealing with angle changes, not with moment diagrams, and that the angle changes occur along the centerline of the beam. Therefore $\bar{x}$ and $\bar{y}$ are *always* measured to the centroid of the M/EI diagram *projected to the centerline of the beam*. Specifically, $\bar{x}$ is the horizontal (or x) component, and $\bar{y}$ the vertical (or y) component, of the distance from the origin to the centroid of the M/EI diagram projected to the centerline of the beam.

Equations 4–20, 4–21, and 4–22 are herein called "graphical" moment area equations. These equations furnish the easiest and quickest way to find deflections or redundant reactions by moment area wherever EI does not vary continuously. The integral equations are superior only when EI varies in an easily expressed equation. Otherwise, it is usually better to divide the structure into a number of segments, using the average M/EI value for the full length of each segment.[8]

Since Exs. 4–5A, 4–5B, 4–5C, and 4–6 were chosen for easy solution by integration, the marked superiority of the graphical approach is not as apparent as it would be for complex problems such as rigid frames.

Equations 4–20, 4–21, and 4–22 give the absolute deflection of a point. But as originally proposed by Greene (and as stated in most textbooks), all but the first term of the right side of each equation were dropped, so that the abridged theorems of Greene give only the deflection *from a tangent* to the elastic curve at the end point of summation. The more general equations presented herein promote a clearer understanding of the basic principles involved. Having obtained a clear understanding of the operation of these equations, you can omit any term you please with perfect comprehension of its effect on the deflection (which will, of course, no longer be a true deflection).

4–8. Deflection of a Cantilever by Graphical Moment Area. The deflection of a cantilever beam uniformly loaded will be found to illustrate the use of the graphical moment area method. Compare this solution with that of Art. 4–5. The approach is exactly the same except that the first term of the equation is solved semi-graphically instead of by integration.

The beam and its loads are shown in Fig. 4–7A. The M/EI diagram is shown in Fig. 4–7B. Since EI is a constant, the moment diagram and the M/EI diagram have the same shape; each is a parabola.

Example 4–8A. *Maximum Deflection.* To find the maximum deflection (which occurs at the free end of the beam), place the coordinate axes through point A, the free end, and write Eq. 4–20

$$\Delta Y = \sum \bar{x} A_{MD/EI} + \sum x\theta + Y \qquad (4\text{–}20)$$

The second and third terms (of the right side) are zero for the reasons explained in Art. 4–5, so for this problem, Eq. 4–20 reduces to

$$\Delta Y_A = \sum_A^B \bar{x} A_{MD/EI}$$

[8] See Art. 6–6.

in which $\bar{x}$ is the distance from point A to the centroid of the M/EI diagram; for a parabola, this distance is $3L/4$. The area of the M/EI diagram is one-third base × altitude,[9] which is $wL^3/6EI$. Then the deflection is

$$\Delta Y_A = \frac{3L}{4}\frac{wL^3}{6EI} = \frac{wL^4}{8EI}$$

This is the same answer found in Art. 4–5 except for the sign, which, as has been explained, is arbitrary anyway.

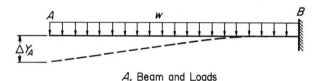

A. Beam and Loads

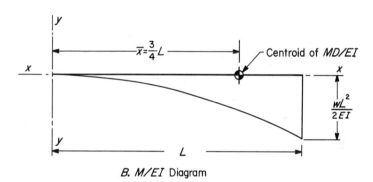

B. M/EI Diagram

Fig. 4–7. Deflection at end of cantilever beam.

Example 4–8B. Maximum Slope. The slope at the end of the beam can be found from Eq. 4–22:

$$\Delta\theta = \sum A_{MD/EI} + \sum \theta \qquad (4\text{--}22)$$

which reduces to

$$\Delta\theta_A = \sum_A^B A_{MD/EI} + 0$$

The area of a parabola is one-third base × altitude, so

$$\Delta\theta_A = \frac{1}{3}L\frac{wL^2}{2EI} = \frac{wL^3}{6EI}$$

Example 4–8C. Deflection at Any Point. To find the deflection at any point—say, the mid-span—pass the coordinate axes through that point and sum angle changes to some other point where the slope and deflection are

[9] See Table 3–1.

known. There are two points where slope and deflection are known: point B, where they are zero, and point A, where the slope is $wL^3/6EI$ and the deflection is $wL^4/8EI$. We shall solve the problem twice in order to obtain a firmer understanding of the fundamentals.

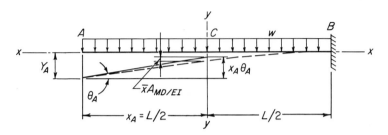

A. Beam, Loads, and Construction

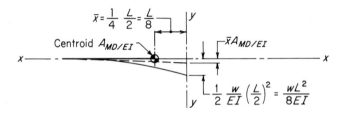

B. M/EI Diagram

**Fig. 4–8. Deflection at center of cantilever beam.
Angle changes from C to A.**

First, let us work with the beam between the center and the free end. Write Eq. 4–20

$$\Delta Y = \sum \bar{x} A_{MD/EI} + \sum x\theta + Y \qquad (4\text{–}20)$$

Placing the coordinate axes at the center (see Fig. 4–8) and summing angle changes from C to A, the equation becomes

$$\Delta Y_C = \sum_{C}^{A} \bar{x} A_{MD/EI} + x_A \theta_A + Y_A$$

In the first term, $\bar{x}$ is one-fourth of the base, which is $(1/4)(L/2)$, or $L/8$; the area of the M/EI diagram is one-third of base × altitude, which is

$$\frac{1}{3}\frac{L}{2}\frac{wL^2}{8EI} = \frac{wL^3}{48EI}$$

In the second term, x_A is $L/2$ and θ_A is $wL^3/6EI$, as found previously. The third term Y_A is $wL^4/8EI$, as also was found previously.

The signs of the terms must be supplied by thinking through the effect of each term. As shown in Fig. 4–8A, ΔY_A is a downward deflection. Whether it is called plus or minus makes no difference, but any decision for this term determines the signs of all other terms. Suppose we call downward deflections plus; then Y_A is plus.

The second term is minus. To determine its sign, consider the effect of θ_A independently of anything else. The slope at A is upward to the right. If there are no other angle changes and no deflection at A, a line sloping upward to the right produces only upward deflections which are minus, according to the decision above. Therefore the sign of the second term is minus.

The first term is plus. The angle changes are concave downward. A line that curves concave downward considered all by itself (with no other angle changes at A and no deflection at A) will curve downward to the right, as shown by the dashed line in Fig. 4–8B. Since downward deflections are plus, the first term is plus.

Writing the proper signs and substituting the values found above for each term, we have

$$\Delta Y_C = +\frac{L}{8}\frac{wL^3}{48EI} - \frac{L}{2}\frac{wL^3}{6EI} + \frac{wL^4}{8EI} = +\frac{17}{384}\frac{wL^4}{EI}$$

in which the plus indicates downward deflection.

The deflection at the center can also be solved by summing angle changes from C to B by writing Eq. 4–20 again:

$$\Delta Y = \sum \bar{x}A_{MD/EI} + \sum x\theta + Y \qquad (4\text{–}20)$$

By considering Fig. 4–9A, the equation reduces to

$$\Delta Y_C = \sum_C^B \bar{x}A_{MD/EI} + 0 + 0$$

The second and third terms are zero because there is no finite angle change at B and no deflection at B. The moment diagram from C to B is only a segment of a parabola, but its area and centroid can be found by the method explained in Art. 3–1, which is universal and holds for any kind of curve, parabola or not. It makes use of the fact that the first moment of an area equals the sum of first moments of its parts. Therefore in Eq. 3–1,

$$\bar{x}A = \bar{x}_1 A_1 + \bar{x}_2 A_2$$

Substituting the proper values and signs shown in Fig. 4–9B gives

$$\frac{L}{4}\frac{wL^3}{6EI} = -\frac{L}{8}\frac{wL^3}{48EI} + \bar{x}_2 \frac{7wL^3}{48EI}$$

from which

$$\bar{x}_2 = \frac{17}{56}L$$

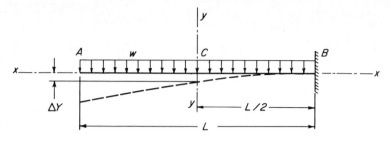

A. Beam and Loads

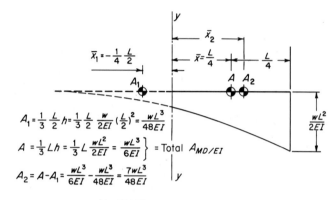

$A_1 = \frac{1}{3}\frac{L}{2}h = \frac{1}{3}\frac{L}{2}\frac{w}{2EI}(\frac{L}{2})^2 = \frac{wL^3}{48EI}$

$\left. \begin{array}{l} A = \frac{1}{3}Lh = \frac{1}{3}L\frac{wL^2}{2EI} = \frac{wL^3}{6EI} \end{array} \right\} = $ Total $A_{MD/EI}$

$A_2 = A - A_1 = \frac{wL^3}{6EI} - \frac{wL^3}{48EI} = \frac{7wL^3}{48EI}$

B. M/EI Diagram from C to B

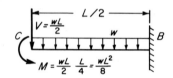

$V = \frac{wL}{2}$

$M = \frac{wL}{2}\frac{L}{4} = \frac{wL^2}{8}$

C. Free Body CB

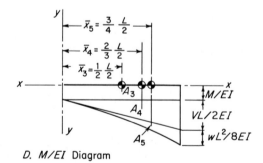

D. M/EI Diagram

Fig. 4–9. Deflection at center of cantilever beam.
Angle changes from C to B.

Substituting in the above equation, we have

$$\Delta Y_C = \bar{x}_2 A_2 = \frac{17}{56} L \frac{7}{48} \frac{wL^3}{EI} = \frac{17}{384} \frac{wL^4}{EI}$$

as before.

Another method of handling the parabolic segment is to replace the load between A and C with a force and a moment, as shown in Fig. 4-9C. The moment diagrams drawn in cantilever parts and shown in Fig. 4-9D consist of a rectangle, a triangle, and a parabola. The area of each of these figures is found as follows:

$$A_3 = \frac{L}{2} \frac{M}{EI} = \frac{L}{2} \frac{wL^2}{8EI} = \frac{wL^3}{16EI}$$

$$A_4 = \frac{1}{2} \frac{L}{2} \frac{VL}{2EI} = \frac{1}{2} \frac{L}{2} \frac{wL}{2} \frac{L}{2EI} = \frac{wL^3}{16EI}$$

$$A_5 = \frac{1}{3} \frac{L}{2} \frac{wL^2}{8EI} = \frac{wL^3}{48EI}$$

Substituting these areas and the centroids (given in Fig. 4-9D) into the above equation for ΔY_C, we have

$$\Delta Y_C = \sum_C^B \bar{x} A_{MD/EI} = \bar{x}_3 A_3 + \bar{x}_4 A_4 + \bar{x}_5 A_5$$

$$\Delta Y_C = \frac{L}{4} \frac{wL^3}{16EI} + \frac{L}{3} \frac{wL^3}{16EI} + \frac{3L}{8} \frac{wL^3}{48EI} = \frac{17}{384} \frac{wL^4}{EI}$$

which agrees with all the previous results.

4-9. Deflection of a Simple Beam by Graphical Moment Area. The speed of the graphical method is somewhat obscured in the preceding articles because of the necessity for explaining each detail. Stripped to bare essentials, however, the graphical method is very fast. In the following solution, explanation is held to a minimum because the operations themselves and the reasons for them have been covered in Arts. 4-6, 4-7, and 4-8.[10]

Example 4-9. Center Deflection. The beam, its loads, and approximate elastic curve are shown in Fig. 4-10A. Two means of constructing moment diagrams are shown in Figs. 4-10B and 4-10C—simple beam moments and cantilever parts from the right respectively. (Cantilever parts from the left are awkward here.) Either is suitable, each involves two parts (the diagram of Fig. 4-10B must be divided into two parts, as shown, to obtain area and centroid), and neither offers particular advantage over the other. We shall use the diagrams of Fig. 4-10C.[11]

[10] These should be reviewed if you encounter any difficulty with Art. 4-9. Article 4-9 is a test of whether you understand the preceding text. You should be able to follow and then to reconstruct every step without difficulty.

[11] You might check the answer by reworking the problem, using Fig. 4-10B. Review Art. 3-2 and Fig. 3-4 if you get an incorrect answer:

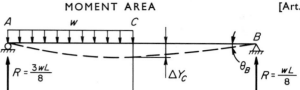

A. Beam and Loads

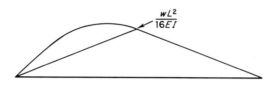

B. Simple Beam (Total) M/EI Diagram

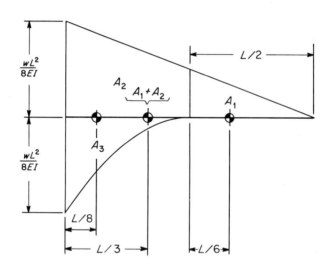

C. M/EI Diagrams. Cantilever Parts

Fig. 4-10. Deflection of simple beam. Graphical moment area.

To find the deflection at the center, place the coordinate axes at the center and write Eq. 4-20:

$$\Delta Y = \sum \bar{x}A_{MD/EI} + \sum x\theta + Y \qquad (4\text{-}20)$$

which reduces to

$$\Delta Y_C = \sum_{C}^{B} \bar{x}A_{MD/EI} + x_B\theta_B + 0$$

Since θ_B is unknown, it must be found by solving the equation for the deflection at point A, which is zero. So Eq. 4–20 reduces to

$$\Delta Y_A = 0 = \sum_A^B \bar{x} A_{MD/EI} + x_B \theta_B + 0$$

Substituting from Fig. 4–10C and noting that the coordinate axes must be shifted to point A, we have

$$0 = \frac{L}{3}\frac{1}{2}L\frac{wL^2}{8EI} - \frac{L}{8}\frac{1}{3}\frac{L}{2}\frac{wL^2}{8EI} + L\theta_B$$

from which

$$\theta_B = \frac{-7}{384}\frac{wL^3}{EI} \qquad \text{concave downward}$$

Now the above equation for ΔY_C can be solved as follows:

$$\Delta Y_C = \frac{L}{6}\frac{1}{2}\frac{L}{2}\frac{wL^2}{16EI} - \frac{L}{2}\frac{7}{384}\frac{wL^3}{EI} = -\frac{5}{768}\frac{wL^4}{EI}$$

The signs are the same as those used in Art. 4–6.

5

STATICALLY INDETERMINATE BEAMS

5–1. Retrospect and Preview. Most of the fundamentals of the moment area method have been covered in the previous chapter. More examples are to come in this chapter, but there will be very little that is completely new. Of course, much of the foregoing theory needs to be clinched, so a large part of the following explanation is detailed and thorough.

All of the problems which follow are statically indeterminate. The internal forces cannot be solved by means of the equations of static equilibrium alone, so other equations—such as moment area equations, for example—must be written. To utilize this method, simply write an equation (or several if necessary) for some deflection or rotation which is known to be zero. Since the equations involve moment diagrams which are in turn dependent upon unknown forces, the unknown forces can be found. Basically, this process is quite simple; practically, it can become involved if the structure is complex or if there are many loads.

5–2. Single Redundant Reaction. Consider a prismatic (constant EI) beam 36 ft long loaded as shown in Fig. 5–1A. In the following examples, let it be required to find:

A. V_B (vertical reaction at B);
B. ΔY_A (vertical deflection at A);
C. $\Delta \theta_A$ (slope at A);
D. $\Delta \theta_B$ (slope at B);
E. ΔY_{max} (position, magnitude, and direction of maximum deflection between B and C).

Example 5–2A. Reactions at B. The beam is statically indeterminate because there are three unknown reaction components, V_B, V_C, and M_C, and there are only two useful equations of static equilibrium

$$\Sigma M = 0 \tag{1–1}$$

$$\Sigma V = 0 \tag{1–3}$$

Equation 1–2

$$\Sigma H = 0 \tag{1–2}$$

is useless here because there are no horizontal forces or horizontal reaction components. With three unknowns and two equations the beam is indeterminate to the first degree. Therefore one other equation must be written

70

before the three unknowns can be found. It must be an equation of elasticity such as one of the moment area equations. Equation 4–20 is the useful one because the deflection at B is known to be zero. Nothing is known about the change of slope at any point (except point C), so Eq. 4–22 is of no use.

Write Eq. 4–20 for the vertical deflection at B by passing the axes through point B, as shown in Fig. 5–1B, and sum the angle changes from B to C. Then Eq. 4–20

$$\Delta Y = \sum \bar{x} A_{MD/EI} + \sum x\theta + Y \qquad (4\text{–}20)$$

reduces to

$$\Delta Y_B = 0 = \sum_{B}^{C} \bar{x} A_{MD/EI} + 0 + 0$$

Now ΔY_B is zero because of an unyielding reaction at B. The term $\sum x\theta$ is zero because there are only infinitesimal angle changes along the elastic curve between B and C, and at point C—the end point of summation of terms—the rotation is zero. The term Y is zero because there is no deflection at the end point of summation, point C.

The moment diagrams from B to C can be evaluated by replacing the load from A to B with an equivalent shear and moment, and by replacing the roller at B by the unknown force V_B, as shown in Fig. 5–1C. The moment diagrams can be drawn in many ways, and one convenient way is in cantilever parts, as shown in Fig. 5–1D. Moment diagrams plotted above the base line are called plus; below the base line, minus. This is purely arbitrary, and opposite signs would yield the same results. The areas and distances to centroids are shown in Table 5–1.

TABLE 5–1

Solution of $\displaystyle\sum_{B}^{C} \bar{x} A_{MD/EI} = 0$

Moment Diagram Part	$\bar{x}$	$A_{MD/EI}$ Coeff. $\times$ Base $\times$ Height	$+\bar{x} A_{MD/EI}$	$-\bar{x} A_{MD/EI}$
A_1	16	$+\dfrac{1}{2} \times 24 \times \dfrac{24 V_B}{EI}$	$16 \times 24 \times 24 V_B/2EI$	
A_2	12	$-1 \times 24 \times \dfrac{48}{EI}$		$12 \times 24 \times 48/EI$
A_3	16	$-\dfrac{1}{2} \times 24 \times \dfrac{288}{EI}$		$16 \times 24 \times 288/2EI$
A_4	18	$-\dfrac{1}{3} \times 24 \times \dfrac{576}{EI}$		$18 \times 24 \times 576/3EI$

Adding the terms in Table 5–1,

$$\frac{16 \times 24 \times 24 \times V_B}{2EI} - \frac{12 \times 24 \times 48}{EI} - \frac{16 \times 24 \times 288}{2EI} - \frac{18 \times 24 \times 576}{3EI} = 0$$

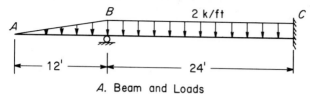

A. Beam and Loads

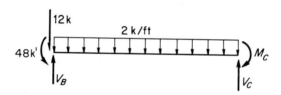

B. Angle Changes from *B* to *C*

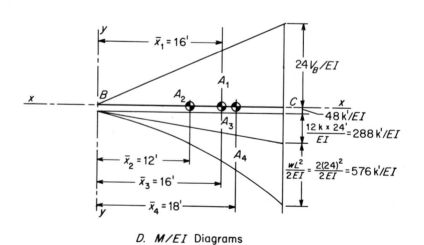

C. Free Body of *BC*

D. M/EI Diagrams

Fig. 5–1. Statically indeterminate reaction.

and solving for V_B, gives

$$V_B = +33.0 \text{ kips} = 33.0 \text{ kips upward}$$

in which the plus sign indicates that the assumed direction of V_B (upward) is correct.

Example 5–2B. Deflection at A. Now that the reaction at B has been found, it can be treated exactly like any other load acting upon the structure. This is always true of any reaction in any structure. The only special feature

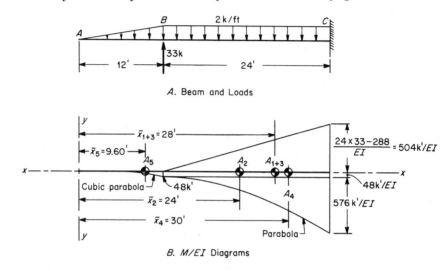

A. Beam and Loads

B. M/EI Diagrams

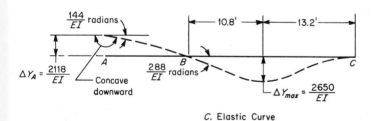

C. Elastic Curve

Fig. 5–2. Deflection of a beam.

of this particular load is that its effect is to cause a deflection of zero. To emphasize this statement, Fig. 5–2 shows the same beam with an upward load of 33 kips acting at B. This beam is statically determinate, and its deflections can be found as in any other statically determinate beam, such as those of Arts. 4–8 and 4–9, for example.

The M/EI diagrams for the entire beam are shown in Fig. 5–2B. Note that the partial MD/EI areas A_1 and A_3 of Fig. 5–1D are combined into a single area for convenience. This is possible only because V_B is now known. To find the deflection at point A, pass the coordinate axes through A and write Eq. 4–20

$$\Delta Y = \sum \bar{x} A_{MD/EI} + \sum x\theta + Y \qquad (4\text{–}20)$$

which reduces to

$$\Delta Y_A = \sum_A^C \bar{x} A_{MD/EI} + 0 + 0$$

if the angle changes are summed from A to C. The only unknown is ΔY_A. All the $\bar{x} A_{MD/EI}$ terms are known. The term $\sum x\theta$ equals zero because there are no finite angle changes between A and C. The term Y is zero because at the end point of summation of terms, point C, there is no deflection. The equation is evaluated in Table 5–2.

TABLE 5–2

Solution of $\Delta Y_A = \sum_A^C \bar{x} A_{MD/EI}$

Part	$\bar{x}$	$A_{MD/EI}$ Coeff. $\times$ Base $\times$ Height	$+\bar{x} A_{MD/EI}$	$-\bar{x} A_{MD/EI}$
A_{1+3}	28	$+\dfrac{1}{2} \times 24 \times \dfrac{504}{EI}$	$169,300/EI$	
A_2	24	$-1 \times 24 \times \dfrac{48}{EI}$		$27,600/EI$
A_4	30	$-\dfrac{1}{3} \times 24 \times \dfrac{576}{EI}$		$138,200/EI$
A_5*	9.60	$-\dfrac{1}{4} \times 12 \times \dfrac{48}{EI}$		$1,382/EI$
			$169,300/EI$	$167,182/EI$

$\Delta Y_A = +169,300/EI - 167,182/EI = +2118/EI = 2118/EI$ upward

* Note that A_5 is a cubic parabola.

The answer cannot be guaranteed to more than one significant figure because the calculations were made with the slide rule. The answer to four places is actually $2074/EI$. Note that the answer is in kip-foot units; therefore EI must be expressed in kip-foot units also. Suppose, for example, the beam is the steel wide-flange section designated 16 W 50. From the AISC Manual it has a moment of inertia of 655.4 in.[4]. Young's modulus for steel is approximately 30,000,000 psi. Then from the conversion constant 1/144,000, developed in Art. 3–4,

$$EI = 655.4 \times 30,000,000 \text{ lb} \times \text{in.}^2 = \frac{655.4 \times 30,000,000}{144,000} \text{ kip-ft}^2$$

$$= 136,000 \text{ kip-ft}^2$$

and

$$\Delta Y_A = \frac{2,118}{136,000} = 0.015 \text{ ft upward}$$

The direction of the deflection is determined by the following reasoning. The moment diagrams are plotted on the compressive side of the beam in Fig. 5–2B. A moment diagram plotted above the beam indicates that the

TABLE 5–3

Solution of $\Delta \theta_A = \sum\limits_{A}^{C} A_{MD/EI}$

Part	$A_{MD/EI}$ Coeff. × Base × Height	$+A_{MD/EI}$	$-A_{MD/EI}$
A_{1+3}	$+\dfrac{1}{2} \times 24 \times \dfrac{504}{EI}$	$6{,}050/EI$	
A_2	$-1 \times 24 \times \dfrac{48}{EI}$		$1{,}152/EI$
A_4	$-\dfrac{1}{3} \times 24 \times \dfrac{576}{EI}$		$4{,}610/EI$
A_5	$-\dfrac{1}{4} \times 12 \times \dfrac{48}{EI}$	$\overline{6{,}050/EI}$	$\dfrac{144/EI}{\overline{5{,}906/EI}}$

$\Delta \theta_A = +6050/EI - 5906/EI = +144/EI$ radians clockwise

elastic curve is concave upward. The beam might be said to bend toward the moment diagrams when they are plotted on the compressive side of the beam. The partial moment diagram labeled A_{1+3} in Fig. 5–2B would tend to create an elastic curve concave upward, and, since the right end is fixed, the point A would tend to move upward. By the same reasoning, all the other moment diagrams would cause point A to move downward. But examination of Table 5–2 shows the effects of A_{1+3} to be greater than the effects of all the other moment diagrams; therefore point A must move upward.

Example 5–2C. Rotation at A. The slope at point A can be found by writing Eq. 4–22

$$\Delta \theta = \sum A_{MD/EI} + \sum \theta \qquad (4\text{–}22)$$

If the angle changes are summed from A to C, the equation reduces to

$$\Delta \theta_A = \sum\limits_{A}^{C} A_{MD/EI} + 0$$

The term $\Sigma \theta$ equals zero because at the end point of summation, point C, the beam is fixed and there is no rotation. The solution is given in Table 5–3.

The direction of rotation can be determined by reasoning the effects of the moment areas. In Table 5–3 moment area A_{1+3} ($6050/EI$) is greater than all other moment areas combined (5906/EI). It is plotted above the beam in Fig. 5–2B, indicating compression in the upper fibers, which produces a curve concave upward. This upward curling results in a clockwise rotation at point A, as shown in Fig. 5–2C. If the beam is a 16 W̄ 50, its EI value is, from Ex. 5–2B, 136,000 kip-ft², and the actual rotation is

$$\Delta\theta_A = 144/EI = 144/136{,}000 = 0.00106 \text{ radian} = 0° \ 04'$$

Example 5–2D. Rotation at B. The rotation at point B can be found by summing angle changes between points B and A or between points B and C. The former summation is a bit more difficult to understand, but it is a more general solution, so let us use it since our purpose is to develop understanding.

The slope is found by writing Eq. 4–22,

$$\Delta\theta = \sum A_{MD/EI} + \sum \theta \qquad\qquad (4\text{–}22)$$

If angle changes are summed from B to A, the equation reduces to

$$\Delta\theta_B = \sum_{B}^{A} A_{MD/EI} + \theta_A$$

At the end point of summation of angle changes, point A, there is an angle change 144/EI clockwise, as found in Ex. 5–2C. The sign of that angle change was plus, but it must be emphasized that signs of angle changes and moment diagrams must be determined anew for each separate part of a problem. There are many instances where a certain angle change called plus for one part of a problem must be termed minus for the next part of the problem. Again, it should be noted that the best way to determine signs in moment area is by reasoning the effects of angle changes and by visualizing the shape of the elastic curve. We can arbitrarily call the slope of the elastic curve at A minus. Change of slope and angle change are synonymous, so the above statement can be reworded to say angle change at A is minus. To visualize the angle change, consider the centerline of the beam at the deflected position of point A to be extended horizontally to the left, as shown in Fig. 5–2C. The angle change is the angle between this extended centerline and the elastic curve. Since it is an angle that is concave downward, it follows that all angle changes concave downward must now be called minus. Thus it follows that moment diagrams plotted below the beam must be called minus whereas those above are plus.

Substituting in the foregoing equation for $\Delta\theta_B$, we have

$$\Delta\theta_B = -\frac{1}{4} \times 12 \times \frac{48}{EI} - \frac{144}{EI} = -\frac{288}{EI} \text{ radians} = \frac{288}{EI} \text{ radians clockwise}$$

From consideration of the foregoing angle changes, the elastic curve rotates clockwise at B; this can be verified by inspection of Fig. 5–2C.

The slope at point B could have been as easily found by summing angle changes between B and C. This involves adding algebraically the terms for parts A_{1+3}, A_2, and A_4 of Table 5–3; the sum of these terms is $+288/EI$. In this instance, the rotation $+288/EI$ can be determined to be clockwise by the reasoning which follows Table 5–3.

Example 5–2E. Maximum Deflection. To find the point between B and C where the deflection is maximum, find the point where the slope is zero. This can be done by passing the coordinate axes through a variable point located x feet from B. (See Fig. 5–2C.) Equation 4–22

$$\Delta\theta = \sum A_{MD/EI} + \sum \theta \qquad (4\text{–}22)$$

reduces to

$$\Delta\theta_x = 0 = \sum_x^B A_{MD/EI} + \theta_B$$

if angle changes are summed from x to B.

The partial areas of the moment diagrams must be expressed in terms of the unknown, x. The partial area of A_{1+3} (Fig. 5–2B) can easily be written by letting y equal the height of the diagram at point x. Then the partial area A_{1+3} is $xy/2$. From similar triangles

$$\frac{y}{x} = \frac{504}{24EI}$$

or

$$y = \frac{21x}{EI}$$

Substituting for y in $xy/2$, the partial area becomes $21x^2/2EI$. The partial area A_2 is $48x/EI$. Again, if we let y be the height of the moment diagram at x, the partial area A_4 is $xy/3$. From properties of parabolas

$$\frac{y}{576/EI} = \left(\frac{x}{24}\right)^2$$

Substituting for y in $xy/3$, the partial area becomes

$$\frac{x}{3}\frac{x^2}{(24)^2}\frac{576}{EI} = \frac{x^3}{3EI}$$

Finally, θ_B is $288/EI$ from Ex. 5–2D.

Substituting in the equation for $\Delta\theta_x$, and letting angle changes concave downward be minus, we have

$$\Delta\theta_x = 0 = +\frac{21x^2}{2EI} - \frac{48x}{EI} - \frac{x^3}{3EI} - \frac{288}{EI}$$

from which[1]

$$x = 10.8 \text{ ft}$$

Instead of setting up a cubic equation, which is usually solved by trial anyway, it may be considered easier to solve for $\Delta\theta_x = 0$ by trial. A value for x can be estimated, the partial areas can be found arithmetically from consideration of the diagrams of Fig. 5–2B, and these areas can then be substituted into the equation for $\Delta\theta_x$. Three trials should be sufficient.

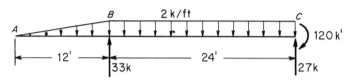

A. Beam and Loads

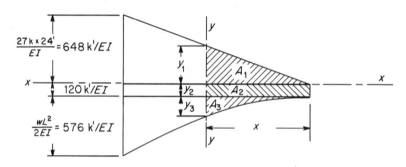

B. M/EI Diagrams. Cantilever Parts from Right

Fig. 5–3. Maximum deflection.

An easier solution is to sum angle changes from x to C. To do so, it would be more convenient to redraw the moment diagrams in cantilever parts starting from C, as shown in Fig. 5–3B. Equation 4–22

$$\Delta\theta = \sum A_{MD/EI} + \sum\theta \qquad (4\text{–}22)$$

reduces to

$$\Delta\theta_x = 0 = \sum_x^C A_{MD/EI} + 0$$

In this equation, $\sum\theta$ is zero because, point C being fixed, there are no finite angle changes.

[1] There are exact methods for solving cubic equations, but they are sufficiently difficult or tedious to justify trial and error for the occasional solution. The best way to solve by trial and error is to substitute a value for x and plot the result on a graph. After one more substitution, other values of x can be chosen intelligently by inspecting the graph.

The shaded partial areas of the moment diagrams must be expressed in terms of x. The partial areas are evaluated by the same method as explained in the foregoing. The terms for each MD/EI area are evaluated in Table 5–4.

TABLE 5–4

Solution of $\displaystyle\sum_{x}^{C} A_{MD/EI} = 0$

Moment Diagram Part	Area	Find y from:	$A_{MD/EI}$
A_1	$+\tfrac{1}{2}y_1 x$	$\dfrac{y_1}{648/EI} = \dfrac{x}{24}$	$+\dfrac{x}{2}\dfrac{x}{24}\dfrac{648}{EI}$
A_2	$-y_2 x$	$y_2 = \dfrac{120}{EI}$	$-\dfrac{120x}{EI}$
A_3	$-\tfrac{1}{3}y_3 x$	$\dfrac{y_3}{576/EI} = \dfrac{x^2}{(24)^2}$	$-\dfrac{x}{3}\dfrac{x^2}{(24)^2}\dfrac{576}{EI}$

From Table 5–4,

$$\frac{648x^2}{2 \times 24EI} - \frac{120x}{EI} - \frac{x^3}{3EI}\frac{576}{(24)^2} = 0$$

Reducing

$$x^2 - 40.5x + 360 = 0$$

and[2]

$$x = 13.2 \text{ ft}$$

The previous solution located the point of maximum deflection 10.8 ft to the right of B. This corresponds exactly to the second solution, 13.2 ft to the left of A. Although both methods give the correct result, the second is a more intelligent approach because it avoids the cubic equation and the trial-and-error solution.

To find the maximum deflection between B and C, which we now know occurs at point x, 13.2 ft from C, write Eq. 4–20

$$\Delta Y = \sum \bar{x}A_{MD/EI} + \sum x\theta + Y \qquad (4\text{–}20)$$

[2] An excellent way to solve quadratic equations is to complete the square by adding such numbers to both sides of the equation that the left side becomes a perfect square, thus

$$x^2 - 40.5x + \left(\frac{40.5}{2}\right)^2 = -360 + \left(\frac{40.5}{2}\right)^2$$

Taking the square root of each side,

$$x - 20.25 = \pm\sqrt{(20.25)^2 - 360} = \pm 7.07$$
$$x = 20.25 - 7.07 = 13.2 \text{ ft}$$

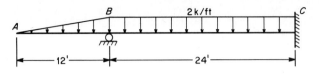

A. Beam and Loads

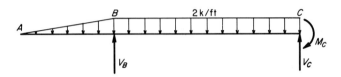

B. Free Body *AC*

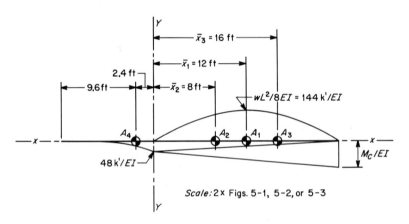

Scale: 2× Figs. 5-1, 5-2, or 5-3

C. M/EI Diagrams. Simple Beam Parts from *B* to *C*

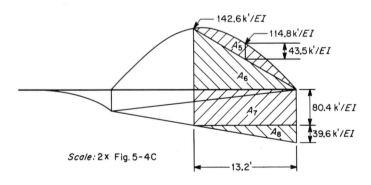

Scale: 2× Fig. 5-4C

D. M/EI Diagrams for Maximum Deflection

Fig. 5–4. Deflection of a beam.

which reduces to

$$\Delta Y_x = \sum_x^C \bar{x} A_{MD/EI} + 0 + 0$$

Both $\sum x\theta$ and Y are zero, because at C (the end of summation) there is no angle change and no deflection. The areas of the moment diagrams are given in terms of x in Table 5–4. Using the computation already completed and substituting 13.2 for x, we solve the above equation as shown in Table 5–5.

TABLE 5–5

Solution of $\Delta Y_x = \sum_x^C \bar{x} A_{MD/EI}$

Moment Diagram Part	$\bar{x}$	$A_{MD/EI}$ from Table 5–4	$+\bar{x} A_{MD/EI}$	$-\bar{x} A_{MD/EI}$
A_1	$\dfrac{1}{3} \times 13.2$	$+ \dfrac{648(13.2)^2}{2 \times 24EI}$	$10,340/EI$	
A_2	$\dfrac{13.2}{2}$	$- \dfrac{120 \times 13.2}{EI}$		$10,450/EI$
A_3	$\dfrac{13.2}{4}$	$- \dfrac{576(13.2)^3}{3(24)^2EI}$		$2,540/EI$
		Summation	$10,340/EI$	$12,990/EI$

$$\Delta Y_x = +10,340/EI - 12,990/EI = -2,650/EI$$

Substituting the value of EI in kip-foot units, we have

$$\Delta Y_x = -\frac{2650}{136,000} = 0.020 \text{ ft downward}^3$$

5–3. Alternate Solution for Beams. There are scores of different approaches to the solution of the problem of Art. 5–2, each differing slightly from the others but all leading to the correct answer. Moment diagrams can be drawn in simple beam parts, or in cantilever parts from the left, or in cantilever parts from the right. Even these three variants do not exhaust all the possibilities in the specific attack on the problem, and the possibilities multiply as the problems become more complex. Some approaches are easy and some are difficult, just as in the solution of a determinate structure, and so it is always wise to consider the approach before commencing any computations. All the solutions given here are practicable, although some are shorter than others.

Example 5–3A. Moment at C. One alternate solution of merit is carried out in a manner somewhat similar to that of Art. 5–2 but with the use of moment diagrams plotted in simple beam parts between B and C, as shown in Fig. 5–4. The one unknown value is the moment at C.

---

[3] Why is the movement downward?

Again, it is necessary to write one equation of elasticity to solve the unknown moment at C. Equation 4–20

$$\Delta Y = \sum \bar{x} A_{MD/EI} + \sum \theta x + Y \qquad (4\text{–}20)$$

reduces to

$$\Delta Y_B = 0 = \sum_B^C \bar{x} A_{MD/EI} + 0 + 0$$

if angle changes are summed from B to C. It should no longer be necessary to state why some of the above terms equal zero, but if explanation is needed, the reasons are precisely those used to explain the same equation in Ex. 5–2A.

The equation is solved in Table 5–6.

TABLE 5–6

Solution of $\displaystyle\sum_B^C \bar{x} A_{MD/EI} = 0$

Moment Diagram Part	$\bar{x}$	$A_{MD/EI}$ Coeff. × Base × Height	$+\bar{x} A_{MD/EI}$	$-\bar{x} A_{MD/EI}$
A_1	12	$+\dfrac{2}{3} \times 24 \times \dfrac{144}{EI}$	$12 \times 16 \times 144/EI$	
A_2	8	$-\dfrac{1}{2} \times 24 \times \dfrac{48}{EI}$		$8 \times 12 \times 48/EI$
A_3	16	$-\dfrac{1}{2} \times 24 \times \dfrac{M_C}{EI}$		$16 \times 12 \times M_C/EI$

so that
$$12 \times 16 \times 144/EI - 8 \times 12 \times 48/EI - 16 \times 12 M_C/EI = 0$$
from which[4]
$$M_C = 120 \text{ kip-ft}$$

Now that M_C is known, the reaction at B can be determined, by use of the equations of static equilibrium, to be 33 kips, which is the same value as that found in Ex. 5–2A.

Example 5–3B. Deflection at A. To find the deflection at A, pass the coordinate axes through A and write Eq. 4–20

$$\Delta Y = \sum \bar{x} A_{MD/EI} + \sum x\theta + Y \qquad (4\text{–}20)$$

which reduces to

$$\Delta Y_A = \sum_A^C \bar{x} A_{MD/EI} + 0 + 0$$

---

[4] It is often advantageous to leave equations in the unsimplified form above so that terms may be easily canceled. It is a small point but, nonetheless, a frequent time saver. One of the hallmarks of the competent professional is the studied use of time-saving devices.

This is the same equation as that in Ex. 5–2B. The solution is given in Table 5–7.

This value for the deflection at A compares favorably with that of Art. 5–2. The small difference is due to slide-rule error. When large numbers are

TABLE 5–7

Solution of $\Delta Y_A = \sum\limits_{A}^{C} \bar{x} A_{MD/EI}$

Moment Diagram Part	$\bar{x}$	$A_{MD/EI}$ Coeff. $\times$ Base $\times$ Height	$+\bar{x} A_{MD/EI}$	$-\bar{x} A_{MD/EI}$
A_1	24	$+\dfrac{2}{3} \times 24 \times \dfrac{144}{EI}$	$55,300/EI$	
A_2	20	$-\dfrac{1}{2} \times 24 \times \dfrac{48}{EI}$		$11,520/EI$
A_3	28	$-\dfrac{1}{2} \times 24 \times \dfrac{120}{EI}$		$40,300/EI$
A_4	9.60	$-\dfrac{1}{4} \times 12 \times \dfrac{48}{EI}$		$1,382/EI$
			$55,300/EI$	$53,202/EI$

$$\Delta Y_A = +55,300/EI - 53,202/EI = 2,098/EI$$

subtracted from large numbers to yield a small-numbered answer, that answer is likely to be considerably in error. For example, if the number 55,300 in Table 5–7 had been called 55,400 (a very slight error indeed), the answer would have been 2198 instead of 2098, a 5 percent difference. Therefore, the slide rule should be manipulated with great care, and even then the answer will not always be correct to more than one or two significant figures.

Example 5–3C. Rotation at A. To find the true slope at A, write Eq. 4–22

$$\Delta\theta = \sum A_{MD/EI} + \sum\theta \qquad (4\text{--}22)$$

which reduces to

$$\Delta\theta_A = \sum_{A}^{C} A_{MD/EI} + 0$$

when the angle changes are summed from A to C. The solution is in Table 5–8.

Example 5–3D. Rotation at B. The slope at B can be determined by summing angle changes from B to C, that is, by using parts A_1, A_2, and A_3 of Table 5–8. The summation of these terms yields $\Delta\theta_A = 289/EI$, which compares well with the answer found in Ex. 5–2D.

Example 5–3E. Maximum Deflection. The moment diagrams of Fig. 5–4 are not convenient for finding the position of the point of maximum deflection because of the complicated expressions for a variable area of a parabolic segment which does not extend to the vertex. So it is much better to use

TABLE 5–8

Solution of $\Delta\theta_A = \sum_A^C A_{MD/EI}$

Moment Diagram Part	$A_{MD/EI}$ Coeff. × Base × Height	$+A_{MD/EI}$	$-A_{MD/EI}$
A_1	$+\dfrac{2}{3} \times 24 \times \dfrac{144}{EI}$	2,304/EI	
A_2	$-\dfrac{1}{2} \times 24 \times \dfrac{48}{EI}$		576/EI
A_3	$-\dfrac{1}{2} \times 24 \times \dfrac{120}{EI}$		1,440/EI
A_4	$-\dfrac{1}{4} \times 12 \times \dfrac{48}{EI}$		144/EI
		2,304/EI	2,160/EI

$\Delta\theta_A = +2{,}304/EI - 2{,}160/EI = +144/EI$ radians clockwise

the moment diagrams of Fig. 5–3 for this purpose. But in order to illustrate how the moment diagrams of Fig. 5–4 can be handled (when necessary), a solution by this method is given.

The point of maximum deflection is the point of zero slope, found by making use of Eq. 4–22

$$\Delta\theta = \sum A_{MD/EI} + \sum\theta \qquad (4\text{–}22)$$

which reduces to

$$\Delta\theta_x = 0 = \sum_x^C A_{MD/EI} + 0$$

This equation should be solved by trial and error to avoid complicated algebraic expressions. By trial and error, the position of the point of zero slope and maximum deflection is found to be 13.2 ft from C, which can be checked as follows: in Fig. 5–4D divide the parabolic segment into two parts, A_5 and A_6. Note that A_5 is a symmetrical segment of a parabola with its vertex on the centerline 6.6 ft from C. Its area is 2/3 base × altitude in which each is, respectively, a horizontal and a vertical projection.[5] The altitude is obtained by finding the simple beam moment due to the uniform load 6.6 ft from C; it is 114.8 kip-ft. The height of A_6 at 6.6 ft from C is 71.3 kip-ft.

[5] Review Art. 3–2 for a more complete explanation.

The altitude of A_5 is then $114.8 - 71.3 = 43.5$ kip-ft.[6] The horizontal projection of the base is, of course, 13.2 ft. The final trial in a series of trials is shown in Table 5–9.

TABLE 5–9

Solution of $\sum\limits_{x}^{C} A_{MD/EI} = 0$

Moment Diagram Part	$A_{MD/EI}$ Coeff. $\times$ Base $\times$ Height	$+A_{MD/EI}$	$-A_{MD/EI}$
A_5	$+\dfrac{2}{3} \times 13.2 \times \dfrac{43.5}{EI}$	$383/EI$	
A_6	$+\dfrac{1}{2} \times 13.2 \times \dfrac{142.6}{EI}$	$940/EI$	
A_7	$-1 \times 13.2 \times \dfrac{80.4}{EI}$		$1{,}060/EI$
A_8	$-\dfrac{1}{2} \times 13.2 \times \dfrac{39.6}{EI}$		$261/EI$
	Summation	$1{,}323/EI$	$1{,}321/EI$

Since the plus areas are very nearly equal to the minus areas, within acceptable limits of slide-rule accuracy, the slope is very nearly zero. This checks the results found in Art. 5–2. As a matter of practicality, it is not often necessary to obtain so close a check as that in Table 5–9. The deflection at another point even as much as a foot away is very nearly equal to the maximum deflection.

The maximum deflection can be found from Eq. 4–20

$$\Delta Y = \sum \bar{x} A_{MD/EI} + \sum x\theta + Y \qquad (4\text{–}20)$$

modified to

$$\Delta Y_x = \sum_{x}^{C} \bar{x} A_{MD/EI} + 0 + 0$$

which can be set in tabular form (Table 5–10), making use of the areas already determined in Table 5–9.

This answer is very close (within slide-rule accuracy) to that found in Ex. 5–2E. Theoretically, the answers should be exactly the same, but this would be true only if the computations were carried out to an infinite number of significant figures.

[6] An easier and more accurate way (though less understandable, perhaps) is to compute the simple beam moment at the center of a 13.2-ft span, thus

$$M = \frac{wL^2}{8} = \frac{2(13.2)^2}{8} = 43.5 \text{ kip-ft}$$

which checks the answer above. Use this method only if you understand why it works.

In reviewing Arts. 5–2 and 5–3, it should be noted that the approach to any part of the problem is always similar. Use is made of Eq. 4–20 or Eq. 4–22, the basic equation being modified to fit the particular limits of summation and the other conditions of the problem. Moment diagrams can be

TABLE 5–10

Solution of $\Delta Y_x = \sum\limits_{x}^{C} \bar{x} A_{MD/EI}$

Moment Diagram Part	$\bar{x}$	$A_{MD/EI}$ (See Table 5–9)	$+\bar{x} A_{MD/EI}$	$-\bar{x} A_{MD/EI}$
A_5	$\frac{1}{2} \times 13.2$	$+383/EI$	$2,530/EI$	
A_6	$\frac{1}{3} \times 13.2$	$+940/EI$	$4,140/EI$	
A_7	$\frac{1}{2} \times 13.2$	$-1,060/EI$		$7,000/EI$
A_8	$\frac{2}{3} \times 13.2$	$-261/EI$		$2,300/EI$
		Summation	$6,670/EI$	$9,300/EI$

$$\Delta Y_x = 6,670/EI - 9,300/EI = -2,630/EI$$

drawn in many ways, any of which can be forced to work, although some make the problem easier than others. Nor is any one type of moment diagram the best for every calculation. The engineer should, therefore, with equal facility, be able to draw moment diagrams in simple beam parts and in cantilever parts from left or right.

5–4. Discussion. The foregoing examples have illustrated the use of moment area for specific solutions, and the reader by now should be familiar with the mechanics of the equations. Other problems are worked out with only minor variations. Some of the variations are now discussed. Most problems will fall into one of these categories.

The beams of Figs. 5–5 to 5–12 represent most of the common types encountered in practice. The kind of loading is immaterial; it is the type of support that dictates the analysis.

Fig. 5–5. Cantilever beam.

The simplest is the cantilever beam. Deflections and rotations can often be solved mentally if the loading is simple. If the moment areas are always summed to point B in Fig. 5–5, all but the first term of each moment area equation become zero because B is fixed.

Unlike the cantilever beam, the simple beam in Fig. 5–6 offers no fixed point at which to end the summation. Since neither A nor B deflects, Eq.

4–20, which can be written for deflection at either A or B (and the moment areas summed between A and B), reduces to

$$\Delta Y_A = 0 = \sum_A^B \bar{x} A_{MD/EI} + x_B \theta_B + 0$$

which determines the slope at B. All deflections and slopes may now be determined by summing MD/EI areas to point B, where the slope is known.

Fig. 5–6. Simple beam.

Nothing further need be said about the supported cantilever of Fig. 5–7, as it has been thoroughly discussed in Arts. 5–2 and 5–3.

Fig. 5–7. Supported cantilever.

Before any deflections or slopes can be found, the reactions must be known so that the moments can be evaluated. The continuous beam of Fig. 5–8 is

Fig. 5–8. Continuous beam.

indeterminate to the first degree because there are three reactions but only two useful equations of statics. Accordingly, we write a moment area equation to solve the unknown reaction, in which some of the moment areas must necessarily be expressed in terms of the unknown reactions. Equation 4–20 could be reduced to

$$\Delta Y_A = 0 = \sum_A^B \bar{x} A_{MD/EI} + x_B \theta_B + 0$$

Note that there are two unknowns in this equation. Some of $A_{MD/EI}$ is unknown because it must be expressed in terms of the unknown reaction and, of course, θ_B is unknown. Therefore, a second equation is necessary. For example, we could write Eq. 4–20 for deflection of point C. The equation reduces to

$$\Delta Y_C = 0 = \sum_C^B \bar{x} A_{MD/EI} + x_B \theta_B + 0$$

in which the same two unknowns appear. These equations can be solved simultaneously, yielding both θ_B and the unknown reaction. Thereafter deflections can be found just as for the beam in Fig. 5–6. If, as often happens in actual practice, the beam and its loads are symmetrical about the center support, then the slope at B must be zero. Each half of the beam then becomes similar to the supported cantilever of Fig. 5–7 and can be analyzed in exactly the same way, thereby eliminating the need for solving two simultaneous equations. Another way of solving the problem is to make use again of either of the above equations; the second term, $x_B\theta_B$, is zero because the slope at B is zero, and this leaves only one unknown in the equation.

The fixed beam of Fig. 5–9 is statically indeterminate to the second degree, so two equations of moment area are required. One could write Eq. 4–20 twice, once for deflection at A and once for deflection at B (both of which are zero). Or one could write Eq. 4–20 for deflection at A and then write Eq. 4–22 for slope at A. These would, respectively, reduce to

$$\Delta Y_A = 0 = \sum_{A}^{B} \bar{x} A_{MD/EI} + 0 + 0$$

and

Fig. 5–9. Fixed beam.

$$\Delta \theta_A = 0 = \sum_{A}^{B} A_{MD/EI} + 0$$

All but the first term of the right side equal zero because rotation and deflection at B are zero.

Fig. 5–10. Articulated beam.

The articulated beam of Fig. 5–10 is unusual. It is included to show how easily the basic principles can be applied to a somewhat complex problem. The beam is statically indeterminate to the first degree; there are four

Fig. 5–11. Beam on elastic foundation.

reaction components[7] (M_A, V_A, V_C, and V_D), two equations of statics ($\Sigma M = 0$, $\Sigma V = 0$), plus one equation of condition ($M_B = 0$). Nevertheless,

---

[7] There are four reaction components only if there are no horizontal loads. If horizontal loads exist, they are resisted at A. This adds another reaction component but also permits the use of $\Sigma H = 0$, with the net result that the beam is still statically indeterminate to the first degree.

one moment area equation does not suffice because of the unknown angle change at B. Regardless of what equations of moment area are written, *this angle change at B must not be ignored*. Equation 4–20 might be reduced to the following two equations

$$\Delta Y_C = 0 = \sum_{C}^{A} \bar{x} A_{MD/EI} + x_B \theta_B + 0$$

$$\Delta Y_D = 0 = \sum_{D}^{A} \bar{x} A_{MD/EI} + x_B \theta_B + 0$$

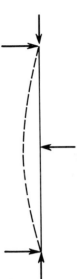

Since some of the moment areas must be expressed in terms of one unknown (a reaction, a shear, or a moment), part of the first term is unknown. Of course, the angle change at B is unknown. This is the reason that two equations are required. As so frequently happens, the hardest part of the problem is the drawing of the moment diagrams. Once they are drawn correctly, the indeterminate structural analysis is simple and straightforward. Remember that for multiple spans moment diagrams are more easily drawn in simple beam parts. Unknowns can be expressed in terms of moments at the reactions.

Beams on elastic foundations (Fig. 5–11) are difficult to solve because there are no fixed points, no known deflections, and no known slopes. However, solutions can be obtained in three practical ways: (1) model analysis, (2)

Fig. 5–12. Beam-column.

special equations, and (3) trial and error. Model analysis is particularly good if the beam is prismatic. Only a wire spline, a box of rubber bands, a drawing board, some small nails, and a balance are needed. If there are several loading conditions, it is also the quickest way. Special equations[8] have been developed, and if applicable they are very practical. They are usually somewhat complicated, however, and their solution is not as easy as one might think. A solution using trial and error is practical when systematic. A method developed by Newmark[9] is rapid when used by a good arithmetician and is well adapted to complex loading conditions and variable moments of inertia. Its disadvantages are that it requires some study to understand and considerable practice to develop speed. It is well worth while, although it is too advanced to include here.

Moment area can be used also to analyze beam-columns such as the example of Fig. 5–12. The Euler column formula can also be developed through moment area. The bending moment due to an axial force must be expressed as deflection times the axial force. Since the curvature even of

[8] M. Hetenyi, *Beams on Elastic Foundations* (Ann Arbor: University of Michigan Press, 1946).

[9] N. M. Newmark, "Numerical Procedure for Computing Deflections, Moments, and Buckling Loads," *Trans. ASCE*, 108: 1161–1188, 1943.

flexible beams is very small, it is accurate enough for practical purposes to assume that the elastic curve is a parabola. The solution is usually a trial-and-error one because the maximum deflection is a function of the bending moment, which for axial forces is, in turn, dependent upon deflection. Usually one can either guess at a maximum deflection or, if there are large transverse loads, use the deflection caused by those transverse loads as a first approximation. The maximum deflection is computed by using both moment due to axial load and moment due to transverse loads. This new deflection is used as a second approximation. Convergence is generally quite rapid so that only two or three trials are necessary.

6

RIGID FRAMES AND ARCHES

6-1. Fixed Rigid Frames. The solution of rigid frames by the graphical moment area equations is not different from the solution for beams. There are, however, some principles of static equilibrium that need to be re-emphasized, some applications of moment area that require explanation, and some useful shortcuts that should be illustrated.

Example 6-1. *Reactions.* The rigid frame of Fig. 6-1 is not, perhaps, a practical structure, but it will illustrate nearly all the principles and applications. It is statically indeterminate to three degrees because there are six reaction components (three at A and three at G) but only three useful equations of static equilibrium. In order to draw moment diagrams and make use of the moment area equations, the structure is cut in two somewhere, and the internal forces at the cut face are replaced with equivalent external forces. Suppose we choose to cut the structure at A; then the reaction from the foundation at A must be replaced by three equivalent forces H, V, and M, as shown in Fig. 6-1B. Of course, we do not know the true direction or sense of H, V, and M, although, by inspection, we can be fairly sure that V acts upward. But we can arbitrarily assume some direction for each of the unknowns. If the assumed direction is incorrect, it will be indicated by a negative answer.[1] Since A is fixed, the x deflection is zero, the y deflection is zero, and the rotation is zero. Expressing these facts with the three moment area equations gives the three additional equations necessary to determine the reactions.

The moment diagrams may be drawn in several ways. One convenient way is to draw them in cantilever parts from the left. There are so many forces acting that the moment diagrams are best shown separated into four groups (Figs. 6-1C, D, E, and F). This is especially good practice for the beginner because it avoids confusion and reduces the hazard of omitting a moment diagram. It is of the utmost importance that every moment diagram be correctly drawn because even one incorrect diagram will nullify the entire solution. Determining the side of compression often seems to trouble the beginner even though, from the consideration of free bodies, there ought to be no doubt whatsoever. To illustrate this point, let us consider several of the

---

[1] The solution of any algebraic equation yields the sign as well as the magnitude of the answer.

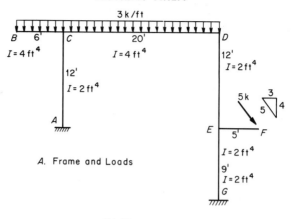

A. Frame and Loads

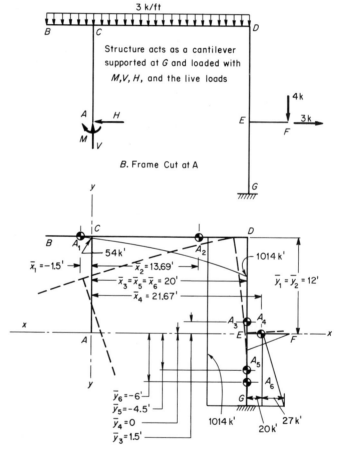

B. Frame Cut at A

Structure acts as a cantilever
supported at G and loaded with
M,V, H, and the live loads

C. Moment Diagrams. Live Load Only

Fig. 6–1. Moment diagrams

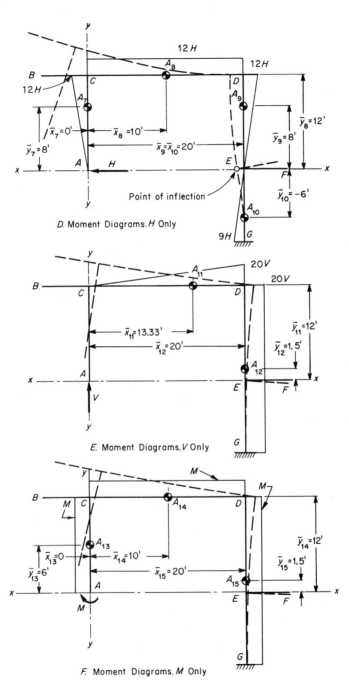

D. Moment Diagrams. H Only

E. Moment Diagrams. V Only

F. Moment Diagrams. M Only

for rigid frame.

moment diagrams. The moment diagram marked A_2 (Fig. 6–1C) caused by the uniform load along the girder CD is plotted on the lower side because the loads to the left cause a counterclockwise moment to act on a free body to the right, as shown in Fig. 6–2, and this produces compression on the lower side.

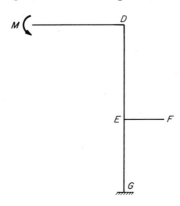

By the same reasoning, the loads along the girder produce a counterclockwise moment acting upon the free body of the right column DG. The load on the outrigger EF is resolved into two components for convenience, as shown in Fig. 6–1B. Both these loads produce compression on the right side of the column. The position of the moment diagram marked A_9 in Fig. 6–1D may be corroborated by the same reasoning. The only force here being considered to the left of point D is H, and about point D, H acts clockwise. The effect of a clockwise moment applied at the top of the column produces compression on the right. At E the moment of the force of H is zero because the line of

Fig. 6–2. Direction of moment due to uniform load.

action of H passes through E. Below E, the moment of H is counterclockwise, and such a moment acting upon a free body of the lower part of the column induces compression on the left side.

Clear, precise reasoning on the effect of angle changes upon the deflection of point A is vital. Note that from Fig. 6–3A angle changes along BC and along EF do not affect the position of point A.[2] Therefore it must follow that moment diagrams along BC and EF *must be omitted* in computing the deflection of point A if the deflection is obtained by summing angle changes from A to G. This does not mean that the loads on BC or EF are ignored; they are not. The effects of these loads are evident in moment diagrams[3] A_2, A_3, A_5, and A_6, which are *not* omitted in computing the deflection of point A.

The effect of angle changes along $ACDEG$ is shown in Figs. 6–3B, C, D, and E. All angle changes have been shown concave inward (that is, concave toward the center of the frame). Such angle changes always produce counterclockwise rotation. Suppose we decide to call all these angle changes

[2] This was explained in another way in Art. 4–2.

[3] Determine area and centroid of A_2 in the manner shown in Fig. 4–9B and described in Art. 4–8. Thus

$$A_1 + A_2 = \tfrac{1}{3} \times \text{base} \times \text{height} = \tfrac{1}{3} \times 26 \times 1014 = 8788$$
$$\text{Subtract } A_1 = \tfrac{1}{3} \times \text{base} \times \text{height} = \tfrac{1}{3} \times 6 \times 54 = \underline{108}$$
$$A_2 = \overline{8680}$$
$$\bar{x}_1 A_1 + \bar{x}_2 A_2 = \bar{x}_{1+2}(A_1 + A_2)$$
$$\tfrac{3}{4} \times 6 \times 108 + \bar{x}_2 \times 8680 = \tfrac{3}{4} \times 26 \times 8788$$
$$\bar{x}_2 = 19.69 \text{ ft from } B = 13.69 \text{ ft from } C$$

positive; then all moment diagrams plotted outside the frame are negative. Suppose we decide also that x is positive to the right and y is positive upward. At A, any deflection to the right must be positive because it is the

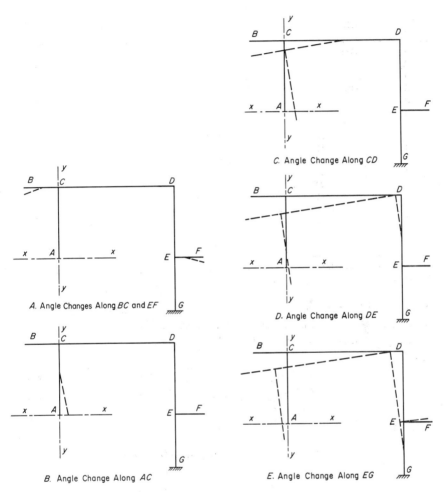

Fig. 6–3. Effect of angle changes on deflection of point A.

product of a positive angle change and a positive y. In Fig. 6–3E, the deflection at A is left, negative—the product of a positive angle change and a negative y. Now since x is positive and the angle changes of Figs. 6–3B, C, D, and E are positive, then it must follow that all downward vertical deflections shown in the figures are positive because such deflections are the result of angle change times x. Note well that deflection is not always positive in the direction in which x or y is positive. When signs are given to the angle

TABLE 6–1

Solution of $\displaystyle\sum_{A}^{G} A_{MD/EI} = 0$

Moment Diagram Part	$A_{MD/EI}$ Coeff. × Base × Height	Coefficient of H	Coefficient of V	Coefficient of M	Constant
A_1	Omit				
A_2	$+ 8,680/4E$				$+ 2,170/E$
A_3	$+1 \times 21 \times 1{,}014/2E$				$+10{,}647/E$
A_4	Omit				
A_5	$-1 \times 9 \times 20/2E$				$-90/E$
A_6	$-\frac{1}{2} \times 9 \times 27/2E$				$-61/E$
A_7	$-\frac{1}{2} \times 12 \times 12H/2E$	$-36/E$			
A_8	$-1 \times 20 \times 12H/4E$	$-60/E$			
A_9	$-\frac{1}{2} \times 12 \times 12H/2E$	$-36/E$			
A_{10}	$+\frac{1}{2} \times 9 \times 9H/2E$	$+20.2/E$			
A_{11}	$-\frac{1}{2} \times 20 \times 20V/4E$		$-50/E$		
A_{12}	$-1 \times 21 \times 20V/2E$		$-210/E$		
A_{13}	$-1 \times 12 \times M/2E$			$-6/E$	
A_{14}	$-1 \times 20 \times M/4E$			$-5/E$	
A_{15}	$-1 \times 21 \times M/2E$			$-10.5/E$	
	Summation	$-111.8/E$	$-260/E$	$-21.5/E$	$+12{,}666/E$

Canceling E, which is common to all terms, and multiplying all terms by -1, we have

$$111.8H + 260V + 21.5M = 12{,}666$$

changes and to x and y, the relation between sign and deflection can always be determined by means of sketches like those in Fig. 6–3.

If angle changes are summed from A to G, the three equations of moment area

$$\Delta Y = \sum \bar{x} A_{MD/EI} + \sum x\theta + Y \qquad (4\text{–}20)$$

$$\Delta X = \sum \bar{y} A_{MD/EI} + \sum y\theta + X \qquad (4\text{–}21)$$

$$\Delta \theta = \sum A_{MD/EI} + \sum \theta \qquad (4\text{–}22)$$

reduce respectively to

$$\Delta Y_A = 0 = \sum_{A}^{G} \bar{x} A_{MD/EI} + 0 + 0$$

$$\Delta X_A = 0 = \sum_{A}^{G} \bar{y} A_{MD/EI} + 0 + 0$$

$$\Delta \theta_A = 0 = \sum_{A}^{G} A_{MD/EI} + 0$$

because there is no rotation or deflection at point G. These equations are evaluated[4] in Tables 6–1, 6–2, and 6–3. (Equation 4–22 is evaluated first so that expressions for $A_{MD/EI}$ may be simplified in a more logical order.)

[4] It is not necessary for the student to check all computations in the following four tables with his slide rule, but, on the other hand, it is absolutely vital that he study each term until he is positive that he understands its derivation including its sign and could develop the term without hesitation or doubt.

TABLE 6–2

Solution of $\sum\limits_{A}^{G} \bar{x} A_{MD/EI} = 0$

Moment Diagram Part	$\bar{x}$ (See Fig. 6–1)	$A_{MD/EI}$ (See Table 6–1)	Coefficients of			Constant
			H	V	M	
A_1		Omit				
A_2	$+13.69$	$+\ 2,170/E$				$+29,707/E$
A_3	$+20$	$+10,647/E$				$+212,940/E$
A_4		Omit				
A_5	$+20$	$-\ \ \ 90/E$				$-1,800/E$
A_6	$+20$	$-\ \ \ 61/E$				$-1,220/E$
A_7	0	$-\ \ 36H/E$				
A_8	$+10$	$-\ \ 60H/E$	$-600/E$			
A_9	$+20$	$-\ \ 36H/E$	$-720/E$			
A_{10}	$+20$	$+\ \ \ 20.2H/E$	$+404/E$			
A_{11}	$+13.33$	$-\ \ 50V/E$		$-\ \ 667/E$		
A_{12}	$+20$	$-\ 210V/E$		$-4,200/E$		
A_{13}	0	$-\ \ \ 6M/E$				
A_{14}	$+10$	$-\ \ \ 5M/E$			$-\ \ 50/E$	
A_{15}	$+20$	$-\ \ 10.5M/E$			$-210/E$	
		Summation	$-916/E$	$-4,867/E$	$-260/E$	$+239,627/E$

Canceling E and multiplying all terms by -1, we have

$$916H + 4867V + 260M = 239,627$$

TABLE 6–3

Solution of $\sum\limits_{A}^{G} \bar{y} A_{MD/EI} = 0$

Moment Diagram Part	$\bar{y}$ (See Fig. 6–1)	$A_{MD/EI}$ (See Table 6–1)	Coefficients of			Constant
			H	V	M	
A_1		Omit				
A_2	$+12$	$+\ 2,170/E$				$+26,040/E$
A_3	$+\ 1.5$	$+10,647/E$				$+15,970/E$
A_4		Omit				
A_5	$-\ 4.5$	$-\ \ \ 90/E$				$+405/E$
A_6	$-\ 6$	$-\ \ \ 61/E$				$+366/E$
A_7	$+\ 8$	$-\ \ 36H/E$	$-288/E$			
A_8	$+12$	$-\ \ 60H/E$	$-720/E$			
A_9	$+\ 8$	$-\ \ 36H/E$	$-288/E$			
A_{10}	$-\ 6$	$+\ \ \ 20.2H/E$	$-121/E$			
A_{11}	$+12$	$-\ \ 50V/E$		$-600/E$		
A_{12}	$+\ 1.5$	$-\ 210V/E$		$-315/E$		
A_{13}	$+\ 6$	$-\ \ \ 6M/E$			$-\ \ 36/E$	
A_{14}	$+12$	$-\ \ \ 5M/E$			$-\ \ 60/E$	
A_{15}	$+\ 1.5$	$-\ \ 10.5M/E$			$-15.75/E$	
		Summation	$-1,417/E$	$-915/E$	$-111.75/E$	$+42,781/E$

Again canceling the constant E and multiplying by -1, we have

$$1417H + 915V + 111.75M = 42,781$$

Solved simultaneously, the equations obtained from Tables 6–1, 6–2, and 6–3 will yield values for H, V, and M. A negative value indicates that the direction (sense) assumed for the reaction component is incorrect; that is, it

TABLE 6–4

Simultaneous Solution of Equations from Tables 6–1, 6–2, and 6–3

Equation	Operation	Left Side of Equations			Right Side of Equations
		Coefficients of			Constant
		H	V	M	
1	(From Table 6–1)	+ 111.8	+ 260	+ 21.5	+ 12,666
2	(From Table 6–2)	+ 916	+4,867	+260	+239,627
3	(From Table 6–3)	+1,417	+ 915	+111.75	+ 42,781
1′	Eq. 1/111.8	+1.000	+2.3255	+0.1923	+113.291
2′	Eq. 2/916	+1.000	+5.3133	+0.2838	+261.601
3′	Eq. 3/1,417	+1.000	+0.6457	+0.0788	+ 30.191
4	Eq. 2′ − Eq. 1′		+2.9878	+0.0915	+148.310
5	Eq. 2′ − Eq. 3′		+4.6676	+0.2050	+231.410
4′	Eq. 4/2.9878		+1.000	+0.0306	+ 49.638
5′	Eq. 5/4.6676		+1.000	+0.0439	+ 49.578
6	Eq. 5′ − Eq. 4′			+0.0133	− 0.061
6′	Eq. 6/0.0133			+1.00	− 4.59
				$M = -$	4.59

4′	Substitute −4.59 for M				
			+1.000		+ 49.638
			$(-1)(-4.59)(+0.0306) =$		+ 0.140
			$V = +$		49.778

1′	Substitute −4.59 for M and +49.778 for V			
		+1.000		+113.291
		$(-1)(-4.59)(+0.1923) =$		+ 0.883
				+114.174
		$(-1)(+49.778)(+2.3255) =$		−115.759
		$H = -$		1.585

That is, $M = -4.59 = 4.59$ kip-ft counterclockwise; $V = +49.78 = 49.78$ kips up; and $H = -1.59 = 1.59$ kips to the right.

acts in the direction opposite to that assumed. The solution of simultaneous equations is an onerous task, and mistakes are only too easy to make, but solutions can be speeded up and the chances for mistakes reduced by using an orderly, tabular form for computations as shown in Table 6–4. Slide-rule accuracy is not usually sufficient for the solution of these simultaneous equations, so a computing machine is preferable. With special care the slide rule can be used for answers of low precision. A meticulous solution by slide rule yielded the following values: $M = -3.8$, $H = -1.4$, and $V = +49.6$.

Because M is minus, its assumed direction, clockwise, was incorrect; it therefore acts counterclockwise. Since V is plus, it acts upward as assumed. As H is minus, it acts to the right instead of to the left as assumed.

Answers should *never* be trusted until checked by substitution into the original equations.

From Table 6–1,

$$111.8(-1.59) + 260(49.78) + 21.5(4-.59) = 12{,}666$$
$$12{,}666 = 12{,}666$$
$$\text{Error} = 0.000 \text{ percent}$$

From Table 6–2,

$$916(-1.59) + 4867(49.78) + 260(-4.59) = 239{,}627$$
$$239{,}629 = 239{,}627$$
$$\text{Error} = 0.001 \text{ percent}$$

From Table 6–3,

$$1417(-1.59) + 915(49.78) + 111.75(-4.59) = 42{,}781$$
$$42{,}782 = 42{,}781$$
$$\text{Error} = 0.002 \text{ percent}$$

Now that H, V, and M are known, the reactions at G can be found by using the three equations of static equilibrium. One convenient way to find them is to consider a free body of the entire frame, cut free from its foundations at A and G. The forces acting upon the frame are shown in Fig. 6–4. From the equations of static equilibrium, we have

$$\Sigma H = 0 \qquad\qquad (1\text{–}2)$$
$$+1.59 + 3 - H_G = 0$$
$$H_G = 4.59 \text{ kips to the left}$$
$$\Sigma V = 0 \qquad\qquad (1\text{–}3)$$
$$+49.78 - 3 \times 26 - 4 + V_G = 0$$
$$V_G = 32.22 \text{ kips upward}$$
$$\Sigma M = 0 \qquad\qquad (1\text{–}1)$$

Summing moments[5] about point G and assuming that M_G acts clockwise, results in

$$1.59 \text{ kips} \times 9 \text{ ft} + 49.78 \text{ kips} \times 20 \text{ ft} - 4.59 \text{ kip-ft} - (3 \text{ kips/ft})$$
$$\times 26 \text{ ft} \times 13 \text{ ft} + 3 \text{ kips} \times 9 \text{ ft} + 4 \text{ kips} \times 5 \text{ ft} + M_G = 0$$
$$M_G = -38.3 \text{ kip-ft} = 38.3 \text{ kip-ft counterclockwise}$$

[5] Many prefer to do this in tabular form—an excellent method—particularly so when there are many forces.

Another approach to the moment at G is to sum, algebraically, the partial moments at G in Figs. 6–1C, D, E, and F. Calling moment diagrams inside positive, we have

$$M_G = \underbrace{+1014 - 20 - 27}_{\text{Fig. 6-1}C} \quad \underbrace{+9H}_{\text{Fig. 6-1}D} \quad \underbrace{-20V}_{\text{Fig. 6-1}E} \quad \underbrace{-M}_{\text{Fig. 6-1}F}$$

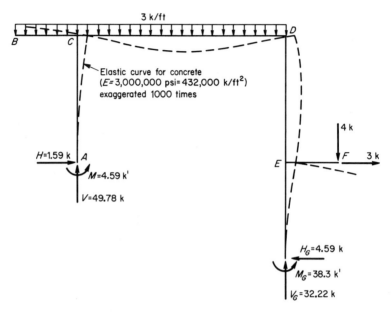

Fig. 6–4. Free body and elastic curve of frame.

and substituting the known values of H, V, and M, we obtain

$$M_G = +1014 - 20 - 27 + 9(-1.59) - 20(49.78) - (-4.59)$$
$$= -38.3 \text{ kip-ft}$$

The minus sign indicates that the moment acts to cause compression on the outside, because compression inside was assumed positive. To cause compression on the outside, the moment must act counterclockwise. Note that the terms in the above equation are each exactly the same as the terms in the substitution for Eq. 1–1.

6–2. Deflection of Rigid Frames. The deflections of points on rigid frames are found in the same way as deflections of beams. However, beams have only one component of deflection (either up or down for horizontal beams) whereas frames deflect both vertically and horizontally. To illustrate the application of moment area equations, the rotation and deflection at point B of the rigid frame of Art. 6–1 will be found.

Example 6–2A. Rotation at B. The easiest way to find the slope at B is to write Eq. 4–22, summing angle changes from B to A thus:

$$\Delta\theta = \sum_A A_{MD/EI} + \sum \theta \qquad (4\text{–}22)$$

$$\Delta\theta_B = \sum_B A_{MD/EI} + 0$$

The only moment diagrams found along the elastic curve from A to C to B are those marked A_1, A_7, and A_{13} in Fig. 6–1. If we decide to call A_1 plus, then the moment diagrams plotted on the left of column AC must also be plus.[6] Therefore A_7 and A_{13}, as shown in Fig. 6–1, are both plus. However, both M and H were found in Art. 6–1 to be minus quantities, so when minus M and minus H are substituted into the plus areas, the areas become minus. Another approach (Table 6–5) would be to redraw the moment diagrams to

TABLE 6–5

Solution of $\Delta\theta_B = \sum_B^A A_{MD/EI}$

Moment Area Part	$A_{MD/EI}$ Coeff. × Base × Height	$+A_{MD/EI}$	$-A_{MD/EI}$
A_1	$+\dfrac{1}{3} \times 6 \times \dfrac{54}{4E}$	$+27/E$	
A_7	$+\dfrac{1}{2} \times 12 \times \dfrac{12(-1.59)}{2E}$		$-57.2/E$
A_{13}	$+1 \times 12 \times \dfrac{(-4.59)}{2E}$		$-27.5/E$
	Summation $+27/E$		$-84.7/E$

$$\Delta\theta_A = +27/E - 84.7/E = -57.7/E \cong 58/E \text{ clockwise}$$

correspond to the known directions of the reactions H, V, and M. Then both A_7 and A_{13} would be plotted on the right side of column AC because H acts to the right and M is counterclockwise.

In this instance the minus sign indicates that A rotates clockwise. To find the numerical value of the rotation, the modulus of elasticity must be expressed in kips per square foot because $\Delta\theta_A$ is in kip-foot units. If the material is concrete with a Young's modulus of 3,000,000 psi, then

$$E = 3,000,000 \frac{\text{lb}}{\text{in.}^2} \times \frac{1\ \text{kip}}{1000\ \text{lb}} \times \frac{144\ \text{in.}^2}{1\ \text{ft}^2} = 432,000\ \text{kips/ft}^2$$

and

$$\Delta\theta_A = \frac{58}{432,000} = 0.00013\ \text{radian} = 27\ \text{sec}$$

[6] For reasons heretofore explained. If by now such statements puzzle the student, he should review this chapter from the beginning.

Example 6–2B. *Deflection at B.* The deflection of point B must be found in components; that is, the x deflection and y deflection must be found, after which the total deflection may be found as the vector sum. The coordinate axes must be passed through point B. We might decide to let x be positive to the right and y be positive downward. There is no particular reason for changing the signs of the moment diagrams from those found in Ex. 6–2A, so the same signs are used although another sign convention would serve as well. Equation 4–20,

$$\Delta Y = \sum \bar{x} A_{MD/EI} + \sum x\theta + Y \qquad (4\text{–}20)$$

reduces to

$$\Delta Y_B = \sum_B^A \bar{x} A_{MD/EI} + 0 + 0$$

This is solved in Table 6–6.

TABLE 6–6

Solution of $\Delta Y_B = \sum_B^A \bar{x} A_{MD/EI}$

Moment Diagram Part	$\bar{x}$ (See Fig. 6–1)	$A_{MD/EI}$ (See Table 6–5)	$+\bar{x}A_{MD/EI}$	$-\bar{x}A_{MD/EI}$
A_1	4.5	$+27/E$	$122/E$	
A_7	6	$-57.2/E$		$343/E$
A_{13}	6	$-27.5/E$		$165/E$
		Summation	$122/E$	$508/E$

$$\Delta Y_B = +122/E - 508/E = -386/E = 386/E \text{ upward}[7]$$

Equation 4–21,

$$\Delta X = \sum \bar{y} A_{MD/EI} + \sum y\theta + X \qquad (4\text{–}21)$$

reduces to

$$\Delta X_B = \sum_B^A \bar{y} A_{MD/EI} + 0 + 0$$

This is solved in Table 6–7.

TABLE 6–7

Solution of $\Delta X_B = \sum_B^A \bar{y} A_{MD/EI}$

Moment Diagram Part	$\bar{y}$ (See Fig. 6–1)	$A_{MD/EI}$ (See Table 6–5)	$+\bar{y}A_{MD/EI}$	$-\bar{y}A_{MD/EI}$
A_1	0	$+27/E$		
A_7	4	$-57.2/E$		$229/E$
A_{13}	6	$-27.5/E$		$165/E$
			Summation	$394/E$

$$\Delta X_B = -394/E = 394/E \text{ right}$$

[7] The direction is determined by thinking about the effects of the angle changes as heretofore explained.

The total deflection is found as the vector sum of ΔX_B and ΔY_B; thus

$$\Delta_B = \sqrt{(\Delta X_B)^2 + (\Delta Y_B)^2} = \frac{1}{E}\sqrt{(394)^2 + (386)^2} = \frac{554}{E} \text{ upward to the right.}$$

6–3. Fixed Rigid Frames. Discussion. There are two ways to consider the structural action involved in the solution of redundant reactions. One is the approach of Art. 6–1 in which the frame is cut in two at some point (point A in Art. 6–1) and the internal forces are replaced by equivalent external forces (H, V, and M). These equivalent external forces act in unison with the loads in such a manner that deflection at A is prevented. Thus, although we have cut the structure at A, we are thinking from first to last of a zero displacement of A.

The other way to conceive of the structural action is to consider separately the effect of each load or force on the "cut-back" structure (the structure as cut in two at A). The live loads bend the structure into an elastic curve shown by the dashed line in Fig. 6–1C. H acting alone produces the elastic curve of Fig. 6–1D; V produces the elastic curve of Fig. 6–1E; and M produces the elastic curve of Fig. 6–1F. (These curves are not drawn to scale and, as the solution of Art. 6–1 shows, both H and M act opposite to the direction shown and produce opposite effects in the elastic curve.) The frame is visualized as bending under the loads so that A moves down, right, and rotates counterclockwise. Then A is partly returned to its original position by H, partly by V, and partly by M. The effect of all three redundant forces is to restore A to its original position. Thus we think of the loads as causing a deflection, and the redundant forces as causing an equal and opposite deflection which finally results in a zero displacement at A.

Each way of visualizing the structural action is entirely valid; indeed, there is no real difference at all. They lead to exactly the same equations. A minor difference in procedure can sometimes be generated by solving the deflections separately, and some authorities make much of this—even to the extent of calling it by special names such as the "general method," the "basic method," or the "method of superposition." Actually both "methods" (or "concepts" of structural action) involve superposition. In the first, the deflections at A are all superimposed before an equation of deflection is written, and in the second, the equations are written for the several deflections which are then superimposed. A distinction between the two is only a matter of sequence.

Some students wonder why it is not possible to avoid solving simultaneous equations. Suppose we consider the frame acted upon only by the loads so that it is bent into the elastic curve of Fig. 6–1C. Why would it not be possible to write a single equation involving only one unknown H, and then compute the value of H required to move A horizontally left to the yy axis, so that $\Delta X_A = 0$? In a similar way, could not a value for V be computed in a single equation such that A would be moved vertically to the xx axis, so

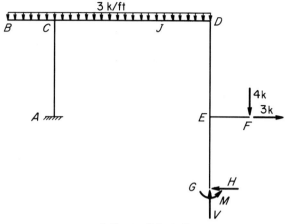

A. Frame Cut at G

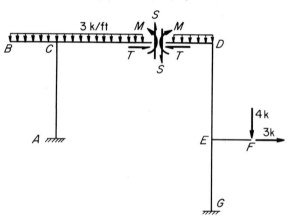

B. Frame Cut at Any Interior Point

Fig. 6–5. Cut-back structures.

that $\Delta Y_A = 0$? And again, could not a value of M be computed so that the rotation at A would be restored to zero? *No, this cannot yield the correct answers!* The reason is that when H is applied to the frame, point A not only moves left, it moves up and rotates as shown in Fig. 6–1D. Similarly, any other force applied at point A results, in general, in three components of deflection, ΔX, ΔY, and $\Delta \theta$. Ignoring the existence of two of the components of deflection certainly could not yield a correct answer. Nor could ignoring the effects of V and M upon the horizontal movement of A lead to a correct value for H.[8]

[8] By extending an inelastic bracket from (and rigidly attached to) A to the "neutral point" (centroid of the frame centerline divided by EI), simultaneous equations can be avoided because a load produces deflection only in the direction of the load. This is the "neutral point method."

The two ways employed to visualize structural action, explained above, depend first upon making the structure statically determinate in some way. In the preceding example, the structure was cut at A and the foundation reactions were replaced by three forces H, V, and M, as shown in Fig. 6–1B. Of course, the structure is not truly a statically determinate one because these forces are unknown. A better term for it is "cut-back structure," which means that enough reactions, or internal stresses, have been cut away and replaced by algebraic symbols so that moment diagrams can be drawn, even though some of them must be drawn in terms of the algebraic symbols.

There are many ways to cut back a structure. Some will increase and some will lessen the difficulty of the solution. The easiest way to visualize and to work with is to cut the frame at a reaction such as was done in Ex. 6–1. The frame could have been cut at point G, as shown in Fig. 6–5A, but note that there would have been several additional moment diagrams due to the forces acting at point F. That is, there would have been one moment diagram for each force (3 kips and 4 kips), from E to D, from D to C, and from C to A—six moment diagrams in all compared with two moment diagrams for the same forces in Fig. 6–1. Thus there is some advantage in cutting the structure at A.

The structure may be cut at some interior point, as shown in Fig. 6–5B. Since there is usually shear, moment, and thrust (axial force) at any interior point, there will be three unknowns unless the frame and its loads are symmetrical. The forces S, T, and M acting on the left portion must be mutually equal and opposite to those acting on the right portion of the frame in order to maintain static equilibrium. The directions of these forces are assumed, and moment diagrams are drawn in cantilever parts for each portion of the frame. The coordinate axes must, of course, pass through the cut point J. Then the three moment area equations can be reduced to the following:

$$\Delta Y_J = \sum_J^G \bar{x} A_{MD/EI} + 0 + 0 = \sum_J^A \bar{x} A_{MD/EI} + 0 + 0$$

$$\Delta X_J = \sum_J^G \bar{y} A_{MD/EI} + 0 + 0 = \sum_J^A \bar{y} A_{MD/EI} + 0 + 0$$

$$\Delta \theta_J = \sum_J^G A_{MD/EI} + 0 = \sum_J^A A_{MD/EI} + 0$$

The chief disadvantage of this approach is that, unless the frame and the loads are symmetrical, three simultaneous equations must be solved even if there are only two—or even one—redundant reactive forces. For example, suppose the frame were pinned at G, there would be an unknown rotation at G, and the terms $\sum x\theta$, $\sum y\theta$, and $\sum \theta$ on the left side of the above equations would not be zero but would instead be $x_G\theta_G$, $y_G\theta_G$, and θ_G, respectively. Thus, although the frame would be statically indeterminate to two degrees only, we would still have to solve three simultaneous equations. A minor disadvantage is that signs are more troublesome. There is one advantage, however, that may in some problems outweigh the disadvantages: The coefficients of H, V, and M are usually smaller and the solution is more accurate. This single advantage can only be overcome in frames cut at a foundation by working to a greater number of significant figures.

When the frame and its loads are symmetrical, some of the redundant forces can be solved by the equations of static equilibrium, thereby eliminating the need for one or more moment area equations.

6–4. Simple Rigid Frames. Problems of frames with fewer redundant reactions can be solved more easily than Ex. 6–1.

Example 6–4A. Two Redundant Reactions. Consider the frame of Fig. 6–6A. If the structure is cut at A, there are only two unknown forces, H and V. These can be found by solving two simultaneous equations. Because $\Delta Y_A = 0$ and $\Delta X_A = 0$, Eqs. 4–20 and 4–21 are the logical equations to use. Since the moment diagrams for live load, H, and V are exactly the same as those shown in Figs. 6–1C, D, and E, the terms for load, H, and V in the equations for this frame are the same as those in Tables 6–2 and 6–3 (Art. 6–1). There is no moment at point A, so the coefficients of M in these two tables are ignored. Thus we have

$$\Delta Y_A = 916H + 4867V - 239,627 = 0 \qquad \text{(from Table 6–2)}$$
$$\Delta X_A = 1417H + 915V - 42,781 = 0 \qquad \text{(from Table 6–3)}$$

from which

$$H = -1.83 = 1.83 \text{ kips right} \qquad V = +49.58 = 49.58 \text{ kips upward}$$

The elastic curve, exaggerated 1000 times, is shown in Fig. 6–6B.

OTHER PROCEDURES. The frame could have been cut at G, as shown in Fig. 6–7A, but this would involve unnecessary labor in the solution. Since point A is not fixed, there is an unknown angle change at A, and this introduces another unknown into the equations for deflection at G. So it is necessary to solve three simultaneous equations instead of two. Actually, there are four unknowns, H, V, M, and θ_A, but since the structure is indeterminate to only two degrees, one of the unknown forces can be expressed in terms of the other two by using the equations of static equilibrium. Thus, there are two unknown forces and the unknown rotation at A. Another way of arriving at the same conclusion is to consider the elastic characteristics of the structure. If it is cut at G, we must somehow express these facts mathematically: there is no vertical deflection of G ($\Delta Y_G = 0$), there is no horizontal deflection at G ($\Delta X_G = 0$), and there is no rotation at G ($\Delta \theta_G = 0$). It requires three equations to do this.

The frame could have been cut at any interior point, as shown in Fig. 6–7B, but this, too, involves unnecessary labor and is, for that reason, poor engineering. Again, there are three unknown forces: shear, thrust, and moment (one of which can be expressed in terms of the other two by an equation of static equilibrium), and an unknown rotation at A, so there are

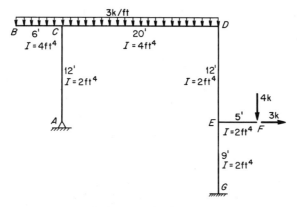

A. Frame and Loads

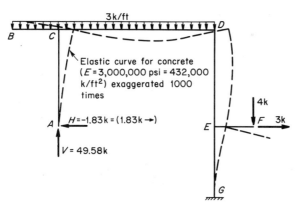

B. Frame Cut at A

Fig. 6–6. Frame with two redundant reactions.

three unknowns. Consequently, three moment area equations must be solved simultaneously. Or, viewed in another way, when the frame is cut at an interior point, the cut faces are free to rotate and move independently of each other. If such movements are to be prevented, we must express mathematically that the relative rotation is zero, the relative axial (thrust) deformation is zero, and the relative shear deformation is zero. Three equations are required here. One of the three internal forces at the cut section can

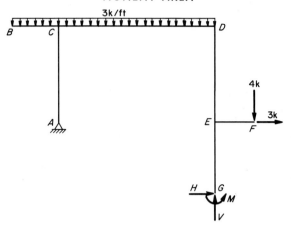

A. Frame and Cut at *G*

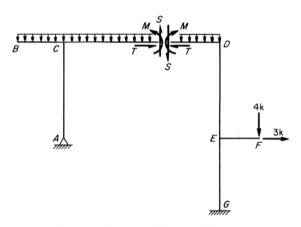

B. Frame Cut at Any Interior Point

Fig. 6–7. Cut-back structures for frame with two redundant reactions.

be expressed in terms of the other two, but, again, there is the unknown rotation at A which makes a third unknown quantity.

Example 6–4B. One Redundant Reaction. Consider the frame in Fig. 6–8 with one redundant reaction. As in Ex. 6–4A, the frame could be cut anywhere, but the only logical place to cut it is at A, replacing the reaction with a single unknown force V.

The horizontal deflection and the rotation at A are unknown, so Eqs. 4–21 (for ΔX_A) and 4–22 (for $\Delta\theta_A$) are useless. The only helpful equation is 4–20 ($\Delta Y_A = 0$). Because the moment diagrams for live load and for V are the same as those shown in Figs. 6–1C and 6–1E, the terms involving load

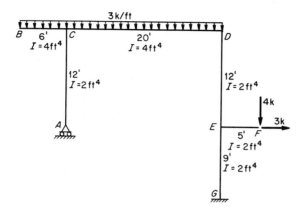

A. Frame and Loads

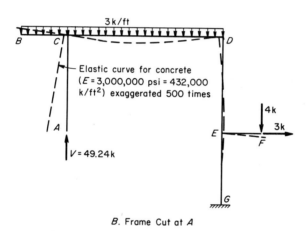

B. Frame Cut at *A*

Fig. 6–8. Frame with one redundant reaction.

and V are the same as those in Table 6–2. Terms for H and M in Table 6–2 are ignored. Thus we have

$$\Delta Y_A = 4867V - 239{,}627 = 0$$

$$V = +49.24 \text{ kips} = 49.24 \text{ kips upward}$$

The elastic curve, exaggerated 500 times, is shown in Fig. 6–8*B*.

6–5. Two-Hinged Frames.

Example 6–5*A. Reactions.* In order to find the reactions for the two-hinged frame in Fig. 6–9*A*, the structure is cut at *A* (or at *G*), as shown in

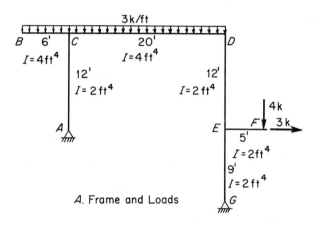

A. Frame and Loads

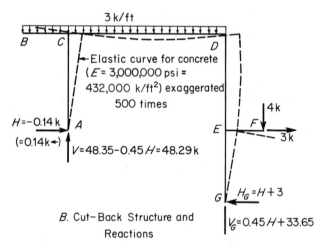

B. Cut-Back Structure and
Reactions

Fig. 6–9. Two-hinged

Fig. 6–9B, and the reactive forces H and V are substituted for the cut away hinge. Since the frame is indeterminate to only one degree, V can be found in terms of H by taking moments about G, thus:

$$\Sigma M_G = 0 = +H \times 9 \text{ ft} + V \times 20 \text{ ft} - (3 \text{ kips/ft})26 \text{ ft} \times 13 \text{ ft}$$
$$+ 4 \text{ kips} \times 5 \text{ ft} + 3 \text{ kips} \times 9 \text{ ft}$$
$$V = 48.35 - 0.45H$$

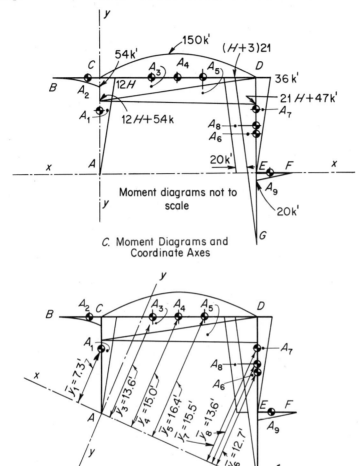

C. Moment Diagrams and
Coordinate Axes

D. Moment Diagrams and Rotated
Axes

rigid frame.

The reactions at G can also be found in terms of H by the equations of static equilibrium.

$$\Sigma H = 0 = H + 3 - H_G$$

$$H_G = H + 3$$

$$\Sigma V = 0 = 48.35 - 0.45H - (3 \text{ kips/ft}) \times 26 \text{ ft} - 4 \text{ kips} + V_G$$

$$V_G = 0.45H + 33.65$$

The moment diagrams could be drawn in a number of ways, but to keep Fig. 6–9C from becoming cluttered with too many moment diagrams, they are drawn in cantilever parts from A for the left column, in cantilever parts from G for the right column, and in simple beam parts between C and D. The controlling simple-beam maximum moments are computed from Fig. 6–9B as follows, calling moments producing compression on the inner fibers positive:

$$M_{CD} = M_{CA} + M_{CB} = 12H + (3 \text{ kips/ft}) \frac{(6)^2}{2} = 12H + 54 \text{ kip-ft}$$

$$M_{\text{mid-point of } CD} = \frac{-WL^2}{8} = \frac{-3(20)^2}{8} = -150 \text{ kip-ft}$$

$$M_{DC} = 4 \text{ kips} \times 5 \text{ ft} - (3 \text{ kips} \times 12 \text{ ft}) + (H + 3)21 \text{ ft}$$
$$= 21H + 47 \text{ kip-ft}$$

Using the moment diagrams and coordinate axes in Fig. 6–9C, Eq. 4–20

$$\Delta Y = \sum \bar{x} A_{MD/EI} + \sum x\theta + Y \qquad (4\text{--}20)$$

reduces to

$$\Delta Y_A = \sum_A^G \bar{x} A_{MD/EI} + x_G\theta_G + 0$$

There are two unknowns in this equation, H and θ_G, so another equation must be written. Equation 4–21

$$\Delta X = \sum \bar{y} A_{MD/EI} + \sum y\theta + X \qquad (4\text{--}21)$$

reduces to

$$\Delta X_A = \sum_A^G \bar{y} A_{MD/EI} + y_G\theta_G + 0$$

in which the same two unknowns H and θ_G appear.

Example 6–5B. Rotated Axes. It is possible—and much more convenient and rapid—to avoid the solution of two simultaneous equations by rotating the axes as in Fig. 6–9D. The moment diagrams and reactive forces are exactly the same as in Figs. 6–9C and 6–9B, but $\bar{x}$ and $\bar{y}$ distances are measured on the slant. Equation 4–21

$$\Delta X = \sum \bar{y} A_{MD/EI} + \sum y\theta + X \qquad (4\text{--}21)$$

reduces to

$$\Delta X_A = 0 = \sum_A^G \bar{y} A_{MD/EI} + (y_G\theta_G = 0) + 0$$

The term $y_G\theta_G$ is zero because the xx axis passes through point G so that y_G is zero. Note that Eq. 4–20 is of no help because its second term $\sum x\theta$ becomes $x_G\theta_G$, which does *not* reduce to zero.

The centroidal or $\bar{y}$ distances are most rapidly obtained by measuring them on a carefully drawn large-scale sketch.[9] The solution of the foregoing equation (which is based on Fig. 6–9D) is found in Table 6–8.

TABLE 6–8

Solution of $\displaystyle\sum_{A}^{G} \bar{y} A_{MD/EI} = 0$

Moment Diagram Part	$\bar{y}$ Scaled on Enlargement of Frame in Fig. 6–9D	$A_{MD/EI}$ Coeff. × Base × Height	Coefficient of H	Constants	
				Plus	Minus
A_1	7.3	$\dfrac{1}{2} \times 12 \times \dfrac{12H}{2E}$	$+\ \ 263H/E$		
A_2		Omit			
A_3	13.6	$\dfrac{1}{2} \times 20 \times \dfrac{12H + 54}{4E}$	$+\ \ 408H/E$	1,836/E	
A_4	15.0	$-\dfrac{2}{3} \times 20 \times \dfrac{150}{4E}$			7,500/E
A_5	16.4	$\dfrac{1}{2} \times 20 \times \dfrac{21H + 47}{4E}$	$+\ \ 861H/E$	1,927/E	
A_6	12.7	$\dfrac{1}{2} \times 21 \times \dfrac{(H + 3)21}{2E}$	$+1,400H/E$	4,200/E	
A_7	15.5	$-\dfrac{1}{2} \times 12 \times \dfrac{36}{2E}$			1,674/E
A_8	13.6	$1 \times 12 \times \dfrac{20}{2E}$		1,632/E	
A_9		Omit			
		Summation	$+2,932H/E$	$+9,595/E$	$-9,174/E$

$$+\frac{2,932H}{E} + \frac{9,595}{E} - \frac{9,174}{E} = 0$$

$$H = -0.14 = 0.14 \text{ kip left}$$

From the equation of static equilibrium developed for V at the beginning of Art. 6–5,

$$V = 48.35 - 0.45(-0.14) = 48.29 \text{ kips up}$$

6–6. Arches and Rings. Moment area is an ideal method for the analysis of two-hinged arches, fixed arches, haunched beams, and closed

---

[9] For a frame of this size, a scale of 5 ft = 1 in. is large enough to obtain $\bar{y}$ to three significant figures.

rings such as those of Fig. 6–10. Most arches and many closed rings are variable in section, continuous beams of concrete are often haunched, and continuous beams of steel are often reinforced over supports (although rarely haunched). There are several ways to analyze structures in which the

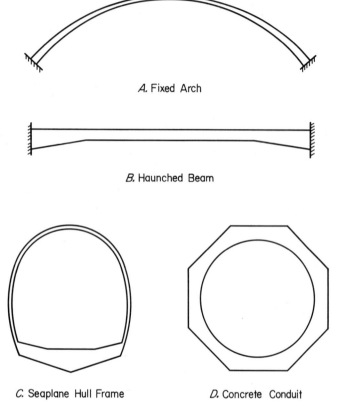

A. Fixed Arch

B. Haunched Beam

C. Seaplane Hull Frame   *D.* Concrete Conduit

Fig. 6–10. Typical arch, haunched beam, and rings.

moment of inertia varies. The most common method is to divide the structure into a number of segments and to assume M/EI to be constant for each separate segment.[10] Another method, often used for beams, is to solve the integral moment area equations by calculus. As shown in Arts. 4–5 and 4–6, integral moment area is very simple for prismatic beams, but as shown in Art.

---

[10] A more accurate variation is Newmark's method (see N. M. Newmark, *op. cit.*, ref. 9, Chapter 5) in which the beam is divided into segments but, instead of assuming constant moment and moment of inertia, the shape of the $A_{MD/EI}$ diagram for each segment is approximated by a trapezoid or by a parabolic segment. For some problems Newmark's method is exact, and for the general problem it is a very accurate approximation. The structure can be divided into fewer segments, and the tabular form of the method permits great speed by a skillful engineer.

10–2, it becomes more complex for haunched beams. It is impractical for arches and rings. A very fast method of analyzing straight members is to plot the M/EI diagrams on a uniform sheet of cardboard (such as Bristol board), cut them out, weigh them to obtain their areas, and balance them to obtain their centroids. This method is accurate if the work is carefully done. It can be applied to rigid frames by treating each moment diagram (for each separate member) separately. The angle changes occur at the centerline of a member, so the centroid of any short segment of the M/EI diagram must fall, mathematically speaking, on the centerline. Centroids of cardboard cut-outs for straight members can be projected to the centerline without error. If the member is curved, error can be eliminated by confining the cardboard cut-outs to a surface perpendicular to the plane of the structure (similar to the M_i and M_s diagrams of Fig. 22–1).

In dividing a beam, arch, or ring into segments, the solution becomes more accurate as the number of segments increases. Although no inflexible rule can be given, practical accuracy can be obtained by dividing arches into 12 to 24 segments, closed rings into 20 to 40 segments. The prismatic portion of a beam can be taken as a single segment provided the true (instead of an average) M/EI diagram is considered. The haunched portion may be divided into two to ten segments, depending upon the length of the haunch.[11]

ACCURACY. It is advantageous to cut a long arch at the crown rather than at one reaction. The lever arms of all the forces (reactive, dead load, and live load) are shorter; therefore, the moments are smaller and, consequently, the accuracy is better. Even so, calculations should be made on a calculator and carried out to five or more significant figures, because the total moments in an arch are quite small, and even a minor error in one moment becomes a large error when all the moments are added algebraically. It is wise to have calculations checked immediately since errors are difficult to avoid.

LIVE LOADS ON ARCHES. Since live loads on arches, especially arch bridges, can act on any portion of the structure, it would ordinarily be necessary to construct many sets of influence lines to determine the positions of live loads that cause maximum stresses. But live loads are usually small compared with dead loads, and influence lines for all arches are very similar. Consequently, arches are usually analyzed for: (1) live load acting on the full span; (2) live load acting on three-eighths of the span (from one end to a point three-eighths of a span from that end); and (3) live load on five-eighths of the span, which by the principle of superposition can be obtained by subtracting item (2) from item (1) if the arch is symmetrical.

TEMPERATURE EFFECTS ON ARCHES. Stresses caused by temperature changes may be considerable. A drop in temperature has the effect of making the arch smaller in every dimension. If unrestrained—as by cutting the left

---

[11] A graphical method for constructing elastic curves was proposed by A. Hoadley in "A Graphical Construction for the Deflection of Structural Members of Variable Moment of Inertia," *Proc. ASCE*, 79 (Separate No. 256), August, 1953.

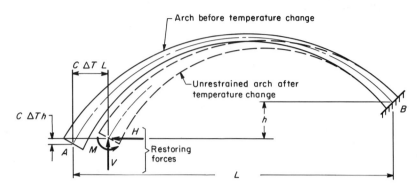

A. Temperature Drop. Left End Cut

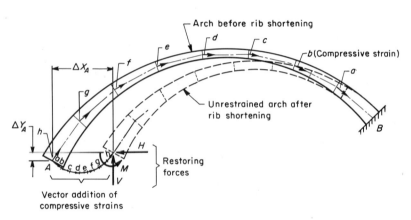

B. Rib Shortening. Left End Cut

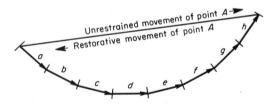

Scale: 4 times strains in figure above

C. Vector Addition of Compressive Strains

Fig. 6–11. Deformations of a fixed arch.

reaction—the arch would contract, as shown by the dashed lines in Fig. 6–11A, without being stressed, and its movement at the left reaction would be

$$\Delta X = C \, \Delta T \, L$$

in which C represents coefficient of thermal expansion, ΔT represents change in temperature, and L represents span.

If the reactions were at different elevations, there would be a vertical movement of the left end

$$\Delta Y = C \, \Delta T \, h$$

in which h represents difference in elevation of the two abutments.

The left abutment of the arch, unrestrained till now, can be visualized as being forced back into position by the vertical, horizontal, and moment reactions H, V, and M, shown in Fig. 6–11A. The three moment area equations become

$$\Delta Y_A = C \, \Delta T \, h = \sum \bar{x} A_{MD/EI} + \sum x\theta + Y$$
$$\Delta X_A = C \, \Delta T \, L = \sum \bar{y} A_{MD/EI} + \sum y\theta + X$$
$$\Delta \theta = 0 = \sum A_{MD/EI} + \sum \theta$$

in which some of the terms may reduce to zero, depending upon the conditions of the problem. Although this problem has been illustrated by cutting the arch at the left abutment, it can be cut just as well at the crown.

RIB SHORTENING. Arches are subject to large axial compressive forces, which induce compressive strains parallel to the arch axis, causing the arch to shorten. Furthermore, fresh concrete tends to shrink, thus making the arch rib shorter. Rib shortening affects the stresses to a lesser degree than temperature change, but it is important, nevertheless. Again, assume the left abutment cut away. The movement of the left end of the arch can be computed by the vector addition of the compressive strain of each segment. The compressive strain for each segment can be taken as the sum of the shrinkage (which is independent of stress) and the compressive strain caused by dead load. The three moment area equations can again be written, letting ΔX equal the horizontal movement as shown in Fig. 6–10B, ΔY equal the vertical movement if any (also shown in Fig. 6–10B), and by letting $\Delta \theta = 0$.

Reactions and stresses due to rib shortening are at best approximate. The amount of shrinkage can only be estimated. The compressive stresses can be determined accurately, but concrete, being subject to plastic flow which varies with a number of factors, does not have a true modulus of elasticity. Hence, final strains can only be approximate.

DESIGN OF ARCHES. The design of arches is not within the scope of this text. The reader is referred to Cross and Morgan,[12] McCullough and Thayer,[13]

---

[12] Hardy Cross and N. D. Morgan, *Continuous Frames of Reinforced Concrete* (New York: John Wiley and Sons, Inc., 1932), pp. 279–338.

[13] Conde B. McCullough and Edward S. Thayer, *Elastic Arch Bridges* (New York: John Wiley & Sons, Inc., 1931).

Maugh,[14] Spofford,[15] Parcel and Maney,[16] Grinter,[17] Hool,[18] Urquhart and O'Rourke,[19] and Michalos.[20] These authors analyze arches by virtual work, column analogy, least work, and by the elastic center method. Any of these methods is suitable and so is moment area. None of these methods of analysis offers outstanding advantages over the others. By avoiding the complex equations of some methods and by using always the same approach for beams, frames, and arches, the moment area method is easier to understand than most.

6–7. Complex Frames. Fig. 6–12 shows some typical complex frames. The double-sewer section of Fig. 6–12A shows a frame indeterminate to six degrees. Such a frame might be cut back as shown, although other cut-back structures are also possible. The analysis requires the solution of six simultaneous equations. This fact, coupled with the curvature and varying moment of inertia, makes this a long and difficult problem. Even so, the moment area method is still practical as compared with other methods of solution.

The continuous arches of Fig. 6–12B contain four bays, and it is necessary to cut the structure in four places in such a manner that moments are determinate at all points. At each cut, there are three unknown forces—12 in all. Although 12 simultaneous equations can be solved, the moment area method (or any other depending on cut-back structures) is impractical, unless an electronic computer can be used. Moment distribution[21,22] can be used for problems of this sort, and it is practical. Model analysis also is a practical method.

Moment area is also impractical for the solution of multistory building frames. Such structures are, however, analyzed easily and quickly by moment distribution.

The Vierendeel truss of Fig. 6–12D is statically indeterminate to 15 degrees. The most practical method of solution is moment distribution; certainly any method that would yield 15 simultaneous equations seems quite impractical unless the equations could be solved by an electronic computer. The

---

[14] L. C. Maugh, *Statically Indeterminate Structures* (New York: John Wiley & Sons, Inc., 1946), pp. 212–238, 288 ff.

[15] C. M. Spofford, *The Theory of Continuous Structures and Arches* (New York: McGraw-Hill Book Company, Inc., 1937).

[16] John Ira Parcel and George Alfred Maney, *An Elementary Treatise on Statically Indeterminate Stresses* (2d ed; New York: John Wiley & Sons, Inc., 1936), pp. 282–348.

[17] Linton E. Grinter, *Theory of Modern Steel Structures* Vol. II (rev. ed; New York: The Macmillan Company, 1949), pp. 239–303.

[18] G. A. Hool, *Reinforced Concrete Construction* Vol. III (2d ed; New York: McGraw-Hill Book Company, Inc., 1928).

[19] Leonard Church Urquhart and Charles Edward O'Rourke, *Design of Concrete Structures* (New York: McGraw-Hill Book Company, Inc., 1954), pp. 350–386.

[20] James Michalos, *Theory of Structural Analysis and Design* (New York: The Ronald Press Co., 1958).

[21] Maugh, *op. cit.*, pp. 230–242.

[22] Michalos, *op. cit.*, pp. 234–252.

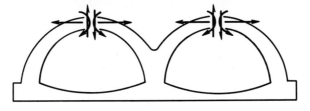

A. Double Sewer

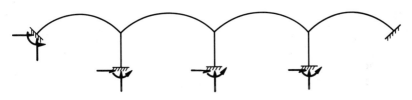

B. Continuous Arches

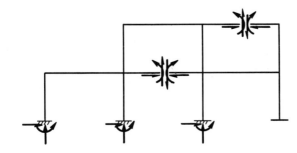

C. Building Frame

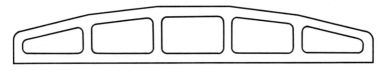

D. Vierendeel Truss

Fig. 6–12. Complex arches and frames.

Vierendeel truss has been used to a limited extent for short bridges. It supports loads by virtue of the bending resistance of its short, heavy members, and it is more efficient than it appears to be.

Part III

VIRTUAL WORK

Virtual work is one of the oldest classical methods of indeterminate structural analysis. The foundation for the method was laid in 1717, when Bernoulli stated the principle of virtual displacements, and in 1833, when Clapeyron showed the equality of internal to external work. In 1846, James Clerk Maxwell adapted these relationships to the solution of statically indeterminate trusses. The method was further developed by Professor Otto Mohr to such an extent that it is sometimes called the Maxwell-Mohr method. Other titles applied to virtual work are virtual velocities (the original but less descriptive title), unit load method, dummy load method, method of work, elastic energy method, and elastic strain-energy method. The last three titles might also be used as alternate terms for some of the other work methods. In 1883 virtual work was introduced into the United States by Professor George Swain, who later added the concept of rotational deflections.

Virtual work is one of a group of closely related strain-energy methods which includes Castigliano's theorems[1] and real work. In common with Castigliano's theorems it is unlimited in scope—adapted to the solution of redundant forces and deflections in trusses, beams, rigid frames, arches, shafts, etc., whether the strains involved are tension, compression, shear, or any combination of these. Any problem that can be solved by any strain-energy method can be solved by virtual work. The concept of Castigliano's theorems is more abstract than that of virtual work, which is straightforward and stripped of non-essential mathematical manipulation. Virtual work is not a rapid method although by using the semi-graphical approach in Chapters 8 and 9, solutions for beams and rigid frames can be obtained nearly as quickly as by the use of moment area. One great advantage of virtual work lies in its (nearly) automatic determination of sign. Considering all its advantages, it is a truly remarkable method of analysis.

[1] See Chapter 24.

7

TRUSSES

7–1. Work and Energy. Work is defined as the product of force times distance. Energy is the capacity for doing work. In a sense work and energy are equivalents and so closely related that a sharp delineation cannot be made.

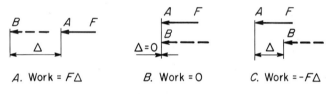

A. Work = $F\Delta$ *B.* Work = 0   *C.* Work = $-F\Delta$

Fig. 7–1. Work.

If a force is constant and moves from A to B along its own line of action, as shown in Fig. 7–1A, the total work done is simply

$$W = F\Delta \tag{7-1}$$

If the force varies, the general expression for the work is

$$W = \int_{s=0}^{s=\Delta} F \, ds$$

In structures which behave elastically, stresses are proportional to strains, so that the force applied is proportional to the distance moved.

$$F = ks \quad \text{or} \quad s = F/k$$

then

$$W = k \int_{s=0}^{s=\Delta} s \, ds = k \left[\frac{s^2}{2} \right]_{s=0}^{s=\Delta} = \left[\frac{ks}{2} s \right]_{s=0}^{s=\Delta} = \left[\frac{Fs}{2} \right]_{s=0}^{s=\Delta} = \frac{F}{2} \Delta \tag{7-2}$$

That is, the work done by a force gradually applied to an elastic structure equals the *average* force times the distance moved.

The distance must always be measured along the line of action of the force. If the point of application of a force moves normal (perpendicular) to the line of action of the force, as from A to B in Fig. 7–1B, no work is done. If a force moves from point A to point B in a path which is oblique to the line of action of the force as in Fig. 7–1C, the work equals the force times the component of the distance measured parallel to the line of action of the force.

The work is positive by definition if the force moves in the direction applied. If the force moves backward as in Fig. 7–1C, the work is negative.

CONSERVATION OF ENERGY. The law of conservation of energy is a basic principle of physics, which states that energy can be neither created nor destroyed. This definition is oversimplified, but it is adequate for the purpose of structural analysis. Specifically, this principle means that, as loads are applied to an elastic structure which is in equilibrium, the energy level of the structure remains fixed. The work done by applied forces is exactly counter-balanced by the energy of internal strains. Thus the total work done—internal and external—must be zero.

7–2. Basic Theory. Indeterminate forces of all kinds must be found—directly or indirectly—by finding one or more deflections. Therefore, statically indeterminate stress analysis is simply the determination of deflections. To

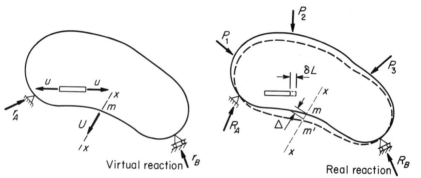

A. Virtual Loads and Reactions   *B.* Real Loads, Distortions, and Reactions

Fig. 7–2. Deflection.

be perfectly general, a method must be capable of determining any component of the deflection at any point in any kind of structure.

To develop such a method, consider any general structure—a truss, beam, rigid frame, or anything else—to be represented by the shapeless mass of Fig. 7–2. Two unyielding reactions show a statically determinate structure, but any number of reactions could be shown and the structure could be indeterminate to any degree without changing the proof in the least. Furthermore, the proof can be extended to include structures on elastic supports.[1] It is necessary only that the structure be stable and in equilibrium. The structure is composed of an infinite number of elements, and a typical element is shown exaggerated in size and strained by an amount δL. The strain may result from shrinkage, temperature, or any other phenomenon, and it may

---

[1] Consider the elastic supports to be a part of the structure. The elastic supports are, in turn, supported by unyielding reactions. Extension of virtual work to include elastic foundations is further discussed in Art. 11–6.

result from stress caused by any sort of loads such as P_1, P_2, and P_3. The source of the strain is of no importance here; all that matters just now is that, owing to some cause, the element elongates (or shortens) an amount δL. A general expression is required for the deflection of any point such as point m along any axis such as xx.

THE VIRTUAL LOAD. Consider all the real loads P_1, P_2, and P_3 to be removed (or consider the structure before temperature changes or shrinkage take place), leaving the structure unstrained. A virtual force U is applied at point m acting in the direction xx as in Fig. 7–2A. It causes reactions r_A and r_B at the supports and induces stresses throughout the structure. The stress acting on the pictured element can be converted to a force u by multiplying the stress by the cross-sectional area of the element.

REAL STRAINS. Now apply the real loads P_1, P_2, and P_3 (or let the temperature change or shrinkage take place) so that real strains occur as in Fig. 7–2B. A typical element will change length by an amount δL. The work done by the virtual force u acting on the element is

$$w_{\text{internal}} = \text{force} \times \text{distance} = u\,\delta L$$

and, of course, the total internal virtual work done on all the elements would be

$$W_{\text{internal}} = \Sigma w_{\text{internal}} = \sum u\,\delta L$$

Except at the reactions, every point along the boundary deflects. Point m moves to m', and the work done by the virtual load U is

$$W_{\text{external}} = \text{force} \times \text{distance} = U\Delta$$

No other external virtual work is done. True, there are virtual reactions (r_A and r_B), but they do not move and hence cause no work, and there are no other external virtual forces to cause work.

From the principle of the conservation of energy, the total energy level of the structure must be unchanged. Thus

$$W_{\text{external}} - W_{\text{internal}} = 0$$

or

$$W_{\text{external}} = W_{\text{internal}}$$

So

$$U\Delta = \sum u\,\delta L \tag{7–3}$$

The virtual load can be left as simply U, and in some of the following examples this will be done. But most engineers prefer to use a unit number for U such as 1 kip or 1 lb. Of course, any other number would serve as well. The use of a unit number is simply a convenience. In this text 1 $\#$ denotes a virtual load and 1 #-ft or 1 #-in., a virtual moment. Equation 7–3 can be expressed, then, as

$$1 \text{ kip } \Delta = \sum u \, \delta L \qquad (7\text{–}3)$$

or

$$1 \, \# \, \Delta = \sum u \, \delta L \qquad (7\text{–}3)$$

In any of these forms the equation has little practical use. It becomes useful for a particular problem only when known quantities can be substituted for δL. The remainder of the chapter is mainly devoted to a study of special expressions for δL.

Discussion. The above proof is as rigorous as necessary. Superficially, it may seem that a more rigorous proof must take into account the total work done by all forces, not just a part of the work as considered above. That can be done,[2] and the same equation results. The proof in the footnote is more complete but, in the last analysis, it is not really more rigorous and it is certainly more complicated. Avoid it if you understand the above development.

It should be emphasized that Eq. 7–3 measures only the deflection caused by the real or actual strains. *The equation does not include deflection due to the virtual load.* Any virtual load—even one that is large compared to real loads—can be used with no effect whatever upon the computed deflection. Note the term for external virtual work, $U\Delta$; the deflection Δ is the deflection due only to the real loads. In the term for internal virtual work, $\sum u \, \delta L$, the

---

[2] Imagine, for the time being, that the virtual load in Fig. 7–2 causes a deflection at point m called Δ_u, and that the element changes in length by an amount δL_u. Then from Eq. 7–2 and the principle of conservation of energy an expression for deflection due only to the virtual load is

$$\tfrac{1}{2} U \Delta_u = \sum \tfrac{1}{2} u \, \delta L_u$$

Now disregard the virtual loads and forces in Fig. 7–2 and consider the work done by the real loads in Fig. 7–2B. Let Δ_1, Δ_2, and Δ_3 be the deflections at loads P_1, P_2, and P_3 respectively. Calling the true force on the element F, the expression for real work is

$$\tfrac{1}{2} P_1 \Delta_1 + \tfrac{1}{2} P_2 \Delta_2 + \tfrac{1}{2} P_3 \Delta_3 = \sum \tfrac{1}{2} F \, \delta L$$

Once again, consider an unloaded structure. Apply first the virtual loads of Fig. 7–2A and then add the real loads of Fig. 7–2B. Writing the expression for the total work, we have

$$\tfrac{1}{2} U \Delta_u + U\Delta + \tfrac{1}{2} P_1 \Delta_1 + \tfrac{1}{2} P_2 \Delta_2 + \tfrac{1}{2} P_3 \Delta_3 = \sum \tfrac{1}{2} u \, \delta L_u + \sum u \, \delta L + \sum \tfrac{1}{2} F \, \delta L$$

From the last equation for *total work* subtract the first equation (for deflection due only to virtual work) and subtract the second equation (for real work). The result is

$$U\Delta = \sum u \, \delta L$$

as before. Note that any deflection caused by the virtual load itself is not included in this equation. Note also that real work has been removed from the final equation. All that is left is the true deflection Δ, whose magnitude is measured by the virtual load. Essentially, the virtual load is only a device—a sort of yardstick—with which to measure true deflection.

strains δL are actual strains, not strains caused partially by the virtual force. The virtual force, then, does not cause deflection. It is used only as a device to convert true strains into strain energy, because strain-energy relations are easy to handle whereas strains *per se* usually are not.

SIGNS. A significant advantage of virtual work is that the determination of signs is automatic. If the sign is plus, the deflection takes the direction of the virtual load. If the sign is minus, the deflection is opposite to the direction of the virtual load. No matter what convention is used for signs, the sign is automatically determined, provided the same convention is used for both real

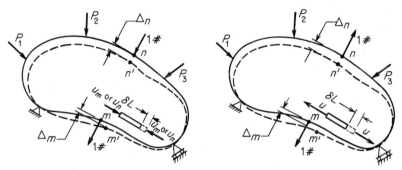

A. Collinear Congruent Virtual Loads   *B*. Collinear Opposite Virtual Loads

Fig. 7–3. Relative deflections.

and virtual loads. This condition is inherent in the development of the general equation. If the internal work is positive, the external work must also be positive, which (according to the definitions[3] in Art. 7–1) indicates that the point must deflect in the direction of the virtual load.

RELATIVE DEFLECTION. It often saves time to compute a deflection relative to another deflection. The long way would be to compute one deflection, then compute the other deflection, and finally subtract one from the other to obtain the difference or the relative deflection. This is illustrated by Fig. 7–3*A*. The deflection of point m is computed as

$$1 \,\#\, \Delta_m = \sum u_m \, \delta L$$

and the deflection of point n is computed as

$$1 \,\#\, \Delta_n = \sum u_n \, \delta L$$

Then the relative deflection is

$$\Delta_{\text{relative}} = \Delta_m - \Delta_n = \frac{\sum u_m \, \delta L - \sum u_n \, \delta L}{1 \,\#}$$

[3] The opposite definition could be assumed, that is, a force moving in the direction in which it is applied does negative work. Then, if the internal work is negative, the external work must also be negative, indicating again that deflection occurs in the direction of the virtual load. Thus the signs do not depend upon the convention; they depend only upon consistency.

Theoretically, the minus sign is not objectionable but, practically, it is. It can be avoided by applying *opposite* virtual loads, as shown in Fig. 7–3B. Now the sign of Δ_n is automatically minus (because it is opposite in direction to the virtual load), so the expressions for virtual work must be added; thus

$$\Delta_{\text{relative}} = \Delta_m + \Delta_n = \frac{\sum u_m\,\delta L + \sum u_n\,\delta L}{1\,\#} = \frac{\sum(u_m + u_n)\,\delta L}{1\,\#}$$

The sequence of adding a column of numbers or a group of algebraic terms does not affect the sum, so the short way to obtain the relative deflection is to apply both virtual loads at once, computing the internal virtual forces u as the sum of u_m and u_n. Then the relative deflection is

$$\Delta_{\text{relative}} = \Delta_m + \Delta_n = \frac{\sum(u_m + u_n)\,\delta L}{1\,\#} = \frac{\sum u\,\delta L}{1\,\#}$$

This expression is the same as Eq. 7–3, in which the internal virtual forces u are those for both virtual loads acting at once. Because the virtual loads are equal and opposite, large portions of the structure may not be stressed by the virtual loads, thus reducing the labor of computation. Relative deflections are important, and this principle will be used again and again.

Rotation. Work can also be expressed as the product of rotation times torque, moment, or couple, where rotation ($\Delta\theta$) is measured in radians. By analogy with the development of Eq. 7–3, rotation can be determined as

$$U\,\Delta\theta = \sum u\,\delta L \qquad\qquad (7\text{–}4)$$

where U is a virtual couple and $\Delta\theta$ is rotation in radians. The internal virtual forces u are those caused by the virtual couple just as similar u forces are caused by virtual loads in Fig. 7–2. Again it is usual to use a virtual couple of unity so that u can be expressed as 1 #-ft or 1 #-in.

The equation for rotation can also be developed from the concept of relative deflections. Suppose the rotation of the boundary at point m of Fig. 7–4 is wanted. Apply equal and opposite unit virtual loads at points q and t a unit distance (say, 1 in.) apart and straddling point m. The relative deflection is

$$\Delta_{\text{relative}} = \Delta_q + \Delta_t = \frac{\sum u\,\delta L}{1\,\#}$$

If the rotation is small, the angle in radians equals the tangent of the angle, so that

$$\Delta\theta_{\text{radians}} = \frac{\Delta_{\text{relative}}}{1\ \text{in.}} = \frac{\sum u\,\delta L}{1\,\# \times 1\ \text{in.}}$$

or

$$1 \text{ \#-in. } \Delta\theta = \sum u\, \delta L \tag{7-4}$$

as before.[4]

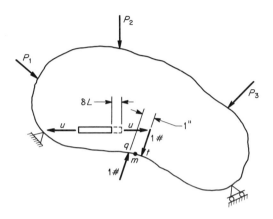

Fig. 7–4. Rotation.

REVIEW AND SUMMARY. To obtain the deflection of a point, apply a virtual load at the point acting in the direction of the desired component of deflection. Evaluate the internal virtual work which is $\sum u\, \delta L$. If the sign is plus, the deflection is in the direction of the virtual force. If the sign is negative, the deflection is opposite to the direction of the virtual force. To obtain the deflection of one point relative to another, apply equal and opposite collinear virtual loads and evaluate $\sum u\, \delta L$, wherein u represents forces due to both virtual loads acting at once. To obtain the rotation at a point, apply a virtual couple at the point and evaluate $\sum u\, \delta L$. Again the sign is automatic—plus if rotation acts in the direction of the virtual couple.

7–3. No-Load Deflections. Trusses are nearly always composed of members that are—or can be assumed to be—prismatic or constant in cross-section between joints. In any member, therefore, strains due to any cause (temperature change, stress, etc.) are usually assumed to be uniformly distributed. Consequently, each member can be considered to be one single large element. When the change of length δL can be evaluated quickly and conveniently, the basic virtual work equation can be used without modification.

Examples of problems adapted to a solution by the basic equation are those in which the change of length is caused by a definite slip in rivets or by an error in the fabricated length, or by deliberately fabricating the member too long or too short.

---

[4] Finite values of pounds and inches were used because it seems easier and more straightforward. The same equation can be obtained by using infinite loads separated by an infinitesimal distance to obtain a virtual torque at a *point*.

CAMBER. Trusses are often cambered (even more than plans may indicate) to allow for slip or play in the joints or to compensate for dead-load or live-load deflection. It is often done by an arbitrary specification which stipulates fabricating certain members longer or shorter than computed lengths by a definite amount.[5]

Example 7–3A. Suppose the truss of Fig. 7–5A is to be cambered by making the length of each tension member (shown by the heavy lines) ⅛ in.

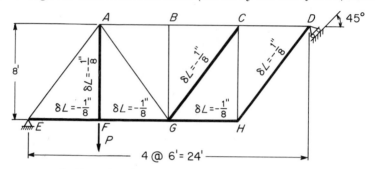

A. Truss Showing Foreshortened Members

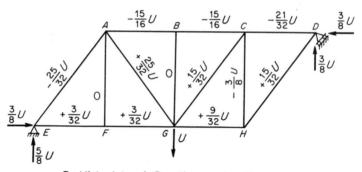

B. Virtual Load, Reactions, and *u* Forces

Fig. 7–5. Cambered truss.

less than that shown on the plans. How much camber (upward deflection disregarding loads) will there be at joint *G*?

Apply virtual load *U* at joint *G* and compute the virtual forces *u* in each element or member. These are shown in terms of the applied virtual load *U* in Fig. 7–5B. The basic virtual work equation is

$$U\Delta = \sum u\,\delta L \qquad (7\text{–}3)$$

in which *u* as applied to this problem is in terms of *U*, as shown in Fig. 7–5B, and *δL* is ⅛ in. for each element or member in tension. Signs are automatic,

---

[5] An AREA specification provides tension members shall be ⅛ in. plus 1/16 in. per 16 ft of length shorter than computed centerline lengths.

as stated before. If tension forces and tension strains (elongation) are assumed positive, the signs of u and δL are those appearing in Table 7–1, and if tensile forces and strains are assumed negative, the signs of u and δL are opposite. But in either case the sign of $\sum u\,\delta L$ is negative, and therefore $U\Delta$ is negative, indicating that deflection is opposite to the virtual force, that is, upward.

TABLE 7–I

Camber of a Truss

$$U\Delta = \sum u\,\delta L \qquad \text{(Eq. 7–3)}$$

Member	u	δL, in.	$u\,\delta L$
AB	$-0.938U$	0	0
BC	$-0.938U$	0	0
CD	$-0.656U$	0	0
EF	$+0.094U$	-0.125	$-0.0118U$
FG	$+0.094U$	-0.125	$-0.0118U$
GH	$+0.281U$	-0.125	$-0.0351U$
EA	$-0.781U$	0	0
HD	$+0.469U$	-0.125	$-0.0586U$
AG	$+0.781U$	0	0
GC	$+0.469U$	-0.125	$-0.0586U$
AF	0	-0.125	0
BG	0	0	0
CH	$-0.375U$	0	0
		$\sum u\,\delta L =$	$-0.1759U$

From Table 7–1

$$U\Delta = -0.1759U$$

let U = 1

Canceling[6] U, which appears on both sides of the equation,

$$\Delta = -0.1759 \text{ in.} \cong 0.18 \text{ in. upward}$$

TEMPERATURE. The change of length of an element due to temperature change is a function of the temperature change ΔT, coefficient of expansion C, and length L.

$$\delta L = C\,\Delta T\,L$$

and this expression can be substituted directly into the basic virtual work equation to produce

$$U\Delta = \sum u\,C\,\Delta T\,L \qquad (7\text{–}5)$$

Example 7–3B. Temperature Effects. Suppose the upper chord of the steel truss of Fig. 7–5A is heated by sunshine to an average temperature 20° F above air temperature. The end posts and web members, receiving only slanting rays of sunlight, are heated 5° F above air temperature, and the lower chord—shaded by the deck—is not heated at all. How much deflection caused by temperature results at joint G?

[6] Note that the virtual force finally cancels, so that no matter what the value of U might have been, it has no effect upon deflection. The deflection is caused by fabrication and not at all by load—virtual or otherwise.

Apply virtual load U at joint G as in Fig. 7–5B. The virtual work equation is evaluated in Table 7–2.

TABLE 7–2
Deflection Due to Temperature Changes

$$U\Delta = \Sigma\, u\, C\, \Delta T\, L \qquad \text{(Eq. 7–5)}$$

Member	ΔT	C	L, in.	u^*	$+u\,C\,\Delta T\,L$	$-u\,C\,\Delta T\,L$
AB	$+20$	0.0000065	72	$-0.938U$		0.00878U
BC	$+20$	0.0000065	72	$-0.938U$		0.00878U
CD	$+20$	0.0000065	72	$-0.656U$		0.00615U
EF	0	0.0000065	72	$+0.094U$		
FG	0	0.0000065	72	$+0.094U$		
GH	0	0.0000065	72	$+0.281U$		
EA	$+5$	0.0000065	120	$-0.781U$		0.00305U
HD	$+5$	0.0000065	120	$+0.469U$	0.00183U	
AG	$+5$	0.0000065	120	$+0.781U$	0.00305U	
GC	$+5$	0.0000065	120	$+0.469U$	0.00183U	
AF	$+5$	0.0000065	96	0		
BG	$+5$	0.0000065	96	0		
CH	$+5$	0.0000065	96	$-0.375U$		0.00117U
				Summation	0.00671U	0.02793U
						$-0.00671U$
				Net sum		0.02122U

* See Table 7–1.

From Table 7–2

$$U\Delta = -0.02122U$$

or

$$\Delta = -0.021 \text{ in.}$$

The minus sign indicates deflection is opposite to the virtual load, that is, upward.

7–4. Deflections Due to Axial Strains in Trusses. Forces in truss members are usually assumed to be co-axial, and because the members are nearly always prismatic, the stresses are uniformly distributed. Again, therefore, each member can be assumed to be one single large element. The change of length of a uniformly strained element is

$$\delta L = \epsilon L$$

in which ϵ is unit strain and L is the length of the element. Young's modulus of elasticity E is defined as the unit stress s, divided by unit strain ϵ. Unit stress equals force F divided by area A. For elastic materials, then

$$\epsilon = \frac{s}{E} = \frac{F/A}{E} = \frac{F}{AE}$$

So by substitution

$$\delta L = \frac{FL}{AE}$$

and Eq. 7–3 becomes

$$UΔ = \sum u \frac{FL}{AE} \tag{7–6}$$

To compute the deflection of a joint in a truss, apply a virtual load at the point, find the virtual reactions, and solve for the virtual forces (u forces) in each member. Find the true forces caused by the real loads. Evaluate $u(FL/AE)$ for every member and add the results algebraically.

7–5. Deflection of a Simple Truss. A statically determinate truss is shown in Fig. 7–6A subjected to a single load. More loads would change only

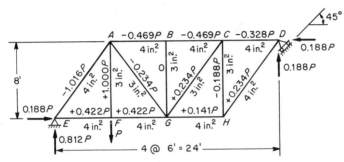

A. Real Loads and Forces

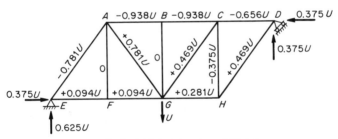

B. Vertical Virtual Loads and Forces

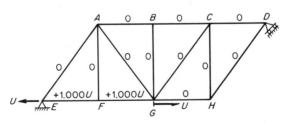

C. Horizontal Virtual Loads and Forces

Fig. 7–6. Deflections of a simple truss.

the real forces in the members, not the method of analysis. Suppose that the absolute deflection of joint G is required. The direction of deflection is unknown, so two components of deflection—one vertical and one horizontal—must be found and combined vectorially.

Example 7–5A. Vertical Deflection. The vertical deflection, called ΔY_G, is found by applying a vertical virtual load at joint G. The reactions are found and the forces in the members are determined (in Fig. 7–6B) just as though

TABLE 7–3

Deflection of Joint G

$$U\,\Delta Y_G = \Sigma\, u(FL/AE) \quad \text{and} \quad U\,\Delta X_G = \Sigma\, u(FL/AE) \qquad \text{(Eq. 7–6)}$$

Member	F	$L,$ in.	$A,$ in.²	FL/A	Vertical, ΔY_G			Horizontal, ΔX_G	
					u	$+u(FL/A)$	$-u(FL/A)$	u	$+u(FL/A)$
AB	$-0.469P$	72	4	$-8.44P$	$-0.938U$	$7.91PU$		0	
BC	$-0.469P$	72	4	$-8.44P$	$-0.938U$	$7.91PU$		0	
CD	$-0.328P$	72	4	$-5.90P$	$-0.656U$	$3.87PU$		0	
EF	$+0.422P$	72	4	$+7.60P$	$+0.094U$	$0.71PU$		$1.00U$	$7.60PU$
FG	$+0.422P$	72	4	$+7.60P$	$+0.094U$	$0.71PU$		$1.00U$	$7.60PU$
GH	$+0.141P$	72	4	$+2.54P$	$+0.281U$	$0.71PU$		0	
EA	$-1.016P$	120	4	$-30.48P$	$-0.781U$	$23.80PU$		0	
HD	$+0.234P$	120	4	$+7.02P$	$+0.469U$	$3.29PU$		0	
AG	$-0.234P$	120	3	$-9.37P$	$+0.781U$		$7.31PU$	0	
GC	$+0.234P$	120	3	$+9.37P$	$+0.469U$	$4.39PU$		0	
AF	$+1.000P$	96	3	$+32.00P$	0			0	
BG	0	96	3	0	0			0	
CH	$-0.188P$	96	3	$-6.02P$	$-0.375U$	$2.26PU$		0	
				Summation		$55.56PU$	$7.31PU$		$15.20PU$
						$-7.31PU$			
				Net sum		$48.25PU$			

the virtual load were a real load. The real forces, which are caused by the real load, are then computed (in Fig. 7–6A) for each member of the truss. The deflection is given by Eq. 7–6. All the pertinent data are shown in Table 7–3. Note that E, the modulus of elasticity, which is common to all members is omitted for brevity in the table. But it must be introduced in the final answer.

Example 7–5B. Horizontal Deflection. The horizontal deflection (called ΔX_G) is found by applying a horizontal virtual load at joint G. The only reaction is an equal and opposite force at the knife edge, with the result that stresses (Fig. 7–6C) are confined to the lower chord only between joints E and G. Note that the virtual forces are precisely those that would be used to obtain the *relative* deflection of joint G with respect to joint E. Of course, joint E cannot move, so that in this instance the relative deflection of G is also the true deflection.

Except for the virtual forces in the members, all the other data including real forces are the same as before for the vertical deflection; thus it saves time and effort to utilize Table 7–3 for horizontal as well as for vertical deflections.

Introducing $E = 30,000$ kips/in.^{2}, the vertical deflection is from Eq. 7–6

$$U\Delta Y_G = \sum u\frac{FL}{AE} = \frac{+48.25PU}{30,000} = +0.0016PU$$

where P is expressed in kips. Note that the virtual load U cancels and that the plus sign indicates that the direction of deflection coincides with the direction of the virtual load.

$$\Delta Y_G = 0.0016P \text{ in. down}$$

The horizontal deflection is from Eq. 7–6

$$U\Delta X_G = \sum u\frac{FL}{AE} = \frac{+15.20PU}{30,000}$$

Again P is expressed in kips, U cancels, and the plus sign indicates deflection in the direction of the virtual load at point G, that is, to the right.

$$\Delta X_G = 0.00051P \text{ in. right}$$

The absolute deflection is obtained as the vectorial sum of the vertical and horizontal deflections

$$\Delta G = \sqrt{(0.0016P)^2 + (0.00051P)^2} = 0.0017P \text{ in. down and right}$$

7–6. Single Redundant Reaction. A truss with a single redundant reaction (statically indeterminate externally to one degree) is shown in Fig. 7–7A. Any one of the three reactions can be considered to be the redundant, and it makes little difference, theoretically or practically, which one it is. The truss is the same as that of Fig. 7–6, and since we already have a stress analysis for the load at F for the truss supported at the ends, it would for this problem save a little work to consider the middle reaction as the redundant.

CUT-BACK STRUCTURE. The structure must be cut back to a statically determinate and stable structure. This is done by removing the center support and replacing it with an unknown force, herein called R, sufficient to prevent any vertical deflection. The structure is, of course, unaffected by this "change" (which really is no change at all), but now there is a means of evaluating R. Since the deflection must be zero, an equation of virtual work can be written to express that fact. The real forces in the members are caused partly by the load P and partly by the unknown force R, which would be the only unknown in the equation and, therefore, readily solved. The cut-back structure and the real forces are shown in Fig. 7–7B. If the principle of superposition is valid (which it is for elastic structures whose deflections are small), the force due to one load is independent of any other loads; thus, when computing forces due to the load P, the load R is totally ignored, and

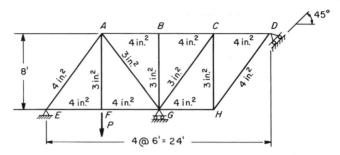

A. Truss and Loads

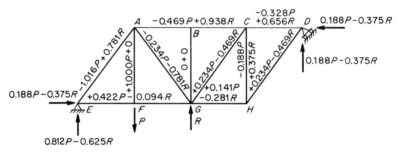

B. Cut-Back Truss, Reactions, and Forces

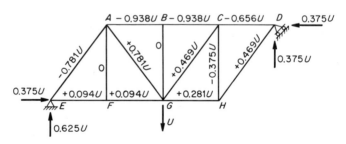

C. Virtual Load and Forces in Members

Fig. 7-7. Truss with redundant reaction.

vice versa. In the structure of Fig. 7–7B, the forces due to P are exactly the same as the forces in the structure of Fig. 7–6A. The forces due to R (which acts upward) are equal and opposite to the forces due to U, the virtual load, which acts downward on the structure in Fig. 7–7C. These forces have been computed before (Fig. 7–6B). That is why this method of working out the problem saves time. The virtual load on the cut-back structure is shown in Fig. 7–7C. The virtual load can be applied acting either up or down; it makes no difference.

The calculations are perfectly straightforward. They are shown in Table 7–4.

TABLE 7–4

Redundant Reaction

$$U \, \Delta Y_G = 0 = \Sigma \, u(FL/AE) \qquad \text{(Eq. 7–6)}$$

Member	F		L, in.	A, in.²	u	u(FL/A) Coefficients of		
						$+P$	$-P$	$-R$
AB	$-0.469P$	$+0.938R$	72	4	$-0.938U$	$7.91U$		$15.84U$
BC	$-0.469P$	$+0.938R$	72	4	$-0.938U$	$7.91U$		$15.84U$
CD	$-0.328P$	$+0.656R$	72	4	$-0.656U$	$3.87U$		$7.75U$
EF	$+0.422P$	$-0.094R$	72	4	$+0.094U$	$0.71U$		$0.16U$
FG	$+0.422P$	$-0.094R$	72	4	$+0.094U$	$0.71U$		$0.16U$
GH	$+0.141P$	$-0.281R$	72	4	$+0.281U$	$0.71U$		$1.42U$
EA	$-1.016P$	$+0.781R$	120	4	$-0.781U$	$23.80U$		$18.30U$
HD	$+0.234P$	$-0.469R$	120	4	$+0.469U$	$3.29U$		$6.60U$
AG	$-0.234P$	$-0.781R$	120	3	$+0.781U$		$7.31U$	$24.40U$
GC	$+0.234P$	$-0.469R$	120	3	$+0.469U$	$4.39U$		$8.80U$
AF	$+1.000P$	0	96	3	0			
BG	0	0	96	3	0			
CH	$-0.188P$	$+0.375R$	96	3	$-0.375U$	$2.26U$		$4.50U$
					Summation	$55.56U$	$7.31U$	$103.77U$
						$-7.31U$		
					Net sum	$48.25U$		

Introducing E (which was omitted from the table), Eq. 7–6 becomes

$$U\Delta Y_G = 0 = \frac{+48.25PU}{E} - \frac{103.77RU}{E}$$

The terms U and E cancel. Solving for R, we obtain (with slide-rule accuracy)

$$R = \frac{+48.25P}{103.77} = +0.465P$$

The plus sign proves that the reaction R acts upward as assumed.

OTHER REDUNDANTS. It has been stated that any one of the three reactions could be considered the redundant and so removed and replaced with an unknown force. But this does not exhaust all the possibilities; any member which, when cut, would make the rest of the structure determinate could be considered as the redundant.

For example, in Fig. 7–8A (which is the same truss as shown in Fig. 7–7A), member AB is considered the redundant. If it were removed, the structure would be stable and determinate. It can be cut, as shown, if the stress in the member is replaced by an equivalent force F. Let us assume the force to be compression. Now a complete stress analysis can be made in terms of P and F. The analyses have been separated to add clarity and simplicity. That for P is shown in Fig. 7–8A, and that for F in Fig. 7–8B. At the point where

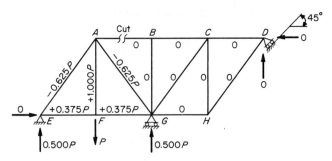

A. Forces Due to External Load P

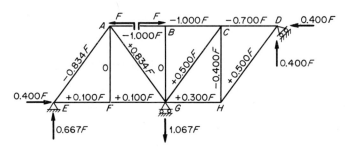

B. Forces Due to Redundant Forces FF

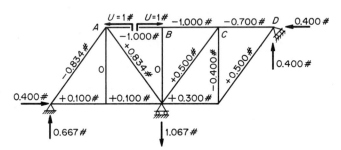

C. Forces Due to Virtual Loads UU

Fig. 7–8. Truss with redundant member.

member AB is cut, the two cut faces must not separate; for if they do, the stresses in the structure would be changed. This is equivalent to saying that the deflection of one cut face relative to the other must be zero. As explained in Art. 7–2, to determine a relative deflection, two equal and opposite virtual forces are applied to the cut faces, as shown in Fig. 7–8C. Whether they are applied in the same direction as the unknown forces F and F is immaterial. The magnitudes of the virtual forces are $1/F$ times that of the redundant forces, and, if the virtual loads are applied in the same direction as the redundant loads, the signs of the forces due to each are the same. If the directions of virtual and redundant forces are different, the signs are opposite. Thus one analysis serves for both the redundant and virtual forces.

Until now, we have called the applied virtual force U, mostly to emphasize that its value does not affect the answer because it always cancels. In the remainder of this Part, unit virtual loads (1 #) are used for convenience. The solution for this example is shown in Table 7–5.

TABLE 7–5

Redundant Member

$$\Delta_{\text{relative}} = 0 = \Sigma \frac{u(FL/AE)}{1\,\#} \qquad \text{(Eq. 7–6)}$$

Member	F		L, in.	A, in.^{2}	u	$u(FL/A)$ Coefficients of		
						$+P$	$-P$	$+F$
AB	0	$-1.000F$	72	4	-1.000			18.00
BC	0	$-1.000F$	72	4	-1.000			18.00
CD	0	$-0.700F$	72	4	-0.700			8.82
EF	$+0.375P$	$+0.100F$	72	4	$+0.100$	0.68		0.18
FG	$+0.375P$	$+0.100F$	72	4	$+0.100$	0.68		0.18
GH	0	$+0.300F$	72	4	$+0.300$			1.62
EA	$-0.625P$	$-0.834F$	120	4	-0.834	15.64		20.85
HD	0	$+0.500F$	120	4	$+0.500$			7.50
AG	$-0.625P$	$+0.834F$	120	3	$+0.834$		20.85	27.80
GC	0	$+0.500F$	120	3	$+0.500$			10.00
AF	$+1.000P$	0	96	3	0			
BG	0	0	96	3	0			
CH	0	$-0.400F$	96	3	-0.400			5.12
					Summation	17.00	20.85	118.07
							-17.00	
							3.85	

Again E and $\#$ (or U) cancel as before, so that we have

$$\Delta_{\text{relative}} = 0 = -3.85P + 118.07F$$

Solving for F gives

$$F = \frac{3.85P}{118.07} = +0.0326P$$

The plus sign indicates that the direction of F is correct, and the force in the member is therefore compression as originally assumed.

The reaction at G can now be computed from Figs. 7–8A and B. The reaction is

$$R = 0.500P - 1.067F = 0.500P - 1.067(0.0326P)$$

$$R = 0.465P$$

which checks the answer previously found.

7–7. Deflection. Statically Indeterminate Trusses. In order to find the deflection of a joint in a statically indeterminate truss, the stresses due to the real loads must be determined first, after which a virtual load must be applied at the joint where the deflection is wanted. Since the truss is statically indeterminate, the virtual forces in the members can be determined by means of some method of indeterminate stress analysis such as virtual work. It is just as easy to compute virtual forces due to a virtual load as it is to find real forces due to a real load, but, even so, that is the long, hard way.

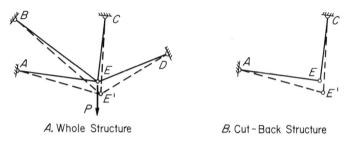

A. Whole Structure   B. Cut–Back Structure

Fig. 7–9. Deflection of a point in a redundant structure.

The easy way to find deflection is to apply the virtual load *to the cut-back structure.* And again, the structure can be cut back in any way that makes it stable and statically determinate.[7]

Consider the structure in Fig. 7–9A, which under the action of the load distorts as shown by the dotted lines. To find the deflection of point E, the true forces in the members must first be found. Then the deflection can be found by applying the virtual load to any cut-back structure such as that in Fig. 7–9B. Since all the members meet at point E, the deflection of that point can be found just as well by using two members as by using all four. The advantage is that the stress analysis for the virtual load is made more easily.

Now consider the structure of Fig. 7–10A to be cut back, as shown in Fig. 7–10B, by removing the middle support and replacing it with its equivalent force, 4.65 kips. This cut-back structure looks exactly like a statically determinate truss simply supported at its ends. If you did not know the truss was statically indeterminate—if Fig. 7–10B represented all the information you had—you would find the deflection at joint H by applying a virtual load to the structure simply supported only at the ends, as shown in Fig. 7–10C. Thus you would unwittingly find the correct deflection by the easiest (and the best) way.

A virtual load can also be applied to the structure cut back in other ways, as shown in Fig. 7–10D, for example. *If the true forces in the members* (shown

---

[7] Of course, we cannot introduce any new reactions since that would alter the problem, but we can always remove as many reactions or members as necessary to produce determinacy and stability.

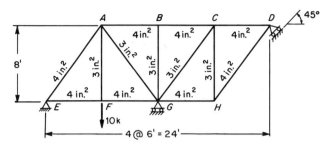

A. Indeterminate Truss and Load

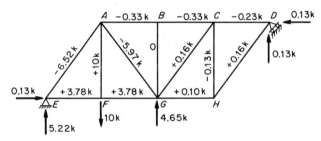

B. Real Forces in Cut-Back Structure

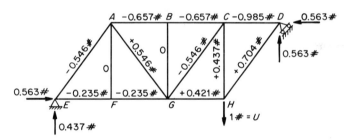

C. Virtual Load and Forces in Cut-Back Structure

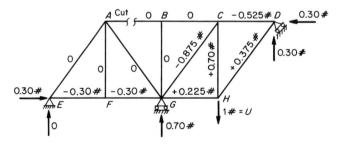

D. Virtual Forces in Structure Cut Back Differently

Fig. 7–10. Deflection of indeterminate truss.

in Fig. 7–10B) *are used to compute the* δL *values* (that is, FL/AE), *the deflection must be correct.* This is true because the virtual forces do not themselves *cause* deflection; they only *measure* deflection.

The use of these different cut-back structures is important. It is just as much a part of virtual work as the equation itself.

Example 7–7. To clinch the foregoing statements, the vertical deflection of joint H is computed in Table 7–6 by using the cut-back structure of Fig. 7–10C and again by using the cut-back structure of Fig. 7–10D.

TABLE 7–6

Deflection of an Indeterminate Truss

$1 \# \Delta Y_H = \Sigma u(FL/AE)$ (Eq. 7–6)

Member	F (from Fig. 7–10B)	L, in.	A, in.²	FL/A	Structure in Fig. 7–10C			Structure in Fig. 7–10D		
					u	+u(FL/A)	−u(FL/A)	u	+u(FL/A)	−u(FL/A)
AB	−0.33	72	4	−5.9	−0.657		3.9	0		
BC	−0.33	72	4	−5.9	−0.657		3.9	0		
CD	−0.23	72	4	−4.1	−0.985		4.0	−0.525	2.2	
EF	+3.78	72	4	+68.0	−0.235		16.0	−0.300		20.4
FG	+3.78	72	4	+68.0	−0.235		16.0	−0.300		20.4
GH	+0.10	72	4	+1.8	+0.421	0.8		+0.225	0.4	
EA	−6.52	120	4	−195.6	−0.546	106.9		0		
HD	+0.16	120	4	+4.8	+0.704	3.4		+0.375	1.8	
AG	−5.97	120	3	−239.0	+0.546	130.7		0		
GC	+0.16	120	3	+6.4	−0.546		3.5	−0.875		5.6
AF	+10.00	96	3	+320.0	0			0		
BG	0	96	3	0	0			0		
CH	−0.13	96	3	−4.2	+0.437		1.8	+0.700		2.9
					Summation	122.9	168.0		4.4	49.3
							−122.9			−4.4
					Net sum		45.1			44.9

The deflections are, within the limitations of slide-rule accuracy, the same. Introducing the modulus of elasticity, which was omitted from Table 7–6, and canceling $\#$ (or U) as before, we have

$$\Delta Y_H = \frac{45.1}{30,000} = 0.0015 \text{ in.}$$

or

$$\Delta Y_H = \frac{44.9}{30,000} = 0.0015 \text{ in.}$$

7–8. Highly Indeterminate Trusses. Highly indeterminate trusses are solved in the same manner as trusses with only one redundant. But there must be as many simultaneous equations of virtual work as there are degrees of indeterminacy. More labor is involved, of course, but there are shortcuts that can be used to reduce the work. These shortcuts have been employed in previous articles, and they are used again herein.

Example 7–8. A truss externally indeterminate to one degree and internally indeterminate to two degrees is shown in Fig. 7–11A. The truss must be cut back to a statically determinate stable structure; one possibility is shown in Fig. 7–11B. The members and supports that are cut must be replaced with

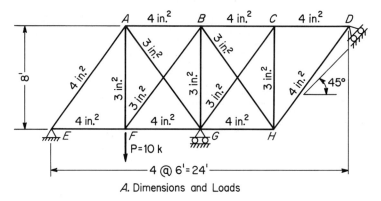

A. Dimensions and Loads

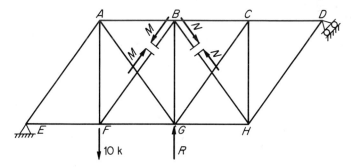

B. Cut-Back Structure and Redundant Forces

Fig. 7–11. Truss with three redundants.

equivalent forces, R, M, and N, as shown. With the redundant reaction and members removed, an analysis for the load is made and the results are shown in Fig. 7–12A. Virtual loads are applied to the *cut-back structure*,[8] as shown in Figs. 7–12B, C, and D. The virtual forces in each member are found for each virtual load separately; that is, a stress analysis is made for Fig. 7–12B, another independent one for Fig. 7–12C, and still another one for Fig. 7–12D. The members stressed by the virtual loads are shown by heavy lines.

Note that the virtual loads are applied to the same members in the same direction as the redundant loads. Therefore one stress analysis serves to evaluate both a virtual force and its corresponding redundant force. For example, the force in any member caused by R is R times as great as the virtual force caused by the virtual load in Fig. 7–12B. Thus the redundant forces are R or M or N times the corresponding virtual forces, and they are so indicated in Table 7–7. In order to identify the virtual forces in Table 7–7, they are labeled u_R, u_M, and u_N as they correspond to redundants R, M, and N.

[8] Review Art. 7–7 for the reasons that make it possible to apply the virtual forces to the cut-back structure.

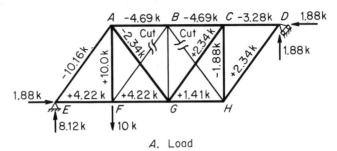

A. Load

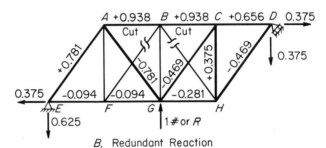

B. Redundant Reaction

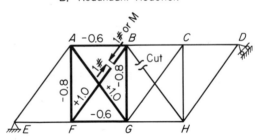

C. Left Redundant Member

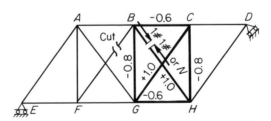

D. Right Redundant Member

Fig. 7–12. Analyses for real load, redundant forces, and virtual loads.
(*Note:* Stressed members shown by heavy lines.)

TABLE 7-7
Solution of Three Redundants *

$$\Delta Y_G = 0 = \frac{\Sigma u_R(FL/A)}{1\#}$$

$$\text{Relative } \Delta_{FB} = 0 = \frac{\Sigma u_M(FL/A)}{1\#}$$

$$\text{Relative } \Delta_{BH} = 0 = \frac{\Sigma u_N(FL/A)}{1\#}$$

			Force due to			$\Sigma u_R(FL/A)$ Coefficients of u_R times:				$\Sigma u_M(FL/A)$ Coefficients of u_M times:				$\Sigma u_N(FL/A)$ Coefficients of u_N times:			
Member	L/A	Load	$u_R R$ (R)	$u_M M$ (M)	$u_N N$ (N)	Load	R	M	N	Load	R	M	N	Load	R	M	N
(1)	(2)	(3)	(4)	(5)	(6)	(7)	(8)	(9)	(10)	(11)	(12)	(13)	(14)	(15)	(16)	(17)	(18)
AB	18	-4.69	+0.938	-0.600	—	-79.1	+15.84	-10.13	—	+50.6	-10.12	+6.48	—	—	—	—	—
BC	18	-4.69	+0.938	—	-0.600	-79.1	+15.84	—	-10.13	—	—	—	—	+50.6	-10.12	—	+6.48
CD	18	-3.28	+0.656	—	—	-38.7	+7.75	—	—	—	—	—	—	—	—	—	—
EF	18	+4.22	-0.094	—	—	-7.1	+0.16	—	—	—	—	—	—	—	—	—	—
FG	18	+4.22	-0.094	-0.600	—	-7.1	+0.16	+1.02	—	-45.6	+1.01	+6.48	—	—	—	—	—
GH	18	+1.41	-0.281	—	-0.600	-7.1	+1.42	—	+3.04	—	—	—	—	-15.2	+3.04	—	+6.48
EA	30	-10.16	+0.781	—	—	-238.0	+18.30	—	—	—	—	—	—	—	—	—	—
HD	30	+2.34	-0.469	—	—	-32.9	+6.60	—	—	—	—	—	—	—	—	—	—
AG	40	-2.34	-0.781	+1.000	—	+73.1	+24.40	-31.22	—	-93.7	-31.22	+40.0	—	—	—	—	—
FB	40	—	—	+1.000	—	—	—	—	—	—	—	+40.0	—	—	—	—	—
BH	40	—	—	—	+1.000	—	—	—	—	—	—	—	—	—	—	—	+40.00
GC	40	+2.34	-0.469	—	+1.000	-43.9	+8.80	—	-18.77	—	—	—	—	+93.7	-18.76	—	+40.00
AF	32	+10.00	—	-0.800	—	—	—	—	—	-256.0	—	+20.48	—	—	—	—	—
BG	32	—	—	-0.800	-0.800	—	—	—	—	—	—	+20.48	+20.48	—	—	+20.48	+20.48
CH	32	-1.88	+0.375	—	-0.800	-22.6	+4.50	—	-9.60	—	—	—	—	+48.1	-9.60	—	+20.48
						-482.5	+103.77	-40.33	-35.46	-344.7	-40.33	+133.92	+20.48	+177.2	-35.44	+20.48	+133.92

* Modulus of elasticity omitted from table. Columns 4, 5, and 6 show numerical values of u_R, u_M, and u_N, respectively.

The total real force F in any bar equals the force due to P plus the force due to R plus the force due to M plus the force due to N. By making use of the relation between virtual forces and redundant forces as explained above, the true force in any bar is

$$F = \text{force due to } P + u_R R + u_M M + u_N N$$

These true forces are shown in columns 3, 4, 5, and 6 of Table 7–7 in terms of coefficients of R, M, and N. To evaluate these three unknowns, three

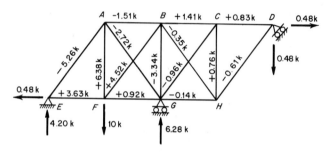

Fig. 7–13. Total forces.

equations of elasticity must be written. The central support does not move vertically, so we can write

$$\Delta Y_G = 0 = \sum u_R \frac{FL}{AE}$$

to express that fact. From Table 7–7, columns 7, 8, 9, and 10, the equation reduces to

$$\Delta Y_G = 0 = -482.5 + 103.77R - 40.33M - 35.46N$$

Note that E, which is constant for all members, has been canceled from both sides of the equation. The cut faces of member FB cannot move relative to each other, and this fact can be expressed as

$$\text{Relative } \Delta_{FB} = 0 = \sum u_M \frac{FL}{AE}$$

From columns 11, 12, 13, and 14, the equation reduces to

$$\text{Relative } \Delta_{FB} = 0 = -344.7 - 40.33R + 133.92M + 20.48N$$

Also the cut faces of member BH cannot move with respect to one another. This yields the equation

$$\text{Relative } \Delta_{BH} = 0 = \sum u_N \frac{FL}{AE}$$

which from columns 15, 16, 17, and 18 becomes

$$\text{Relative } \Delta_{BH} = 0 = +177.2 - 35.44R + 20.48M + 133.92N$$

Solving[9] the above three equations simultaneously yields

$$R = +6.28 \text{ kips}$$
$$M = +4.52 \text{ kips}$$
$$N = -0.35 \text{ kip}$$

With the redundant forces known, the true forces in each member can be computed from the equation previously given in this article. The results are shown in Fig. 7–13.

7–9. Deflection. Highly Indeterminate Trusses. Regardless of how highly indeterminate a structure may be, if the forces in its members are known, the deflection of any point can be determined as easily as for a

TABLE 7–8

Deflection of a Highly Indeterminate Truss

$$1 \# \Delta Y_H = \Sigma \, u(FL/AE) \qquad (\text{Eq. 7–6})$$

Member	F^*	L/A†	u‡	$+u(FL/A)$	$-u(FL/A)$
AB	-1.51	18	0		
BC	$+1.41$	18	0		
CD	$+0.83$	18	-0.525		-7.84
EF	$+3.63$	18	-0.300		-19.60
FG	$+0.92$	18	-0.300		-4.97
GH	-0.14	18	$+0.225$		-0.57
EA	-5.26	30	0		
HD	-0.61	30	$+0.375$		-6.86
AG	-2.72	40	0		
FB	$+4.52$	40	0		
BH	-0.35	40	0		
GC	-0.96	40	-0.875	33.60	
AF	$+6.38$	32	0		
BG	-3.34	32	0		
CH	$+0.76$	32	$+0.700$	17.02	
			Summation	50.62	39.84
				-39.84	
			Net sum	10.78	

* From Fig. 7–13.
† From Table 7–7, column 2.
‡ From Fig. 7–10D.
Note: Modulus of elasticity is omitted in table.

determinate structure. That is because the virtual load can be applied to the cut-back structure, as explained in Art. 7–7.

Example 7–9. Suppose the vertical deflection of joint H in the truss of Fig. 7–11A is wanted. The virtual load can be applied to the structure cut back in any way desired. Either of the cut-back structures shown in Figs. 7–10C and 7–10D is suitable, and since analyses have been made for the

[9] See Table 6–4, Art. 6–1, for a logical way to solve simultaneous equations. A slide rule is not accurate enough to obtain three (or even two) significant numbers.

virtual loads, it would reduce the labor to use one of these figures. There are more unstressed members in Fig. 7–10D than in Fig. 7–10C, so that Fig. 7–10D requires fewer computations and is, therefore, preferred. The true forces in the members of the truss are obtained from Fig. 7–13. The solution is presented in Table 7–8.

Since the modulus of elasticity ($E = 30,000$ kips/in.^{2}) was omitted from the table, it must be considered now, so the deflection becomes

$$\Delta Y_H = \frac{+10.78}{30,000} = +0.00036 \text{ in. downward.}$$

8

BEAMS

8–1. Deflection Due to Bending. The deflection of beams and rigid frames is caused by bending, shear, and axial strains. Bending is by far the most important; shear and axial strains usually account for less than 2 or 3 percent of the total and they are, for that reason, commonly ignored. Deflection caused by shear may be important for short, deep beams, and this subject is discussed in Chapter 11.

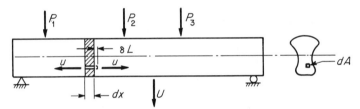

Fig. 8–1. Virtual work for bending.

To convert the basic equation of virtual work into a form useful for evaluating deflection at any point due to bending, consider the beam of Fig. 8–1. Two supports and three loads are shown, but any number of supports and loads could be shown without changing the following development. Furthermore, a rigid frame could be shown just as well, and the development of the equation would still be exactly the same. Imagine the beam to be composed of an infinite number of infinitesimal elements, one of which is shown exaggerated in size. The basic equation of virtual work is

$$U\Delta = \sum u \, \delta L \qquad (7\text{–}3)$$

Now, δL for any element equals unit strain times length, and unit strain equals unit stress divided by Young's modulus. Therefore,

$$\delta L = \epsilon \, dx = \frac{s}{E} \, dx$$

The stress on any element can be computed from the general flexure formula, $s = My/I$, so by substitution

$$\delta L = \frac{My}{EI} \, dx$$

where M is the bending moment at the cross-hatched section caused by the real loads P_1, P_2, and P_3. The term u is the *force* on the element caused by the virtual load. Force equals stress times area (the area of the element is dA), and again stress equals my/I, where m is the bending moment at the cross-hatched section caused by the virtual load. Therefore

$$u = \text{stress} \times \text{area} = \frac{my}{I} \, dA$$

Then

$$u \, \delta L = \frac{Mmy^2 \, dA \, dx}{EI^2}$$

To find the sum of $u \, \delta L$ for all elements, we must integrate (sum) the elements over the cross-sectional area and then integrate the elements over the full length of the beam. That is,

$$U\Delta = \int_0^L \int_0^A \frac{Mmy^2 \, dA \, dx}{EI^2}$$

The expression $\int_0^A y^2 \, dA$ is I, the moment of inertia. Substituting I for $\int_0^A y^2 \, dA$ and canceling, gives

$$U\Delta = \int_0^L \frac{Mm \, dx}{EI} \tag{8–1}$$

As stated before, U is written as $1 \, \#$ for convenience and identification.

DISCUSSION. To find the deflection of a point on a beam, apply a virtual load at the point. Write an expression[1] for M (usually a variable) which is the moment caused by the real loads, and another expression for m (also a variable, usually) which is the moment caused by the virtual load. Substitute them into Eq. 8–1 and integrate over the full length of the beam. If there are concentrated loads, no single expression for moment is valid for the entire beam; thus separate expressions must be written for each segment of the beam, each segment integrated separately, and then the segments added to obtain the total integral.

RELATIVE DEFLECTIONS. As with trusses, relative deflections can be found by applying equal and opposite virtual forces at the two points for which relative deflections are required. As shown in Art. 7–2, the equation of virtual work for relative deflection is

$$\Delta_{\text{relative}} = \frac{\sum u \, \delta L}{U} = \int_0^L \frac{(Mm/EI) \, dx}{U}$$

which is exactly the same as Eq. 8–1. M is the moment due to the real loads, and m is the moment due to both virtual loads acting simultaneously.

[1] See Art. 2–4.

ROTATION. Rotations or slopes must often be computed, particularly for finding points of maximum deflection. True rotation or slope is found by applying a virtual couple at the point where the slope is required. As shown in Art. 7-2, the equation of virtual work is

$$U \, \Delta\theta = \sum u \, \delta L = \int_0^L \frac{Mm \, dx}{EI} \tag{8-2}$$

in which M is the moment due to the real loads, m is the moment due to the applied virtual couple U which is usually unity (1 #-ft or 1 #-in.)

SIGNS. As explained in Art. 7-2, signs for virtual work expressions are automatic, and this applies to the above equations for beams and frames. It is only necessary to use the same convention for M as for m. If the sign is negative, the deflection or the redundant is opposite in sense to the applied virtual load; if positive, it corresponds in sense to the applied virtual load.

8-2. Deflection. Cantilever Beam. The beam of Fig. 8-2A is a simple, prismatic (E and I are constant) cantilever supporting a uniform load. The application of virtual work to beams can be aptly illustrated by computing the maximum deflection and slope and the deflection and slope at some intermediate point such as B, located, say $\frac{3}{4}L$ from the fixed end.

Example 8-2A. Maximum Deflection. The maximum deflection occurs at A, so apply a virtual load at A, as shown in Fig. 8-2B. The deflection is given by the equation

$$1 \, \# \, \Delta Y_A = \int_0^L \frac{Mm \, dx}{EI} \tag{8-1}$$

in which EI is a constant and M and m are variables. The real moment M can be most easily expressed (in terms of any variable distance x) when x is measured to the free end. Then the real moment is

$$M = \text{force} \times \text{distance} = wx \, \frac{x}{2} = \frac{wx^2}{2}$$

The virtual moment m due to the virtual load must be expressed in terms of the same x, that is, x as measured from the free end. The virtual moment is

$$m = \text{force} \times \text{distance} = 1 \, \# \, x$$

Since EI is constant, it may be placed before the integral sign in Eq. 8-1 for deflection:

$$1 \, \# \, \Delta Y_A = \int_0^L \frac{Mm \, dx}{EI} = \frac{1}{EI} \int_0^L \frac{wx^2}{2} \, 1 \, \# \, x \, dx$$

Canceling the 1 # from both sides, we have

$$\Delta Y_A = \frac{1}{EI} \int_0^L \frac{wx^3}{2} \, dx = \frac{1}{EI} \left[\frac{wx^4}{8} \right]_0^L = \frac{wL^4}{8EI}$$

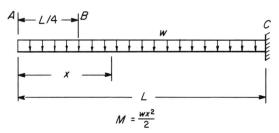

$$M = \frac{wx^2}{2}$$

A. Beam, Loads, and Moment Equation

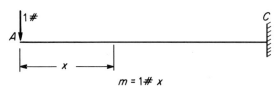

$m = 1\# \, x$

B. Virtual Load and Virtual Moment Equation

$m = 1\# - \text{in.}$

C. Virtual Couple and Virtual Moment Equation

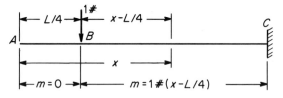

$m = 0$ $m = 1\#(x - L/4)$

D. Virtual Load at *B* and Virtual Moment Equations

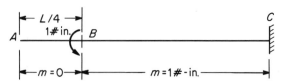

$m = 0$ $m = 1\# - \text{in.}$

E. Virtual Couple at *B* and Virtual Moment Equations

Fig. 8–2. Deflections of a cantilever beam.

Example 8–2B. Maximum Slope. The maximum slope also occurs at A, so a couple of 1 #-in. is applied at A, as shown in Fig. 8–2C. The virtual moment is constant, that is, 1 #-in. The real moment is the same as before. Then the equation for rotation is

$$1\ \#\text{-in.}\ \Delta\theta_A = \int_0^L \frac{Mm\,dx}{EI} = \frac{1}{EI}\int_0^L \frac{wx^2}{2}\,1\ \#\text{-in.}\ dx \tag{8–2}$$

Canceling 1 #-in. from both sides, we have

$$\Delta\theta_A = \frac{1}{EI}\int_0^L \frac{wx^2}{2}\,dx = \frac{1}{EI}\left[\frac{wx^3}{6}\right]_0^L = \frac{wL^3}{6EI}$$

Example 8–2C. Deflection at B. The virtual load is applied at B, as shown in Fig. 8–2D. Again it is probably most convenient to express x in terms of distance from the free end, so the equation for the real moment is the same as before. But the equation for virtual moment follows from consideration of Fig. 8–2D. From $x = 0$ to $x = L/4$, the virtual moment is zero and, therefore, the virtual work is zero also. From $x = L/4$ to $x = L$, the virtual moment is

$$m = 1\ \# \left(x - \frac{L}{4}\right)$$

The equation of virtual work for deflection at B is

$$1\ \#\ \Delta Y_B = \frac{1}{EI}\int_{L/4}^L \frac{wx^2}{2}\,1\ \#\left(x - \frac{L}{4}\right)dx$$

$$1\ \#\ \Delta Y_B = \frac{1\ \#}{EI}\int_{L/4}^L \left(\frac{wx^3}{2} - \frac{wLx^2}{8}\right)dx = \frac{1\ \#}{EI}\left[\frac{wx^4}{8} - \frac{wLx^3}{24}\right]_{L/4}^L$$

$$\Delta Y_B = \frac{1}{EI}\left(\frac{wL^4}{8} - \frac{wL^4}{24} - \frac{wL^4}{8\times256} + \frac{wL^4}{24\times64}\right) = \frac{171wL^4}{2048EI}$$

Example 8–2D. Rotation at B. A virtual couple of 1 #-in. is applied at B. From $x = 0$ to $x = L/4$, the virtual moment is zero, therefore the virtual work is zero. From $x = L/4$ to $x = L$, the virtual moment is 1 #-in. The real moment is the same as before. Writing Eq. 8–2 for rotation, we have

$$1\ \#\text{-in.}\ \Delta\theta_B = \int_{L/4}^L \frac{Mm\,dx}{EI} = \frac{1}{EI}\int_{L/4}^L \frac{wx^2}{2}\,1\ \#\text{-in.}\ dx$$

Canceling the 1 #-in. from both sides gives

$$\Delta\theta_B = \frac{1}{EI}\int_{L/4}^L \frac{wx^2}{2}\,dx = \frac{1}{EI}\left[\frac{wx^3}{6}\right]_{L/4}^L = \frac{w}{6EI}\left[L^3 - \left(\frac{L}{4}\right)^3\right] = \frac{21wL^3}{128EI}\ \text{radians}$$

8–3. Maximum Deflection. In the example of Art. 8–1 it was obvious that the maximum deflection occurred at the free end of the cantilever. However, it is often impossible, by inspection only, to establish the point where the maximum deflection occurs. In such cases one does not know

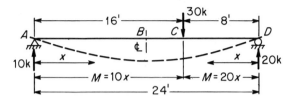

A. Beam, Load, and Moment Equations

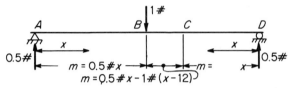

B. Virtual Load at Center and Virtual Moment Equations

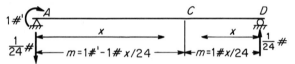

C. Virtual Couple and Virtual Moment Equations

D. Equivalent Cantilever Beam and Loads

E. Virtual Couple at Any General Point on Equivalent Cantilever Beam. Virtual Moment Equations

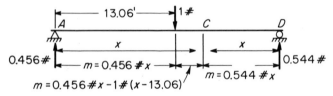

F. Virtual Load at Point of Maximum Deflection. Virtual Moment Equations

Fig. 8–3. Maximum deflection of a simple beam.

where to place the virtual load. Therefore any equation of virtual work must be written for a variable position of the virtual load. Of course, it is possible to estimate the location of the maximum deflection and compute the deflection at the estimated point and also at points straddling it. By plotting a graph, the maximum deflection can be found accurately enough for practical purposes. But this is not an elegant solution, and it takes more time than the exact method to be presented herein. If a cruder approximation of the maximum deflection is permissible, the calculation of a single deflection at the estimated point of maximum deflection is usually fairly close to the true maximum.

The beam of Fig. 8–3A is a representative example. It can be seen by inspection that the deflection will be a maximum at some point between the 30-kip load and the center of the beam. The deflection at the center would be very nearly the maximum, so it will be computed for comparison with the maximum.

Example 8–3A. *Center Deflection.* The real moments can be written in two equations, as shown in Fig. 8–3A, in which one x is the distance from the left reaction and the other x is the distance from the right reaction. They are not the same x, so they must be used in separate expressions and integrated separately. The moment $M = 10x$ is valid only between points A and C, whereas the moment $M = 20x$ is valid only between points D and C.

The virtual load is applied at the center, as shown in Fig. 8–3B. Equations for the virtual moment between points A and C must be written in terms of x as measured from the left reaction in order to be compatible with the x for the real moment between points A and C. For the same reason, the equation of virtual moment between D and C must be written in terms of x as measured from the right reaction. Thus the virtual moments are

$$\text{From } A \text{ to } B \qquad m = 0.5 \,\# \, x$$
$$\text{From } B \text{ to } C \qquad m = 0.5 \,\# \, x - 1 \,\# \, (x - 12)$$

(This is the moment of the virtual reaction minus the moment of the virtual load.)

$$\text{From } D \text{ to } C \qquad m = 0.5 \,\# \, x$$

Since the limits of integration are different and the two x's are different, the integral of $(Mm\,dx)/EI$ must be evaluated in three separate terms, which must then be added thus:

$$1 \,\# \, \Delta Y_B = \int_0^{12} \frac{10x(0.5 \,\# \, x)\,dx}{EI} + \int_{12}^{16} \frac{10x[0.5 \,\# \, x - 1 \,\# \, (x - 12)]\,dx}{EI}$$

$$+ \int_0^8 \frac{20x(0.5 \,\# \, x)\,dx}{EI}$$

$$\Delta Y_B = \frac{5}{EI}\int_0^{12} x^2\,dx + \frac{1}{EI}\int_{12}^{16} (120x - 5x^2)\,dx + \frac{10}{EI}\int_0^8 x^2\,dx$$

Integrating, substituting limits, and clearing terms result in

$$\Delta Y_B = \frac{7360}{EI} \text{ exactly}$$

Example 8–3B. Point of Maximum Deflection. To find the point of maximum deflection we must find the point of zero slope (by applying a virtual couple at that point). Since the location of the point of zero slope is unknown, a *shifting* virtual couple must be applied (to a varying point). Applied to a simply supported beam, a shifting couple is difficult to use, but it is easy to work with a shifting couple on a cantilever. A useful shortcut is, therefore, to transform a simple beam into a cantilever.

In making a simple beam into a cantilever beam, the true elastic curve must not be disturbed. This means the moments must remain the same (although other, but equivalent, expressions for moment can be used) and the rotation at the supports must remain unchanged. An equivalent cantilever beam is shown in Fig. 8–3*D*. Note that the loads and reactions are the same as those of Fig. 8–3*A*, and that the fixed support has been rotated downward so the slope at point *A* is the same for both beams. The similarity of the two beams is thus assured.

The slope at point *A* in Fig. 8–3*A* must be determined so that the necessary rotation can be applied at point *A* in the cantilever beam of Fig. 8–3*D*. To find the slope, apply a virtual couple at point *A*, as shown in Fig. 8–3*C*. The virtual moments are

$$\text{From } A \text{ to } C \qquad m = 1 \text{ \#-ft} - 1 \text{ \#} \frac{x}{24}$$

$$\text{From } D \text{ to } C \qquad m = 1 \text{ \#} \frac{x}{24}$$

The equation of virtual work is

$$1 \text{ \#-ft } \Delta\theta_A = \int_0^L \frac{Mm \, dx}{EI} = \frac{1}{EI} \int_0^{16} 10x\left(1 \text{ \#-ft} - 1 \text{ \#} \frac{x}{24}\right) dx$$
$$+ \frac{1}{EI} \int_0^8 20x\left(1 \text{ \#} \frac{x}{24}\right) dx$$

from which

$$\Delta\theta_A = \frac{853}{EI} \text{ radians}$$

The point of zero slope can be found by applying a virtual couple at any point located a variable distance *x* from the fixed end. Think of *x* varying until it locates the point of zero slope. Then, since the rotation of the beam at this point is zero, the external virtual work, 1 #-ft $\Delta\theta_x$, must also be zero, making it possible to solve for *x*.

Note that, in addition to the virtual work due to bending, $\int(Mm \, dx)/EI$, there is virtual work due to the rotation at point *A*. The virtual work caused by bending is negative (for M is opposite in sign to m), but the virtual work due to rotation is positive because the beam rotates in the same direction as the virtual couple—clockwise.[2] The equation of virtual work is

$$1 \text{ #-ft } \Delta\theta_x = 0 = \frac{1}{EI} \int_0^x 10x(-1 \text{ #-ft}) \, dx + \Delta\theta_A 1 \text{ #-ft}$$

$$= -\frac{10 \text{ #-ft}}{EI} \int_0^x x \, dx + \frac{853}{EI} \times 1 \text{ #-ft}$$

Integrating and canceling E, I, and #-ft, yields

$$0 = -5x^2 + 853$$

$$x = 13.06 \text{ ft}$$

Now that we know the point of maximum deflection is 13.06 ft from point A, it is necessary only to apply a virtual load at that point, as shown in Fig. 8–3F, and find the deflection.

$$1 \text{ # } \Delta Y_{\max} = \frac{1}{EI} \int_0^{13.06} 10x(0.456 \text{ # } x) \, dx + \frac{1}{EI} \int_{13.06}^{16} 10x[0.456 \text{ # } x$$

$$- 1 \text{ # } (x - 13.06)] \, dx + \frac{1}{EI} \int_0^8 20x(0.544 \text{ # } x) \, dx$$

$$\Delta Y_{\max} = \frac{7434}{EI}$$

which is, after all, very close to the deflection at the center.

8–4. Indeterminate Beams. As with trusses, redundant reactions for indeterminate beams are found by cutting the structure back to a determinate one, substituting equivalent forces for the redundant reactions, and writing an equation of virtual work setting the deflection equal to zero.

Example 8–4. A beam, statically indeterminate to one degree is shown in Fig. 8–4A. Any one of the three reaction components can be considered as the redundant, but it is probably most convenient to take the reaction at point B as the redundant, leaving a cantilever beam as the cut-back structure in Fig. 8–4B. The deflection at point B is zero, so a virtual load is applied at B, and the external virtual work is equated to zero. The expression for virtual moment from B to C is

$$m = 1 \text{ # } x$$

No expression for real moment from A to B is necessary because the virtual moment there is zero, and, therefore, the virtual work will be zero also. An equation for real moment between B and C can be developed as follows: The total load between A and B is 6 kips and its line of action is 4 ft to the

---

[2] Another line of reasoning is this: Imagine the support to be unmoved—not to rotate—and instead imagine the beam forcibly bent down to produce a permanent set resulting in an angle equal to $853/EI$. The lower elements must shorten, that is, compress. The virtual couple also produces compressive forces on the lower elements; therefore the virtual work must be positive.

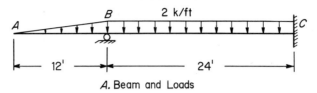

A. Beam and Loads

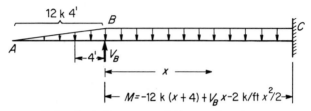

B. Cut–Back Structure and Moment Equation

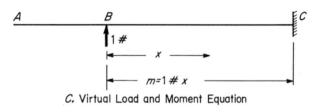

C. Virtual Load and Moment Equation

Fig. 8–4. Reaction of a statically indeterminate beam.

left of B. Its moment to the right of B is 12 kips $(x + 4)$. The moment of the reaction, V_B, is $V_B x$. The moment of the uniform load from B to C is $(2 \text{ kips/ft})x^2/2$. Calling moments positive when they produce compression in the upper fibers and adding

$$M = -12 \text{ kips } (x + 4) + V_B x - (2 \text{ kips/ft}) \frac{x^2}{2}$$

The equation for virtual work is

$$1 \,\#\, \Delta Y_B = 0 = \int_0^L \frac{Mm\, dx}{EI} = \frac{1 \,\#}{EI} \int_0^{24} (-12x^2 - 48x + V_B x^2 - x^3)\, dx$$

Solving

$$0 = \left[-\frac{12x^3}{3} - \frac{48x^2}{2} + \frac{V_B x^3}{3} - \frac{x^4}{4} \right]_0^{24}$$

$$0 = -4(24)^3 - 24(24)^2 + \frac{V_B(24)^3}{3} - \frac{(24)^4}{4}$$

$$V_B = +33 \text{ kips}$$

Because the answer is plus, the reaction acts upward as assumed.

8–5. Deflection. Indeterminate Beams. In computing deflections of statically indeterminate beams or frames, the virtual load can be applied to any valid cut-back structure, that is, any cut-back structure which does not violate support conditions of the real structure and which is stable and determinate. The reasons are the same as those explained for the deflection of trusses in Art. 7–7. Thus to find the deflection at any point along the beam in Fig. 8–5A, the cut-back structure may consist of a simple cantilever beam

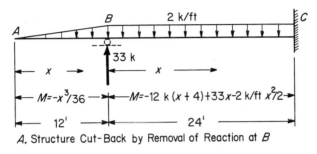

A. Structure Cut-Back by Removal of Reaction at *B*

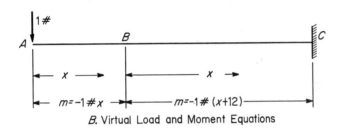

B. Virtual Load and Moment Equations

Fig. 8–5. Deflection of a statically indeterminate beam.

fixed at point *C* and loaded with the distributed loads plus the upward load of 33 kips at point *B*. Of course, the upward load is in reality a reaction or support, but the support can be considered to be the same as any other load.

Example 8–5. To find the deflection at point *A*, for example, apply a virtual load at *A*, as shown in Fig. 8–5*B*. For portion *AB* it is easiest to let x be measured from *A*, and the virtual moment is then

$$m = 1 \,\#\, x$$

The real moment from *A* to *B* is written

$$M = \text{force} \times \text{lever arm} = \frac{xy}{2}\frac{x}{3}$$

where y is the intensity of load at a distance x from *A*. From similar triangles we can write

$$\frac{y}{x} = \frac{2\ \text{kips/ft}}{12} \qquad \text{or} \qquad y = \frac{x}{6}$$

so

$$M = \frac{x^2 y}{6} = \frac{x^3}{36}$$

Real moments from B to C can be written in terms of an x measured from point A, but from Art. 8–4 we already have an equation for moment in terms of x measured from point B. It would save some work to use it. The equation was

$$M = -12 \text{ kips } (x + 4) + V_B x - (2 \text{ kips/ft}) \frac{x^2}{2}$$

But V_B was found to be 33 kips. So the equation becomes

$$M = -12 \text{ kips } (x + 4) + 33x - (2 \text{ kips/ft}) \frac{x^2}{2}$$

To be compatible, the virtual work equation for portion BC must be written in terms of x measured from B. Then, from B to C,

$$m = -1 \,\#\, (x + 12)$$

The equation of virtual work is

$$1 \,\#\, \Delta Y_A = \frac{1}{EI} \int_0^{12} \frac{x^3}{36} (1 \,\#\, x) \, dx$$

$$+ \frac{1}{EI} \int_0^{24} [-12(x + 4) + 33x - x^2][-1 \,\#\, (x + 12)] \, dx$$

from which

$$\Delta Y_A = \frac{2074}{EI}$$

8–6. Semi-graphical Integration. Writing an algebraic expression for moments, integrating, and substituting limits is a tedious operation and, because of the many terms involved, it is difficult to avoid mistakes. Since the curves of moment are nearly always simple curves consisting of straight lines or parabolas, properties of the curves and areas enclosed by them can be expressed by simple formulas.[3] Whenever it is possible to represent a complex integral by a simple formula, it would be foolish—and poor engineering—to use the calculus.

The expression $\int_A^B (Mm \, dx)/EI$ can be separated into groups like this: $\int_A^B m \times M/EI \times dx$. M/EI plotted as a curve is simply the moment diagram divided by EI, as shown in Fig. 8–6B. If EI is constant, the M/EI diagram has the same shape as the moment diagram. The term $\int_A^B (M/EI) \, dx$ is the area of the M/EI diagram—herein called $A_{MD/EI}$—between points A and B

[3] See Table 3–1.

in Fig. 8–6B. The quantity m is the virtual moment; it is, in other words, the ordinate of the virtual moment diagram. The virtual moment diagrams for beams or rigid frames (composed of straight members) always consist of

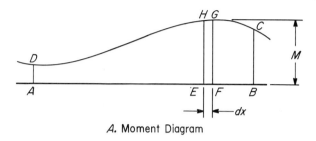

A. Moment Diagram

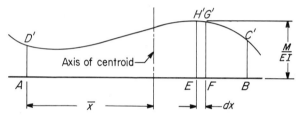

B. Moment Diagram Divided by EI, MD/EI

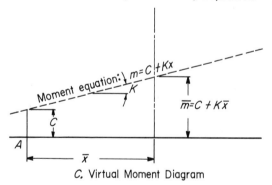

C. Virtual Moment Diagram

Fig. 8–6. Semi-graphical integration of $\int (Mm/EI)\, dx$.

straight lines or a series of straight lines. Therefore, the algebraic expressions for m are always simple, first-degree equations. The equation of any straight line (including m) can be expressed as $C + Kx$, where C and K are constants. C is the ordinate at point A, and K is the tangent of the slope of the line as shown in Fig. 8–6C. Therefore,

$$\int_A^B m\, \frac{M}{EI}\, dx = \int_A^B (C + Kx)\, \frac{M}{EI}\, dx = C \int_A^B \frac{M}{EI}\, dx + K \int_A^B \frac{M}{EI}\, x\, dx$$

But $\int_A^B (M/EI)x \, dx$ can be written $\int_A^B yx \, dx$ where y is M/EI. From calculus, $\int_A^B yx \, dx$ is the first moment of the area about point A. Algebraically expressed, it is $A\bar{x}$, where A is the area and $\bar{x}$ is *the distance from point A to the centroid of the area.*

By substitution, then,

$$C \int_A^B \frac{M}{EI} \, dx + K \int_A^B \frac{M}{EI} x \, dx = CA_{MD/EI} + K\bar{x}A_{MD/EI}$$

or

$$\int_A^B m \frac{M}{EI} \, dx = (C + K\bar{x})A_{MD/EI}$$

Since $\bar{x}$ is the distance from point A to the centroid of $A_{MD/EI}$ as shown at Fig. 8–6B, the expression $C + K\bar{x}$ (see Fig. 8–6C) is the virtual moment at the centroid of $A_{MD/EI}$ and is herein called $\bar{m}$. Therefore $\int_A^B (Mm/EI) \, dx = \bar{m}A_{MD/EI}$, and deflection can be expressed as

$$U\Delta = \bar{m}A_{MD/EI}$$

This is to say: *internal virtual work equals the area under the M/EI diagram multiplied by the virtual moment at the centroid of the M/EI diagram.* This relationship is true only if x (and therefore m) is a continuous function, that is, if the virtual moment diagram is an unbroken straight line. However, if the virtual moment diagram does have a break, the M/EI diagram can be broken into segments such that for any segment the virtual moment diagram is a straight unbroken line.

In general, the areas of the M/EI diagrams are more conveniently handled in parts, each part being multiplied by its own $\bar{m}$, and the several products thus obtained being added algebraically to obtain the total. Thus the virtual work equation for deflection becomes

$$U\Delta = \sum \bar{m}A_{MD/EI} \qquad (8\text{–}3)$$

In the same manner Eq. 8–2 for rotation can be expressed

$$U\Delta\theta = \sum \bar{m}A_{MD/EI} \qquad (8\text{–}4)$$

It must be remembered that all the principles that apply to the integral calculus solution apply to the semi-graphical procedure as well. The only difference between the two procedures is that the tedium of writing a moment equation, integrating, and substituting limits is replaced by some simple formulas; but the formulas themselves are no substitute for thinking and for an understanding of the basic principles. Quite the reverse. Far from being "foolproof," the semi-graphical procedure requires a clearer understanding than does the one using integral calculus. Once the understanding is acquired it is faster and, therefore, to be preferred on all counts both for learning and for practical office use.

SUMMARY. To integrate the expression $\int (Mm/EI)\, dx$ semi-graphically, plot the M/EI diagram, then plot the m diagram. Compute the area under the M/EI diagram, $A_{MD/EI}$. Locate the centroid of the M/EI diagram and calculate the virtual moment $\bar{m}$ at that point. Calculate the virtual work as $\bar{m}A_{MD/EI}$. If the virtual moment diagram is not a continuous straight line, break both diagrams into suitable sections or segments, evaluate the product $\bar{m}A_{MD/EI}$ for each section, and add all these products algebraically. Semi-graphical integration may be performed in cantilever parts or in simple beam parts if desired. Formulas for areas and centroids of moment diagrams are given in Table 3–1 and for partial moment diagrams in Art. 3–2.

8–7. Deflection of a Cantilever Beam. Semi-graphical Integration. The rest of this chapter will be devoted to the semi-graphical procedure wherever practicable. To illustrate the operation of the procedure and to compare it with integral calculus, the problems of Arts. 8–2, 8–3, and 8–5 will be worked by the semi-graphical procedure. Since these are comparatively simple problems well adapted to integral calculus, the advantages of the semi-graphical procedure are less apparent than usual.

The beam shown in Fig. 8–7A is the same as that of Fig. 8–2A, and the following solution should be compared with that of Art. 8–2 for parallelism.

Example 8–7A. *Maximum Deflection.* The M/EI diagram of the real beam is shown in Fig. 8–7B. The curve is a parabola and its area is

$$A_{MD/EI} = \frac{1}{3} bh = \frac{1}{3} L \frac{wL^2}{2EI} = \frac{wL^3}{6EI}$$

Its centroid is located three-quarters of the span length ($\frac{3}{4}L$) from the free end, point A.

The deflection is maximum at point A, so the virtual load is applied at that point. The virtual moment diagram is shown in Fig. 8–7C. The virtual moment at the centroid of the M/EI diagram above it is

$$\bar{m} = \tfrac{3}{4} \times 1 \,\#\, L$$

The deflection is from Eq. 8–3,

$$1 \,\#\, \Delta Y_A = \sum \bar{m} A_{MD/EI} = \frac{wL^3}{6EI} \frac{3}{4} \times 1 \,\#\, L$$

$$\Delta Y_A = \frac{wL^4}{8EI}$$

which checks the answer in Art. 8–2.

Example 8–7B. *Maximum Slope.* To find the maximum slope, which occurs at point A, a virtual couple is applied at that point, resulting in the virtual moment diagram shown in Fig. 8–7D.

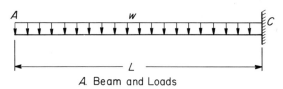

A. Beam and Loads

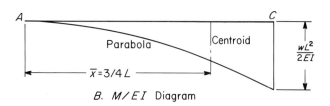

B. M/EI Diagram

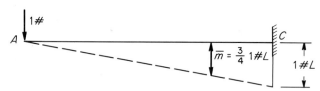

C. Virtual Load and Moment Diagram for Deflection

D. Virtual Couple and Moment Diagram for Rotation

Fig. 8–7. Maximum deflection of a cantilever beam.
Semi-graphical integration.

The slope is, from Eq. 8–4,

$$1 \#\text{-ft}\ \Delta\theta_A = \sum \bar{m} A_{MD/EI} = \frac{wL^3}{6EI} 1 \#\text{-ft}$$

$$\Delta\theta_A = \frac{wL^3}{6EI}$$

as before.

Example 8–7C. Deflection at B. To find the deflection at any other point, such as point *B*, a virtual load is applied at point *B*, producing the virtual moment diagram shown in Fig. 8–8*E*. Note that the virtual moment is zero from *A* to *B* and, therefore, no virtual work is done between *A* and *B*. That means that the MD/EI area between points A and B is omitted from the computations, which leaves then only the partial moment diagram from B to C, marked A_2 in Fig. 8–8B.

The area and centroid of the portion of the MD/EI area marked A_2 can be treated as a unit or in parts. Although Arts. 3–2 and 3–3 explain calculation of partial moment diagrams, three different ways are explained in the following, partly as a memory refresher and partly to show the relation between partial diagrams and $\bar{m}$. The three ways are shown in Figs. 8–8B, C, and D. In Fig. 8–8B, area A_2 is found as the total area minus area A_1, thus:

$$A_2 = A_{\text{total}} - A_1 = \frac{wL^3}{6EI} - \frac{1}{3}\frac{wL^2}{32EI}\frac{L}{4} = \frac{63wL^3}{6 \times 64EI}$$

and the centroid (measured from point A) is found from the equation

$$\bar{x}A_{\text{total}} = \bar{x}_1 A_1 + \bar{x}_2 A_2$$

$$\frac{3L}{4}\frac{wL^3}{6EI} = \frac{3}{4}\frac{L}{4}\frac{wL^3}{6 \times 64EI} + \bar{x}\frac{63wL^3}{6 \times 64EI}$$

where x in all terms is referred to as the distance from point A. Then

$$\bar{x} = \frac{765L}{63 \times 16} \text{ from point } A \text{ or } \frac{513L}{63 \times 16} \text{ from point } B$$

and

$$\bar{m} = 1 \# \frac{513}{63 \times 16} L \text{ at a point } \frac{513L}{63 \times 16} \text{ from point } B$$

The deflection at point B is, from Eq. 8–3,

$$1 \# \Delta Y_B = \sum \bar{m}A_{MD/EI} = \frac{513L}{63 \times 16}\frac{63wL^3}{6 \times 64EI}$$

$$\Delta Y_B = \frac{171}{2048}\frac{wL^3}{EI}$$

which equals the value found by integration in Art. 8–2.

In Fig. 8–8C, the area of the M/EI diagram between B and C is split into a rectangle, a triangle, and a parabola by resolving the loads from A to B into an equivalent shear plus a moment. Instead of finding the area and centroid of the entire segment, it is easier to leave it in parts and multiply each part by $\bar{m}$ at the centroid of that part. Thus we have,

$$1 \# \Delta Y_B = \sum \bar{m}A_{MD/EI} = \bar{m}_3 A_{MD/EI_3} + \bar{m}_4 A_{MD/EI_4} + \bar{m}_5 A_{MD/EI_5}$$

in which

$$A_{MD/EI_3} = hb = \frac{wL^2}{32EI}\frac{3}{4}L = \frac{3wL^3}{128EI}$$

$$\bar{m}_3 = m \text{ at centroid of } A_3 = \tfrac{1}{2} \times 1 \# \tfrac{3}{4}L = \tfrac{3}{8}L1 \#$$

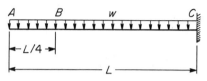

A. Beam and Loads

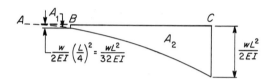

B. M/EI Diagram from B to C

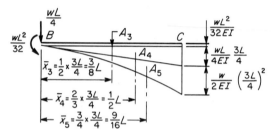

C. M/EI Diagram (in Parts) from B to C

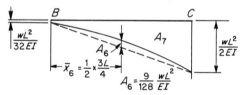

D. M/EI Diagram (in Parts) from B to C

E. Virtual Load and Moment Diagram

F. Virtual Couple and Moment Diagram

Fig. 8–8. Deflection of a point on a cantilever beam. Semi-graphical integration.

Remember that the slope of the moment diagram equals the shear. The shear at B is $wL/4$, so the ordinate at C equals slope times distance $= (wL/4EI)$ $\times (3L/4)$, which divided by EI is $3wL^2/16EI$. So

$$A_{MD/EI_4} = \frac{1}{2}\,hb = \frac{1}{2} \times \frac{3wL^2}{16EI}\frac{3}{4}\,L = \frac{9wL^3}{128EI}$$

$$\bar{m}_4 = \frac{2}{3} \times 1 \,\#\, \frac{3}{4}\,L = 1\,\#\,\frac{L}{2}$$

$$A_{MD/EI_5} = \frac{1}{3}\,hb = \frac{1}{3} \times \frac{9wL^2}{32EI}\frac{3}{4}\,L = \frac{9wL^3}{128EI}$$

$$\bar{m}_5 = \tfrac{3}{4} \times 1 \,\#\, \tfrac{3}{4}L = 1\,\#\,\tfrac{9}{16}L$$

Substituting gives

$$1\,\#\,\Delta Y_B = 1\,\#\,\frac{3L}{8}\frac{3wL^3}{128EI} + 1\,\#\,\frac{L}{2}\frac{9wL^3}{128EI} + 1\,\#\,\frac{9}{16}\,L\,\frac{9wL^3}{128EI}$$

$$\Delta Y_B = \frac{171wL^4}{2048EI}$$

In Fig. 8–8D, the area of the M/EI diagram is found as the area of the trapezoid (A_{6+7}) minus the area of the parabolic segment marked A_6. The centroid of the trapezoid may be found, or the trapezoid itself may be divided into more conveniently shaped portions, such as two triangles or a rectangle and triangle. The location of the centroid of a trapezoid is given by the formula

$$\bar{x} = \frac{n + 2m}{3(n + m)}\,b$$

where m is one altitude, n is the other altitude, b is the base, and $\bar{x}$ is the distance from the end of altitude n. The area of the trapezoid is

$$A_{\text{trapezoid}} = A_{MD/EI_{6+7}} = \frac{n + m}{2}\,b = \frac{1}{2}\left(\frac{wL^2}{32EI} + \frac{wL^2}{2EI}\right)\frac{3}{4}\,L = \frac{51}{256}\frac{wL^3}{EI}$$

and the centroid from point B is

$$\bar{x}_{6+7} = \frac{\frac{1}{32} + 2 \times \frac{1}{2}}{3(\frac{1}{32} + \frac{1}{2})} \times \frac{3}{4}\,L = \frac{33}{68}\,L$$

$$\bar{m}_{6+7} = 1\,\#\,\tfrac{33}{68}L \text{ at a point } \tfrac{33}{68}L \text{ from } B$$

The area of the parabola is

$$A_{MD/EI_6} = \tfrac{2}{3}hb$$

where h is the height and b is the horizontal projection of the base. The height can be found by subtracting the total moment midway between points B and C from the height of the trapezoid at the same point which is located $\tfrac{3}{8}L$ from point B and $\tfrac{5}{8}L$ from point A:

$$h = \frac{wL^2}{EI}\frac{1}{2}\left(\frac{1}{32} + \frac{1}{2}\right) - \frac{w}{EI}\frac{1}{2}\left(\frac{5}{8}\,L\right)^2 = \frac{9}{128}\frac{wL^2}{EI}$$

Therefore

$$A_6 = \frac{2}{3} \times \frac{9}{128} \frac{wL^2}{EI} \frac{3L}{4} = \frac{9}{256} \frac{wL^3}{EI}$$

The centroid of the parabola is midway between points B and C, so $\bar{m}$ for the parabola is

$$\bar{m}_6 = 1 \# \tfrac{3}{8} L$$

From Eq. 8–3

$$1 \# \Delta Y_B = \sum \bar{m} A_{MD/EI} = \bar{m}_{6+7} A_{MD/EI_{6+7}} - \bar{m}_6 A_{MD/EI_6}$$

Substituting

$$1 \# \Delta Y_B = 1 \# \frac{33}{68} L \frac{51}{256} \frac{wL^3}{EI} - 1 \# \frac{3}{8} L \frac{9}{256} \frac{wL^3}{EI} = \frac{171}{2048} \frac{wL^4}{EI}$$

As can be seen, the computations can be simple or involved depending on how the M/EI diagrams are handled. It requires more acumen to get the best out of this method than is required for the integral calculus procedure.

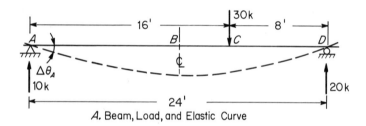

A. Beam, Load, and Elastic Curve

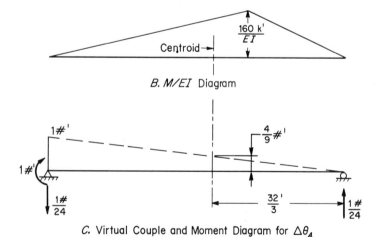

B. M/EI Diagram

C. Virtual Couple and Moment Diagram for $\Delta\theta_A$

Fig. 8–9. Maximum deflection.

Example 8–7*D*. *Rotation at B*. A virtual couple is applied at point *B* producing the moment diagram shown in Fig. 8–8*F*. Note that $\bar{m}$ is 1 #-ft everywhere between points *B* and *C*. Writing Eq. 8–4 for rotation gives

$$1 \text{ \#-ft } \Delta\theta = \sum \bar{m} A_{MD/EI} \tag{8–4}$$

Taking the area evaluated for Fig. 8–8*B*, we have

$$1 \text{ \#-ft } \Delta\theta_B = 1 \text{ \#-ft } \frac{63}{6 \times 64} \frac{wL^3}{EI}$$

$$\Delta\theta_B = \frac{21}{128} \frac{wL^3}{EI}$$

8–8. Maximum Deflections. Semi-Graphical Procedure. The procedure of finding the point of maximum deflection, explained in Art. 8–3, can be followed even more expeditiously by semi-graphical integration.

Example 8–8. The beam shown in Fig. 8–9*A* is the same beam discussed in Art. 8–3. As before, the procedure is to find the point of zero slope.

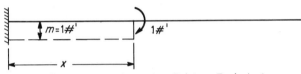

D. Virtual Couple at Any Point on Equivalent
Cantilever Beam and Virtual Moment Diagram

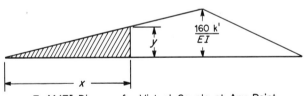

E. M/EI Diagram for Virtual Couple at Any Point

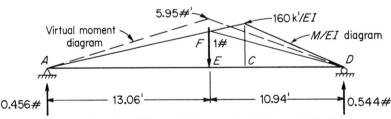

F. Virtual Load and Moment Diagram for Maximum Deflection

Semi-graphical integration.

That point is also the point of maximum deflection. However, as explained in Art. 8–3, to find the point of zero slope, the slope at some other point must be found first.

The slope at point A is the most convenient one to find, because—using it as a starting point—the M/EI diagram from that point to the point of zero slope is a triangle. A virtual couple of 1 #-ft is applied to A, resulting in the virtual moment diagram shown in Fig. 8–9C. The area of the M/EI diagram is

$$A_{MD/EI} = \frac{160 \times 24}{2EI} = \frac{1920}{EI}$$

The distance from point D to the centroid of the M/EI diagram is

$$\bar{x} = \frac{2a + b}{3} = \frac{2CD + AC}{3} = \frac{2 \times 8 + 16}{3} = \frac{32 \text{ ft}}{3}$$

From Fig. 8–9C we have

$$\bar{m} = \frac{32 \text{ ft}}{3} \times \frac{1 \#}{24} = \frac{4}{9} \text{ #-ft}$$

So the rotation at A is, from Eq. 8–4,

$$1 \text{ #-ft } \Delta\theta_A = \sum \bar{m} A_{MD/EI} = \frac{1920}{EI} \times \frac{4}{9} \text{ #-ft}$$

$$\Delta\theta_A = \frac{853}{EI}$$

The answer is positive, so the rotation is clockwise, corresponding to the direction of the virtual couple.

The simple beam is converted to an equivalent cantilever, as explained in Art. 8–3. The true moments must not change (otherwise the cantilever beam would not be an equivalent one), so there is no virtue in redrawing the beam insofar as the real loads are concerned, because we already have the true moment diagram anyway. (An equivalent beam is shown in Fig. 8–3D.) The equivalent cantilever beam must be drawn for the virtual couple, however, and this is shown in Fig. 8–9D together with the virtual moment diagram resulting from the couple applied at any point a distance x from point A.

It must be borne in mind that the equivalent cantilever beam has a slope at point A, so there will be virtual work done at point A equal to the rotation (or slope) times virtual moment. The sign is plus since the rotation and the virtual moment act in the same direction. On the other hand, the sign of the real moments and the virtual moments are opposite, so the virtual work due to the moments must be minus. Adding these two sources of virtual work and equating to zero to obtain the point of zero rotation or zero slope, results in

$$1 \text{ #-ft } \Delta\theta_x = 0 = m \Delta\theta_A - \sum \bar{m} A_{MD/EI}$$

The area of the M/EI diagram of length x and altitude y as shown in Fig. 8–9E is

$$A_{MD/EI} = \frac{xy}{2}$$

where

$$\frac{y}{x} = \frac{160/EI}{16}$$

$$A_{MD/EI} = \frac{5x^2}{EI}$$

The virtual moment m is 1 #-ft everywhere, so

$$0 = 1 \text{ #-ft} \frac{853}{EI} - 1 \text{ #-ft} \frac{5x^2}{EI}$$

$$x = 13.06 \text{ ft}$$

which is the point of maximum deflection measured from point A.

The maximum deflection can now be found by applying a virtual load at a point 13.06 ft from A (as found above) either to the simple beam or to the equivalent cantilever. Actually the use of the equivalent cantilever is a little quicker, and the maximum deflection is computed both ways for comparison.

Using the true beam, that is, the simple beam in Fig. 8–9A, a virtual load is applied 13.06 ft from point A, producing the virtual moment diagram shown in Fig. 8–9F. Note that the virtual moment diagram is discontinuous at the virtual load (at point E) and, therefore, the M/EI diagram must be broken into at least two segments[4] so that for each segment the virtual moment diagram is a straight line. The M/EI diagram is redrawn in Fig. 8–9F for convenience in showing the segments. The segment between points A and E is triangular in shape and easily solved. Its area[5] is

$$A_{A\text{-}E} = 10 \text{ kips} \times 13.06 \text{ ft} \times \frac{13.06 \text{ ft}}{2EI} = \frac{853}{EI}$$

and $\bar{m}$ is

$$\bar{m} = \tfrac{2}{3} \times 5.95 \text{ #-ft} = 3.97 \text{ #-ft}$$

The M/EI diagram between points E and D is an irregular quadrangle. Its area and centroid can be found in several ways. One of the most practical ways is to divide it into triangles and find the area and centroid of each triangle. These can be combined into a single area with a single $\bar{m}$ by adding the products of each area times its own separate $\bar{m}$ to produce the total. Perhaps the easiest solution here is to make use of our previous work. It was

[4] As explained in Art. 8–6.
[5] This area $853/EI$ equals the value found for $\Delta\theta_A$. Why?

found previously in this article that the total M/EI area is $1920/EI$ and the centroid is $32\frac{2}{3}$ ft from point D. Therefore the area between points E and D is

$$A_{E\text{-}D} = \frac{1920}{EI} - \frac{853}{EI} = \frac{1067}{EI}$$

Making use of the fact that the first moment of an area equals the sum of the first moment of its parts

$$\sum A\bar{x} = A_1\bar{x}_1 + A_2\bar{x}_2 + \cdots \tag{3–1}$$

$$\frac{1920}{EI} \times \frac{32}{3} = \frac{853}{EI}\left(10.94 + \frac{13.06}{3}\right) + \frac{1067}{EI}\,\bar{x}$$

$$\bar{x} = 6.97$$

At 6.97 ft from point D, $\bar{m}$ is

$$\bar{m} = 0.544\ \# \times 6.97\ \text{ft} = 3.79\ \#\text{-ft}$$

From Eq. 8–3 the deflection is

$$1\ \#\ \Delta Y_{\max} = \sum \bar{m}A_{MD/EI} = 3.97\ \#\text{-ft}\,\frac{853}{EI} + 3.79\ \#\text{-ft}\,\frac{1067}{EI}$$

$$\Delta Y_{\max} = \frac{7430}{EI}$$

In Art. 8–3 it was shown that the simply supported beam could be transformed into an equivalent cantilever beam. The advantage was the simpler virtual moment equation. This procedure can be applied to the semi-graphical method with equally advantageous results. Figure 8–10 shows the M/EI diagram (which is the same as that in Fig. 8–9B) and the virtual load and moment diagram applied to the equivalent cantilever. As before, the total internal virtual work equals the work due to bending plus the work due to the rotation of the beam at point A. The virtual work due to bending is minus because the true and virtual moments are of opposite sign. The work due to rotation is plus because the direction of rotation (see Fig. 8–9A) is the same as the virtual moment at that point. Note that the only part of the true moment diagram that is used is that part between points A and E. Between points E and D, the virtual moment (and consequently, the virtual work) equals zero. The maximum deflection is, then,

$$1\ \#\ \Delta Y_{\max} = \sum \bar{m}A_{MD/EI} + m\ \Delta\theta_A = -4.35\ \#\text{-ft}\,\frac{853}{EI} + 13.06\ \#\text{-ft}\,\frac{853}{EI}$$

$$\Delta Y_{\max} = \frac{7430}{EI}$$

as before.

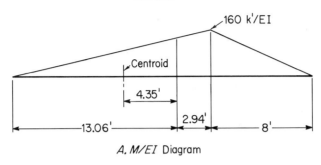

A, M/EI Diagram

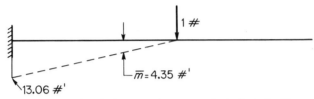

B, Virtual Load and Moment Diagram on Equivalent Cantilever

Fig. 8–10. Maximum deflection. Semi-graphical integration.

8–9. Indeterminate Beams. Semi-graphical Integration.

The discussion of Art. 8–4 on the solution of statically indeterminate beams applies equally well to the semi-graphical procedure. Figure 8–11A shows the same beam and loads discussed in Art. 8–4 and shown in Fig. 8–5A.

Example 8–9A. Redundant Reaction. The beam is statically indeterminate to one degree, and any of the reaction components can be considered as the redundant. A convenient one is the support at point B. Accordingly, the structure is cut back by replacing the support at B with the reaction R, as shown in Fig. 8–11B, which results in the M/EI diagrams[6] in Fig. 8–11C.

The virtual moment diagram for deflection at point B is shown in Fig. 8–11D together with $\bar{m}$ values for each M/EI part in the figure above. The solution of the equation of virtual work can be expedited by using a tabular form (Table 8–1).

From Table 8–1,

$$0 = \frac{152{,}064}{EI} - \frac{4608R}{EI}$$

$R = +33.0$ kips upward as assumed because the sign is plus

Example 8–9B. Deflection at A. Now that R has been determined, the deflection at any point can be computed. For example, to compute deflection

---

[6] Similar moment diagrams are developed in Arts. 5–2 and 5–3.

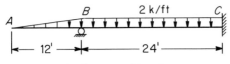

A. Beam and Loads

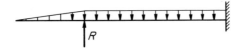

B. Cut-Back Structure

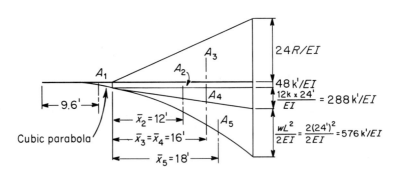

C. M/EI Diagrams

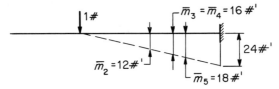

D. Virtual Load and Moment Diagram for ΔY_B

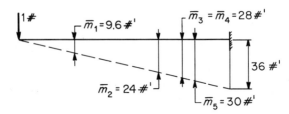

E. Virtual Load and Moment Diagram for ΔY_A

Fig. 8-11. Redundant beam. Semi-graphical integration.

TABLE 8–I
Redundant Reaction

$$1 \# \Delta Y_B = 0 = \Sigma \, \bar{m} A_{MD/EI} \qquad \text{(Eq. 8–3)}$$

Moment Diagram Part	$A_{MD/EI}$ Coeff. × Base × Height	$\bar{m}$	$+\bar{m}A_{MD/EI}$	$-\bar{m}A_{MD/EI}$
A_1	$-\dfrac{1}{4} \times 12 \times \dfrac{48}{EI}$	0		
A_2	$-1 \times 24 \times \dfrac{48}{EI}$	-12	$13{,}824/EI$	
A_3	$+\dfrac{1}{2} \times 24 \times \dfrac{24R}{EI}$	-16		$4{,}608R/EI$
A_4	$-\dfrac{1}{2} \times 24 \times \dfrac{288}{EI}$	-16	$55{,}296/EI$	
A_5	$-\dfrac{1}{3} \times 24 \times \dfrac{576}{EI}$	-18	$82{,}900/EI$	
		Summation	$152{,}064/EI$	$4{,}608R/EI$

at point A, apply a virtual load at A which results in the virtual moment diagram and the values of $\bar{m}$ for each M/EI part, as shown in Fig. 8–11E. The deflection at A is computed in Table 8–2.

TABLE 8–2
Deflection of Redundant Beam

$$1 \# \Delta Y_A = \Sigma \, \bar{m} A_{MD/EI} \qquad \text{(Eq. 8–3)}$$

Moment Diagram Part	$A_{MD/EI}$ Coeff. × Base × Height	$\bar{m}$	$+\bar{m}A_{MD/EI}$	$-\bar{m}A_{MD/EI}$
A_1	$-\dfrac{1}{4} \times 12 \times \dfrac{48}{EI}$	-9.6	$1{,}382/EI$	
A_2	$-1 \times 24 \times \dfrac{48}{EI}$	-24	$27{,}648/EI$	
A_3	$+\dfrac{1}{2} \times 24 \times \dfrac{24 \times 33}{EI}$	-28		$266{,}112/EI$
A_4	$-\dfrac{1}{2} \times 24 \times \dfrac{288}{EI}$	-28	$96{,}768/EI$	
A_5	$-\dfrac{1}{3} \times 24 \times \dfrac{576}{EI}$	-30	$138{,}240/EI$	
		Summation	$264{,}038/EI$	$266{,}112/EI$

From Table 8–2, the deflection is

$$\Delta Y_A = \frac{264{,}038}{EI} - \frac{266{,}112}{EI}$$

$$= \frac{-2074}{EI} = \frac{2074}{EI} \text{ upward because the sign is negative}$$

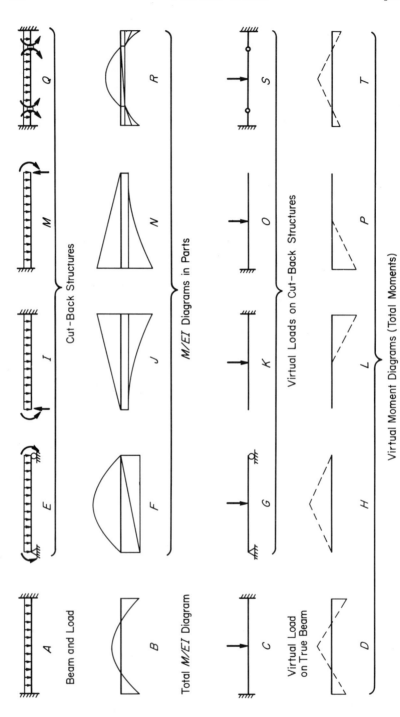

Fig. 8-12. Deflection of a statically indeterminate beam.

8–10. Deflection of Indeterminate Beams. As stated in previous articles, an indeterminate structure can be cut back in any manner whatsoever that leaves the structure stable and determinate. Those forces that are chosen to be the redundants are treated as loads, and deflections can be found by applying the virtual load to the cut-back structure. This is tantamount to considering the cut-back structure as the actual one. These statements have far-reaching implications, which can result in some very peculiar cut-back structures that are, incredibly enough, perfectly valid. Furthermore, the statements are general and apply to other methods of analysis (such as neutral-point or column analogy) as well as to virtual work. They seem to be most spectacular and yet, with all, more conveniently explained by virtual work than by other methods.

To explore this subject fully would require too much explanation, so the student should recognize that the following example only suggests some of the possibilities. The philosophy and principles of the example can be applied to a great many entirely different problems—even to problems worked by other methods.

To illustrate these principles, consider a beam fixed at both ends and subjected to a uniform load, as shown in Fig. 8–12A. Suppose the maximum deflection (which occurs at the center) is wanted. Before any deflection can be computed, all unknown reactions must first be determined, and it is to be understood that this has been done in each case as a prelude to the following discussion. Note that the sketches of Fig. 8–12 are in definite sequence. The assumed beam (cut-back in Fig. 8–12E, I, M, and Q) is at the top; the M/EI diagrams are second; the virtual load on the assumed beam is third; and the resulting virtual moment diagram is last. There are many possible cut-back structures of which only a few are indicated in the figure.

Of course, it is possible to solve the deflection by using the total M/EI diagram and a virtual load on the indeterminate structure, as in sequence $ABCD$. Possible but foolish, since the M/EI diagrams are inconvenient and the virtual moment diagram must itself be found by indeterminate analysis. Or it is possible—and much more convenient—to assume one of the cut-back beams of Fig. 8–12E, I, or M with their corresponding M/EI diagrams and virtual moment diagrams. We could even use the cut-back beam of Fig. 8–12Q, assuming the moments at the hinges to be the redundants. (It is hardly convenient here, but it could be for other structures, especially rigid frames.)

All the M/EI diagrams are equal to one another. The diagrams of Figs. 8–12F, J, N, and R are only different ways of expressing the diagram of Fig. 8–12B in parts. Now, therefore, if the virtual moments of, say, Fig. 8–12H can be used in conjunction with the M/EI diagrams of Fig. 8–12F directly above, it can also be used in conjunction with any other M/EI diagram. For example, the virtual moments of Fig. 8–12H can be used in conjunction with the M/EI diagram of Fig. 8–12N. But this virtual moment diagram derives from a cut-back structure that is simply supported at each end (Fig. 8–12G), whereas the M/EI diagram is drawn for a cut-back structure that is a cantilever fixed at the left end (Fig. 8–12M).

Thus it follows that a structure may be cut back in one manner for the real loads, whereas it may be cut back in an entirely different manner for the virtual load. At face value, this may seem illogical, but considered in the light of the foregoing paragraph, it is not only logical but also of the utmost rationality. It applies moreover to frames, trusses, and other structures. These principles can—and should—be utilized in practice to simplify and shorten the labor of computing deflections in all sorts of indeterminate structures.

9

RIGID FRAMES

9–1. Fixed Rigid Frames. The principles of virtual work as discussed for beams apply without modification to the solution of redundant reactions and deflections of rigid frames. Again, as with beams, signs are automatic; it is only necessary to employ the same convention for real moments and for virtual moments.

Example 9–1. *Reactions.* An example of the application of virtual work to a rigid frame is illustrated in Fig. 9–1. The frame, its loads, and its dimensions are shown in Fig. 9–1A. Although a great many cut back structures are possible,[1] the one shown in Fig. 9–1B is probably as convenient as any. The moment diagrams for loads and for the three redundant forces are shown in separate drawings (Figs. 9–1C, D, E, and F) to avoid confusion.[2]

The frame is statically indeterminate to three degrees, and therefore three equations of virtual work are required. They can be obtained from the consideration that the horizontal deflection at point A is zero ($\Delta X_A = 0$), the vertical deflection at point A is zero ($\Delta Y_A = 0$), and the rotation at A is zero ($\Delta \theta_A = 0$). To develop the first equation, apply a horizontal virtual load at point A as in Fig. 9–2A, and draw the virtual moment diagrams. Then

$$1 \mathbin{\#} \Delta X_A = 0 = \sum \bar{m} A_{MD/EI} \tag{8–3}$$

in which each moment diagram area in Figs. 9–1C, D, E, and F is multiplied by its $\bar{m}$ (shown in Fig. 9–2A), divided by E and I, and the results are added algebraically as shown in Table 9–1. The only moment diagram requiring explanation is A_2. The area and centroid are computed by methods explained in Art. 3–2. The specific solution for A_2 is found in Art. 6–1. No signs are shown in columns 2 and 3 because any sign convention can be used. Of course, the signs would change with different sign conventions. Regardless of the sign convention used for any particular M/EI area, the signs in columns 4, 5, 6, and 7 will be as shown because the same sign convention must be used for the real and virtual moments.

The second equation is developed by applying a vertical virtual load at point A and multiplying the moment diagram areas by the $\bar{m}$ values found from Fig. 9–2B and dividing by E and I. The calculations are shown in Table 9–2.

---

[1] More on cut-back structures is found in Arts. 6–3 and 9–4.
[2] A detailed explanation of the M/EI diagrams is given in Art. 6–1.

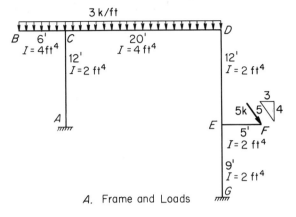

A. Frame and Loads

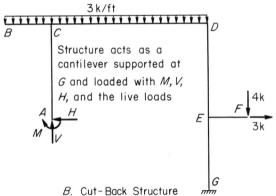

B. Cut-Back Structure

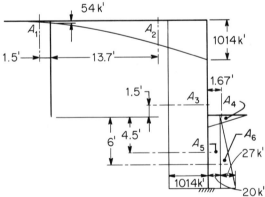

C. Moment Diagrams for Live Load Only

Fig. 9-1. Moment diagrams

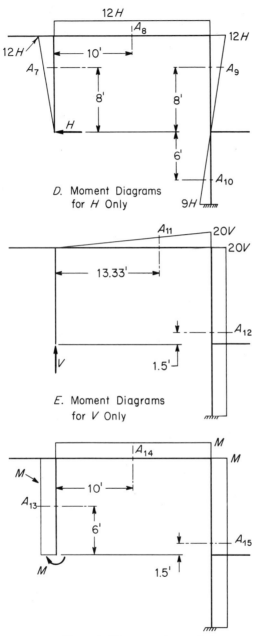

D. Moment Diagrams
for H Only

E. Moment Diagrams
for V Only

F. Moment Diagrams for M Only

for rigid frame.

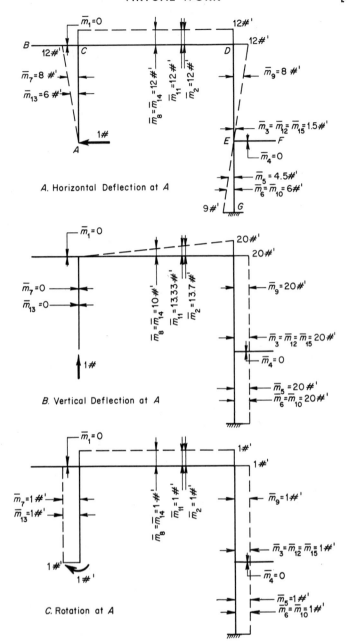

Fig. 9–2. Virtual loads, moment diagrams, and m values.
(Subscripts refer to moment diagram parts in Fig. 9–1.)

TABLE 9–I
Horizontal Deflection

$$1 \# \Delta X_A = 0 = \Sigma \bar{m} A_{MD/EI} \qquad \text{(Eq. 8–3)}$$

| Moment Diagram Part | $A_{MD/EI}$ Coeff. $\times$ Base $\times$ Height | $\bar{m}$ (Fig. 9–2A) | $\bar{m}A_{MD/EI}$ Coefficient of | | | |
			H	V	M	Constant
(1)	(2)	(3)	(4)	(5)	(6)	(7)
A_1	$\frac{1}{3} \times 6 \times \frac{54}{4E}$	0				
A_2	$\frac{8,679}{4E}$	12				$-26{,}040/E$
A_3	$1 \times 21 \times \frac{1,014}{2E}$	1.5				$-15{,}970/E$
A_4	$\frac{1}{2} \times 5 \times \frac{20}{2E}$	0				
A_5	$1 \times 9 \times \frac{20}{2E}$	4.5				$-405/E$
A_6	$\frac{1}{2} \times 9 \times \frac{27}{2E}$	6				$-366/E$
A_7	$\frac{1}{2} \times 12 \times \frac{12H}{2E}$	8	$+288/E$			
A_8	$1 \times 20 \times \frac{12H}{4E}$	12	$+720/E$			
A_9	$\frac{1}{2} \times 12 \times \frac{12H}{2E}$	8	$+288/E$			
A_{10}	$\frac{1}{2} \times 9 \times \frac{9H}{2E}$	6	$+121/E$			
A_{11}	$\frac{1}{2} \times 20 \times \frac{20V}{4E}$	12		$+600/E$		
A_{12}	$1 \times 21 \times \frac{20V}{2E}$	1.5		$+315/E$		
A_{13}	$1 \times 12 \times \frac{M}{2E}$	6			$+36/E$	
A_{14}	$1 \times 20 \times \frac{M}{4E}$	12			$+60/E$	
A_{15}	$1 \times 21 \times \frac{M}{2E}$	1.5			$+15.75/E$	
	Summation		$+1{,}417/E$	$+915/E$	$+111.75/E$	$-42{,}781/E$

Canceling the constant E, we have $1{,}417H + 915V + 111.75M = 42{,}781$

TABLE 9–2
Vertical Deflection

$$1 \,\#\, \Delta Y_A = 0 = \Sigma \, \bar{m} A_{MD/EI} \qquad \text{(Eq. 8–3)}$$

Moment Diagram Part	$A_{MD/EI}$ Coeff. × Base × Height	$\bar{m}$ (Fig. 9–2B)	$\bar{m}A_{MD/EI}$			
			H	Coefficient of V	M	Constant
(1)	(2)	(3)	(4)	(5)	(6)	(7)
A_1	$\dfrac{1}{3} \times 6 \times \dfrac{54}{4E}$	0				
A_2	$\dfrac{8{,}679}{4E}$	13.69				$-29{,}707/E$
A_3	$1 \times 21 \times \dfrac{1{,}014}{2E}$	20				$-212{,}940/E$
A_4	$\dfrac{1}{2} \times 5 \times \dfrac{20}{2E}$	0				
A_5	$1 \times 9 \times \dfrac{20}{2E}$	20				$+1{,}800/E$
A_6	$\dfrac{1}{2} \times 9 \times \dfrac{27}{2E}$	20				$+1{,}220/E$
A_7	$\dfrac{1}{2} \times 12 \times \dfrac{12H}{2E}$	0				
A_8	$1 \times 20 \times \dfrac{12H}{4E}$	10	$+600/E$			
A_9	$\dfrac{1}{2} \times 12 \times \dfrac{12H}{2E}$	20	$+720/E$			
A_{10}	$\dfrac{1}{2} \times 9 \times \dfrac{9H}{2E}$	20	$-404/E$			
A_{11}	$\dfrac{1}{2} \times 20 \times \dfrac{20V}{4E}$	13.33		$+667/E$		
A_{12}	$1 \times 21 \times \dfrac{20V}{2E}$	20		$+4{,}200/E$		
A_{13}	$1 \times 12 \times \dfrac{M}{2E}$	0				
A_{14}	$1 \times 20 \times \dfrac{M}{4E}$	10			$+50/E$	
A_{15}	$1 \times 21 \times \dfrac{M}{2E}$	20			$+210/E$	
		Summation	$+916/E$	$+4{,}867/E$	$+260/E$	$-239{,}627/E$

Canceling E, we have $916H + 4{,}867V + 260M = 239{,}627$

TABLE 9–3
Rotation

$$1 \text{ \#-ft } \Delta\theta_A = 0 = \Sigma \, \bar{m} A_{MD/EI} \qquad \text{(Eq. 8–3)}$$

Moment Diagram Part	$A_{MD/EI}$ Coeff. × Base × Height	$\bar{m}$ (Fig. 9–2C)	$\bar{m} A_{MD/EI}$			
			H	Coefficient of V	M	Constant
(1)	(2)	(3)	(4)	(5)	(6)	(7)
A_1	$\frac{1}{3} \times 6 \times \frac{54}{4E}$	0				
A_2	$\frac{8,679}{4E}$	1				$-2,170/E$
A_3	$1 \times 21 \times \frac{1,014}{2E}$	1				$-10,647/E$
A_4	$\frac{1}{2} \times 5 \times \frac{20}{2E}$	0				
A_5	$1 \times 9 \times \frac{20}{2E}$	1				$+90/E$
A_6	$\frac{1}{2} \times 9 \times \frac{27}{2E}$	1				$+61/E$
A_7	$\frac{1}{2} \times 12 \times \frac{12H}{2E}$	1	$+36/E$			
A_8	$1 \times 20 \times \frac{12H}{4E}$	1	$+60/E$			
A_9	$\frac{1}{2} \times 12 \times \frac{12H}{2E}$	1	$+36/E$			
A_{10}	$\frac{1}{2} \times 9 \times \frac{9H}{2E}$	1	$-20.2/E$			
A_{11}	$\frac{1}{2} \times 20 \times \frac{20V}{4E}$	1		$+50/E$		
A_{12}	$1 \times 21 \times \frac{20V}{2E}$	1		$+210/E$		
A_{13}	$1 \times 12 \times \frac{M}{2E}$	1			$+6/E$	
A_{14}	$1 \times 20 \times \frac{M}{4E}$	1			$+5/E$	
A_{15}	$1 \times 21 \times \frac{M}{2E}$	1			$+10.5/E$	
	Summation		$+111.8/E$	$+260/E$	$+21.5/E$	$-12,666/E$

Canceling E, we have $111.8H + 260V + 21.5M = 12,666$

The third equation is developed by applying a virtual moment at point A, again multiplying the moment diagram areas by the $\bar{m}$ values found from Fig. 9–2C, and dividing by E and I. These figures are shown in Table 9–3.

The three equations[3] resulting from Tables 9–1, 9–2, and 9–3 are solved simultaneously[4] for H, V, and M, yielding

$$H = -1.59 \text{ kips} = 1.59 \text{ kips to the right}$$

$$V = +49.78 \text{ kips} = 49.78 \text{ kips upward}$$

$$M = -4.59 \text{ kip-ft} = 4.59 \text{ kip-ft counterclockwise}$$

DEFLECTION. The deflection of any point of the structure can be found by using the cut-back structure of Fig. 9–1B and the real moment diagrams of Figs. 9–1C, D, E, and F by substituting the above values for H, V, and M respectively. According to the discussion of Art. 8–10, these moment diagrams could also be used with any other valid (that is, stable and determinate) cut-back structure.

9–2. Fewer Redundants. As the number of redundants increases, the solution becomes longer and more involved. Fewer redundants result in shorter solutions. This can be quickly illustrated by using the solution of Art. 9–1 as a starting point.

Example 9–2A. Two Redundants. Consider the frame of Art. 9–1 to be supported as shown in Fig. 9–3. The frame is statically indeterminate to two degrees, and a convenient cut-back structure would be one fixed at G and free at A with the two redundants H and V acting at point A as shown in the figure. The moment diagrams are exactly the same as those shown in Figs. 9–1C, D, and E. There is no redundant moment at point A, so the moment diagrams of Fig. 9–1F do not exist for this problem. The horizontal and vertical deflections at point A are zero, so the virtual loads and moment diagrams of Figs. 9–2A and B can be utilized for two equations of virtual work that can be solved simultaneously for the redundant forces. However, the rotation at point A is not zero, so the virtual couple and moment diagram of Fig. 9–2C cannot yield an equation that would be of any help in solving the redundant forces. The equation for deflection at point A can be taken

---

[3] Note that these three equations are identical to the equations in Art. 6–1, which were developed from equations of moment area, and that the tabulated figures in Tables 9–1, 9–2, and 9–3 are identical to those in Tables 6–3, 6–2, and 6–1 respectively. Thus, the two different concepts that produce identical equations are closely related, and it is interesting to note that the $\bar{x}$ and $\bar{y}$ of moment area is numerically equal to the $\bar{m}$ of virtual work. Using moment area, the effect of each moment diagram must be carefully considered. It is not an automatic method, and so it requires a deeper insight into structural theory. On the other hand, virtual work is nearly automatic, so that comparatively less explanation and less structural sense are required.

[4] The detailed solution is given in Table 6–4.

directly from Tables 9–1 and 9–2 by dropping all terms involving the redundant moment M. The resulting equations are

$$1417H + 915V = 42{,}781$$

$$916H + 4867V = 239{,}627$$

from which

$$H = -1.83 \text{ kips} = 1.83 \text{ kips to the right}$$

$$V = +49.58 \text{ kips} = 49.58 \text{ kips upward}$$

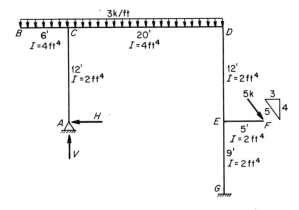

Fig. 9–3. Rigid frame with two redundant reactions.

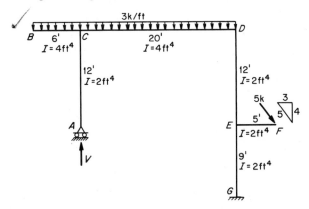

Fig. 9–4. Rigid frame with one redundant reaction.

Example 9–2B. One Redundant. If the rigid frame is statically indeterminate to only one degree as, for example, in Fig. 9–4, the moment diagrams of Figs. 9–1C and E apply. The vertical deflection at point A is zero, so the virtual load and moment diagrams of Fig. 9–2B can be utilized to write a single equation of virtual work which is sufficient to evaluate the single redundant. This equation can be obtained from Table 9–2 by dropping all terms involving the redundants H and M (since they are zero for this frame). The equation is, then

$$4867V = 239{,}627$$

from which

$$V = +49.24 \text{ kips} = 49.24 \text{ kips upward}$$

9–3. Two-Hinged Frame

Example 9–3. *Reactions.* A two-hinged frame, statically indeterminate to one degree, is shown in Fig. 9–5A. Because it is indeterminate only to one degree, it must be cut back by introducing only one degree of freedom because it must be stable. One possible cut-back structure is shown in Fig. 9–5B, where one knife-edge support is replaced by rollers and a redundant force H (which is shown in Fig 9–5D). All the reactions can be found in terms of known loads and the unknown H, and the moment diagrams are found in Figs. 9–5C and D.

Since there is only one redundant force, only one equation of virtual work is required. That equation can be based on the fact that the horizontal deflection at point G must be zero. Thus a horizontal virtual load would be applied at point G, as shown in Fig. 9–5E. However, the structure must be in static equilibrium under the action of the virtual load. Summing moments about point G shows that a vertical force must act at point A and, using the other two equations of static equilibrium, equal and opposite forces must react at point G. Now the resultant of the forces at point G must pass through point A and the resultant of the forces at point A must pass through point G. Thus the virtual loads are reduced to equal and opposite virtual loads at points A and G. Again see Fig. 9–5E. From the discussion of Art. 7–2, the virtual loads automatically measure[5] the deflection of point G with respect to point A.

Now suppose we had originally introduced the problem with the idea of equating to zero the deflection of point A with respect to point G. We would probably have used equal and opposite unit (1 #) virtual forces at points A and G, as shown in Fig. 9–5F. Of course, the amount of the virtual load can have no effect upon the answer; it affects only the ordinates of the virtual moment diagrams, which vary in direct proportion to the virtual load.

The virtual moments in Fig. 9–5F can be determined analytically or graphically. To find the moments graphically, scale[6] the distance from any point on the frame to the line of action of the virtual force. Since the virtual force is unity, the moment at the point is numerically equal to the distance to the line of action of the force, as shown by Fig. 9–5F. Thus, instead of computing $\bar{m}$ at the centroid of each moment diagram, just measure $\bar{m}$ from the drawing. For example, the moment diagram marked A_5 (Fig. 9–5C) is a

---

[5] It has been stated before that virtual work is a nearly automatic method.

[6] The largest convenient drawing to fill an 8½-by-11-in. sheet is usually adequate.

triangle, and its centroid is 4 ft below point D. The virtual moment $\bar{m}_5$ at the centroid of A_5 is represented graphically to some scale by the line pq in Fig. 9–5F. The value of pq can be either computed algebraically or found graphically by scaling the distance pr, which is numerically equal to $\bar{m}_5$, as

TABLE 9–4

Redundant Reaction

$$1 \ \# \ \Delta X_A = 0 = \Sigma \, \bar{m} A_{MD/EI} \qquad \text{(Eq. 8–3)}$$

Moment Diagram Part	$A_{MD/EI}$ Coeff. × Base × Height	$\bar{m}$ (Scaled from Fig. 9–5F)	$\bar{m}A_{MD/EI}$		$\bar{m}$ (Computed from Fig. 9–5E)	$\bar{m}A_{MD/EI}$	
			Coefficient of H	Constant		Coefficient of H	Constant
(1)	(2)	(3)	(4)	(5)	(6)	(7)	(8)
A_1	$\frac{1}{3} \times 6 \ \times \frac{54}{4E}$	0			0		
A_2	$\frac{1}{2} \times 20 \times \frac{54}{4E}$	13.7		$-1{,}850/E$	15		$-2{,}025/E$
A_3	$\frac{2}{3} \times 20 \times \frac{150}{4E}$	15.1		$+7{,}550/E$	16.5		$+8{,}249/E$
A_4	$\frac{1}{2} \times 20 \times \frac{47}{4E}$	16.5		$-1{,}939/E$	18		$-2{,}115/E$
A_5	$\frac{1}{2} \times 12 \times \frac{36}{2E}$	15.5		$+1{,}674/E$	17		$+1{,}836/E$
A_6	$1 \times 12 \times \frac{20}{2E}$	13.7		$-1{,}644/E$	15		$-1{,}800/E$
A_7	$\frac{1}{2} \times 21 \times \frac{63}{2E}$	12.8		$-4{,}234/E$	14		$-4{,}630/E$
A_8	$\frac{1}{2} \times 5 \ \times \frac{20}{2E}$	0			0		
A_9	$\frac{1}{2} \times 12 \times \frac{12H}{2E}$	7.3	$-263H/E$		9	$-324H/E$	
A_{10}	$\frac{1}{2} \times 20 \times \frac{12H}{4E}$	13.7	$-411H/E$		15	$-450H/E$	
A_{11}	$\frac{1}{2} \times 20 \times \frac{21H}{4E}$	16.5	$-866H/E$		18	$-945H/E$	
A_{12}	$\frac{1}{2} \times 21 \times \frac{21H}{2E}$	12.8	$-1{,}411H/E$		14	$-1{,}544H/E$	
	Summation		$-2{,}951H/E$	$-443/E$		$-3{,}263H/E$	$-485/E$

stated above. Other values of $\bar{m}$ are determined in the same way, and the computations[7] are shown in Table 9–4. The tabulated values of $\bar{m}$ were actually scaled from a drawing twice as large as Fig. 9–5F. Values of $\bar{m}$ computed from Fig. 9–5E are also shown in the table for comparison. Note that there is no difference in the result. Parenthetically, it might be added that, for this problem, the algebraically obtained values of $\bar{m}$ in Fig. 9–5E

[7] Again, note the similarity between virtual work and moment area. The $\bar{m}$ of virtual work in this example is numerically equal to the $\bar{y}$ of moment area in the same example of Fig. 6–9.

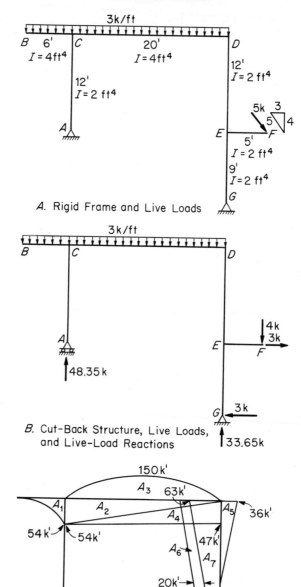

A. Rigid Frame and Live Loads

B. Cut-Back Structure, Live Loads, and Live-Load Reactions

C. Live-Load Moment Diagrams in Parts

Fig. 9-5. Two-hinged

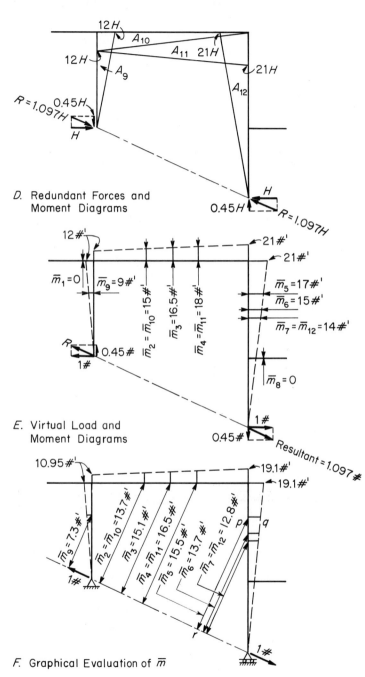

D. Redundant Forces and
   Moment Diagrams

E. Virtual Load and
   Moment Diagrams

F. Graphical Evaluation of $\bar{m}$

rigid frame.

lead to a somewhat quicker solution than the graphically obtained values of $\bar{m}$ in Fig. 9–5*F*. The reverse would be true, however, if the frame were quite irregular or if some members were sloping.

From columns 4 and 5 we have, canceling E which is constant,

$$-2951H - 443 = 0$$

$$H = -0.15 \text{ kip} = 0.15 \text{ kip acting opposite to the}$$
$$\text{direction shown in Fig. 9–5}D$$

From columns 6 and 7

$$-3263H - 485 = 0$$

$$H = -0.149 \text{ kip} \cong 0.15 \text{ kip as before}$$

9–4. Other Cut-Back Structures. Several times in the preceding discussion it was suggested that different cut-back structures could be used.

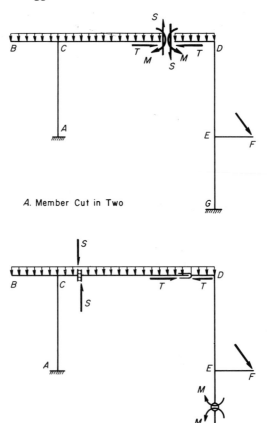

A. Member Cut in Two

B. Shear Guide, Thrust Guide, and Hinge

Fig. 9–6. Other cut-back structures.

In the articles on trusses some alternate ones were shown, and Fig. 8–12 shows several alternates for a beam. This discussion is limited here because the possibilities are themselves almost unlimited.

As stated before, a structure can be cut back in any way that makes it determinate and stable. To illustrate this, consider the rigid frame of Fig. 9–1*A*. In Art. 9–1 this same structure was cut back by removing one reaction, as shown in Fig. 9–1*B*. A different cut-back structure in which a member is completely cut through is illustrated in Fig. 9–6*A*. In general it requires three reactions to restrain the members at such a cut—shear, thrust, and moment. If the structure is statically indeterminate to less than three degrees, the creation of three such internal reactions usually adds to the labor of the solution, unless use of symmetry is made. Sometimes, the added labor can be reduced by selecting one or two (as the situation demands) of these internal reactions to be the redundants and expressing the other internal reactions in terms of the redundants. Often the labor can be reduced still more by assuming a cut that permits only one degree of freedom. A hinge is such a cut. It permits rotation but resists shear and thrust. A guided cut is one that resists moment but permits free movement in either shear or thrust. Guided cuts are impractical to construct physically, but they are just as feasible mathematically as are hinges. Fig. 9–6*B* shows a cut-back structure utilizing three different kinds of cuts (a hinge, a guided shear cut, and a guided thrust cut) to produce three degrees of freedom. Still other kinds of cut-back structures can be constructed. The sketches in Fig. 9–6 suggest only some of the possibilities.

Usually the structure cut back by the removal of a reaction (such as those in the examples previously solved) is to be preferred because it is simpler. But many engineers prefer the type of cut-back structure shown in Fig. 9–6*A*, particularly for arches, because arithmetical accuracy is better.

10

NON-PRISMATIC MEMBERS

10-1. Beams, Rigid Frames, and Arches. Continuous beams are often haunched at the supports, and members in rigid frames are often haunched at the knees to provide deeper sections, better able to resist the higher moments. Sometimes members in rigid frames and arches are tapered for their full length. There are several ways to treat such problems:

1. The haunches may be ignored.
2. If an integrable expression can be written for the moment of inertia, the problem can be solved by integration.
3. The member may be divided into segments short enough so that the real and virtual moments and the moment of inertia can be considered constant for each segment.
4. The member may be divided into segments short enough so that the M/EI curve can be approximated by a series of straight lines.
5. Or models may be used.

NEGLECTING THE HAUNCHES. Needless to say, neglecting the haunches or the taper causes error in the analysis although not, perhaps, as much as might be supposed. When the haunches are short or quite shallow, it may be fairly safe to ignore them, but when the haunches are pronounced, the error may be excessive. In general (though it may not always be true), a haunch reduces the bending moment in the shallow portion and increases it at the haunch. By comparing "precise" and approximate solutions for typical problems, reasonably safe correction factors for approximate solutions can be obtained but, to be safe, they must be high and are, therefore, uneconomical. This seems justifiable only when the structure is so small that greater precision is not economically justified. It may be quite satisfactory for preliminary design.

As an example of the comparison between moments obtained by an approximate method (neglecting the haunches) and a "precise" method (including them in the analysis), the gabled, haunched, rigid frame of Fig. 14-13 yields the values[1] shown in Table 10-1.

INTEGRATION. The integration of the virtual work equation provides the most accurate analysis. But even so, the analysis is not absolutely exact

---

[1] These values were obtained by moment distribution, not by virtual work. But it makes no difference, because answers obtained by all methods must be the same provided the same assumptions are made for each method.

unless the virtual work due to shear and axial strains is also included, and the virtual work equation for bending corrected for the slope of the haunch, where the formula $s = My/I$, is not strictly valid. To include all these refinements is quite impractical, and they are commonly omitted. Nevertheless, the results are usually reasonably accurate as shown by good correlation with model studies.

TABLE 10–1

Comparison of "Precise" and Approximate Moments

Point on Frame	Description	Bending Moments, kip-ft	
		"Precise" (Haunches Included in Analysis)	Approximate (Haunches Ignored in Analysis)
A	Reaction—no haunch	157	116
B	Knee—haunched	94	99
C	Ridge—haunched	88	39
D	Knee—haunched	250	211
E	Reaction—no haunch	0	0
$(A + B)/2$	Mid-point—straight	31.5	8.5
$(B + C)/2$	Mid-point—straight	63	40
$(C + D)/2$	Mid-point—straight	124	168
$(D + E)/2$	Mid-point—straight	125	105.5

Even though it provides accurate answers, integration is rarely used except for single beams, because the expressions that result are often quite complex, difficult, and tedious to integrate. In Art. 10–2 certain constants used for moment distribution—stiffness, carry-over factor, and fixed-end moments—are solved by integration for a parabolically haunched beam.

SUMMATION. Because integration, as applied to arches and rings, is so complex, such structures are best divided into a number of segments. The real moment, virtual moment, and moment of inertia are determined for the center of the segment, and these values are assumed to be constant over the length of the segment. The accuracy of the solution depends upon the number of segments; more segments insure greater accuracy.

To illustrate the summation procedure, which is the same for arches and rings as for beams, the stiffness and carry-over factor are found for a parabolically haunched beam in Art. 10–3.

A more accurate variation of the summation process is to divide the member into segments as described above. The curved M/EI diagram can be represented by broken straight lines, and the areas and centroids of the resulting trapezoidal sections can be found and multiplied by the $\bar{m}$ values. However, such a solution adds greatly to the labor.

MODELS. Models may be prepared from plastic or a good grade of cardboard, and fixed-end moments, stiffnesses, and carry-over factors may be determined by measuring rotations, couples, and loads. Unless some suitable instrument is available, this method is impractical. Ondra[2] proposed making large three-dimensional models of the M/EI diagrams and weighing each end to find their "areas" and centroids.

10-2. Integration. Moment Distribution Constants.

Certain constants are necessary in order to work problems by moment distribution. They are stiffness, carry-over factor, and fixed-end moment. Stiffness is defined as the moment required to rotate one end of a beam through an angle of 1 radian while the other end is held fixed. To distinguish it from other moments, which are often abbreviated M, it is called K. It usually appears with subscripts such as K_{AB}, which indicates the stiffness at end A of the member AB. Carry-over factor is the ratio of the moment induced at a fixed end to the moment applied at the rotated end of a beam. It is designated C and usually appears with subscripts like C_{AB}, which means the carry-over factor from end A to end B. Fixed-end moments are the moments at the fixed ends caused by the loads on the beam. They are designated M or when necessary to distinguish them from other moments, FEM. They, too, appear with subscripts like M_{AB}, which indicate the moment at end A of member AB.

These constants cannot be determined by moment distribution, but virtual work is a practical method. Two purposes are served by developing these constants here: the solution of non-prismatic members by virtual work is illustrated by a practical type of problem, and the derivation of the constants in Appendix A is given in such a way that specific constants can be computed if they are not to be found in the Appendix. An incidental advantage is that this solution by virtual work invites comparison with the solution by moment area given in *Handbook of Rigid Frame Constants*.[3]

Example 10-2A. *Carry-over Factor.* One end of the unsymmetrical haunched beam shown in Fig. 10-1B is rotated through an angle of 1 radian while the other end remains fixed. Note that both true and virtual moments are shown in simple beam parts.

The carry-over factor can be found by writing an equation of virtual work (which is zero) for the rotation of point B. A unit couple is applied at point B. Then Eq. 8-2 becomes, for this special application,

$$1 \text{ \#-ft } \Delta\theta_B = 0 = \int_A^B \frac{Mm \, dx}{EI} \tag{10-1}$$

---

[2] Otakar Ondra, "Moment Distribution Constants from Models," *J. Structural Div. ASCE*, 82 (ST 5): 1058-1 to 1058-29, 1956.

[3] Portland Cement Association, 33 West Grand Ave., Chicago 10, Ill. To avoid confusion, the terminology, formulas, integrals, and—as a result—the explanations herein are either taken from or closely follow those of *Handbook of Rigid Frame Constants*. One exception is the sign of the carry-over factor, which is herein termed plus to correspond with the sign convention of Part IV.

Using the expression for moments shown in Figs. 10–1C and D, we have

$$M = M_A \frac{L - x}{L} - M_A C_{AB} \frac{x}{L}$$

$$m = 1 \text{ \#-ft } \frac{x}{L}$$

Noting that M_A, C_{AB}, L, and E are always[4] constants and so may be placed outside the integral sign, we have

$$0 = \frac{M_A}{EL^2} \int_A^B \frac{(L - x)x \, dx}{I_x} - \frac{M_A C_{AB}}{EL^2} \int_A^B \frac{x^2}{I_x} \, dx \qquad (10\text{--}2)$$

Solving for C_{AB} gives

$$C_{AB} = \frac{\displaystyle\int_A^B [(L - x)x/I_x] \, dx}{\displaystyle\int_A^B (x^2/I_x) \, dx} = \frac{\displaystyle\int_A^B (Lx/I_x) \, dx - \int_A^B (x^2/I_x) \, dx}{\displaystyle\int_A^B (x^2/I_x) \, dx} \qquad (10\text{--}3)$$

If the beam is prismatic, I_x (the subscripts denote I at any point located a variable distance x from A) is constant and can be placed outside the integral and canceled. The limits A and B can be replaced by the limits 0 and L, respectively, because the expressions are continuous from one end to the other, that is, from $x = 0$ to $x = L$. Thus, for prismatic beams, the carry-over factor becomes

$$C_{AB} = \frac{\displaystyle\int_0^L Lx \, dx - \int_0^L x^2 \, dx}{\displaystyle\int_0^L x^2 \, dx} = \frac{[Lx^2/2]_0^L - [x^3/3]_0^L}{[x^3/3]_0^L} = \frac{(L^3/2) - (L^3/3)}{L^3/3} = \frac{1}{2}$$

A more direct solution could have been obtained by substituting limits into Eq. 10–2, but this would have avoided the more general Eq. 10–3, which must be developed for non-prismatic members. Equation 10–3 is applicable to any beam whether prismatic or not, so it can be used to find the stiffness factor of any beam if an integrable expression can be written for I_x.

If the haunch is a parabola with its vertex at the shallow end of the haunch, the depth at any point x distance from A is

$$h_x = h_c + r_A h_c \left(\frac{a_A L - x}{a_A L}\right)^2 = h_c \left[1 + r_A \left(1 - \frac{x}{a_A L}\right)^2\right]$$

[4] Rarely, E may not be a constant. Then it too must be placed under the integral.

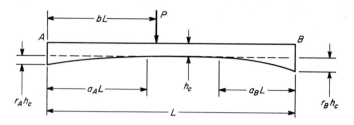

A. Beam and Dimensions

B. Free Body of Beam

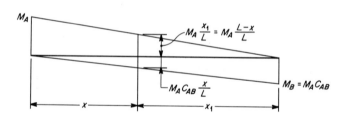

C. Moment Diagrams in Simple Beam Parts

Fig. 10–1. Stiffness and

and since the moment of inertia is proportional to the cube of the depth, I_x in terms of I_c (the moment of inertia for which the depth is h_c) is, between points A and C,

$$I_x = I_c\left(\frac{h_x}{h_c}\right)^3 = I_c\left[1 + r_A\left(1 - \frac{x}{a_A L}\right)^2\right]^3$$

Therefore

$$\int_A^B \frac{Lx}{I_x}\,dx = \frac{L}{I_c}\int_0^{a_A L} \frac{x\,dx}{\{1 + r_A[1 - (x/a_A L)]^2\}^3} + \frac{L}{I_c}\int_{a_A L}^{(1-a_B)L} x\,dx$$

$$+ \frac{L}{I_c}\int_{a_B L}^{2a_B L} \frac{(1 - 2a_B)(L + x)\,dx}{\{1 + r_B[1 - (x/a_B L)]^2\}^3} \qquad (10\text{–}4)$$

The last term may require explanation. The formula for moment of inertia I_x must be expressed in terms of x measured from point A because the real

and virtual moments are so expressed. Consider the mirror image of the right
haunch, as shown by the dotted lines in Fig. 10–2. Its moment of inertia can
be expressed in the same manner as that of the left haunch,

$$I_x = I_c \left[1 + r_B \left(1 - \frac{x'}{a_B L} \right)^2 \right]^3$$

where x' is measured from the left end of this haunch just as x is measured
from the left end of the left haunch, and x can be expressed as

$$x = (L - 2a_B L) + x' = (1 - 2a_B)L + x'$$

Of course dx can be expressed as dx'. As for limits, the real haunch extends
from $x' = a_B L$ to $x' = 2a_B L$, which are the lower and upper limits, respec-

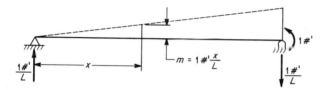

D. Virtual Couple and Moment Diagram for Rotation at B

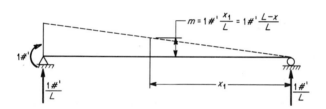

E. Virtual Couple and Moment Diagram for Rotation at A

carry-over factor.

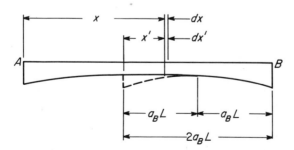

Fig. 10–2. Mathematical expression for right haunch.

tively. The last term then becomes

$$\int_{x=L-a_BL}^{x=L} \frac{Lx\,dx}{I_x} = \frac{L}{I_c}\int_{x'=a_BL}^{x'=2a_BL} \frac{[(1-2a_B)L+x']\,dx'}{\{1+r_B[1-(x'/a_BL)]^2\}^3}$$

which becomes, on dropping the primes (converting x' to x), the last term of Eq. 10–4. Thus we have

$$\int_A^B \frac{x^2\,dx}{I_x} = \frac{1}{I_c}\int_0^{a_AL} \frac{x^2\,dx}{\{1+r_A[1-(x/a_AL)]^2\}^3} + \frac{1}{I_c}\int_{a_BL}^{(1-a_B)L} x^2\,dx$$

$$+ \frac{1}{I_c}\int_{a_BL}^{2a_BL} \frac{[(1-2a_B)L+x]^2\,dx}{\{1+r_B[1-(x/a_BL)]^2\}^3} \qquad (10–5)$$

Numerical values for the integrals in Eq. 10–3 may be found by substituting the dimension ratios $(a_A, r_A, a_B,$ and $r_B)$ into the Evaluated Integrals $2a, 2b, 1a,$ and $2c$ in Table 58 of Appendix A. Assume, for example that $a_A = 0.4$, $r_A = 0.6$, $a_B = 0.3$, and $r_B = 1.0$; then we have

$$L\int_A^B \frac{x\,dx}{I_x} = [0.06355 + 0.16500 + 0.06534 + 0.06588]\frac{L^3}{I_c} = 0.35977\frac{L^3}{I_c}$$

$$\int_A^B \frac{x^2\,dx}{I_x} = [0.01843 + 0.09300 + 0.02614 + 0.05270 + 0.02748]\frac{L^3}{I_c}$$

$$= 0.21775\frac{L^3}{I_c}$$

Therefore, from Eq. 10–3, we have

$$C_{AB} = \frac{0.35977 - 0.21775}{0.21775} = 0.652$$

which is the value in Table 9, line 13 of Appendix A. The value of C_{BA} can be found in a similar manner by substituting x_1 for x in Eqs. 10–3, 10–4, and 10–5, integrating from B to A, and noticing that r_B must be used between B and a_BL and r_A between a_AL and A. Using the same dimension ratios as before, we find

$$C_{BA} = \frac{0.36402 - 0.22200}{0.22200} = 0.640$$

Example 10–2B. *Stiffness Factor.* The stiffness factor can be found from a virtual work equation for the rotation at point A which is 1 radian (unity). Thus, we have

$$1\ \#\text{-ft}\ \Delta\theta_A = 1\ \#\text{-ft}\times 1 = \int_A^B \frac{Mm\,dx}{EI}$$

From Figs. 10–1C and E, we have

$$M = M_A\frac{x_1}{L} - M_A C_{AB}\frac{x}{L} = M_A\frac{x_1}{L} - M_A C_{AB}\frac{L-x_1}{L}$$

$$m = 1\ \#\text{-ft}\frac{x_1}{L}$$

$$1 = \frac{M_A}{EL^2}\int_B^A \frac{x_1^2\,dx_1}{I_x} - \frac{M_A C_{AB}}{EL^2}\int_B^A \frac{(L-x_1)x_1}{I_x}\,dx_1 \qquad (10–6)$$

In this form the equation is advantageous because the integral terms correspond to those of Eq. 10–2. The moment M_A is called K_A, as explained previously, to distinguish the stiffness from other moments. As will be seen,

$$K_A = \frac{k_A EI}{L} \tag{10-7}$$

in which k_A is a dimensionless constant. Solving Eq. 10–6 for M_A, we have

$$M_A = K_A = \frac{k_A EI}{L} = \frac{EL^2}{\int_B^A (x_1^2/I_x)\,dx_1 - C_{AB}\int_B^A [(L-x_1)x_1/I_x]\,dx_1} \tag{10-8}$$

Likewise, if the beam is fixed at A and rotated 1 radian at B, we have

$$M_B = K_B = \frac{k_B EI}{L} = \frac{EL^2}{\int_A^B (x^2/I_x)\,dx - C_{BA}\int_A^B [(L-x)x/I_x]\,dx} \tag{10-9}$$

If the beam is prismatic, the moment of inertia is a constant, C_{AB} is 1/2 as previously found, and Eq. 10–8 becomes

$$K_A = \frac{IEL^2}{\int_0^L x_1^2\,dx_1 - \frac{1}{2}\int_0^L (Lx_1 - x_1^2)\,dx_1} = \frac{IEL^2}{L^3/3 - \frac{1}{2}[(L^3/2)-(L^3/3)]} = \frac{4EI}{L}$$

From Eq. 10–7,

$$k_A = \frac{LK_A}{EI} = 4$$

The stiffness factors for the haunched beam with the dimension ratios used before ($a_A = 0.4$, $r_A = 0.6$, $a_B = 0.3$, and $r_B = 1.0$) can be computed by using the numerical values for the integrals found for the carry-over factors:

$$k_A = \frac{L^3}{I_c[0.22200 - 0.652(0.36402 - 0.22200)](L^3/I_c)} = 7.73$$

$$k_B = \frac{L}{I_c[0.21775 - 0.640(0.35977 - 0.21775)](L^3/I_c)} = 7.88$$

and these are the stiffness factors in Table 9, line 13, of Appendix A.

Example 10–2C. *Fixed-End Moments. Uniform Load.* General expressions for fixed-end moments due to a uniform load can be developed by writing virtual work equations for the end slopes of the beam which are zero by definition. According to the moment diagrams shown in simple beam parts in Fig. 10–3A, the real moments for the uniformly loaded beam can be written as

$$M = -M_A \frac{x_1}{L} - M_B \frac{x}{L} + \left(\frac{wLx}{2} - \frac{wx^2}{2}\right)$$

$$= -M_A \frac{(L-x)}{L} - \frac{M_B x}{L} + \frac{wx}{2}(L-x)$$

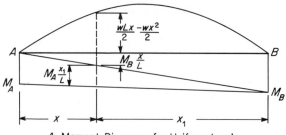

A. Moment Diagrams for Uniform Load

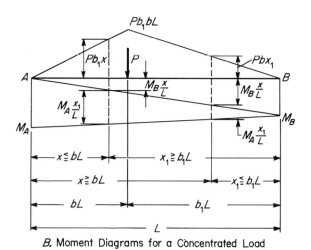

B. Moment Diagrams for a Concentrated Load

Fig. 10–3. Fixed-end moments.

And from Fig. 10–1D, the virtual moment is

$$m = 1 \text{ \#-ft} \frac{x}{L}$$

$$1 \text{ \#-ft } \Delta\theta_B = 0 = \int_A^B \frac{Mm \, dx}{EI}$$

$$= 1 \text{ \#-ft} \int_A^B \left[-\frac{M_A(L-x)x}{L^2 EI_x} - \frac{M_B x^2}{L^2 EI_x} + \frac{wx^2(L-x)}{2LEI_x} \right] dx$$

But L and E are constant and may be placed outside the integral. Multiplying each term by $-EL^2$ reduces the above equation to

$$0 = M_A \int_A^B \frac{(L-x)x \, dx}{I_x} + M_B \int_A^B \frac{x^2 \, dx}{I_x} - \frac{wL}{2} \int_A^B \frac{(L-x)x^2 \, dx}{I_x} \qquad (10\text{-}10)$$

If the beam is prismatic, I_x is a constant and may be canceled. Also M_A equals M_B by symmetry. Equation 10–10 then becomes

$$0 = M_A \int_0^L (Lx - x^2)\, dx + M_B \int_0^L x^2\, dx - \frac{wL}{2} \int_0^L (Lx^2 - x^3)\, dx$$

from which

$$M_A = M_B = \frac{wL^2}{12}$$

If the beam is not prismatic, another equation must be written for the slope at B, which also is zero. Substituting x_1 for x and M_A for M_B in Eq. 10–10, gives

$$0 = M_A \int_B^A \frac{x_1^2\, dx_1}{I_x} + M_D \int_B^A \frac{(L - x_1)x_1\, dx_1}{I_x} - \frac{wL}{2} \int_B^A \frac{(L - x_1)x_1^2\, dx_1}{I_x}$$

$$(10\text{--}11)$$

The first and second terms of the above two equations were evaluated in the solution for the carry-over factors. The third term (of Eq. 10–10) can be expanded:

$$\frac{wL}{2} \int_A^B \frac{(L - x)x^2\, dx}{I_x} = \frac{wL}{2} \left[L \int_A^B \frac{x^2\, dx}{I_x} - \int_A^B \frac{x^3\, dx}{I_x} \right]$$

The first term in the brackets has also been evaluated, but the last term has not. It can be integrated in parts as follows:

$$\int_A^B \frac{x^3\, dx}{I_x} = \frac{1}{I_c} \int_0^{a_A L} \frac{x^3\, dx}{\{1 + r_A[1 - (x/a_A L)]^2\}^3} + \frac{1}{I_c} \int_{a_A L}^{1 - a_B L} x^3\, dx$$

$$+ \frac{1}{I_c} \int_{a_B L}^{2a_B L} \frac{[(1 - 2a_B L)L + x]^3\, dx}{\{1 + r_B[1 - (x/a_B L)]^2\}^3} \quad (10\text{--}12)$$

Numerical values for the integrals in Eq. 10–12 may be found by substituting the proper dimension ratios in Evaluated Integrals 4a, 4b, 1a, 2 of Table 58 of Appendix A. Using the same dimension ratios as before,

$$\int_A^B \frac{x^3\, dx}{I_x} = [0.00578 + 0.05363 + 0.064 \times 0.16335$$

$$+ 0.48 \times 0.06588 + 1.2 \times 0.02748 + 0.01186] \frac{L^4}{I_c} = 0.14632 \frac{L^4}{I_c}$$

Substituting this value along with others previously obtained into Eq. 10–10, we have

$$0 = 0.14202 M_A + 0.21775 M_B - (0.21775 - 0.14632) \frac{wL^2}{2I_c}$$

and Eq. 10–11 becomes, in like manner,

$$0 = 0.22200 M_A + 0.14202 M_B - (0.22200 - 0.15141) \frac{wL^2}{2I_c}$$

Solving these two equations simultaneously yields

$$M_A = 0.0928 wL^2$$

$$M_B = 0.1035 wL^2$$

These are the same coefficients to be found in Table 9, line 13, of Appendix A.

Example 10–2D. Fixed-End Moments. Concentrated Load. The procedure for determining fixed-end moments due to concentrated load is similar to that for uniform loads, but the limits for the various parts depend upon the position of the load, that is, whether or not it is located within one of the haunches. In accordance with the simple beam parts shown in Fig. 10–3B, the real moments for the slope at B can be written as:

From A to bL

$$M = -M_A \frac{x_1}{L} - M_B \frac{x}{L} + Pb_1 x$$

From bL to B

$$M = -M_A \frac{x_1}{L} - M_B \frac{x}{L} + Pbx_1$$

The virtual moment from A to B is, from Fig. 10–3D,

$$m = 1 \text{ \#-ft} \frac{x}{L}$$

and after multiplication by $-EL^2$, the virtual work equation for slope at B is

$$-EL^2 \text{ \#-ft } \Delta\theta_B = 0 = -L^2 \int_A^B \frac{Mm \, dx}{I} = M_A \int_A^B \frac{(L-x)x \, dx}{I_x}$$

$$+ M_B \int_A^B \frac{x^2 \, dx}{I_x} - Pb_1 L \int_A^{bL} \frac{x^2 \, dx}{I_x} - PbL \int_{bL}^B \frac{(L-x)x \, dx}{I_x} \quad (10\text{--}13)$$

Likewise, the virtual work equation for the slope at A can be written as

$$0 = M_A \int_B^A \frac{x_1^2 \, dx_1}{I_x} + M_B \int_B^A \frac{(L-x_1)x_1 \, dx_1}{I_x}$$

$$- PbL \int_B^{b_1 L} \frac{x_1^2 \, dx_1}{I_x} - Pb_1 L \int_{b_1 L}^A \frac{(L-x_1)x_1 \, dx_1}{I_x} \quad (10\text{--}14)$$

The first two terms of Eqs. 10–13 and 10–14 occur also in Eqs. 10–10 and 10–11, and their evaluation has been illustrated. The third and fourth terms must be integrated in parts, depending upon the location of the load with respect to the haunches. For example when b is less than a_A, the fourth term in Eq. 10–13 must be integrated in three parts by noting the identity

$$PbL \int_{bL}^{B} \frac{(L - x)x \, dx}{I_x} = PbL \int_{B}^{b_1 L} \frac{(L - x_1)x_1 \, dx_1}{I_x}$$

$$= PbL \left[L \int_{0}^{a_B L} \frac{x_1 \, dx_1}{I_x} + L \int_{a_B L}^{(1-a_A)L} \frac{x_1 \, dx_1}{I_x} \right.$$

$$+ L \int_{a_A L}^{(2a_A - b)L} \frac{[(1 - 2a_A)L + x_1] \, dx_1}{I_x} - \int_{0}^{a_B L} \frac{x_1{}^2 \, dx_1}{I_x}$$

$$\left. - \int_{a_B L}^{(1-a_A)L} \frac{x_1{}^2 \, dx_1}{I_x} - \int_{a_A L}^{(2a_A - b)L} \frac{[(1 - 2a_A)L + x_1]^2 \, dx_1}{I_x} \right] \qquad (10\text{–}15)$$

And similarly, the third term of Eq. 10–14 becomes

$$PbL \int_{B}^{b_1 L} \frac{x_1{}^2 \, dx_1}{I_x} = PbL \left[\int_{0}^{a_B L} \frac{x_1{}^2 \, dx_1}{I_x} + \int_{a_B L}^{(1-a_A)L} \frac{x_1{}^2 \, dx_1}{I_x} \right.$$

$$\left. + \int_{a_A L}^{(2a_A - b)L} \frac{[(1 - 2a_A)L + x_1]^2 \, dx_1}{I_x} \right] \qquad (10\text{–}16)$$

The fourth term of Eq. 10–14 becomes

$$Pb_1 L \int_{b_1 L}^{A} \frac{(L - x_1)x_1 \, dx_1}{I_x} = Pb_1 L \int_{A}^{bL} \frac{(L - x)x \, dx}{I_x}$$

$$= Pb_1 L \left[L \int_{0}^{bL} \frac{x \, dx}{I_x} - \int_{0}^{bL} \frac{x^2 \, dx}{I_x} \right] \qquad (10\text{–}17)$$

The last term and the fourth from the last term in Eq. 10–15 and the last term in Eq. 10–16 are evaluated most conveniently by substituting the numerical values of the limits directly into Integrals 1, 2, and 3 in Table 58, Appendix A, so no evaluated integrals are included in that table for limits $a_A L$ to $(2a_A - b)L$. The other terms in Eqs. 10–15 and 10–16 are evaluated by substituting Integrals 2a, 2b, 3a, and 3b, and the two terms in Eq. 10–17 are evaluated by means of Integrals 2 and 3. Using the same dimension ratios as before and placing the load P at $0.3L$ ($b = 0.3$) from point A, Eqs. 10–13 and 10–14 become

$$0 = 0.21775 M_B + 0.14202 M_A - 0.00454 PL - 0.03564 PL$$

$$0 = 0.14202 M_B - 0.22200 M_A - 0.03327 PL + 0.01627 PL$$

from which

$$M_A = 0.1802 PL$$

$$M_B = 0.0699 PL$$

These values are found in Table 9 of Appendix A.

10–3. Summation. Moment Distribution Constants. As mentioned in Art. 10–1, the summation method usually provides the most practical solution for beams, arches, and rings in which the moment of inertia varies. The integral form of the virtual work equation

$$U\Delta = \int_0^L \frac{Mm\,dx}{EI} \tag{8–1}$$

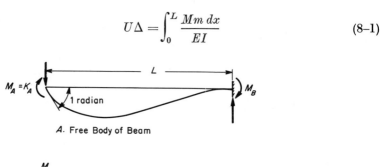

A. Free Body of Beam

B. True Moment Diagrams

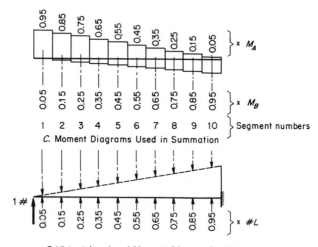

C. Moment Diagrams Used in Summation

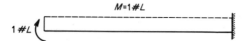

D. Virtual Load and Moment Diagram for Deflection

E. Virtual Couple and Moment Diagram for Rotation

Fig. 10–4. Stiffness and carry-over factor for prismatic beam. Summation process.

is expressed as

$$U\Delta = \sum m\,\frac{M\,\Delta L}{EI} \qquad\qquad (10\text{--}18)$$

In like manner, Eq. 8–2,

$$U\,\Delta\theta = \int_0^L \frac{Mm\,dx}{EI} \qquad\qquad (8\text{--}2)$$

can be expressed as

$$U\,\Delta\theta = \sum m\,\frac{M\,\Delta L}{EI} \qquad\qquad (10\text{--}19)$$

in which dx becomes ΔL (a finite length or segment of the structure), and m, M, E, and I are the respective values of these quantities at the middle of each of the segments into which the structure is divided. To provide comparison with exact values, the summation method will be used to compute the stiffness and the carry-over factor for a prismatic beam and again for a haunched beam.

Example 10–3A. *Carry-over Factor.* Figure 10–4A shows a prismatic beam rotated at one end through an angle of 1 radian. The moment required to do this is the stiffness. The moment induced at the other end of the beam equals the stiffness times the carry-over factor. True moment diagrams are pictured in Fig. 10–4B, whereas the moment diagrams as actually used in the summation process are shown in Fig. 10–4C. The carry-over factor is computed first by writing an expression for the deflection, which is zero at point A. This is best done in tabular form (Table 10–2).

TABLE 10–2

Carry-over Factor

$$1\,\#\,\Delta Y_A = 0 = \sum m\,\frac{M\,\Delta L}{EI} \qquad (\text{Eq. 10--18})$$

Segment	M		$(M\,\Delta L)/EI$		m	$(m\,M\,\Delta L)/EI$	
	M_A	M_B	M_A	M_B		M_A	M_B
1	0.95	0.05	$0.095L/EI$	$0.005L/EI$	$0.05\,\#\,L$	$0.00475\,\#\,L^2/EI$	$-0.00025\,\#\,L^2/EI$
2	0.85	0.15	$0.085L/EI$	$0.015L/EI$	$0.15\,\#\,L$	$0.01275\,\#\,L^2/EI$	$-0.00225\,\#\,L^2/EI$
3	0.75	0.25	$0.075L/EI$	$0.025L/EI$	$0.25\,\#\,L$	$0.01875\,\#\,L^2/EI$	$-0.00625\,\#\,L^2/EI$
4	0.65	0.35	$0.065L/EI$	$0.035L/EI$	$0.35\,\#\,L$	$0.02275\,\#\,L^2/EI$	$-0.01225\,\#\,L^2/EI$
5	0.55	0.45	$0.055L/EI$	$0.045L/EI$	$0.45\,\#\,L$	$0.02475\,\#\,L^2/EI$	$-0.02025\,\#\,L^2/EI$
6	0.45	0.55	$0.045L/EI$	$0.055L/EI$	$0.55\,\#\,L$	$0.02475\,\#\,L^2/EI$	$-0.03025\,\#\,L^2/EI$
7	0.35	0.65	$0.035L/EI$	$0.065L/EI$	$0.65\,\#\,L$	$0.02275\,\#\,L^2/EI$	$-0.04225\,\#\,L^2/EI$
8	0.25	0.75	$0.025L/EI$	$0.075L/EI$	$0.75\,\#\,L$	$0.01875\,\#\,L^2/EI$	$-0.05625\,\#\,L^2/EI$
9	0.15	0.85	$0.015L/EI$	$0.085L/EI$	$0.85\,\#\,L$	$0.01275\,\#\,L^2/EI$	$-0.07225\,\#\,L^2/EI$
10	0.05	0.95	$0.005L/EI$	$0.095L/EI$	$0.95\,\#\,L$	$0.00475\,\#\,L^2/EI$	$-0.09025\,\#\,L^2/EI$
				Summation		$0.16750\,\#\,L^2/EI$	$-0.33250\,\#\,L^2/EI$

Thus, from Table 10–2, we have

$$0 = \frac{0.16750 M_A\,\#\,L^2}{EI} - \frac{0.33250 M_B\,\#\,L^2}{EI}$$

from which the carry-over factor is

$$C_{AB} = \frac{M_B}{M_A} = 0.504$$

The exact value is one-half, so the summation process here results in an error of only about 1 percent.

Example 10–3*B*. *Stiffness.* To find the stiffness, write an expression for the rotation, which is unity at point *A*. The virtual moment diagram is shown in Fig. 10–4*E*, and the values of M_A and M_B are taken from Table 10–2. The solution is given in Table 10–3.

TABLE 10–3

Stiffness

$$1 \# L \, \Delta\theta_A = 1 \# L = \Sigma m \frac{M \, \Delta L}{EI} \qquad \text{(Eq. 10–19)}$$

Segment	(M ΔL)/EI		m	(mM ΔL)/EI	
	M_A	M_B		M_A	M_B
1	0.095L/EI	0.005L/EI	1 # L	0.095 # L²/EI	−0.005 # L²/EI
2	0.085L/EI	0.015L/EI	1 # L	0.085 # L²/EI	−0.015 # L²/EI
3	0.075L/EI	0.025L/EI	1 # L	0.075 # L²/EI	−0.025 # L²/EI
4	0.065L/EI	0.035L/EI	1 # L	0.065 # L²/EI	−0.035 # L²/EI
5	0.055L/EI	0.045L/EI	1 # L	0.055 # L²/EI	−0.045 # L²/EI
6	0.045L/EI	0.055L/EI	1 # L	0.045 # L²/EI	−0.055 # L²/EI
7	0.035L/EI	0.065L/EI	1 # L	0.035 # L²/EI	−0.065 # L²/EI
8	0.025L/EI	0.075L/EI	1 # L	0.025 # L²/EI	−0.075 # L²/EI
9	0.015L/EI	0.085L/EI	1 # L	0.015 # L²/EI	−0.085 # L²/EI
10	0.005L/EI	0.095L/EI	1 # L	0.005 # L²/EI	−0.095 # L²/EI
			Summation	0.500 # L²/EI	−0.500 # L²/EI

From Table 10–3 we have

$$1 \# L = \frac{0.500 M_A \# L^2}{EI} - \frac{0.500 M_B \# L^2}{EI}$$

$$1 = \frac{0.500 M_A L}{EI} - \frac{0.500(0.504 M_A)L}{EI}$$

$$M_A = K_A = \frac{4.03 EI}{L}$$

The exact value is $4EI/L$, so again the error is approximately 1 percent.

Examination of Table 10–3 shows the fifth and sixth columns to be numerically similar to the second and third columns because *m* is unity for each segment. Therefore Table 10–3 could have been dispensed with and columns 4 and 5 of Table 10–2 could have been totaled instead with the same results, provided the proper signs and the proper factor $\# L^2/EI$ were supplied to the totals. This will be done in the example of the haunched beam that follows.

Example 10–3C. *Stiffness and Carry-over Factor for Haunched Beam.* The beam is shown in Fig. 10–5A. Since the haunches are parabolic, the depth at any point can be computed as

$$d = \left(\frac{x}{aL}\right)^2 rh_c$$

where x is the distance from the vertex of the haunch and the other symbols correspond to those in Fig. 10–1A. The true moment diagrams are shown in Fig. 10–5C. The beam is divided into ten segments, and the moment at the

TABLE 10–4

Stiffness and Carry-over Factor

$$1 \# \Delta Y_A = 0 = \Sigma \, m \, \frac{M \, \Delta L}{EI} \qquad \text{(Eq. 10–18)}$$

$$1 \# L \, \Delta \theta_A = 1 \# L = \Sigma \, m \, \frac{M \, \Delta L}{EI} \qquad \text{(Eq. 10–19)}$$

| Segment | $(M \, \Delta L)/EI$ | | m | $(mM \, \Delta L)/EI$ | |
	M_A	M_B		M_A	M_B
1	$0.03056L/EI$	$0.00161L/EI$	$0.05 \# L$	$+0.00153 \# L^2/EI$	$-0.00008 \# L^2/EI$
2	$0.04519L/EI$	$0.00797L/EI$	$0.15 \# L$	$+0.00678 \# L^2/EI$	$-0.00120 \# L^2/EI$
3	$0.05881L/EI$	$0.01960L/EI$	$0.25 \# L$	$+0.01470 \# L^2/EI$	$-0.00490 \# L^2/EI$
4	$0.06320L/EI$	$0.03403L/EI$	$0.35 \# L$	$+0.02212 \# L^2/EI$	$-0.01191 \# L^2/EI$
5	$0.05500L/EI$	$0.04500L/EI$	$0.45 \# L$	$+0.02475 \# L^2/EI$	$-0.02025 \# L^2/EI$
6	$0.04500L/EI$	$0.05500L/EI$	$0.55 \# L$	$+0.02475 \# L^2/EI$	$-0.03025 \# L^2/EI$
7	$0.03500L/EI$	$0.06500L/EI$	$0.65 \# L$	$+0.02275 \# L^2/EI$	$-0.04225 \# L^2/EI$
8	$0.02303L/EI$	$0.06908L/EI$	$0.75 \# L$	$+0.01727 \# L^2/EI$	$-0.05181 \# L^2/EI$
9	$0.00768L/EI$	$0.04353L/EI$	$0.85 \# L$	$+0.00653 \# L^2/EI$	$-0.03700 \# L^2/EI$
10	$0.00102L/EI$	$0.01953L/EI$	$0.95 \# L$	$+0.00097 \# L^2/EI$	$-0.01855 \# L^2/EI$
Σ	$0.36449L/EI$	$0.36035L/EI$		$+0.14215 \# L^2/EI$	$-0.21820 \# L^2/EI$

middle of each segment is divided by I to produce the M/I diagrams shown in Fig. 10–5D. If E were also variable, it would be necessary to divide M by E also. The calculations, shown in Table 10–4, follow the same course as in the previous example. First the carry-over factor is computed. Then, with the known relation between M_A and M_B, the stiffness can be found. The values of m can be obtained from Figs. 10–4D and E or from Tables 10–2 and 10–3.

From Table 10–4 we have

$$0 = + \frac{0.14215 M_A \# L^2}{EI} - \frac{0.21820 M_B \# L^2}{EI}$$

$$C_{AB} = \frac{M_B}{M_A} = \frac{0.14215}{0.21820} = 0.65147$$

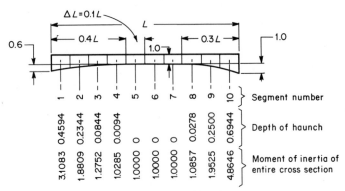

A. Beam, Dimensions, and Moments of Inertia

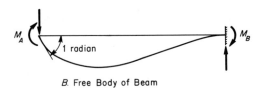

B. Free Body of Beam

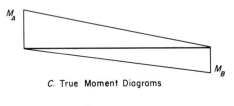

C. True Moment Diagrams

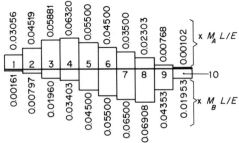

D. Values of $M \Delta L / EI$

Fig. 10-5. Stiffness and carry-over factor for haunched beam.
Summation process.

Note that every value of m in Fig. 10–4E is unity times $\# L$. Therefore the sum of columns two and three in Table 10–4 is $mM \, \Delta L/EI$ when multiplied by $\# L$. Thus we have

$$1 \# L = \frac{0.36449 M_A \# L^2}{EI} - \frac{0.36025 M_B \# L^2}{EI}$$

$$1 = \frac{0.36449 M_A L}{EI} - \frac{0.36025(0.65147 M_A)L}{EI}$$

$$M_A = K_A = \frac{7.7043 EI}{L}$$

from which

$$k_A = 7.70$$

These values of C_{AB} and k_A (0.651 and 7.70 respectively) compare closely with those obtained by integration (0.652 and 7.73 respectively). So the summation process is not only quicker than the integration process,[5] but it is also accurate enough for most practical purposes. Of course, fixed-end moments can also be obtained by the same process.

10–4. Arches, Rings, and Complex Structures. Virtual work, like moment area, is also an ideal method for the solution of arches and rings whether they are variable in section or not. Summation is nearly always used in preference to integration, which (particularly for non-prismatic arches or rings) is usually very complicated, as might be imagined from the discussion in Art. 10–2.

The procedure is very similar to that for haunched beams (as covered in Art. 10–3). The arch or ring is divided into a number of segments and is cut back to a statically determinate structure. To obtain suitable accuracy, arches must be divided into 20 to 30 segments and rings into 32 to 48 segments. Real and virtual loads are applied just as they are for rigid frames (Arts. 9–1 through 9–3). So all the principles and most of the procedures have already been covered in this Part.

Arches, and sometimes rings, are subject to stresses caused by temperature and axial strains due to stress. Although it is possible to solve for these effects simultaneously, this is rarely done. Sufficient accuracy can be obtained by solving for each of them independently and superimposing them upon the effects due to bending. These effects are discussed in Art. 6–6. All that is said about moment area in Art. 6–6 applies equally to virtual work, and any moment area equation can be supplanted by a corresponding virtual work equation.[6]

---

[5] Except for the preparation of extensive tables.

[6] It is not necessary to read the preceding part of Part II in order to understand Art. 6–6.

Complex frames such as double sewer sections, multi-story frames and other structures statically indeterminate to many degrees are not well suited to solutions by virtual work because of the many simultaneous equations required. Other methods, such as moment distribution, are superior where they can be used. Moment distribution can be used for the solution of multiple arches.[7,8] The use of models also is practical.

[7] L. C. Maugh, *Statically Indeterminate Structures* (New York: John Wiley & Sons, Inc., 1946), pp. 212–255.

[8] James Michalos, *Theory of Statically Indeterminate Structures* (New York: The Ronald Press Co., 1958), pp. 234–252.

11

SHEAR AND COMPOSITE ACTION

11-1. Shear. Basic Theory. To develop a basic equation for deflection due to shear, consider any general structure to be represented by Fig. 11–1A. Two unyielding reactions are shown, but any number could be shown without changing the proof, and the proof can be extended to include structures on

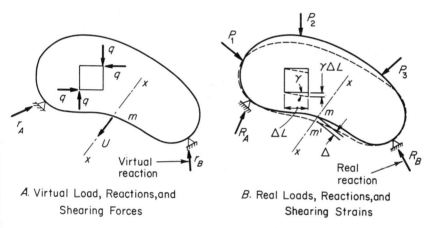

A. Virtual Load, Reactions, and
Shearing Forces

B. Real Loads, Reactions, and
Shearing Strains

Fig. 11–1. Deflection due to shear.

elastic supports.[1] It is necessary only that the structure be stable and be in equilibrium. The structure is composed of an infinite number of elements, one of which, greatly enlarged, is shown in Fig. 11–1A. The element is strained in shear by the loads P_1, P_2, and P_3 in Fig. 11–1B. If the length of the element is ΔL, and the shearing strain is defined as the angle γ, the shearing detrusion is $\gamma \, \Delta L$, provided that the strain is small.

In general, shearing strains would also be accompanied by normal strains, that is, by changes in the length and width of the elements. But since it is more convenient to deal separately with the two kinds of strains, only shearing strains are considered herein. If normal strains do occur, they can be included as shown in Art. 11–6 on composite structures.

[1] By making the elastic supports a part of the structure. The elastic supports in turn are supported by unyielding reactions.

VIRTUAL LOAD. Consider the real loads to be removed so that all the elements are unstrained. To find the deflection at point m caused by shear, the virtual load U is applied at point m acting in the direction of the desired component of deflection. The internal virtual shearing stresses acting on the faces of the element are converted to virtual shearing *forces* q by multiplying the shearing stress acting on each face of the element by the corresponding area of the face. Each face of a square element is equally stressed in shear (if the element is small), so the four virtual shearing forces shown in Fig. 11–1A are equal.

REAL STRAINS. Now apply the real loads P_1, P_2, and P_3, and permit the real shearing strains to occur. The typical element distorts as shown[2] by the dashed lines. The horizontal virtual forces do no work because the relative deflection (parallel to the forces) is zero. The vertical virtual forces do suffer a relative (vertical) displacement which is $\gamma \, \Delta L$, and the virtual work done on the element is

$$w_{\text{internal}} = q\gamma \, \Delta L$$

and the total internal virtual work done on all the elements is

$$W_{\text{internal}} = \sum q\gamma \, \Delta L$$

The external virtual work is

$$W_{\text{external}} = U\Delta$$

and since external work must equal internal work, the basic equation of virtual work is

$$U\Delta = \sum q\gamma \, \Delta L \qquad (11\text{–}1)$$

This development parallels that of Art. 7–2 so closely that it could have been omitted entirely in favor of a statement to the effect that Eq. 11–1 follows from Eq. 7–1 by analogy.

Unlike normal strains which may be caused by temperature variations or some other phenomenon not associated with stress, shearing strains are always caused by shearing stresses. If the material is elastic, the equation

$$\gamma = \frac{S_s}{G}$$

---

[2] Actually the element may be translated and rotated. But the virtual work on the element due to both translation and rotation is zero. Work of translation is zero, because for each virtual force there is an equal opposite force. Therefore, from the discussion of relative deflections in Art. 7–2, the virtual forces measure only *relative* distortion, that is, change of size or shape but not rotation or change of location. Work of rotation is zero because the four virtual forces can be thought of as two equal and opposite couples and, if the element rotates, the work done by one couple is canceled by the opposing work done by the other. Therefore, if the element is rotated by the real forces, it can be rotated back into the position shown without causing more work and, therefore, without affecting the virtual work due to shear.

holds, where S_s is the shearing stress and G is the modulus of rigidity.[3] Substituting this expression in place of γ in Eq. 11–1, we have

$$U\Delta = \sum q \frac{S_s}{G} \Delta L \qquad (11\text{–}2)$$

ROTATION. Since work can also be expressed as the product of couple and rotation in radians, rotation due to shear can be determined as

$$U \, \Delta\theta = \sum q \frac{S_s}{G} \Delta L \qquad (11\text{–}3)$$

where U is an applied virtual couple and $\Delta\theta$ is rotation in radians.

RELATIVE DEFLECTIONS. Relative deflections due to shear are computed just as are relative deflections due to normal strains—by applying equal and opposite virtual loads to the structure at the points where relative deflection is wanted. Relative deflection is computed from Eq. 11–2, where the virtual shearing forces q are those due to the two virtual loads acting at once. The explanation is parallel to that of Art. 7–2.

RELATIVE ROTATIONS. Even relative rotation can be computed by applying equal and opposite virtual couples to the structure at the two points for which relative rotation is wanted. Again, the virtual forces q are those due to the two couples acting at once. Relative rotation is given directly by Eq. 11–3.

11–2. Equation of Shearing Deflection. Beams. Either of the basic equations for virtual work due to shear (Eq. 11–2 or 11–3) contains two terms q and S_s that ordinarily vary from point to point, making a direct solution impossible. But these variables can usually be expressed in terms of formulas which contain terms that can be evaluated. Shearing stress in beams is given by the formula[4]

$$S_s = \frac{VA\bar{y}}{Ib} \qquad (11\text{–}4)$$

in which S_s is shearing stress, V is total shear on the cross-section (ordinate of the shear diagram), A is the area of the portion of the cross-section on one side of a line through the point where shearing stress is wanted, $\bar{y}$ is the distance from the neutral axis to the centroid of the area A, I is the moment

---

[3] If the material is elastic, homogeneous, and isotropic, and if the strains are small, it can be shown by mechanics that the relation between modulus of rigidity and modulus of elasticity is

$$G = \frac{E}{2(1 + \mu)}$$

where μ is Poisson's ratio. Poisson's ratio is about 0.2 for concrete, 0.3 for steel, 0.33 for aluminum alloys, and 0.35 for many plastics.

[4] If the reader is not thoroughly conversant with the development of this formula, the remainder of this article will be difficult to understand.

of inertia, and b is the width or thickness of the section where the shearing stress is wanted.

GENERAL EQUATION. To convert Eq. 11-2 into a form suitable for beams, consider Fig. 11-2 and let

$$\Delta L = dx$$

$$q = \text{virtual stress} \times \text{area} = \frac{vA\bar{y}}{Ib}\, b\, dy$$

where v is the shearing stress at the cross-section due to the applied virtual load U. Then we have

$$q\frac{S_s}{G}\Delta L = \frac{vA\bar{y}}{Ib}\, b\, dy\, \frac{VA\bar{y}}{Ib}\frac{dx}{G} = \frac{vV(A\bar{y})^2}{I^2bG}\, dy\, dx$$

But $A\bar{y}$ itself is a variable and different at every level on the cross-section. Since A is the (parallel-ruled) area above the cross-hatched element in Fig. 11-2B and $\bar{y}$ is the distance to its centroid, $A\bar{y}$ can be expressed in terms of b and dy thus:

$$A\bar{y} = \int_y^c by\, dy$$

Substituting in the equation above, and summing the virtual work on all the elements in the cross-section by integrating from $-c$ to $+c$, and summing the virtual work on all cross-sections by integrating over the full length of the beam, we have

$$U\Delta = \int_0^L \int_{-c}^{+c} \frac{vV\left[\int_y^c by\, dy\right]^2}{I^2bG}\, dy\, dx \tag{11-5}$$

which cannot be simplified unless the shape of the cross-section is known.

RECTANGULAR BEAMS. If the cross-section is rectangular, b is a constant, the neutral axis is at the mid-height, and c equals $d/2$, so Eq. 11-5 can be evaluated step by step, thus:

$$\int_y^{c=d/2} by\, dy = b\left[\frac{y^2}{2}\right]_y^{d/2} = \frac{b}{2}\left(\frac{d^2}{4} - y^2\right)$$

$$\int_0^L \int_{-c}^{+c} \frac{V\left[\frac{b}{2}\left(\frac{d^2}{4} - y^2\right)\right]^2}{I^2bG}\, dy\, dx = 2\int_0^L \int_0^{d/2} \frac{vV}{I^2bG}\frac{b^2}{4}\left(\frac{d^4}{16} - \frac{2d^2y^2}{4} + y^4\right) dy\, dx$$

$$= \frac{2}{4}\int_0^L \frac{vVb}{I^2G}\left[\frac{d^4y}{16} - \frac{d^2y^3}{2\times3} + \frac{y^5}{5}\right]_0^{d/2} dx$$

$$= \frac{1}{120}\int_0^L \frac{vVbd^5}{I^2G}\, dx$$

If $bd^3/12$ is substituted for I, the last expression above becomes

$$\frac{1}{120}\int_0^L \frac{vVbd^5}{(b^2d^6/144)G}\,dx = \frac{6}{5}\int_0^L \frac{vV}{bdG}\,dx$$

and since bd equals the cross-sectional area, the virtual work equation for rectangular beams becomes

$$U\Delta = \frac{6}{5}\int_0^L \frac{vV\,dx}{AG} \tag{11-6}$$

in which v is the shear due to the virtual load U, V is the shear due to the real loads, A is the total cross-sectional area, and G is the modulus of rigidity.

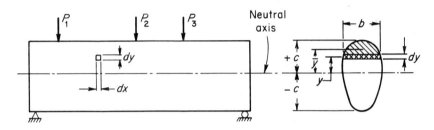

A. Beam and Loads   *B.* Cross-Section

Fig. 11-2. Shear in beams.

Equation 11-6 is not an exact equation. It is based on Eq. 11-4 which, in turn, is developed from the flexure formula ($s = My/I$), and so it is subject to all the errors and assumptions of the flexure formula, plus the assumption that concentrations of shearing stress can be ignored. Like the flexure formula, it is adequate for beams that are several times as long as their depths. Very short beams are subject to concentrations of load and such aberrations of stress that deflections can be accurately determined only by the mathematical theory of elasticity or by some experimental method.

OTHER SHAPES. For circular beams, Van den Broek[5] reports the coefficient of the integral in Eq. 11-6 to be $10/9$. The coefficient for flanged beams (where A is taken as the area of the web only) is very nearly unity, as will be discussed in Art. 11-4.

11-3. Deflection of a Rectangular Cantilever Beam. To compare deflection due to shear with that due to bending, consider a cantilever beam of length L supporting a uniform load of w per unit length. (This is the beam of Fig. 8-2.)

[5] J. A. Van den Broek, *Elastic Energy Theory* (2d ed.; New York: John Wiley & Sons, Inc., 1942), p. 172.

Let x be any distance from the free end. To find the maximum deflection which occurs at the free end, apply a virtual load of $U = 1 \#$ at the free end. Then the virtual shear at any point is

$$v = U = 1 \#$$

and the real shear at any point x from the free end is

$$V = wx$$

Substituting in Eq. 11–6, we have

$$1 \# \, \Delta Y_A = \frac{6}{5} \int_0^L \frac{1 \# \, wx}{AG} \, dx = \frac{6 \#}{5AG} \left[\frac{wx^2}{2} \right]_0^L$$

and

$$\Delta Y_A = \frac{3}{5} \frac{wL^2}{AG}$$

From Art. 8–2 the deflection due to bending is

$$\Delta Y_A = \frac{wL^4}{8EI}$$

Example 11–3. If the beam were of steel 2 in. wide, 6 in. deep, and 24 in. long, the deflection due to shear would be

$$\Delta Y_A = \frac{3}{5} \frac{wL^2}{AG} = \frac{3}{5} \frac{w(24)^2}{12 \times 11,000,000} = 2.62 \times 10^{-6} w$$

which is only 6.6 percent of the deflection due to bending,

$$\Delta Y_A = \frac{wL^4}{8EI} = \frac{w(24)^4}{8 \times 29,000,000 \times 36} = 3.97 \times 10^{-5} w$$

RELATION BETWEEN SHEAR AND BENDING. To find the length for which deflection for shear and bending is equal, equate the deflections, thus:

$$\frac{3wL^2}{5AG} = \frac{wL^4}{8EI}$$

$$L = \sqrt{\frac{24EI}{5AG}} = 0.894d\sqrt{1 + \mu}$$

So, at a span approximately equal to the depth, half the deflection of a cantilever beam is caused by shear and the other half by bending. At greater span lengths, the deflection due to shear decreases rapidly in comparison to that due to bending.

Since the span lengths of simple beams are rarely less than ten times the depth, and for cantilevers rarely less than four times the depth, the deflection due to shear is of minor importance. Even for short beams an approximate expression for deflection due to shear would be adequate.

Parcel and Moorman[6] report that, for beams simply supported at both ends and supporting a uniform load, the ratio of deflection due to shear (Δ_v) to deflection due to bending (Δ_b) is

$$\frac{\Delta_v}{\Delta_b} = C\left(\frac{d}{L}\right)^2$$

where C, tabulated for I-beams and wide-flanged beams, varies from 6.5 to 20, the mean value being about 11. For rectangular beams, C is 1.9. For central concentrated loads C is 1.25 times the values above. Thus for a span-depth ratio of 10, the deflection due to shear would usually be about 11 percent (and could be as high as 25 percent) of the deflection due to bending. If the deflection must be known accurately, shear must not be ignored but, on the other hand, neither can other factors be ignored—such as flooring, which usually adds considerably to the stiffness of a beam and is very often of more significance than the shear.

Even though the proportion of the deflection due to shear may be high, neglecting shear in solving indeterminate reactions results in errors that are quite small,[7] so it is nearly always safe to neglect shear in the computation of redundants.

11–4. Approximate Shearing Deflection. Beams. The true distribution of shearing stress[8] in rectangular beams is parabolic, as is shown in

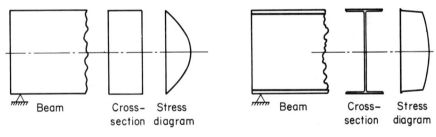

Beam   Cross- Stress   Beam   Cross- Stress
        section diagram   section diagram

A. Rectangular Beam   *B.* Wide-Flange Beam

Fig. 11–3. Distribution of shearing stress in beams.

Fig. 11–3*A*. But in flanged beams, the distribution of shearing stress[9] is approximately rectangular, as shown in Fig. 11–3*B*. Note that the shearing stresses in the flanges are very small. There would be little error in assuming that the shearing stress in the web is uniform and equal to the total shear V, divided by the area of the web A_w.

[6] John I. Parcel and Robert B. B. Moorman, *Analysis of Statically Indeterminate Structures* (New York: John Wiley & Sons, Inc., 1955), pp. 37–40.

[7] Parcel and Moorman, *op. cit.*, p. 41.

[8] Computed from $S_s = VA\bar{y}/Ib$ (Eq. 11–4).

[9] Shown true to scale for a 14 W 30 beam.

In Eq. 11–2, then, we have

$$S_s = \frac{V}{A_w}$$

$$q = \text{virtual stress} \times \text{area of element} = \frac{v}{A_w} dA_w$$

$$\Delta L = dx$$

and the internal virtual work on a single element is

$$q \frac{S_s}{G} \Delta L = \frac{v}{A_w} dA_w \frac{V}{A_w G} dx$$

The total virtual work must be obtained by summing the virtual work on all elements in the cross-section (integrating over the area of the cross-section) and summing all the cross-sections in the beam (integrating over the full length of the beam). The total virtual work is

$$U\Delta = \int_0^L \int_0^{A_w} \frac{vV}{A_w^2 G} dA_w \, dx$$

But

$$\int_0^{A_w} dA_w = A_w$$

so the above equation becomes

$$U\Delta = \int_0^L \frac{vV \, dx}{A_w G} \tag{11-7}$$

Not only is Eq. 11–7 fairly accurate for flanged beams, but it is only 20 percent in error for rectangular beams (where $A_w = A$), as can be seen by comparing Eqs. 11–7 with 11–6. Since shearing deflections are usually small anyway, Eq. 11–7 is sufficiently accurate for most problems regardless of the shape of the beam.

Note the similarity between the expression $\int_0^L (vV/A_w G) \, dx$ and $\int_0^L (Mm/EI) \, dx$. By the same reasoning that developed the expression

$$\int_0^L \frac{Mm \, dx}{EI}$$

into

$$\sum \bar{m} A_{MD/EI}$$

Equation 11–7 can be expressed as

$$U\Delta = \sum \bar{v} A_{SD/AG} \tag{11-8}$$

where $A_{SD/AG}$ is the area of the shear diagram divided by $A_w G$ and $\bar{v}$ is the virtual shear at the centroid of $A_{SD/AG}$. The same limitations that apply to semi-graphical integration for deflection due to bending apply also to semi-graphical integration for deflection due to shear.

Example 11–4. Cantilever Beam. To find the deflection due to shear at the free end of a uniformly loaded cantilever beam of span length L supporting a uniform load of w per unit length, plot the shear diagram as in Fig. 11–4B and plot the virtual shear diagram due to the virtual load, as shown in Fig. 11–4C. Then from Eq. 11–8,

$$1 \# \, \Delta Y_A = \sum \bar{v} A_{SD/AG}$$
$$= \frac{(wL)L}{2A_w G} \, 1 \#$$

and

$$\Delta Y_A = \frac{wL^2}{2A_w G}$$

If the beam were rectangular, we would substitute A for A_w, and noting the "exact" deflection to be $\frac{6}{5}$ times the approximate deflection, the "exact" deflection would be

$$\Delta Y_A = \frac{6}{5} \frac{wL^2}{2AG} = \frac{3wL^2}{5AG}$$

which is the same expression found in Art. 11–3 by integral calculus.

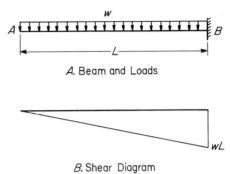

A. Beam and Loads

B. Shear Diagram

C. Virtual Shear Diagram

Fig. 11–4. Deflection due to shear. Semi-graphical integration.

11–5. Torsion. Shearing stress due to torsion is given by the formula

$$S_s = \frac{Tr}{J} \tag{11–9}$$

in which S_s is shearing stress, T is the torque or twisting moment, r is the radius to any point from the center, and J is the polar moment of inertia. The formula is accurate only for long, round shafts. It simply does not fit square shafts, but (although stresses in square shafts must always be inaccurate when calculated from this formula) rotations can be found by substituting an "effective" polar moment of inertia, J_e for J.

Stresses and rotations in thin rectangular shafts[10] or shafts composed of thin rectangular elements can be approximated by modifying Eq. 11–9 to

$$S_s = \frac{Tc}{J_e} \tag{11–10}$$

where c is the (total) thickness of the element and J_e is $\frac{1}{3} \sum c^3 d$, where d is the width of the element.

[10] I-beams and wide-flange beams subject to torsion are composed of elements (flanges and web) that are thin with respect to their widths.

Stresses and rotations in thin, hollow shafts can be found from the formula

$$S_s = \frac{T}{2At} \qquad (11\text{--}11)$$

where A is the enclosed cross-sectional area and t is the wall thickness.

ROUND SHAFTS. An equation for round shafts which can also be used for thin, rectangular shafts (by substituting J_e for J) can be developed from Eqs. 11–2 and 11–9 as follows. First, consider any single element. Now

$$S_s = \frac{Tr}{J} \qquad (11\text{--}9)$$

$$q = \frac{Ur}{J}\,dA$$

in which U is the virtual torque on the shaft, dA is the area of a face of the element, and

$$\Delta L = dx$$

a differential distance along the axis of the shaft. Then we have

$$q\frac{S_s}{G}\,\Delta L = \frac{Ur\,dA}{J}\frac{Tr}{JG}\,dx = \frac{TUr^2\,dA}{J^2G}\,dx$$

The total virtual work must be obtained by summing the virtual work on all elements in the cross-section (integrating over the area of the cross-section) and summing all the cross-sections in the shaft (integrating over the full length of the shaft). Then

$$U\,\Delta\theta = \int_0^L \int_0^A \frac{UTr^2\,dA}{J^2G}\,dx$$

But $\int_0^A r^2\,dA$ is, by definition, equal to J, so substituting J for $\int_0^A r^2\,dA$ in the numerator and canceling, we have

$$U\,\Delta\theta = \int_0^L \frac{UT}{JG}\,dx$$

from which

$$\Delta\theta = \frac{TL}{JG} \qquad (11\text{--}12)$$

where L is the length of the shaft.

11–6. Composite Structures. Composite structures are those in which deflections and stresses result from two or more kinds of stresses. Thus an arch is a composite structure because the forces in the arch result from both bending and axial compression. (Shearing strain also has some effect on the forces but its effect in the ordinary arch is entirely negligible.) The deflection of a beam on elastic supports is the result of bending of the beam combined with the deformation of the elastic supports. Such structures are analyzed by the same principles already studied. The structure is cut back to make it statically determinate, and virtual work equations are written for each kind of stress produced. Suppose the deflection of some point on a rectangular beam resulted partly from shear and partly from bending; the deflection can be expressed as the sum of the internal virtual work due to shear plus that due to bending. Hence, by combining Eqs. 8-1 and 11-6, we have

$$1 \,\#\, \Delta = \int_0^L \frac{Mm\,dx}{EI} + \frac{6}{5}\int_0^L \frac{vV\,dx}{AG}$$

Example 11-6. *Trussed Beam.* One of the commonest examples of composite structures is the trussed beam. The Big Horn Trail Bridge of Fig. 11-5 is a king truss—a type often used for short bridges on dirt roads. The timbers for this particular bridge were furnished in short lengths because they had to be transported by pack horse. The significant stresses are those due to bending of the deck and to the axial forces in all members.

Although the reactions are statically determinate (if the frictional forces resulting from the sliding of the deck upon the sills at each end are ignored), the bridge itself is internally statically indeterminate to the first degree. It could be cut back in a number of ways, as by putting a hinge at the middle of the deck, by cutting one of the cables, or by cutting the post. One way is about as good as another, and in this example the post CD is cut as shown in Fig. 11-6A. When a member in a free body is cut, the internal stresses must be replaced by equivalent external forces. These forces are marked P in Fig. 11-6A. The redundant forces P cause redundant axial forces of $1.83P$ tension in the cable, and of $1.76P$ compression in the deck. These values are found from principles of static equilibrium.

The bending moment diagrams are shown in parts in Fig. 11-6B. The part labeled A_1 and A_2 is due only to a snow load of 50 psf acting on the cut-back structure. The part labeled A_3 and A_4 is due only to the indeterminate forces P in the post. Together they account for all bending in the deck.

By applying equal and opposite virtual loads to the cut faces of the post, we can write a virtual work expression for the relative movement of one cut face with respect to the other. The relative movement is, of course, zero. The virtual work in the structure is that due to bending plus that due to axial deformation. Thus the expression is the simple addition of Eqs. 7-6 and 8-3

$$U \,\Delta_{\text{relative}} = 0 = \sum \bar{m}A_{MD/EI} + \sum u\frac{FL}{AE} \qquad (7\text{-}6 + 8\text{-}3)$$

Before the equation can be set up in final form, we must determine the areas, the moduli of elasticity, and the moments of inertia of the various members. In a real structure this is not always a simple task. For example, the deck of the bridge is laminated, not solid. How effective are the nails

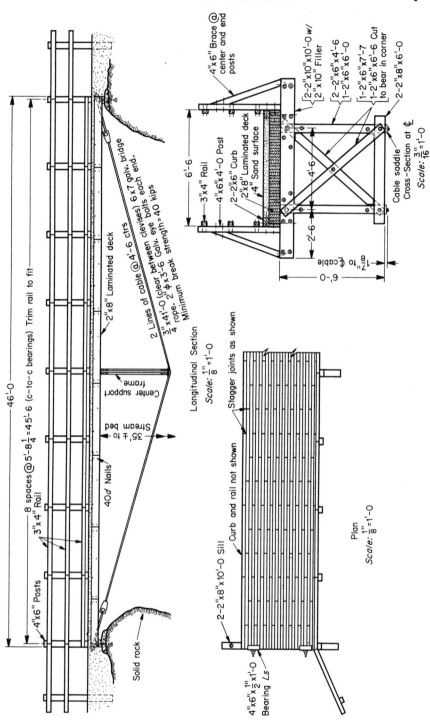

Fig. 11–5. Big Horn Trail Bridge, Payette National Forest.

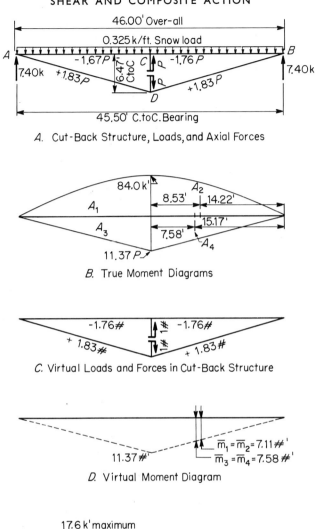

A. Cut-Back Structure, Loads, and Axial Forces

B. True Moment Diagrams

C. Virtual Loads and Forces in Cut-Back Structure

D. Virtual Moment Diagram

E. Total Moment Diagram

Fig. 11–6. Analysis of trussed beam (Big Horn Trail Bridge).

holding the laminations? Furthermore, the modulus of elasticity varies almost 100 percent with moisture changes, and it varies with duration of loading and other factors. The modulus of elasticity of wire ropes varies from about 14,000,000 psi to about 25,000,000 psi, depending on the type of rope and whether it is prestretched. Even the post offers uncertainties. It, too, is laminated and the laminations are of different lengths, some butting against the deck and rope saddle and some butting against a floor beam and a brace. Can we be sure these staggered butt joints are equally tight? Furthermore, the post contains a cross-brace. Most engineers would ignore the brace, even though it actually would carry some of the post load. But how much? It does not matter much in this instance because the virtual work in the post is very small anyway. These are only samples of the uncertainties in the structure, and this structure is quite simple in comparison with many.

We shall assume the deck to be two-thirds as effective as a solid deck. We shall assume the post to extend from the centerline of the cable to the centerline of the deck, and the cross-bracing is to be ignored. The physical dimensions and constants of the bridge are assumed to be as follows:

Deck:

Modulus of elasticity = 1,600,000 psi = 230,000 kips/ft^2

$$\text{Area} = \frac{2}{3} \times 6.5 \times \frac{7.5}{12} = 2.71 \text{ ft}^2$$

$$\text{Moment of inertia} = \frac{2}{3}\frac{bd^3}{12} = \frac{2}{3} \times \frac{6.5(0.625)^3}{12} = 0.0882 \text{ ft}^4$$

Length = 46.0 ft

Post:

Modulus of elasticity = 1,600,000 psi = 230,000 kips/ft^2

Area = $6 \times 1\frac{5}{8} \times 5\frac{5}{8} \times \frac{1}{144} = 0.381 \text{ ft}^2$

Length = 6.47 ft

Tension members (cable):

Modulus of elasticity = 18,000,000 psi = 2,590,000 kips/ft^2

Area = $2 \times 0.2705 \text{ in.}^2 = 0.541 \text{ in.}^2 = 0.00376 \text{ ft}^2$

Length = 41.0 ft

Tension members (eyebolts):

Modulus of elasticity = 30,000,000 psi = 4,320,000 kips/ft^2

Area = $2 \times 3.14 \text{ in.}^2 = 6.28 \text{ in.}^2 = 0.0436 \text{ ft}^2$

Length = 6.8 ft

The areas of the moment diagrams are as follows:

$$A_1 = A_2 = \frac{2}{3} \times \frac{45.50}{2} \times 84.0 = 1274 \text{ kip-ft}^2$$

$$A_3 = A_4 = -\frac{1}{2} \times \frac{45.50}{2} \times 11.37P = -129.2P \text{ ft}^2$$

The following expressions of virtual work are obtained for the bending in the deck due to

Snow load $\qquad 2\left[\dfrac{(-7.11)1274}{230,000 \times 0.0882}\right] = -0.894$

Redundant $\qquad 2\left[\dfrac{(-7.58)(-129.2P)}{230,000 \times 0.0882}\right] = +0.0965P$

And the following expressions of virtual work for axial deformations due to the redundant force P in the post are obtained for:

Deck $\qquad \dfrac{(-1.76)(-1.76P)46.0}{230,000 \times 2.71} = +0.000229P$

Post $\qquad \dfrac{(-1)(-P)(6.47)}{230,000 \times 0.381} = +0.000074P$

Cable $\qquad \dfrac{(1.83)(1.83P)41.0}{2,590,000 \times 0.00376} = +0.0141P$

Eyebolts $\qquad \dfrac{(1.83)(1.83P)(6.8)}{4,320,000 \times 0.0436} = +0.000121P$

Adding all these expressions for virtual work, we have

$$\Delta_{\text{relative}} = 0 = -0.894 + 0.111P$$

from which

$$P = 8.05 \text{ kips}$$

Substituting 8.05 for P in Fig. 11–6B and adding the two moment diagrams (one for the snow load and one for the redundant force), we obtain the total moment diagram of Fig. 11–6E. A better distribution of moments can be obtained by further tightening of the nuts on the eyebolts. This pre-tensions the cable, introduces camber into the deck, increases the negative moment, and decreases the positive moments.

Part IV

MOMENT DISTRIBUTION

Moment distribution was first presented to the public in 1930 by Professor Hardy Cross, who had been teaching it for eight years. The 145 pages of discussion following his ten-page monumental paper[1] bespeak the importance attached to it by far-sighted men. For the vast majority of practicing engineers, moment distribution, wherever applicable, has largely supplanted all other methods of indeterminate structural analysis.

Moment distribution possesses several inherent advantages over other methods of analysis: it is rapid, easy to use, and practically automatic (thus reducing blunders to a minimum), and it affords the user a clear picture of how the structure is behaving during each step of the analysis. Being a method of successive approximations, it is adapted to solutions of any degree of accuracy—from rough approximate answers that can be quickly obtained to answers of high precision.

This method has the one disadvantage that its use is confined to the solution of bending moments. For example, it cannot be used to solve axial forces in indeterminate trusses and space frames, although it is unexcelled for the solution of secondary stresses (stresses due to flexure) in trussed structures. This limitation is not very important because most indeterminate structures are of the continuous-beam or rigid-frame type and are admirably suited for analysis by moment distribution. It has not been common practice to design indeterminate trusses except for certain types of monumental bridges.

In essence, moment distribution is the solution by successive approximations of the slope deflection equations which were presented by Professor George Maney in 1915. The slope deflection equations were, in turn, extended from other equations originally proposed by Manderla and Mohr. Since the introduction of moment distribution, many variants of the method have appeared; some of these are shortcuts or "improvements" of the original method, whereas others are somewhat similar methods—for example, the solution of angle changes rather than of moments. With the exception of two improvements,[2] none of these variants has achieved much popularity. The original Cross method, modified by these two improvements, is presented herein.

[1] Hardy Cross, "Analysis of Continuous Frames by Distributing Fixed-End Moments," *Trans. ASCE*, 96: 1–10, 1932.

[2] These are (a) the use of clockwise and counterclockwise sign convention and (b) the writing of the balancing and carry-over moments for a single joint at a time.

12

JOINT ROTATION

12–1. Definitions. FIXED-END MOMENT. This moment is one which would exist at the end of a member if its end were fixed against rotation.

Fixed-end moments are abbreviated FEM. Where no confusion could exist, the abbreviation is shortened to M. Figure 12–1 shows these moments for common loads acting on prismatic (constant E and I) members. They should be memorized because they will be used over and over again. Fixed-end moments for unusual loadings can ordinarily be obtained by superimposing one load type upon another. Fixed-end moments may be caused also by the deflection of one end with respect to the other, as explained in Art. 13–1. Fixed-end moments for non-prismatic members must be calculated by a suitable method (moment area, for example), determined experimentally,[1] or found from charts or tables.[2] For partial loads they can be obtained by the method shown in Art. 13–3.

SIGN CONVENTION. Moments which act upon a free body of the member in a clockwise direction are considered positive; those acting counterclockwise are negative. Figure 12–2 illustrates the sign convention graphically.

In the original Cross method, moments which cause compression in the upper fibers of a beam are considered positive. This convention (called "designer's" convention in this text) is all right for continuous beams (it is often used though not necessarily superior for certain shortcut methods[3]), but it is cumbersome for ordinary rigid frames and confusing for complex rigid frames with sloping members. The "clockwise" sign convention has several advantages over "designer's" convention: most important, it avoids confusion at joints connecting several sloping members; it makes the balancing operation completely automatic, thereby reducing chances for mistakes; it is easier to learn; by using it, one need make no distinction at all among horizontal, vertical, and sloping members—all joints and all members are treated in exactly the same way. A complete analysis involves use of free bodies for finding reactions and other forces, so it is advantageous to be able to apply the final end moments obtained from moment distribution directly to such free bodies.

[1] W. J. Eney, "Fixed-End Moments by Cardboard Models," *Eng. News Record*, Dec. 12, 1935.
[2] Appendix A.
[3] *Continuity in Concrete Building Frames* (Portland Cement Assn., Chicago).

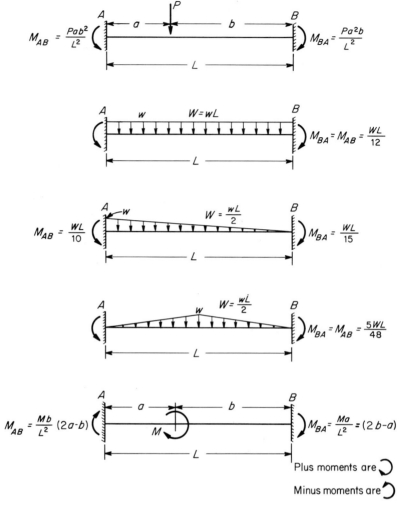

Fig. 12–1. Fixed-end moments for prismatic beams.

STIFFNESS. Stiffness is that moment which is required to rotate one end of a member through an angle of 1 radian.

The stiffness is designated as K and equals $4EI/L$ for fixed prismatic members.[4] For non-prismatic members, stiffness, like fixed-end moments, must be calculated analytically, determined experimentally, or found from charts or tables.[5]

[4] K can be derived by moment area or virtual work (see Art. 10–2). A derivation by conjugate beam is shown in Ex. 20–4A.

[5] Appendix A.

CARRY-OVER FACTOR. If one end of a member is rotated (but not other-wise displaced) by an applied moment while the other end is held fixed, as shown in Fig. 12–3, some moment is induced at the fixed end. The ratio of the moment at the fixed end to the moment at the rotated end is called the carry-over factor.

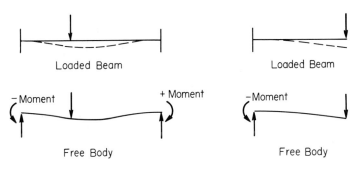

Fig. 12–2. Sign convention.

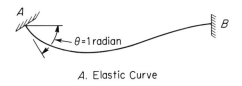

A. Elastic Curve

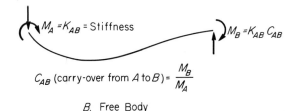

C_{AB} (carry-over from A to B) $= \dfrac{M_B}{M_A}$

B. Free Body

Fig. 12–3. Stiffness and carry-over.

The carry-over factor is designated as C and equals $+\frac{1}{2}$ for prismatic members. For non-prismatic members, the carry-over factor, like stiffness and fixed-end moments, must be determined analytically or experimentally.

Stiffness and carry-over factor are illustrated in Fig. 12–3. Note that in Fig. 12–3A the left end is rotated 1 radian while the right end remains fixed. In the free-body diagram of Fig. 12–3B, the member is in equilibrium under the action of a moment and a force at each end. In order to hold the member bent as shown, both moments must act clockwise upon the free body. Then M_A multiplied by the carry-over factor C_{AB} equals M_B. Thus, if one end of of an otherwise fixed-ended member is rotated, a portion of the moment is "carried over" to the fixed end. If the moment at the rotating end is clockwise, the carry-over moment is also clockwise. If the rotating moment is counterclockwise, the carry-over moment is also counterclockwise. The carry-over factor is, then, *always* positive.[6]

Both stiffness and carry-over factor are functions only of the elastic properties of the member. Neither is affected by other loads acting upon the member.

SUBSCRIPTS. Subscripts are used for identification as follows: The first letter indicates the end to which the moment, stiffness, or carry-over factor

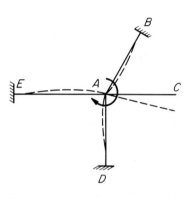

Fig. 12–4. Rotation of a rigid joint.

applies, and the second letter identifies the member. For example, suppose members AB, AC, AD, and AE are rigidly connected together at point A. Then M_{AB} means the moment at point A in member AB, K_{AB} means the stiffness at the A end of member AB, and C_{AB} means the carry-over factor from end A to end B in the member AB.

DISTRIBUTION FACTOR. When a joint composed of several rigidly connected members rotates, moments are induced into the members. The proportion of the total moment that is induced into each member is the "distribution" factor.

Figure 12–4 shows four members rigidly connected at point A; three are fixed at their outer ends, but one, member AC, is free at its outer end. Now suppose the joint A rotates to the position shown by the dashed lines. Members AB, AD, and AE are flexed by the rotation, and moment is induced in each. Member AC rotates freely and thus is not flexed, and no moment is induced in it. If the joint rotates exactly 1 radian, the total moment required to force it to rotate is, from the discussion of stiffness factor,

$$M_{\text{total}} = K_{AB} + K_{AC} + K_{AD} + K_{AE}$$

But from the definition of stiffness (moment required to rotate one end of a member through an angle of 1 radian) and from the fact that no moment at all is induced into member AC, it follows that

$$K_{AC} = 0$$

That is, *members with one free end have no stiffness at all.* Therefore

$$M_{\text{total}} = K_{AB} + 0 + K_{AD} + K_{AE} = \Sigma K$$

---

[6] The carry-over factor is always positive when using the sign convention of this chapter. The carry-over factor is negative in designer's convention.

where ΣK is the sum of stiffness factors of those members which are rigidly connected at the joint being considered.

If the members are elastic, stresses are proportional to strains and moments are proportional to angles of rotation. Therefore the proportion of the moment absorbed by any one member, say AB, is $K_{AB}/\Sigma K$, regardless of the amount of rotation. The ratio $K_{AB}/\Sigma K$ is the distribution factor, abbreviated D_{AB}. The distribution factors for all the members are

$$D_{AB} = \frac{K_{AB}}{\Sigma K}$$

$$D_{AC} = \frac{0}{\Sigma K} = 0$$

$$D_{AD} = \frac{K_{AD}}{\Sigma K}$$

$$D_{AE} = \frac{K_{AE}}{\Sigma K}$$

Note that the sum of the distribution factors is

$$\Sigma D_A = \frac{K_{AB}}{\Sigma K} + \frac{K_{AD}}{\Sigma K} + \frac{K_{AE}}{\Sigma K} = \frac{K_{AB} + K_{AD} + K_{AE}}{\Sigma K}$$

$$= \frac{K_{AB} + K_{AD} + K_{AE}}{K_{AB} + K_{AD} + K_{AE}} = 1$$

The *sum of the distribution factors at any joint must always equal unity.*

12–2. Concepts. DISTRIBUTING MOMENTS. In the structure shown in Fig. 12–5A, the members are rigidly connected at points A, E, and G. To solve any problem by moment distribution, we isolate and solve one joint at a time. Consider joint A, isolated in Fig. 12–5B. Imagine a brake at A which prevents rotation of the joint. Now let the load P be applied at point C. The member AC would bend somewhat, and since the joint A is fixed, a fixed-end moment, $(FEM)_{AC}$, would be developed at A acting counterclockwise on a free body of AC, as shown in Fig. 12–5C. According to our sign convention, this moment is negative and its magnitude is, from consideration of static equilibrium, $P \times AC$. The moments at joint A are now in equilibrium with $(FEM)_{AC}$ acting counterclockwise on free body AC and $P \times AC$ acting clockwise on the brake.

Now suppose the brake to be released. The joint is no longer in equilibrium because the $(FEM)_{AC}$ is no longer opposed by the brake. The moments at the joint are "unbalanced," so the joint begins to rotate clockwise, as shown in Fig. 12–5D. This rotation continues until members AB, AD, and AE are flexed enough to develop a resisting or "balancing" moment equal

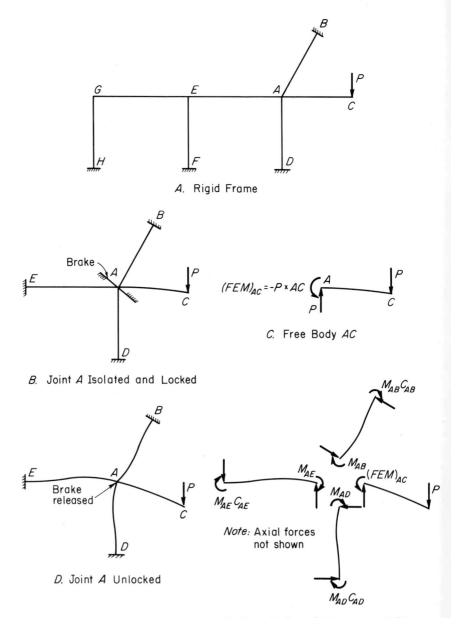

A. Rigid Frame

B. Joint A Isolated and Locked

$(FEM)_{AC} = -P \times AC$

C. Free Body AC

D. Joint A Unlocked

Note: Axial forces not shown

E. Free Bodies of Members of Joint A

Fig. 12–5. Distribution of moments at a joint.

to $P \times AC$. From consideration of the distribution factor, the rotational moment absorbed by each member is

$$M_{AB} = D_{AB} \times P \times AC \text{ clockwise}$$

$$M_{AC} = 0, \text{ because } D_{AC} = 0$$

$$M_{AD} = D_{AD} \times P \times AC \text{ clockwise}$$

$$M_{AE} = D_{AE} \times P \times AC \text{ clockwise}$$

Note that the "balancing" moments are opposite in sign to the fixed-end moment $(FEM)_{AC}$. Thus, *the "balancing" moments are always opposite in sign to the "unbalanced" moments.* The total moments acting at the joint are now in static equilibrium. If we sum the moments at joint A, we have

$$\Sigma M_A = M_{AB} - (FEM)_{AC} + M_{AD} + M_{AE} = 0 \qquad (1\text{–}1)$$

The rotational moment induced in members AB, AD, and AE causes carry-over moments at the opposite end of these members. Thus, as shown in the exploded sketch of Fig. 12–5E, members AB, AD, and AE are in equilibrium under the action of rotational moment, carry-over moment, and the shears induced by these moments.

The joint A can again be locked in its rotated position and joint E can be unlocked. It will rotate counterclockwise because of the moment carried over from A to E. Moments are balanced as explained above. Then joint E is relocked and joint G unlocked, balanced, and relocked. Then joint A is unlocked and balanced again. The process is repeated until the desired accuracy is obtained.

MOMENT DISTRIBUTION PROCEDURE. The following procedure is general; it applies to rigid frames of any sort as well as to continuous beams and to members of variable as well as constant EI.

1. Compute stiffnesses and carry-over factors for each member. For prismatic members these are $4EI/L$ and $+\frac{1}{2}$, respectively.

2. Determine the distribution factors for each member at each joint from the stiffnesses. Make a sketch of the structure and record the distribution factors in a box at each joint. The sum of the distribution factors at each joint must equal unity.

3. Compute the fixed-end moments for each loaded member. Record them on the sketch of the structure.

4. Select any joint where the fixed-end moments are unbalanced, preferably the one with the greatest unbalanced moment. Unlock the joint by multiplying the unbalanced moment by the distribution factor for each member. Note that the balancing moments are opposite in sign to the unbalanced moment. Record the results and draw a line under the balancing moments to indicate that the joint is in equilibrium. Now consider the joint to be relocked in its present rotated position.

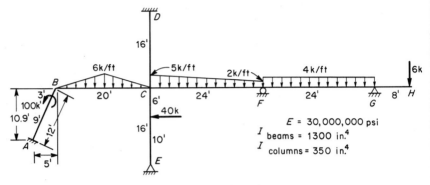

A. Frame and Loads

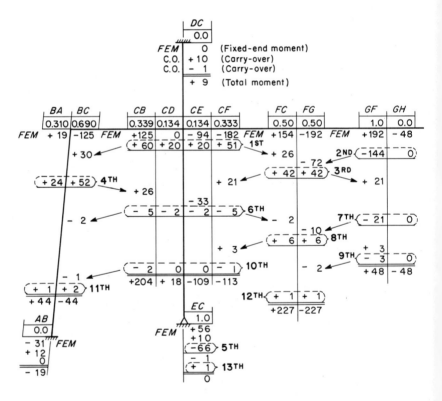

B. Distribution of Moments

Fig. 12-6. Moment distribution for rigid frame with no
joint deflection.

5. Record the carry-over moments at the opposite end of each member so balanced.

6. Select any other joint and repeat steps 4 and 5. Balance carry-over moments as well as fixed-end moments.

7. Continue to unlock, balance, and carry over, and relock each joint one by one, until the structure is gradually relaxed into equilibrium at all joints.

Always think of moment distribution as a physical occurrence and picture the structural action at each step.

The beams are loaded or otherwise distorted while the joints are held against rotation; one joint is then allowed to rotate with accompanying distribution of the unbalanced moment at that joint and the resulting moments are carried-over to the adjacent joints; then another joint is allowed to rotate while the others are held against rotation; and the process is repeated until all the joints are "eased down" into equilibrium.[7]

12–3. Example of a Rigid Frame. The following example problem (see Fig. 12–6) has been chosen because, except for joint deflection or translation (sidesway), it represents every facet of the moment distribution process as applied to either continuous beams or rigid frames either with or without sloping members on both hinged and fixed supports. Complete computations are shown in Fig. 12–6 and in the text; those which might prove troublesome are explained.

This exposition forms the basis for all that follows, and the reader should follow each step of the computations, making sure he understands each number and each sign before proceeding. Note that the steps in the procedure explained in Art. 12–2 are followed exactly.

Simple as moment distribution is, students *can* get confused by thinking of too many things at once. Since it is a step-by-step process, think of it in just that way. That is, make a computation, then, after writing the result, forget about it. The mind is then cleared for action on the next step—not cluttered up with a multitude of details about stiffnesses, fixed-end moments, and distribution factors in a hopeless jumble.

STIFFNESSES AND CARRY-OVER FACTORS. The members are all prismatic, so the stiffnesses equal $4EI/L$ and the carry-over factors equal $\frac{1}{2}$. Note that member GH has no stiffness because it has no support at H. It is similar to member AC of Fig. 12–5. Although member CE is hinged at E, the hinge (like a joint) can be considered locked temporarily, so its stiffness factor is computed just as for a fixed member.[8] Remember that each joint is locked against rotation at the start of the process; if joint E is locked, it becomes, in effect, fixed and is therefore treated as a fixed joint.

---

[7] Cross, *op. cit.*, p. 3.

[8] It is possible to modify the expression for stiffness of members not fully fixed, as is shown in Art. 14–3. The use of the modified stiffness shortens the labor but is often a source of confusion for beginners. The author believes that it should not be used until the student has gained a mastery of the basic process.

For convenience in avoiding large numbers, all values are best expressed in kip-foot units. Then we have

EI values:

$$EI = \frac{30{,}000{,}000 \text{ psi} \times 1300 \text{ in.}^4}{144{,}000(\text{in.}^2/\text{ft})(\text{lb}/\text{kip})} = 271{,}000 \text{ kip-ft}^2 \quad \text{for the beams}$$

$$EI = \frac{30{,}000{,}000 \times 350 \text{ in.}^4}{144{,}000(\text{in.}^2/\text{ft})(\text{lb}/\text{kip})} = 73{,}000 \text{ kip-ft}^2 \quad \text{for the columns}$$

Column stiffnesses:

$$K_{AB} = \frac{4EI}{L} = \frac{4 \times 73{,}000}{12} = 24{,}300 \text{ kip-ft}$$

$$K_{CE} = K_{CD} = \frac{4EI}{L} = \frac{4 \times 73{,}000}{16} = 18{,}200 \text{ kip-ft}$$

Beam stiffnesses:

$$K_{BC} = \frac{4EI}{L} = \frac{4 \times 271{,}000}{20} = 54{,}200 \text{ kip-ft}$$

$$K_{CF} = K_{FG} = \frac{4EI}{L} = \frac{4 \times 271{,}000}{24} = 45{,}200 \text{ kip-ft}$$

$$K_{GH} = 0 \quad \text{because there is no support at one end}$$

DISTRIBUTION FACTORS. At fixed supports such as A or D, there is no rotation, so there can be no rotational (balancing) moment. The joint is never "unlocked," so moments are never distributed. Another viewpoint is that the "stiffness" of a fixed support is infinite, so the sum of stiffnesses at any fixed support such as A is infinity for the support plus K_{AB}. The distribution factor for AB would be, then,

$$D_{AB} = \frac{K_{AB}}{\infty + K_{AB}} = 0$$

showing there is no moment distributed into the member at a fixed support.

On the other hand, the distribution factor is 1.00 for a single member that terminates at a hinge support or knife edge such as at E, but not at F because there are two members at F. The knife edge or hinge can take no moment, so the member itself must absorb all the unbalanced moment. As before, the other viewpoint is that the "stiffness" of a knife edge or a hinge is zero, so the sum of stiffnesses at a joint such as E is K_{EC} plus zero for the knife edge. The distribution factor for EC is, then,

$$D_{EC} = \frac{K_{EC}}{0 + K_{EC}} = 1.00$$

By the same reasoning, the distribution factor for GF at the joint G is 1.00 because neither the knife-edge support nor member GH possesses any stiffness.

Distribution at joint C:

$$\Sigma K_C = K_{CB} + K_{CF} + K_{CD} + K_{CE}$$

$$= 54{,}200 + 45{,}200 + 18{,}200 + 18{,}200 = 135{,}800$$

$$D_{CB} = \frac{K_{CB}}{\Sigma K_C} = \frac{54{,}200}{135{,}800} = 0.399$$

$$D_{CD} = \frac{K_{CD}}{\Sigma K_C} = \frac{18{,}200}{135{,}800} = 0.134$$

$$D_{CE} = D_{CD} \qquad\qquad = 0.134 \qquad \text{because } K_{CE} = K_{CD}$$

$$D_{CF} = \frac{K_{CF}}{\Sigma K_C} = \frac{45{,}200}{135{,}800} = 0.333$$

$$\overline{\Sigma D_C = 1.000} \qquad \text{check}$$

Distribution at joint F:

$$D_{FC} = D_{FG} = 0.50$$

by inspection, because the two spans are equal in length, modulus of elasticity, and moment of inertia. They are therefore of equal stiffness. Or the distribution factor can be computed as

$$D_{FC} = \frac{K_{FC}}{\Sigma K_F} = \frac{45{,}200}{45{,}200 + 45{,}200} = 0.50$$

Distribution at joint B:

$$D_{BA} = \frac{K_{BA}}{\Sigma K_B} = \frac{24{,}300}{24{,}300 + 54{,}200} = 0.31$$

$$D_{BC} = \frac{K_{BC}}{\Sigma K_B} = \frac{54{,}200}{78{,}500} = 0.69$$

$$\overline{\Sigma D_B = 1.00} \qquad \text{check}$$

These distribution factors are written on a sketch of the frame, as shown in Fig. 12–6B. It should be noted that the distribution factors could have been computed by using any factor *proportional* to stiffness, I/L, for example. However, when dealing with non-prismatic members, the true stiffness must be used; then too, the actual rotations can be computed only by using the true stiffness; and finally, the use of the true stiffness is a bit more fundamental. It is not important but it seems just as well to use the true stiffness.

FIXED-END MOMENTS. See Fig. 12–1 for the appropriate formulas.

$$M_{AB} = \frac{Mb}{L^2}(2a-b) = \frac{-100\times 3}{(12)^2}(2\times 9 - 3) = -31 \text{ kip-ft}$$

$$M_{BA} = \frac{Ma}{L^2}(2b-a) = \frac{-100\times 9}{(12)^2}(2\times 3 - 9) = +19 \text{ kip-ft}$$

Note that signs of the fixed-end moments as explained in Art. 12–1 are determined automatically by the formula.

$$M_{BC} = -\frac{5}{48}WL = -\frac{5}{48}\frac{(6\text{ kips/ft})20}{2}20 = -125 \text{ kip-ft}$$

$$M_{CB} = +125 \text{ kip-ft}$$

The signs are determined by inspection of free-body diagrams like those in Fig. 12–2.

$$M_{CE} = -\frac{Pab^2}{L^2} = -\frac{40\text{ kips}\times 6(10)^2}{(16)^2} = -94 \text{ kip-ft}$$

$$M_{EC} = +\frac{Pa^2b}{L^2} = +\frac{40\text{ kips}\times (6)^2 10}{(16)^2} = +56 \text{ kip-ft}$$

Note that the joint at E is considered locked (fixed) for computing fixed-end moments.

M_{CF} is found by superimposing a triangular load of 3 kips/ft at the peak upon a uniform load of 2 kips/ft.

$$M_{CF} = -\frac{WL}{10} - \frac{WL}{12} = -\frac{(3\text{ kips/ft})24}{2}\times\frac{24}{10} - (2\text{ kips/ft})24\times\frac{24}{12}$$

$$= -182 \text{ kip-ft}$$

$$M_{FC} = +\frac{WL}{15} + \frac{WL}{12} = +\frac{(3\text{ kips/ft})24}{2}\times\frac{24}{15} + (2\text{ kips/ft})24\times\frac{24}{12}$$

$$= +154 \text{ kip-ft}$$

$$M_{FG} = -\frac{WL}{12} = -\frac{(4\text{ kips/ft})24\times 24}{12} = -192 \text{ kip-ft}$$

$$M_{GF} = +192 \text{ kip-ft}$$

$$M_{GH} = -PL = -6\times 8 = -48 \text{ kip-ft}$$

These fixed-end moments, labeled *FEM*, are written on the sketch of the structure in Fig. 12–6B. There are several popular schemes for recording them. Some authorities use a tabular form. Others use a sketch and write the fixed-end moments alongside the corresponding members, and there are several variations of this scheme. The method used here is a combination of the two forms. It has most of the advantages of each system. The principal advantage is that the distributed moments are recorded together, not scattered around on the structure, and thus it makes the process a little easier to follow. The other methods are also satisfactory, however.

DISTRIBUTING MOMENTS. As stated under *Moment distribution procedure* in Art. 12–2, the joints can be balanced in any order, but it reduces the labo- if the joints with the greatest unbalanced moments are treated first. Rememr ber that a joint is balanced by multiplying the total unbalanced moment by the distribution factor for each member. Immediately after balancing, moments are carried over to the opposite ends of the members, and the joint is then relocked.

First Distribution. The unbalanced moment at joint C is

$$M_C = +125 + 0 - 94 - 182 = -151$$

The minus sign shows it to be counterclockwise. As the joint is unlocked, it rotates clockwise, thus inducing clockwise (plus) rotational moments into each member as shown in "1st," Fig. 12–6B. Multiplying the unbalanced moment by distribution factors previously found and recorded in Fig. 12–6B, gives:

$$\text{In } CB \quad M = 151 \times 0.399 = \ +60$$
$$\text{In } CD \quad M = 151 \times 0.134 = \ +20$$
$$\text{In } CE \quad M = 151 \times 0.134 = \ +20$$
$$\text{In } CF \quad M = 151 \times 0.333 = \ \underline{+51}$$
$$+151$$

These moments are recorded and a short line is now drawn under the distributed moments to indicate the joint is now in equilibrium—that ΣM_C is now truly zero, as shown below.

$$\Sigma M_C = +125 - 94 - 182 + 60 + 20 + 20 + 51 = 0 \quad \text{check}$$

After balancing, the moments should always be checked to see if the sum equals zero.

The carry-over moments are recorded immediately. To forget one would be disastrous. We have

$$+60 \times \tfrac{1}{2} = +30 \quad \text{at } BC$$
$$+20 \times \tfrac{1}{2} = +10 \quad \text{at } EC$$
$$+20 \times \tfrac{1}{2} = +10 \quad \text{at } DC$$
$$+51 \times \tfrac{1}{2} = +26 \quad \text{at } FC \quad \text{(to the nearest even number)}$$

The carry-over moments are, wherever convenient, shown by arrows.

The joint C is now relocked. This same process is repeated at the other joints, balancing both fixed-end and carry-over moments until all joints are as near to equilibrium as desired.

Second Distribution. At joint G, the unbalanced moment is

$$\Sigma M_G = +192 - 48 = +144$$

and the balancing moment (opposite in sign to the unbalanced moment) is

$$-144 \times 1.00 = -144 \text{ to } GF$$

The carry-over is

$$-144 \times \tfrac{1}{2} = -72 \text{ to } FG$$

Third Distribution. At joint F the unbalanced moment due both to fixed-end moments and to carry-over moments is

$$\Sigma M_F = +154 - 192 + 26 - 72 = -84$$

and the distribution is

$$+84 \times 0.50 = +42 \text{ to } FC \quad \text{and} \quad +42 \text{ to } FG$$

The carry-over moments are

$$+42 \times \tfrac{1}{2} = +21 \text{ to } CF \quad \text{and} \quad +21 \text{ to } GF$$

Note that these carry-over moments unbalance joints C and G, which were previously balanced, but the new unbalanced moments are much smaller than the previous ones.

Fourth Distribution. At joint B the unbalanced moment is

$$\Sigma M_B = +19 - 125 + 30 = -76$$

and the distribution is

$$+76 \times 0.310 = +24 \text{ to } BA$$
$$+76 \times 0.690 = +52 \text{ to } BC$$

Carry-over moments are recorded at AB and CB.

Fifth Distribution. It would be unwise to balance joint C again before joint E is balanced and its carry-over moment included in the balance of joint C.

$$\Sigma M_E = +56 + 10 = +66$$

and the balancing moment is

$$-66 \times 1.0 = -66 \text{ to } EC$$

The carry-over is

$$-66 \times \tfrac{1}{2} = -33 \text{ to } CE$$

Sixth Distribution. Joint C, once balanced, is unbalanced now by carry-over moments which total

$$\Sigma M_C = +26 - 33 + 21 = +14$$

which are balanced as shown in Fig. 12–6B.

The process is continued until the desired accuracy has been obtained. In this problem, moments are computed to the nearest kip-foot. Such accuracy is sufficient for the usual problem. Always end with a balance operation; never leave a carry-over moment unbalanced.

Note that moments at joints A and D are never balanced. The supports are fixed, do not permit rotation, and hence are never unlocked, so there is never any "balance" at a fixed joint.

FINAL MOMENTS. A double line (to distinguish summation from balancing) is drawn under the moments at each joint as shown, and the sum of the moments in each column recorded below the double line. These are the final end moments. They are those moments which would act upon free bodies of the individual members.

The final moments should be totaled for every member at each joint to see if the sum is zero as it should be. Slide-rule mistakes and mistakes in signs can often be discovered in this way, but this is by no means a sure check.

ROTATION. Mentally picture the rotation of each joint as it is balanced. In this way you can "see" the structure settling into its final distorted shape. This helps to build a "structural sense"—the ability to visualize what happens to a structure under load.

Occasionally, it is desirable to compute the rotation of a joint. It can be done using moment area or virtual work and a free-body diagram of any one of the members of the joint. But it is much easier to make use of the distributed moments and the stiffness. Suppose, for example, that the rotation of joint C is wanted. We could select any member, CB, for instance, noting its stiffness to be 54,200 kip-ft. From Fig. 12–6B it was balanced (rotated) by

$+60$ kip-ft in the 1st distribution

-5 kip-ft in the 6th distribution

-2 kip-ft in the 10th distribution

a total of $+53$ kip-ft. If 54,200 kip-ft cause 1 radian (57.3°) of rotation, $+53$ kip-ft cause

$$\theta_C = \frac{+53}{54,200} \times 1 \text{ radian} = +0.00098 \text{ radian} = +0.056° = 3' \, 22''$$

From the discussion of Art. 12–2, the rotation is clockwise because the balancing or rotation moment is plus.

REACTIONS. The reactions can be determined by applying the equations of static equilibrium to the proper free-body diagrams. For example, the horizontal force at E is found by taking moments about C of free body CE, shown in Fig. 12–7B. Thus we have

$$\Sigma M_C = 0 = -109 \text{ (from moment distribution)} + 6 \text{ ft} \times 40 \text{ kips} - 16H_E$$

(1–1)

from which

$$H_E = 8.2 \text{ kips to the right}$$

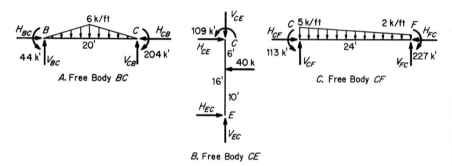

A. Free Body BC

B. Free Body CE

C. Free Body CF

Fig. 12–7. Free bodies of rigid frame in Fig. 12–6.

The vertical component at E must be equal to the shear in CB at C (V_{CB}) plus the shear in CF at C (V_{CF}); there is no vertical reaction at D, unless D is assumed to be a "sky hook." From Fig. 12–7A we have,

$$\Sigma M_B = 0 = -44 \text{ kip-ft} + (6 \text{ kips/ft}) \frac{20 \text{ ft}}{2} \times 10 \text{ ft} + 204 \text{ kip-ft} - 20V_{CB}$$

$$V_{CB} = 38.0 \text{ kips up}$$

and from Fig. 12–7C we have,

$$\Sigma M_F = 0 = -113 \text{ kip-ft} + V_{CF} \times 24 \text{ ft} - \frac{(3 \text{ kips/ft})24 \text{ ft}}{2} \times \frac{2 \times 24 \text{ ft}}{3}$$

$$- (2 \text{ kips/ft})24 \text{ ft} \times \frac{24 \text{ ft}}{2} + 227 \text{ kip-ft}$$

(1–1)

$$V_{CF} = 43.2 \text{ kips up}$$

The vertical reaction at E is, then,

$$V_E = V_{CB} + V_{CF} = 38.0 + 43.2 = 81.2 \text{ kips up}$$

Most other reactions are determined similarly. The determination of the reaction at A is more involved because AB is a sloping member. One method

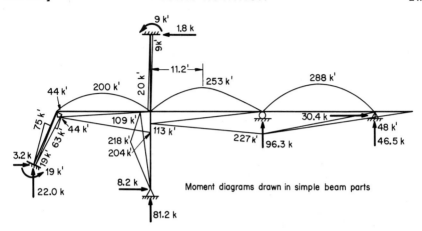

Fig. 12–8. Reactions and moment diagrams. (See Fig. 12–6 for end moments.)

is to write two equations for the vertical and horizontal components at A by summing moments: (1) about B of free body AB and (2) about C of free body ABC; these are solved simultaneously.

The reactions and moment diagrams plotted by simple beam parts are shown in Fig. 12–8. These should be verified by the student before proceeding.

13

SIMPLE JOINT DEFLECTION

13–1. Fixed-End Moments for Joint Deflection. In the preceding article, moments were caused only by fixed-end moments and rotation. Joint deflections were prevented by the supports. But moments due to joint deflections are important in many rigid frames.

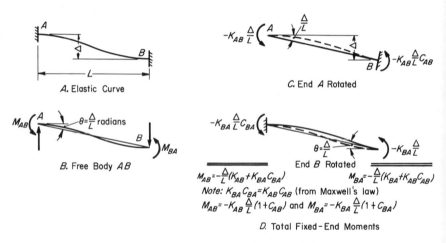

A. Elastic Curve

C. End A Rotated

B. Free Body AB

End B Rotated

$$M_{AB} = -\frac{\Delta}{L}(K_{AB} + K_{BA}C_{BA})$$

$$M_{BA} = -\frac{\Delta}{L}(K_{BA} + K_{AB}C_{AB})$$

Note: $K_{BA}C_{BA} = K_{AB}C_{AB}$ (from Maxwell's law)

$$M_{AB} = -K_{AB}\frac{\Delta}{L}(1 + C_{AB})$$ and $$M_{BA} = -K_{BA}\frac{\Delta}{L}(1 + C_{BA})$$

D. Total Fixed–End Moments

Fig. 13–1. Fixed-end moments for joint deflection.

If one end of a member is deflected relative to the other end while the joints are locked against rotation, fixed-end moments are developed, as shown in Fig. 13–1B. These fixed-end moments are treated just like fixed-end moments due to load. Fixed-end moments due to deflection can be found by using moment area or virtual work. However, the following method is not only much faster but also much better since it is perfectly general and applies to both prismatic and non-prismatic members. The approach is through the following steps:

1. Imagine that member AB is hinged at both ends.
2. Joint B is now deflected an amount Δ, leaving AB straight but rotated clockwise through an angle of Δ/L radians.
3. Now imagine both ends relocked with the beam still straight.

4. Unlock A and apply enough moment to rotate end A counterclockwise Δ/L radians and relock it.

5. Unlock B and apply enough moment to rotate end B counterclockwise Δ/L radians.

The beam is now deflected and the joints are in their original, unrotated position.

Step 4 is illustrated in Fig. 13–1C. The moment at A required to cause a rotation of Δ/L radians is $-K_{AB}(\Delta/L)$ and the moment carried over to B is $-K_{AB}(\Delta/L)C_{AB}$. Joint A is relocked, and in step 5 (Fig. 13–1D) joint B is rotated Δ/L radians, making the two ends parallel. The moment at B required to rotate the joint is $-K_{BA}(\Delta/L)$ and there is a carry-over of $-K_{BA}(\Delta/L)C_{BA}$ to joint A. The total fixed-end moments at A due to rotation and carry-over is the sum of the end moments at point A in Figs. 13–1C and 13–1D, which is

$$M_{AB} = -K_{AB}\frac{\Delta}{L} - K_{BA}\frac{\Delta}{L}C_{BA} = -\frac{\Delta}{L}(K_{AB} + K_{BA}C_{BA})$$

But, from Maxwell's law (or it can be readily shown by virtual work)

$$K_{BA}C_{BA} = K_{AB}C_{AB}$$

Therefore the fixed-end moments become

$$M_{AB} = -K_{AB}\frac{\Delta}{L}(1 + C_{AB})$$

and

$$M_{BA} = -K_{BA}\frac{\Delta}{L}(1 + C_{BA})$$

If the members are prismatic, the fixed-end moment becomes

$$M_{AB} = M_{BA} = -\frac{3}{2}\frac{K\Delta}{L} = -\frac{6EI\,\Delta}{L^2}$$

You can memorize these formulas if you wish, but it is just as easy to remember the method of Fig. 13–1 and solve the fixed-end moments. After a little practice you can solve the fixed-end moments mentally and almost instantaneously. The signs of the moments can be so easily determined by inspection[1] or visualization that there is no point in stating the rule for them.

13–2. Example of Known Joint Translation. Figure 13–2 is illustrative of a general type of problem in which the amount of deflection is known. The distribution factors are determined by inspection. The beam is uniform in section and all spans are equal; therefore all stiffnesses are equal, which makes all the distribution factors equal to 0.5 for each member, except at A and D. The situation at A and D has been explained in Art. 12–3.

---

[1] Make sketches of the deflected structure if necessary.

Converting the deflections from inches to feet, the fixed-end moments are

$$M_{AB} = M_{BA} = \frac{-6EI\,\Delta}{L^2} = \frac{-6 \times 4{,}320{,}000(0.0064)(3\ \text{in.}/12)}{(20)^2}$$

$$= -104\ \text{kip-ft}$$

$$M_{BC} = M_{CB} = \frac{6 \times 4{,}320{,}000(0.0064)(2\ \text{in.}/12)}{(20)^2} = +69\ \text{kip-ft}$$

$$M_{CD} = M_{DC} = \frac{6 \times 4{,}320{,}000(0.0064)(1\ \text{in.}/12)}{(20)^2} = +35\ \text{kip-ft}$$

The balancing and carry-over operations follow the same pattern explained in Art. 12–3. The balancing process was stopped at joint C while the moments

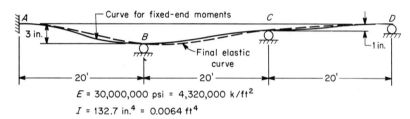

$E = 30{,}000{,}000$ psi $= 4{,}320{,}000$ k/ft^2

$I = 132.7$ in.^{4} $= 0.0064$ ft^4

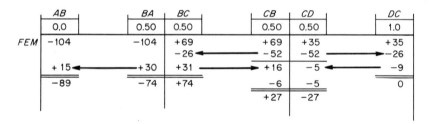

	AB		BA	BC		CB	CD		DC
	0,0		0.50	0.50		0.50	0.50		1.0
FEM	−104		−104	+69		+69	+35		+35
				−26		−52	−52		−26
	+15		+30	+31		+16	−5		−9
	−89		−74	+74		−6	−5		0
						+27	−27		

Fig. 13–2. Settlement of supports.

were still somewhat large, just to show that it can be stopped at any time. Even so, the maximum error is only about 2 kip-ft.

The final moments are the true[2] moments due to deflection. If there are moments due to loads on the spans, these can be included by adding fixed-end moments due to load to those due to deflection before distributing the moments. When analyzing a real structure, it is usually better to distribute the two sets of fixed-end moments separately and add the final results. A designer generally wants to know the effect of each set of loads or distortions independently.

13–3. Fixed-End Moments for Complex Loads. The simplest problem involving an unknown deflection is the determination of fixed-end moments for partial (or "patch") loads by moment distribution. Although

[2] Within the limits of accuracy desired—in this instance, 2 kip-ft.

formulas can be found for some partial loadings,[3] they cannot be found for all of them and, furthermore, it is unwise to be utterly dependent on formulas, particularly when the following general solution is so quick and easy.

The partial loading on the beam of Fig. 13–3 is typical of beams around stair wells. The approach is through the following steps:

1. Introduce a temporary support at point C, compute fixed-end moments for beam CB, balance and carry over (as for any continuous beam), as illustrated in Fig. 13–3B.

2. Find the force exerted by the temporary support at point C by equations of static equilibrium applied to free bodies, as shown in Fig. 13–3C.

3. Cancel the temporary support at point C by applying an equal and opposite reactive force at C, as shown in Fig. 13–3D, and compute the fixed-end moments acting on the beam by making use of the formulas in Fig. 12–1.

4. Add the moments shown at points A and B in Figs. 13–3C and 13–3D to obtain the final correct fixed-end moments.

Another example of the need for a temporary support to find fixed-end moments occurs when a span is divided into two segments (or more) with different, but constant, moments of inertia. This situation occurs, for example, in multiple I-beam bridges where the beams are strengthened over the supports by cover plates, which also increase the moment of inertia. The formulas of Fig. 12–1 cannot be applied to such beams because they are not prismatic over the entire span. Except for step 3, which entails the use of the formulas of Fig. 12–1, the procedure is the same as outlined above. To find fixed-end moments for "an equal and opposite reactive force at C," it is necessary to perform step 3 as follows:

a. Deflect point C (without rotation) any convenient, arbitrary amount. Compute fixed-end moments for temporary span AC and CB from the formula $M = 6EI \, \Delta/L^2$ or from the formulas in Fig. 13–1.

b. Distribute the moments by performing the balance and carry-over operations.

c. Using free bodies of temporary spans AC and CB, compute the reaction at C.

d. Multiply the reaction at C by the constant that makes it equal and opposite to the reaction found in step 2. Then multiply the final moments in part b by the same constant. These are the correct step-3 moments. If the beam were prismatic, the moments obtained in this manner would equal the moments obtained by fixed-end-moment formulas.

The principles involved in parts a through d are clarified by the discussion in Art. 13–4.

Fixed-end moments for most complex loadings can be obtained by combining the loadings shown in Fig. 12–1 in appropriate ways, implemented

---

[3] Hardy Cross and N. D. Morgan, *Continuous Frames of Reinforced Concrete* (New York: John Wiley & Sons, Inc., 1932), p. 85.

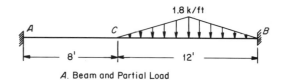

A. Beam and Partial Load

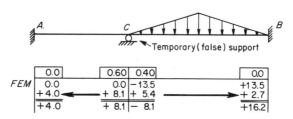

B. End Moments with Temporary Support

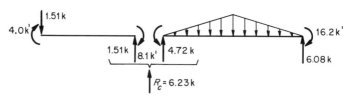

C. Reaction for Temporary Support

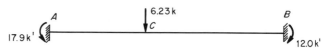

D. Fixed-End Moments for Canceling Temporary
Support

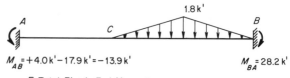

$M_{AB} = +4.0 \text{k}' - 17.9 \text{k}' = -13.9 \text{k}'$ $M_{BA} = 28.2 \text{k}'$

E. Total Fixed-End Moments

Fig. 13–3. Fixed-end moments for a partial load.

when necessary by the method of introducing one or more temporary
reactions as explained above. Thus, by memorizing the first four fixed-end
moments of Fig. 12–1, you can find nearly any fixed-end moment. Fixed-end
moments for an applied moment (the last drawing in Fig. 12–1) can also be
worked by the method of introducing a temporary support, so it is not really
essential to memorize that formula.

Fixed-end moments for the beam of Fig. 13–4A, for example, can be obtained by adding fixed-end moments for a single, concentrated load acting at C, D, and E. If loads occur at the quarter points, the addition can be done algebraically, as follows:

$$M = \sum P \frac{ab^2}{L^2} = \frac{P}{L^2}\left[\frac{L}{4}\left(\frac{3L}{4}\right)^2 + \frac{L}{2}\left(\frac{L}{2}\right)^2 + \frac{3L}{4}\left(\frac{L}{4}\right)^2\right] = \frac{5}{16}PL$$

thus rapidly obtaining a general formula for fixed-end moments.

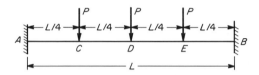

A. Concentrated Loads

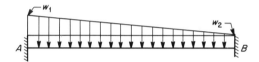

B. Uniformly Varying Load

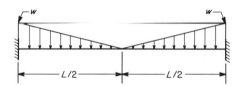

C. Uniformly Varying Load

Fig. 13–4. Fixed-end moments for complex loads.

As shown in Art. 12–3, loads of the type shown in Fig. 13–4B can be handled by breaking the load into a uniform load plus a load varying uniformly to a maximum at one end. Fixed-end moments are computed for each load separately and then added to obtain the total. In Fig. 13–4C, the fixed-end moments are found by subtraction. Fixed-end moments are found for a load varying from zero at the ends to a maximum of w at the center and, again, for a uniform load of w. The difference is the true fixed-end moment. If the loading of Fig. 13–4C were unsymmetrical, fixed-end moments could be found by the method of introducing a temporary support at the point of zero load.

Fixed-end moments for loads which do not vary uniformly must be solved by moment area or virtual work (or by some comparable method). But such loads are rarely encountered in practice, so that such solutions are of only academic interest.

13–4. Example of Sidesway of Single-Story Frames. Another form of deflection analysis is involved in the single-story rigid frame of Fig. 13–5A.

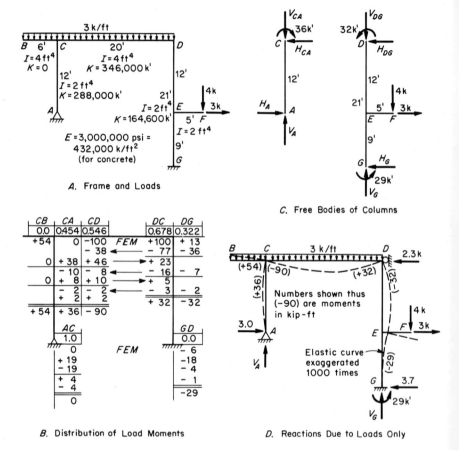

A. Frame and Loads

C. Free Bodies of Columns

B. Distribution of Load Moments

D. Reactions Due to Loads Only

Fig. 13–5. Analysis of single-story frame for load moments only.

In this type of problem, the lateral deflection of the horizontal beam is unknown and a direct solution (one involving predetermined fixed-end moments for deflection) is impossible. Nevertheless, a solution—albeit indirect—can be made by using equations of static equilibrium.

PROCEDURE. There are several well-recognized procedures for handling such problems. Most of them are quite satisfactory and, in spite of any claims to the contrary, one involves about as much labor as another. Speed is a matter of familiarity more than of method. The following method is presented, then, not necessarily because it is better than others, but because beginners seem to understand it more readily. In practice it is about as fast as any method for frames up to three stories, and it possesses the virtue of being readily applicable to all problems without modification.

In general, problems involving sidesway or any other form of unknown joint deflection are solved in several parts. Moments are found for loads first, then for deflections, and finally the two are added. If there are several stories, the moments caused by deflection for each story are found separately.

MOMENTS DUE TO LOAD. Joint deflection is prevented by a temporary (or "false") reaction at D, as shown in Fig. 13–5D. Thus we are enabled to find moments caused by load only. The computation of stiffnesses, distribution factors, and fixed-end moments is straightforward. Therefore, except for the right column, they are not shown here.

Fixed-end moments for the right column are best found by replacing member EF and its loads by equivalent forces[4] at E acting on column DG. Thus the 4-kip load at F produces a clockwise moment at E of 4 kips $\times$ 5 ft $= 20$ kip-ft, and the 3-kip load at F is simply transferred directly to E. Then the fixed-end moments at G are

$$M_{GD} = \frac{Pab^2}{L^2} + \frac{Mb}{L^2}(2a - b)$$

$$= \frac{-3 \times 9(12)^2}{(21)^2} + \frac{20 \text{ kip-ft} \times 12}{(21)^2}(2 \times 9 - 12)$$

$$= 8.8 + 3.3 = -5.5 \text{ kip-ft, say, } -6 \text{ kip-ft}$$

and the fixed-end moments at D are

$$M_{DG} = \frac{Pa^2b}{L^2} + \frac{Ma}{L^2}(2b - a) = \frac{+3(9)^2 12}{(21)^2} + \frac{20 \text{ kip-ft} \times 9}{(21)^2}(2 \times 12 - 9)$$

$$= +6.6 + 6.1 = +12.7 \text{ kip-ft, say, } +13 \text{ kip-ft}$$

REACTIONS DUE TO LOAD. After distributing the load moments in Fig. 13–5B, the horizontal reactions at the lower supports (A and G) are found from free bodies of the columns drawn in Fig. 13–5C. To find H_A, we sum moments at C:

$$\Sigma M_C = 0 = +36 \text{ kip-ft} - 12H_A$$

$$H_A = 3.0 \text{ kips right}$$

---

[4] The "joint" at E is not truly a joint in the sense that moments can be balanced at E; that is because joint E is free to deflect laterally. It is possible, though impractical, to treat E as a true joint, but sidesway corrections are required for it in addition to sidesway corrections for the girder. Corrections for sidesway are thereby complicated needlessly.

To find H_G, sum moments at D:

$$\Sigma M_D = 0$$
$$= -32\text{ kip-ft} - 29\text{ kip-ft} + 4\text{ kips} \times 5\text{ ft} - 3\text{ kips} \times 12\text{ ft} + 21H_G$$
$$H_G = 3.7\text{ kips left}$$

To find the horizontal reaction at the girder (point D), sum horizontal forces acting on a free body of the entire frame. There are such forces acting at A, D, F, and G.

$$\Sigma H = 0 = 3.0\text{ kips} - H_D + 3\text{ kips} - 3.7\text{ kips}$$
$$H_D = 2.3\text{ kips left}$$

MOMENTS DUE TO DEFLECTION. If the horizontal deflection of the girder were known, the moments due to deflection could be solved directly, as in the example of Art. 13-2. Unfortunately the deflection is not known, but even so, a solution is possible through the use of the equations, of statics.

One criterion of the amount of deflection is useful. The deflection must be such that the temporary (or "false") reaction at D constraining the frame against sidesway is exactly counterbalanced by an equal and opposite force caused by sidesway. To explain this in more detail, imagine that our frame is forced to deflect any arbitrary distance to the right. For such deflection the fixed-end moments can be computed and distributed, and from the final moments the horizontal force which holds the frame in its deflected position can be found. Because the deflection was only estimated, it is unlikely that the horizontal force will exactly counterbalance the temporary reaction. But deflections, forces, moments, and reactions are all proportional; therefore they can all be corrected at once if multiplied by a factor such that the horizontal force does counterbalance the temporary reaction. These corrected moments are added algebraically to the moments caused by load alone to obtain the correct total moments. This procedure is clarified in the continuation of the example.

Fixed-end moments are computed for any arbitrary joint deflection, say, 0.003 ft, pictured in Fig. 13-6A, as follows:

$$M_{AC} = M_{CA} = \frac{-3\,\Delta K}{2L} = \frac{-3 \times 0.003 \times 288{,}000}{2 \times 12} = -108\text{ kip-ft}$$

$$M_{GD} = M_{DG} = \frac{-3\,\Delta K}{2L} = \frac{-3 \times 0.003 \times 164{,}600}{2 \times 21} = -35\text{ kip-ft}$$

They are distributed in Fig. 13-6B.

REACTIONS DUE TO SIDESWAY. The horizontal reactions at the supports A and G are found as before from free bodies of the columns. Taking moments at C of free body AC in Fig. 13-6C, we have

$$\Sigma M_C = 0 = -37\text{ kip-ft} + 12H_A$$
$$H_A = 3.1\text{ kips left}$$

Taking moments about D of free body DG, we have

$$\Sigma M_D = 0 = -29 \text{ kip-ft} - 31 \text{ kip-ft} + 21 H_G$$

$$H_G = 2.9 \text{ kips left}$$

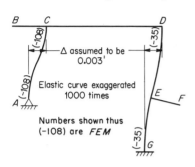

A. Deflected Frame. Sidesway
Fixed-End Moments

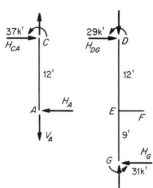

C. Free Bodies of Columns

CB	CA	CD		DC	DG
0.0	0.454	0.546		0.678	0.322
0	-108	0	*FEM*	0	-35
	+54	+12	←	+24	+11
0	+19	+23	→	+12	
	-5	-4	←	-8	-4
0	+4	+5	→	+2	
	-1			-1	-1
0	.0	+1		+29	-29
0	-37	+37			

AC			GD	
1.0			0.0	
-108	*FEM*		-35	
+108			+6	
+10			-2	
-10			-31	
+2				
-2				
0				

B. Distribution of Sidesway Moments

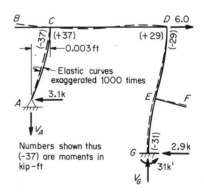

D. Uncorrected Sidesway

Fig. 13-6. Analysis of single-story frame for uncorrected sidesway.

Again the force at the girder required to hold the frame in its deflected position is computed by summing horizontal forces on a free body of the entire frame.

$$\Sigma H = 0 = -3.1 \text{ kips} - 2.9 \text{ kips} + H_D$$

$$H_D = 6.0 \text{ kips right}$$

as shown in Fig. 13-6D.

CORRECTED SIDESWAY. The true sidesway force at the girder must be 2.3 kips to the right so that when the forces and moments due to sidesway are added to those due to load, the total external force at D will be canceled.

The estimated sidesway has resulted in a force of 6.0 kips at D, but it can be corrected to 2.3 kips by multiplying by the correction ratio 2.3/6.0, thus

$$6.0 \text{ kips} \times \frac{2.3}{6.0} = 2.3 \text{ kips}$$

The 6.0 kips can only be corrected this way if all other forces, moments, and the deflections too are multiplied by the same ratio. Thus the true deflection must be

$$\Delta = 0.003 \text{ ft} \times \frac{2.3}{6.0} = 0.0012 \text{ ft}$$

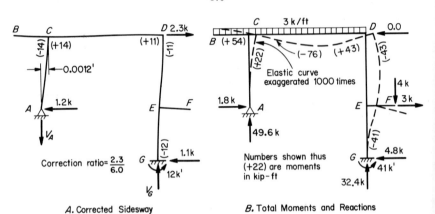

A. Corrected Sidesway   B. Total Moments and Reactions

Fig. 13–7. Corrected sidesway and total moments for single-story frame.

Had this value been used for computing fixed-end moments, the resulting final force[5] at D would have been 2.3 kips. These corrections are possible because deflections, forces, and moments are all mutually proportional. Figure 13–7A shows the moments, shears, and deflections corrected by the ratio 2.3/6.0. These are the true sidesway values.

SUPERPOSITION. The total moments, forces, and elastic curves are found by adding true (corrected) moments, forces, and deflections due to sidesway to those due to load. The results are shown in Fig. 13–7B.

To make sure that the moments have been properly corrected and added, the temporary reactive force at point D should be checked. If it is not zero, then the temporary reaction has not been canceled and the solution is wrong. Summing horizontal forces in Fig. 13–7B, we have, for the entire frame

$$\Sigma H = +1.8 \text{ kips} + 3.0 \text{ kips} - 4.8 \text{ kips} = 0$$

as it should be. This single check does not, however, guarantee that the solution is correct. Methods of checking solutions are discussed in Chapter 15.

[5] Try it.

Discussion. The entire procedure is summarized in outline form and keyed to the figures as follows.

Frame constants:
  1. Compute all K and D values (Fig. 13–5A and B).

Load moments:
  2. Compute fixed-end moments (Fig. 13–5B).
  3. Distribute (Fig. 13–5B).
  4. Compute shears (Fig. 13–5C).
  5. Compute temporary reactions (Fig. 13–5D). If there are none—that is, if they are zero—there is no sidesway and the solution is finished.

Deflection moments:
  6. Compute moments by estimating the deflection (Fig. 13–6A).
  7. Distribute (Fig. 13–6B).
  8. Compute shears (Fig. 13–6C).
  9. Compute the restraint—the force required to hold the frame in its deflected position (Fig. 13–6D).
  10. Correct the restraint to equal the temporary reaction in step 5 (Fig. 13–7A). At the same time correct moments, shears, and deflections.

Combination:
  11. Determine the total moments by adding load moments from step 3 to corrected deflection moments and reactions from step 10 (Fig. 13–7B). Check the temporary support to see if it is truly canceled.

The many figures shown may engender the feeling that the solution is very complicated. That is not so. These figures are shown to add to the clarity and avoid the confusion of too much data per figure. With more experience comes the ability to visualize elastic curves and free-body diagrams so that such figures as 13–5C become superfluous. Then, too, the data in some of the other figures can be combined, thus still further reducing the required number of figures. The entire solution, scratchwork and all, can be easily put on one page. Contrast this with a solution by any of the classical methods such as moment area or virtual work.

An often puzzling point is this: If the horizontal force at the top of the girder is known, why not compute fixed-end moments from the known force? However, this cannot be done because the distribution process changes the moments, the column shears, and the force at the girder. For example, in Fig. 13–6A, the force at the girder can be determined to be 21.3 kips from equations of static equilibrium, but, after the moments are distributed, the force becomes 6.0 kips. Until the moments due to sidesway are distributed, the force causing sidesway cannot be computed.

It is usually unnecessary to compute fixed-end moments due to sidesway by estimating a deflection. Instead, a fixed-end moment can be assumed, which saves a little arithmetic. But whether the fixed-end moments are computed from assumed deflections or from assumed forces, or whether they

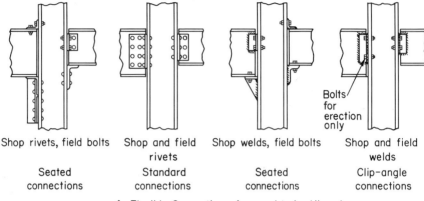

A. Flexible Connections Assumed to be Hinged

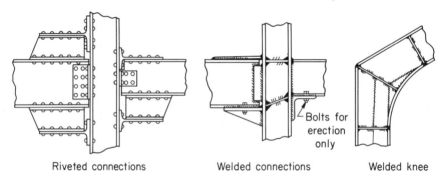

B. Rigid Connections

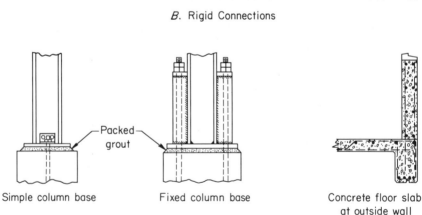

C. Semirigid Supports

Fig. 13-8. Typical joints.

are assumed directly, they must bear the proper relationship to each other. The relationship is that moments are proportional to $I\Delta/L^2$ (assuming E to be constant) and to $1/L^2$ if E, I, and Δ are the same for both columns. In this example the ratio of fixed-end moments must be

$$\frac{M_{\text{left column}}}{M_{\text{right column}}} = \frac{108}{35}$$

The advantage of estimating deflection is that the true deflection is determined by the correction factor. It is often advantageous to know the deflections, and continued use enhances one's structural sense. The only disadvantage is that the fraction $6EI\Delta/L^2$, which contains large numbers, must be evaluated.

Although moments are figured to the nearest kip-foot and forces to the nearest 0.1 kip, systematic errors may be expected to result in errors in the answer of about 2 kip-feet in moment and of about 0.2 kip in force. Such accuracy is ordinarily acceptable. But any degree of accuracy desired can be obtained by carrying figures to a suitable number of significant places. Moment distribution is a method of successive approximations, not an approximate method.

13–5. Partial Fixity. Heretofore the discussion has been limited to reactions that were either fixed or hinged and to joints that were rigid. Actually, there are few such joints outside the laboratory. True hinges have been used in bridges and monumental buildings, but tests show that even these sometimes develop considerable moment.

FLEXIBLE AND RIGID JOINTS. Typical flexible joints are shown in Fig. 13–8A. Whether bolted, riveted, or welded, these are built flexible enough so that the joints are incapable of resisting much moment. Members so connected are treated as though they were on knife-edge supports. The assumption is a good one and on the safe side.

Rigid connections are shown in Fig. 13–8B. It requires a regiment of rivets and massive construction to approach true rigidity in a riveted joint. In contrast, a rigid welded joint is clean and simple. But even welded joints can bristle with diaphragms and welds when beams of different sizes frame into a column from four directions. Although there is some elastic deformation in all these joints, and the possibility of some slip in the riveted joints, common practice is well justified in treating them as rigid.

SEMI-RIGID JOINTS. It is possible to consider slip in riveted or bolted joints by analyzing first as though for rigid joints. Then, where moments are large enough to cause slip, the rotation due to slip is computed (estimated might be a better word). The moments due to this rotation are computed, treated just like fixed-end moments, and distributed in the usual manner. The total moments are those from the first analysis made for rigid joints added to those due to slip.[6] Elastic joint deformation can be considered in a somewhat similar manner.[7]

REACTIONS. The fixity or rigidity of reactions is not usually so clear cut as that of joints; that is, reactions are usually semi-rigid in contrast to joints which are usually either flexible or rigid. The simple (or "flexible") column base of Fig. 13–8C can develop considerable moment because the lower end of the column is milled, and grout is packed tightly under the base plate. On the other hand, the "fixed" column base cannot be truly rigid because, although the joint itself is rigid, the pedestal and footing deform slightly, and the entire unit can rotate as a whole upon the yielding soil. The outside beam and wall, which is the support for the floor slab, can rotate elastically between columns. Thus, even though the joint itself is rigid, the reaction is neither fixed nor hinged.

In conclusion, it is usually safe to regard joints as either completely flexible or completely rigid. But such practice may often be unsafe for column bases and other supports, which should usually be considered partially fixed.

DEFINITION OF PARTIAL FIXITY. For our purposes a partially fixed support is one which resists rotation elastically. For convenience the fixity is expressed as a percentage directly convertible to a distribution factor by the formula

$$D = 1 - \frac{\text{percent fixity}}{100}$$

Thus if a support has a fixity of zero percent, it is a hinge or knife edge, and the distribution factor is 1.00, as explained before in Art. 12–3. If a support is rigid, its fixity is 100 percent, and, according to the above formula, the distribution factor is zero. If a support is 75 percent fixed, the distribution factor for the member at the support is 0.25.

The percentage of fixity can be visualized as a physical concept. Imagine the partially fixed support replaced by a knife-edge support and the member extended to an imaginary fixed support. The distribution factors at the knife-edge support can be varied at will by varying the extended length. A support of zero fixity, then, can be replaced by a knife-edge reaction and the member extended to infinity. If the support is 75 percent fixed, the member can be visualized as extending one-third of its length beyond the knife edge to the imaginary fixed support.

PERCENTAGE OF PARTIAL FIXITY. In practice, the percentage of partial fixity is simply estimated. This may seem speculative, but in reality it is not more so than the assumption of, say, a rigid reaction. Certainly it is

[6] Bruce Johnson and E. H. Mount, "Analysis of Building Frames with Semi-Rigid Connections." *Trans. ASCE*, 107: 993–1019, 1942.

[7] J. C. Rathbun, "Elastic Properties of Riveted Connections," *Trans. ASCE*, 101: 524–596, 1936.

better practice to estimate a certain percentage of partial fixity than it is to ignore the possibility of joint rotation entirely. The consequences of estimating a partial fixity are no more serious than those of other assumptions that the designer makes constantly.

The estimation can be a sheer guess or it can be determined by calculations based on laws of mechanics with suitable assumptions. For example, the rotation of a footing on soft clay soil can be computed with reasonable accuracy from principles of soil mechanics. This rotation added to that due to flexure in the footing pad, the pedestal, and the joint itself can be equated to the rotation of the member extended to the imaginary fixed support by suitably adjusting the extension of the member. A few such computations made in his spare time will give the designer a "feeling" for the percentage of fixity that should be assigned. There is no such thing as a "safe" guess here; that is, one cannot estimate the partial fixity at 25 percent, and then double it to make sure. The only sure analysis is the wasteful one of using both zero percent and 100 percent fixity and making certain the structure is safe for everything between.

14

COMPLEX JOINT DEFLECTION

14–1. Multiple-Story Frames. Sidesway analysis for multi-story frames is very similar to analysis of two-story frames. The principles of the analysis of two-story frames are directly applicable to multi-story frame analysis and to other complex frames as well. In the single-story frame we have only one deflection to consider. In multi-story frames, there are several

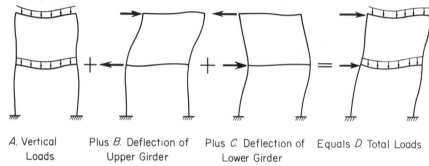

| A. Vertical | Plus B. Deflection of | Plus C. Deflection of | Equals D. Total Loads |
| Loads | Upper Girder | Lower Girder | |

Fig. 14–1. Analysis of multi-story frames.

(or at least two) deflections. Neither the amount of deflection nor the relation between the several deflections is known, and multi-story sidesway analysis is complicated by the fact that each deflection has a considerable effect on every temporary, or false, reaction.

PROCEDURE. Sidesway analysis for multi-story frames is exemplified by the two-story frame of Fig. 14–1. If the frame and vertical loads are symmetrical, there will be no joint deflection, and the elastic curve is as shown in Fig. 14–1A. But if the frame or the loads are unsymmetrical or if there are horizontal forces (which may be caused by wind or earthquake[1]), then sidesway corrections are required. Sidesway analysis is made by:

    1. Deflecting first the upper girder and solving for the acting forces using free bodies and the principles of equilibrium (Fig. 14–1B).

    2. Deflecting the lower girder and again solving for the acting forces (Fig. 14–1C).

---

[1] Earthquake forces are usually approximated by assuming horizontal static forces acting at each floor level.

3. Correcting the moments due to sidesway by equating the forces causing deflection to the forces known to exist. There are two sets of forces (one at the top girder and one at the lower girder), so two equations must be solved simultaneously.

4. Adding moments due to: (*a*) vertical load; (*b*) corrected deflection of the upper girder; and (*c*) corrected deflection of the lower girder to obtain the final moments for the total loads in Fig. 14–1*D*.

This procedure is the same whether sidesway is caused by horizontal forces or by only vertical loads accompanied by dissymmetry.

14–2. Example of Two-Story Frame. The illustrative example of Fig. 14–2*A* is that of a single-bay two-story symmetrical frame subjected to intrapanel[2] loads and to horizontal forces acting at the girders. The column bases are partially fixed. It should be noted that the procedure is the same whether the sidesway is caused by unsymmetrical loads, by an unsymmetrical frame, or by horizontal forces.

The stiffnesses rather than the moments of inertia have been assumed directly. They correspond roughly to 10-in. and 14-in. steel wide-flange beams and to 10-in. wide-flange columns. The loads and spans shown closely represent those commonly encountered.

MOMENTS WITHOUT SIDESWAY. The frame is first analyzed without sidesway by introducing temporary or false reactions at D and E. With these temporary reactions preventing joint translation, the horizontal concentrated loads cannot cause fixed-end moments, so the only fixed-end moments are those caused by the uniform loads. These are distributed in Fig. 14–2*B*.

FALSE REACTIONS. The determination of the false reactions often troubles beginners, therefore these calculations are completely described. This part of the problem is statically determinate, and so the principles are simple: calculate the shear in the columns, draw free-body diagrams of the upper story and the whole frame, and apply Eq. 1–2 ($\Sigma H = 0$) to each free body to find the unknown false reactions.

Column shears in the upper story are calculated from the free bodies shown in Fig. 14–2*C*. Note that these columns are cut between the girders, that is, short of the girders. Thus neither the girders nor the loads at the joints (such as the 3-kip load at point C) are shown. To find the shear at B, sum moments about point C.

$$\Sigma M_C = 0 = 37\,\text{kip-ft} + 41\,\text{kip-ft} + (0.14\,\text{kip/ft})16\,\text{ft} \times 8\,\text{ft} - 16H_B$$

$$H_B = +3.8\,\text{kips} = 3.8\,\text{kips right}$$

[2] Intrapanel loads are those which occur between joints as distinguished from panel point loads which act at the joints.

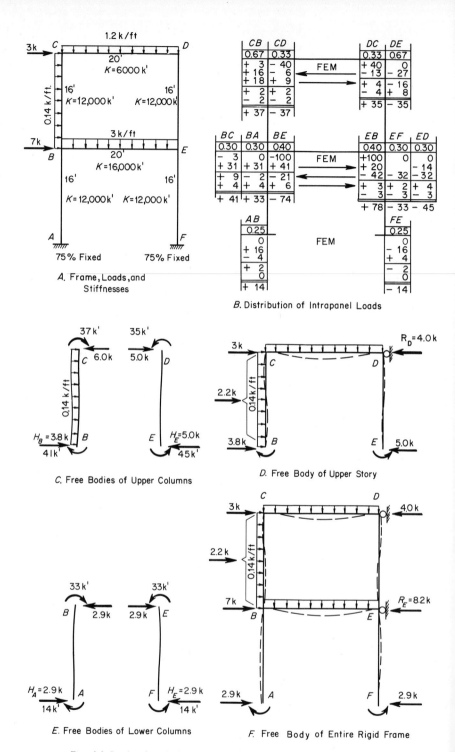

Fig. 14–2. Analysis of two-story frame for intrapanel loads.

In the same way, sum moments about point D to find the shear at the base of the right column.

$$\Sigma M_D = 0 = -35 \text{ kip-ft} - 45 \text{ kip-ft} + 16 H_C$$
$$H_C = +5.0 \text{ kips} = 5.0 \text{ kips left}$$

Now from the free body of the upper story (Fig. 14–2D),

$$\Sigma H = 0 = +3.8 \text{ kips} + 2.2 \text{ kips} + 3 \text{ kips} - R_D - 5.0 \text{ kips}$$
$$R_D = +4.0 \text{ kips} = 4.0 \text{ kips left}$$

Column shears at the base of the lower columns are calculated from the free-body diagrams of Fig. 14–2E. Again note that these columns are cut between the joints so that loads at the joints (such as the 7-kip load at point B) are not shown. Find shears at the base of each column by writing moments about the upper end:

$$\Sigma M_B = 0 = +33 \text{ kip-ft} + 14 \text{ kip-ft} - 16 H_A$$
$$H_A = +2.9 \text{ kips} = 2.9 \text{ kips right}$$
$$\Sigma M_E = 0 = -33 \text{ kip-ft} - 14 \text{ kip-ft} - 16 H_F$$
$$H_F = -2.9 \text{ kips} = 2.9 \text{ kips left}$$

Now draw a free body of the entire frame, as shown in Fig. 14–2F. The horizontal loads are the shears at A and F, the panel point loads of 7 kips and 3 kips at B and C, the uniform load between B and C, the false reaction of 4.0 kips at D, and the unknown false reaction at E. Equate the horizontal forces to zero.

$$\Sigma H = 0$$
$$= +2.9 \text{ kips} + 7 \text{ kips} + 2.2 \text{ kips} + 3 \text{ kips} - 4.0 \text{ kips} - R_E - 2.9 \text{ kips}$$
$$R_E = +8.2 \text{ kips} = 8.2 \text{ kips left}$$

DEFLECTION OF UPPER GIRDER. The upper girder is assumed to be deflected to the right some arbitrary distance, say 0.05 ft. The fixed-end moments are

$$M = \frac{3K\Delta}{2L} = \frac{-3}{2} \times \frac{12{,}000 \times 0.05}{16} = -56 \text{ kip-ft}$$

The minus sign is determined by inspection. The moments are distributed in Fig. 14–3A.

The horizontal forces acting on the frame to hold it in its deflected position are figured from the free bodies shown in Fig. 14–3B. Summing moments about the top of the upper left column, we have

$$\Sigma M_C = 0 = -21 \text{ kip-ft} - 31 \text{ kip-ft} + 16 H_{BC}$$
$$H_{BC} = 3.2 \text{ kips left}$$

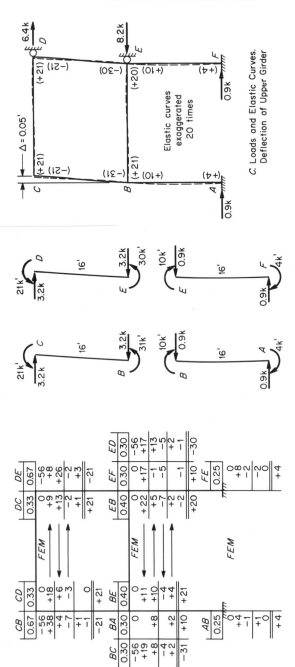

C. Loads and Elastic Curves. Deflection of Upper Girder.

B. Free Bodies of Columns. Vertical Forces Not Shown

A. Distribution. Deflection of Upper Girder

Fig. 14-3. Analysis of two-story frame for deflection of upper girder.

at the bottom of the column and, similarly, the shear at the bottom of the upper right column is

$$H_{ED} = 3.2 \text{ kips left}$$

Now taking the entire upper story of the frame as a free body and summing horizontal forces, we have

$$\Sigma H = 0 = -3.2 \text{ kips} - 3.2 \text{ kips} + R_D$$
$$R_D = 6.4 \text{ kips right}$$

as shown in Fig. 14–3C.

The reaction at E is found by computing first the shears at the foundations (points A and F) and then summing horizontal forces on the entire frame. Summing moments about the top of the lower left column, we have

$$\Sigma M_B = 0 = +10 \text{ kip-ft} + 4 \text{ kip-ft} - 16H_A$$
$$H_A = 0.9 \text{ kip right}$$

at the base of the column, and the shear at the base of the right column is, similarly,

$$H_F = 0.9 \text{ kip right}$$

Taking the entire frame as a free body, as shown in Fig. 14–3C, and summing horizontal forces, we have

$$\Sigma H = 0 = +6.4 \text{ kips} + 0.9 \text{ kip} + 0.9 \text{ kip} - H_E$$
$$H_E = 8.2 \text{ kips left}$$

DEFLECTION OF LOWER GIRDER. The lower girder is assumed to be deflected to the right any arbitrary distance. If the distance is 0.05 ft, the fixed-end moments are again 56 kip-ft in both the upper and lower columns. Moments in the upper columns are plus while those in the lower columns are minus, as determined from inspection of the deflected structure.

The moments are distributed in Fig. 14–4A. The column free bodies are pictured in Fig. 14–4B. The horizontal reactions in Fig. 14–4C are determined in exactly the same manner as explained for the deflection of the upper girder.

TOTAL MOMENTS. The total moments are those due to the intrapanel (uniform) loads plus the corrected moments due to deflection of the upper girder plus the corrected moments due to deflection of the lower girder.

As with the single-story example, we do not know the amount of the deflection of either of the two girders. But we do know that the temporary reactions at D and E must be zero; that is, the deflections must be such as to eliminate them. They can be eliminated by adding the correct proportion of the deflection of the upper girder and the correct proportion of the deflection of the lower girder to the moments due to intrapanel loads. Calling the

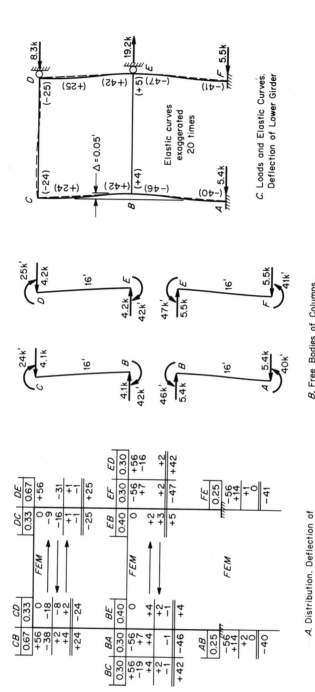

C. Loads and Elastic Curves.
Deflection of Lower Girder.

B. Free Bodies of Columns.
Vertical Forces Not Shown

A. Distribution. Deflection of
Lower Girder

Fig. 14–4. Analysis of two-story frame for deflection of lower girder.

correct proportion of the deflection of the upper girder x and the correct proportion of the lower girder y, two simultaneous equations can be written, thus:

$$\text{Reaction at } D = 0 = +6.4x - 8.3y - 4.0 \text{ kips}$$

$$\text{Reaction at } E = 0 = -8.2x + 19.2y - 8.2 \text{ kips}$$

from which

$$x = 2.64$$

$$y = 1.55$$

The corrected deflection of the upper girder is, then

$$\Delta_C = 0.05 \times 2.64 = 0.132 \text{ ft}$$

and the corrected deflection of the lower girder is

$$\Delta_B = 0.05 \times 1.55 = 0.078 \text{ ft}$$

The final end moments in Fig. 14–3A are multiplied by the correction factor 2.64, and the final end moments in Fig. 14–4A are multiplied by the correction factor 1.55. These are the corrected sidesway moments. When they are added to the intrapanel load moments of Fig. 14–2B, the total moments of Fig. 14–5A are obtained.

These total moments should always be checked to see whether the false reactions have been truly eliminated. Computations for the check are made from the free bodies shown in Fig. 14–5B. They show the horizontal forces to be 3.2 kips and 6.9 kips at C and B, respectively. The error is indicative of the required number of significant figures in the computations. The last digit, although unreliable, is seldom greatly in error in moment distribution calculations. The 6 percent error in this example represents good practical accuracy.

The total loads acting on the structure are shown in Fig. 14–5C together with the final moments in parentheses. The elastic curves are exaggerated 20 times. The amount of deflection is quite typical of steel structures which are, in general, much more flexible than reinforced concrete structures.

A separate figure has been drawn to clarify each step of the computations. Actually, only Figs. 14–2B, 14–3A, and 14–4A are required, so the problem is much less complicated than the number of drawings would make it seem.

14–3. Modified Constants for Partial Fixities.

A great many shortcuts have been invented for moment distribution. But the basic method is so simple and fast that it is not generally worth while to clutter the mind with variations. One shortcut, however, is so simple that its advantages far outweigh its disadvantage. Furthermore, its use sometimes makes simple problems balance to the exact answer in the first distribution.

In the examples illustrated thus far, a hinged reaction (such as that in Figs. 12–6 and 13–2) is treated as follows: moments from the adjacent joint are carried over to the reaction, distributed, and carried back again. This

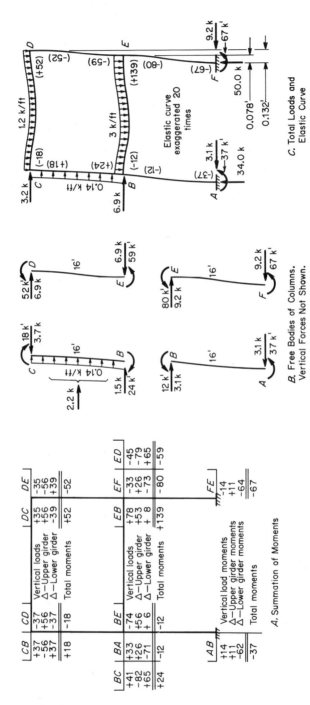

C. Total Loads and Elastic Curve.

B. Free Bodies of Columns. Vertical Forces Not Shown.

A. Summation of Moments

Fig. 14-5. Analysis of two-story frame. Total moments, forces, and elastic curve.

procedure can be shortened by modifying the stiffness factors and the distribution factors so that carry-over to the reaction is eliminated. Physically this means that the joint at the reaction is unlocked and remains unlocked and free to rotate throughout every step in the solution. This is a departure from the basic method of keeping *every* joint locked except the joint at which moments are being distributed.

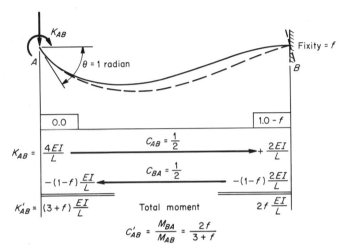

Fig. 14–6. Modified stiffness and carry-over for partial fixity. Prismatic members.

This modification can be extended to include joints that are partially fixed. There is a slight difference in that moments are carried over to the reaction, but there the difference ceases, for there is no distribution and no moment is carried back. Physically, as with the hinged reaction, the joint remains unlocked throughout the entire solution, and it is free to rotate within the constraint of its degree of partial fixity.

PRISMATIC MEMBERS. Member AB of Fig. 14–6 is a free body of one member of a rigid frame partially fixed at B. To find the stiffness at A, lock the joint at B and rotate the end 1 radian at A. The moment required is $K_{AB} = 4EI/L$, and half of this moment is carried to B. Now relock joint A and unlock joint B and balance it. According to the definition of partial fixity (Art. 13–5), the balancing moment is $-(1 - f)(2EI/L)$. Half of this moment is carried over to joint A. The total moment at joint A is the modified stiffness (abbreviated K').

$$K'_{AB} = (3 + f)\frac{EI}{L}$$

If the fixity at B is zero (a hinge), the modified stiffness is $3EI/L$ which is $\frac{3}{4}$ of the unmodified stiffness.

The modified carry-over factor from A to B is found by dividing the total moment at B by the total moment at A, which yields

$$C'_{AB} = \frac{2f}{3+f}$$

This reduces to zero if B is a hinge, showing that no moment is carried over to a hinge joint by this shortcut method.

MODIFIED FIXED-END MOMENTS. If the partially fixed or hinged joints are to remain unlocked from the beginning of the solution, the fixed-end

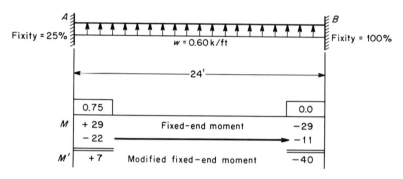

Fig. 14–7. Computation of modified fixed-end moments.

moments must be modified accordingly. It is possible to start with unmodified moments and modify them as the solution proceeds. But this is sometimes confusing, and therefore it is better to start the problem with modified moments.

In the beam of Fig. 14–7 the unmodified fixed-end moments are

$$M = \frac{WL^2}{12} = \frac{0.60(24)^2}{12} = 29 \text{ kip-ft}$$

From the definition of partial fixity, the distribution factor at A is 0.75. Joint A is unlocked; the balancing moment is

$$-0.75(+29) = -22$$

and half of this moment is carried over to B. The total moments are the modified fixed-end moments (abbreviated FEM' or M').

NON-PRISMATIC MEMBERS. It is possible to develop formulas for non-prismatic members, but they are so cumbersome that it is easier to use the method of Fig. 14–6 for finding stiffnesses and carry-over factors and the method of Fig. 14–7 for fixed-end moments. The unmodified starting values must be determined first either by means of tables, as explained in Art. 14–5, or by some other suitable method such as moment area, virtual work, or the use of models.

14–4. Example of a Split-Level Rigid Frame. The following example illustrates both the use of modified constants and the extension of moment distribution for solving more complex problems. The frame, acted upon by horizontal loads caused by wind, is shown in Fig. 14–8. The columns (10 W⁻ 49) and girders (14 W⁻ 34) are about the proper size for this frame.

The final moments would result in large deflections and in serious over-stress at one point (*E*). To reduce the overstress, the support at that point could be built semi-rigid; to reduce the deflections, the other two supports

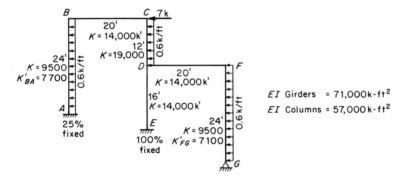

Fig. 14–8. Split-level rigid frame and wind loads.

should be more rigid. Thus, proper foundation design would redistribute the moments in such a way that stresses would be more uniform and within (or at least close to) the allowable stresses. The frame and its conditions of fixity were, then, chosen to demonstrate moment distribution—not good design practice.

STIFFNESSES. The unmodified stiffnesses (*K*) are shown in Fig. 14–8. If modified constants are to be used, the modified stiffness of column *AB* is

$$K'_{BA} = \frac{(3+f)EI}{L} = \frac{3.25 \times 57,000}{24} = 7700 \text{ kip-ft}$$

and the modified stiffness of column *FG* is

$$K'_{FG} = \frac{(3+f)EI}{L} = \frac{3.0 \times 57,000}{24} = 7100 \text{ kip-ft}$$

The stiffnesses of the girders and of the center columns cannot be modified because their ends are fixed or rigidly attached to other members.

The distribution factors are computed in the usual way, using the modified stiffnesses for the outside columns and the unmodified stiffnesses for the other members.

CARRY-OVER FACTORS. If the modified constants are used, the carry-over factors for the outside columns must be modified as follows.

For member AB, the carry-over factor from B to A is

$$C'_{BA} = \frac{2f}{3+f} = \frac{2 \times 0.25}{3 + 0.25} = 0.15$$

and the carry-over factor from F to G is

$$C'_{FG} = \frac{2f}{3+f} = \frac{2 \times 0}{3 + 0} = 0$$

All the other carry-over factors are $\frac{1}{2}$ and none of them can be modified.

FIXED-END MOMENTS. When modified constants are used, the fixed-end moments in members partially fixed *must* be modified also. The modified fixed-end moments for column AB are shown in Fig. 14–7. The modified fixed-end moment for column FG (or for any member pinned at one end) can be computed mentally if the unmodified fixed-end moment is known. The procedure is as follows:

	G		F	
	1.0		0.0	
M	$+29$		-29	(unmodified fixed-end moment)
	-29	$\longrightarrow$	-14	(distribution and carry-over)
M'	0		-43	(modified fixed-end moment)

So for any prismatic member symmetrically loaded and pinned at one end, the modified fixed-end moment is always equal to 1.5 times the unmodified moment at the fixed end. It is zero at the pinned end.

All other members are either fixed or rigidly attached to other members, so no other fixed-end moments can be modified. The 7-kip force at C causes only deflection fixed-end moments, which are to be treated with sidesway and are to be ignored for the present.

MOMENTS WITHOUT SIDESWAY. Moments are distributed in the usual way, except that moments are not balanced at A and G because these two joints are kept continuously unlocked; that is, they are always in balance through the modification of stiffnesses and fixed-end moments. Therefore, the distribution factors at A and G are now zero, as shown in Fig. 14–9A. The column shears are computed from the free bodies shown in Fig. 14–9B.

As with the two-story frame, there are temporary (or false) reactions that prevent joint deflection. These are computed by summing all horizontal forces acting on free body $ABCD$, Fig. 14–9C:

$$\Sigma H = 0 = -(0.6 \text{ kip/ft})24 \text{ ft} - (0.6 \text{ kip/ft})12 \text{ ft} - 7 \text{ kips} + 2.4 \text{ kips}$$
$$+ 6.5 \text{ kips} + R_B$$
$$R_B = 19.7 \text{ kips right}$$

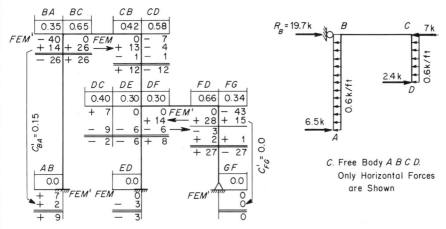

A. Distribution of Load Moments

C. Free Body A B C D.
Only Horizontal Forces
are Shown

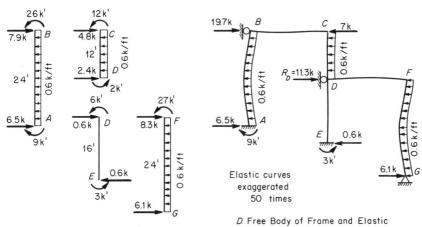

B. Free Bodies of Columns. Vertical
Forces not Shown

D. Free Body of Frame and Elastic
Curves. Vertical Forces not Shown

Elastic curves
exaggerated
50 times

Fig. 14–9. Analysis of split-level frame for intrapanel loads.

Next, sum horizontal forces on a free body of the entire frame, as shown in Fig. 14–9D:

$$\Sigma H = 0 = -(0.6 \text{ kip/ft})24 \text{ ft} - (0.6 \text{ kip/ft})12 \text{ ft} - (0.6 \text{ kip/ft})24 \text{ ft}$$
$$- 7 \text{ kips} - 0.6 \text{ kip} + 19.7 \text{ kips} + 6.5 \text{ kips} + 6.1 \text{ kips} + R_D$$

$$R_D = 11.3 \text{ kips right}$$

DEFLECTION OF THE UPPER GIRDER. The upper girder is assumed to be deflected to the left some arbitrary distance, say 0.20 ft, as shown in the inset

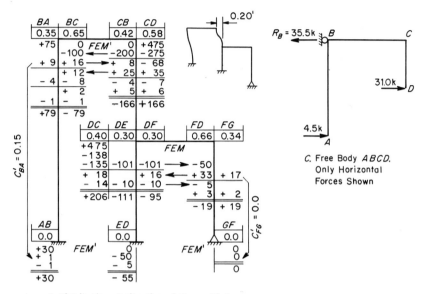

A. Distribution. Deflection of Upper Girder

C. Free Body ABCD.
Only Horizontal
Forces Shown

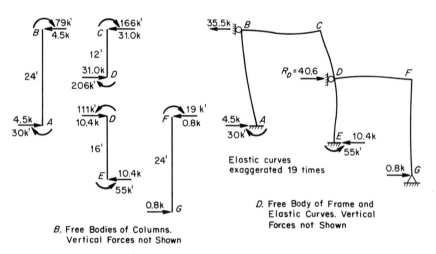

B. Free Bodies of Columns.
Vertical Forces not Shown

D. Free Body of Frame and
Elastic Curves. Vertical
Forces not Shown

Fig. 14-10. Analysis of split-level frame for deflection of upper girder.

of Fig. 14–10A. The unmodified fixed-end moments acting on column AB are

$$FEM = \frac{6EI\Delta}{L^2} = \frac{6 \times 57{,}000 \times 0.20}{24 \times 24} = 119 \text{ kip-ft}$$

Or we could compute the fixed-end moment from the formula developed in Fig. 13–1:

$$FEM = K\frac{\Delta}{L}(1 + C) = \frac{3K\Delta}{2L} = \frac{3 \times 9500 \times 0.20}{2 \times 24} = 119 \text{ kip-ft}$$

Note well that the stiffness used above is the *unmodified* stiffness K; *modified stiffnesses K' cannot be used in this formula.*

Now the fixed-end moment above must be modified in the manner illustrated in Fig. 14–7. The computations are:

	A		B
	0.75		0.0
FEM	+119		+119
	−89	———————→	−44
FEM'	+30		+75

The fixed-end moments in column CD are

$$FEM = \frac{6EI\Delta}{L^2} = \frac{6 \times 57{,}000 \times 0.20}{12 \times 12} = 475 \text{ kip-ft}$$

These moments are not to be modified because the member is not partially fixed.

As only columns AB and CD are deflected, there are no other fixed-end moments. The moments are distributed in Fig. 14–10A.

The temporary reactions are computed in the manner already explained in this article under the subhead *Moments Without Sidesway*. Shear at the base of each column is computed as shown in Fig. 14–10B, by using a free body of only the column in question.

Then compute one false reaction, using a free body that contains only that one false reaction, as illustrated by the free body $ABCD$ of Fig. 14–10C. The equation is

$$\Sigma H = 0 = +4.5 \text{ kips} + 31.0 \text{ kips} - R_B$$
$$R_B = 35.5 \text{ kips left}$$

Next compute the other temporary reaction by using a free body that contains only that one unknown force, although it may contain any other *known* temporary reactions. For example, from the free body of the entire frame shown in Fig. 14–10D, we can write an equation of static equilibrium for horizontal forces, thus:

$$\Sigma H = 0 = -35.5 \text{ kips} + 4.5 \text{ kips} - 10.4 \text{ kips} + 0.8 \text{ kip} + R_D$$
$$R_D = 40.6 \text{ kips right}$$

Another free body that might be used just as effectively is $EDFG$. Note that the shear in column CD just above point D is 31.0 kips and acts left on the free body. The equation is

$$\Sigma H = 0 = -31.0 \text{ kips} - 10.4 \text{ kips} + 0.8 \text{ kip} + R_D$$
$$R_D = 40.6 \text{ kips right}$$

DEFLECTION OF LOWER GIRDER. The lower girder is assumed to be deflected to the left some arbitrary distance, say 0.10 ft. The fixed-end moments in column CD are

$$M = \frac{6EI\Delta}{L^2} = \frac{-6 \times 57{,}000 \times 0.10}{12 \times 12} = -237 \text{ kip-ft}$$

In column DE, they are

$$M = \frac{6EI\Delta}{L^2} = \frac{+6 \times 57{,}000 \times 0.10}{16 \times 16} = +134 \text{ kip-ft}$$

In column FG, the unmodified fixed-end moments are

$$M = \frac{6EI\Delta}{L^2} = \frac{+6 \times 57{,}000 \times 0.10}{24 \times 24} = +59 \text{ kip-ft}$$

But these moments in FG must be modified for the hinged reaction at G as follows:

	G		F
	1.0		0.0
FEM	+59		+59
	−59	⟶	−30
FEM'	0		+29

The moments are distributed in Fig. 14–11A. Column shears and temporary reactions, which are shown in Fig. 14–11B, are found in exactly the same manner as described before.

TOTAL MOMENTS. The total moments are those due to intrapanel loads, plus the corrected moments due to deflection of the upper girder, plus the corrected moments due to the deflection of the lower girder. The problem is similar to that for the two-story frame of Art. 14–2.

The temporary reactions at B and D must be eliminated by equating them to zero. Calling the correct proportion of the deflection of the upper girder x and that of the lower girder y, two simultaneous equations may be written:

$$\text{Reaction at } B = 0 = +19.7 - 35.5x + 20.6y$$

$$\text{Reaction at } D = 0 = +11.3 + 40.6x - 38.3y$$

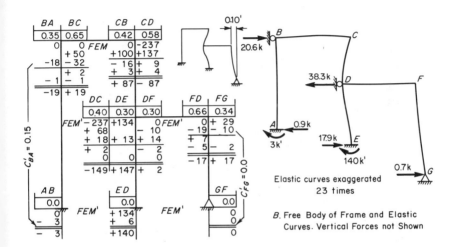

A. Distribution. Deflection of Lower Girder

Fig. 14-11. Analysis of split-level frame for deflection of lower girder.

from which

$$x = 1.89$$

$$y = 2.30$$

The corrected deflection of the upper girder is, then,

$$\Delta_B = 0.20 \text{ ft} \times 1.89 = 0.38 \text{ ft}$$

and that of the lower girder is

$$\Delta_D = 0.10 \text{ ft} \times 2.30 = 0.23 \text{ ft}$$

The final end moments from Fig. 14-10A are multiplied by 1.89 and the final end moments of Fig. 14-11A are multiplied by 2.30. These are added to the final end moments of Fig. 14-9A to obtain the total moments, which are shown in Fig. 14-12A. The elastic curves and the true forces are shown in Fig. 14-12B. Note that the force at B is not exactly 7 kips and that there is a force at D which should be zero. These inaccuracies are the result of rounding off the column shears to the nearest 0.1 kip; the simultaneous equations are very sensitive to small changes in the coefficients. Therefore the computed correction factors are not particularly accurate. In problems of this sort it is well to compute shears and temporary reactions to the nearest 0.01 kip, then round off the final answer to the nearest 0.1 kip.

The elastic curves were constructed in the following manner. First the problem was reworked by using *unmodified* constants. The solution illustrated in Figs. 14–9 through 14–12 cannot be used. Joint rotations were computed[3]

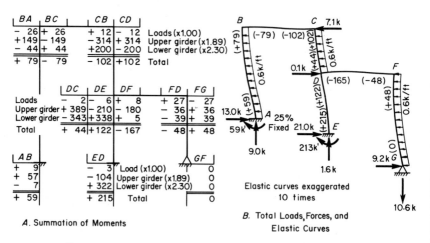

Fig. 14–12. Analysis of split-level frame. Total moments, forces, and elastic curve.

as explained in Art. 12–3. The deflection from a straight line joining the two ends of a member can be computed by using the curve in Fig. 12–3. That curve results from an end rotation of 1 radian, but if the rotation is less, the deflections are less in the same proportion, and since rotation is proportional to the *balancing moment*, the following formula for deflection at the center is obtained from the curve:

$$\Delta_{center} = \frac{M_{balancing}L}{8K}$$

If both ends of the member rotate (as they usually do), the deflections from rotation of each end are added either algebraically or graphically. If there are loads acting on the member, add algebraically the deflection due to load. For a fixed-ended member, the deflection due to a uniform load is

$$\Delta_{center} = \frac{WL^3}{384EI}$$

[3] Rotation equals the sum of *balancing moments* in a member (at the end for which joint rotation is wanted) divided by the stiffness. The result is rotation in radians.

The deflection due to a concentrated center load is

$$\Delta_{center} = \frac{PL^3}{192EI}$$

The elastic curves are drawn through the known points of deflection and tangent to the known rotations at the joints. Together with the total moments (which give some idea of the amount of curvature), the above data are quite sufficient for constructing reasonably accurate elastic curves. But remember, this cannot be done by using modified constants.

The only excuse for this shortcut is to decrease the labor of the distribution process. But in this particular example, the use of the modified constants decreases the labor very little; the number of cycles of distribution is reduced about 30 percent by using modified constants. But since the constants themselves require a little extra work, the advantage is lost to some extent. Where high accuracy is needed (requiring many cycles) or where members with large moments are pinned or nearly so, the modified constants are well worth while. For those who use moment distribution rarely, this shortcut is best avoided.

14–5. Non-prismatic Members. Tapered and haunched members are widely used in modern practice, especially in reinforced concrete construction. For such members the stiffnesses, carry-over factors, and fixed-end moments are usually much different from those for prismatic moments. Unless the member is symmetrical, the values for one end are different from those for the other end.

Extensive tables[4] of constants are found in Appendix A for parabolic haunches (Tables 1 to 26), for straight haunches (Tables 27 to 52), and for certain special members (Tables 53 to 57). In general, the tables are self-explanatory, but their use is illustrated in Art. 14–6.

INTERPOLATION. Interpolation for approximate analyses can usually be made by observation, particularly when only one dimension ratio varies from those given in the tables. For more precise analyses, when more than one dimension ratio varies, and when the constants diverge appreciably from a straight line, it is best to interpolate by plotting curves of the values.

But even the plotting of curves is inadequate for obtaining fixed-end moments for concentrated loads, especially at the maximum ordinate of the curve, because of the uncertainty of the curvature. A simple aid to increase the accuracy of the curves is a spline,[5] which can be forced into position at all known points. The elastic limit of the spline must not be exceeded; that is, it must not be bent so far that it does not spring back straight again. Although the spline should, theoretically, be haunched in the same manner as the beam, this is not ordinarily convenient. However, since the spline is forced into

---

[4] Reprinted by permission from *Handbook of Rigid Frame Constants*, (Chicago, Ill. Portland Cement Association).

[5] A $\frac{1}{16}$-in. or $\frac{3}{32}$-in. oxy-acetylene welding rod 3 ft long is ideal and readily available.

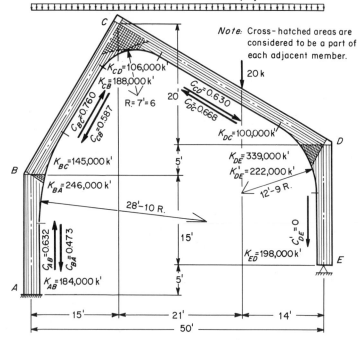

A. Frame, Loads, and Elastic Constants

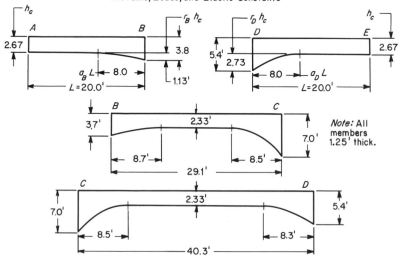

B. Assumed Dimensions of Members and Haunches

Fig. 14-13. Gabled frame.

position at seven points, the accuracy is very good, even though the spline is prismatic.

Another method of interpolation is to fit a curve by means of Simpson's rule for finding areas. The total area under the curve must equal the uniform load coefficient. This method is not quite as fast as the use of a spline, but it is excellent if no spline is available. It is illustrated as a check on the spline in Art. 14–6.

14–6. Example of a Gabled Frame. The gabled frame has gained wide popularity in recent years. It is a representative example of a certain class of complex problems in which the deflection of one member causes related but different deflections in other members. The example in Fig. 14–13A was made unsymmetrical in every important respect so that its solution is as general as possible.

STIFFNESSES, CARRY-OVER FACTORS, AND FIXED-END MOMENTS. The dimensions used for determining the constants are usually scaled from a large-scale drawing. A scale of $\frac{1}{2}$ in. = 1 ft, 0 in. was used for this example. These dimensions are shown in Fig. 14–13B, and the following calculations are based on them:

Member AB:

$$a_A = 0 \qquad a_B = \tfrac{8}{20} = 0.4$$

$$r_A = 0 \qquad r_B = \frac{3.8 - 2.67}{2.67} = 0.424, \text{ say } 0.4$$

The justification for assuming $r_B = 0.4$ is twofold. First, it would require a change of depth at B of only $\frac{3}{4}$ in. to make r_B exactly 0.4. Uncertainties in the interpretation of haunch dimensions of members intersecting at odd angles make greater refinement unjustifiable. Second, examination of Appendix A, Table 26, shows little change in values between $r_B = 0.4$ and $r_B = 0.6$; interpolation would yield values very close indeed to those of $r_B = 0.4$. (For example, by straight-line interpolation, the value of k_{BA} is 5.85 for $r_B = 0.424$ as compared with $k_{BA} = 5.76$ for $r_B = 0.4$.) From Appendix A, Table 26, we have

$$C_{AB} = 0.632 \qquad C_{BA} = 0.473$$

$$k_{AB} = 4.31 \qquad k_{BA} = 5.76$$

The true stiffnesses equal kEI/L. Assuming $E = 3,000,000$ psi $= 432,000$ kips/ft², and $I = bd^3/12 = [1.25(2.67)^3]/12 = 1.98$ ft⁴, the stiffnesses are

$$K_{AB} = \frac{4.31 \times 432,000 \times 1.98}{20} = 184,000 \text{ kip-ft}$$

$$K_{BA} = \frac{5.76 \times 432,000 \times 1.98}{20} = 246,000 \text{ kip-ft}$$

From Maxwell's law of reciprocal deflections,[6] we have

$$C_{AB}K_{AB} = C_{BA}K_{BA}$$
$$0.632 \times 184,000 = 0.473 \times 246,000$$
$$116,000 = 116,000 \quad \text{check}$$

Member BC:

There is no well-established rule for treating the deep circular haunch at C. It seems reasonable to approximate the circular haunch with a parabola, making the curves fit closely at the shallow part of the haunch and ignoring discrepancies at the deep end. The beam is so stiff at the deep end of the haunch that even large changes in depth there would have less effect upon the elastic curve (and therefore upon the constants) than smaller changes elsewhere. The parabolas at C are shown by the dotted lines in Fig. 14–13A.

$$a_B = \frac{8.7}{29.1} = 0.299, \text{ say } 0.30 \qquad a_C = \frac{8.5}{29.1} = 0.292, \text{ say } 0.30$$

$$r_B = \frac{3.7 - 2.33}{2.33} = 0.588, \text{ say } 0.6 \qquad r_C = \frac{7.0 - 2.33}{2.33} = 2.00$$

From Appendix A, Table 8, without interpolation we have

$$C_{BC} = 0.760 \qquad C_{CB} = 0.587$$
$$k_{BC} = 7.42 \qquad k_{CB} = 9.60$$
$$m_{BC} = 0.0810 \qquad m_{CB} = 0.1213$$

For $I = [1.25(2.33)^3]/12 = 1.32$, the true stiffnesses are:

$$K_{BC} = \frac{7.42 \times 432,000 \times 1.32}{29.1} = 145,000 \text{ kip-ft}$$

$$K_{CB} = \frac{9.60 \times 432,000 \times 1.32}{29.1} = 188,000 \text{ kip-ft}$$

$$C_{BC}K_{BC} = C_{CB}K_{CB}$$
$$760 \times 145,000 = 0.587 \times 188,000 \quad \text{check}$$

Member BC slopes at an angle of $\tan^{-1} 25/15 = 59.0°$. The total vertical load is $W = 15$ ft $\times$ 1 kip/ft $= 15$ kips and the total load normal (perpendicular) to the member is $15 \cos 59.0°$. The fixed-end moment for the normal load is, then,

$$M_{BC} = -0.0810(15 \cos 59.0°)29.1 = -18.2 \text{ kip-ft, say } -18 \text{ kip-ft}$$

However, the above figures can be advantageously rearranged thus:

$$M_{BC} = -0.0810 \times 15(29.1 \cos 59.0°)$$

[6] See Art. 18–2.

But since $29.1 \cos 59.0° = 15$, the equation for moment can be again rewritten

$$M_{BC} = -0.0810 \times 15 \text{ kips} \times 15 \text{ ft} = -0.0810(1 \text{ kip/ft})(15 \text{ ft})^2$$

$$= -18.2 \text{ kip-ft, say } -18 \text{ kip-ft}$$

Therefore, fixed-end moments can always be found by using the total vertical load in conjunction with the horizontal projection of the member. This is the easiest way and will always be used henceforth. We find, also,

$$M_{CB} = +0.1213(1 \text{ kip/ft})(15 \text{ ft})^2 = +27 \text{ kip-ft}$$

Member CD:

$$a_C = \frac{8.5}{40.3} = 0.211, \text{ say } 0.2 \qquad a_D = \frac{8.3}{40.3} = 0.206, \text{ say } 0.2$$

$$r_C = \frac{7.0 - 2.33}{2.33} = 2.00 \qquad r_D = \frac{5.4 - 2.33}{2.33} = 1.32$$

By straight-line interpolation between $r_D = 1.0$ and 1.5 in Appendix A, Table 22, we have

$$C_{CD} = 0.630 \qquad C_{DC} = 0.668$$

$$k_{CD} = 7.52 \qquad k_{DC} = 7.10$$

The uniform load coefficients are

$$m_{CD} = 0.1033 \qquad m_{DC} = 0.0936$$

The concentrated load coefficients are

m_{CD}	b	m_{DC}
0.0971	0.1	0.0018
0.2027	0.3	0.0497
0.1598	0.5	0.1423
0.0613	0.7	0.1877
0.0034	0.9	0.0947

Using a spline to obtain the proper curves through the ten points obtained above, we find the coefficients at the point where b equals 0.6 to be

$$m_{CD} = 0.111 \qquad m_{DC} = 0.178$$

By straight-line interpolation m_{CD} would be 0.1106, which is very close, but m_{DC} would be 0.1650, which is in error by 7 percent.

As mentioned in Art. 14–5, the accuracy of a curve can be checked by the use of Simpson's rule for finding areas. The rule is

$$\text{Area} = \frac{d}{3} \left(h_e + 2h_{\text{odd}} + 4h_{\text{even}} + h'_e \right)$$

in which d is the common interval between offsets, h_e and h'_e are the end offsets, h_{odd} are odd offsets (3rd, 5th, 7th), and h_{even} are even offsets (2nd, 4th, 6th, 8th). Note that there must be an odd number of offsets. Applying the rule to the values found by means of the spline, we have the results shown in Table 14–1.

These checks are rather exceptional, and such apparent accuracy cannot always be expected. The true error of any *one* point is somewhat greater than the average errors indicated above. With reasonable care, though, errors should not exceed 3 or 4 percent if the elastic limit of the spline is not reached.

TABLE 14–1
Check on Accuracy of Spline

Offset No.	b	m_{CD}	m_{DC}
1	0.0	$0.0000 \times 1 = 0.0000$	$0.0000 \times 1 = 0.0000$
2	0.1	$0.0971 \times 4 = 0.3884$	$0.0018 \times 4 = 0.0072$
3	0.2	$0.167 \ \times 2 = 0.334$	$0.020 \ \times 2 = 0.040$
4	0.3	$0.2027 \times 4 = 0.8108$	$0.0496 \times 4 = 0.1984$
5	0.4	$0.197 \ \times 2 = 0.394$	$0.095 \ \times 2 = 0.190$
6	0.5	$0.1598 \times 4 = 0.6392$	$0.1423 \times 4 = 0.5692$
7	0.6	$0.111 \ \times 2 = 0.222$	$0.178 \ \times 2 = 0.356$
8	0.7	$0.0613 \times 4 = 0.2452$	$0.1877 \times 4 = 0.7508$
9	0.8	$0.024 \ \times 2 = 0.048$	$0.158 \ \times 2 = 0.316$
10	0.9	$0.0034 \times 4 = 0.0136$	$0.0947 \times 4 = 0.3788$
11	1.0	$0.0000 \times 1 = 0.0000$	$0.0000 \times 1 = 0.0000$
		$30\overline{)3.0952}$	$30\overline{)2.8064}$
		0.10317	0.09355

These numbers should equal the uniform load coefficients, which are:

0.1033	0.0937
Error = 0.2 percent	Error = 0.2 percent

It is entirely unnecessary to check the accuracy of the spline by Simpson's rule. It is included here to illustrate the method and to show the accuracy obtainable.

The true stiffnesses are

$$K_{CD} = \frac{7.52 \times 432{,}000 \times 1.32}{40.3} = 106{,}000 \text{ kip-ft}$$

$$K_{DC} = \frac{7.10 \times 432{,}000 \times 1.32}{40.3} = 100{,}000 \text{ kip-ft}$$

$$C_{CD}K_{CD} = C_{DC}K_{DC}$$

$$0.630 \times 106{,}000 = 0.668 \times 100{,}000 \quad \text{check}$$

The fixed-end moments due to the uniform load are found by using the vertical load for w and the horizontal projection for L.

$$
\begin{aligned}
M_{CD} &= -0.1033wL^2 & M_{DC} &= +0.0936wL^2 \\
&= -0.1033(1 \text{ kip/ft})(35 \text{ ft})^2 & &= +0.0936(1 \text{ kip/ft})(35 \text{ ft})^2 \\
&= -127 \text{ kip-ft} & &= +115 \text{ kip-ft}
\end{aligned}
$$

The fixed-end moments due to the concentrated load are also found by using the vertical load with the horizontal projection of member CD for L.

$$M_{CD} = -0.111PL \qquad\qquad M_{DC} = +0.178PL$$
$$= -0.111 \times 20 \text{ kips} \times 35 \text{ ft} \qquad = +0.178 \times 20 \text{ kips} \times 35 \text{ ft}$$
$$= -78 \text{ kip-ft} \qquad\qquad = +125 \text{ kip-ft}$$

The total fixed-end moments are

$$M_{CD} = -127 - 78 = -205 \text{ kip-ft} \qquad M_{DC} = +115 + 125 = +240 \text{ kip-ft}$$

Member DE:

$$a_D = \frac{8.0}{20.0} = 0.4 \qquad\qquad a_E = 0$$

$$r_D = \frac{5.4 - 2.67}{2.67} = 1.04 \cong 1.0 \qquad r_E = 0$$

From Appendix A, Table 26, the unmodified factors are:

$$C_{DE} = 0.450 \qquad C_{ED} = 0.768$$
$$k_{DE} = 7.93 \qquad k_{ED} = 4.64$$

The true stiffnesses are

$$K_{DE} = \frac{7.93 \times 432,000 \times 1.98}{20} = 339,000 \text{ kip-ft}$$

$$K_{ED} = \frac{4.64 \times 432,000 \times 1.98}{20} = 198,000 \text{ kip-ft}$$

$$C_{DE}K_{DE} = C_{ED}K_{ED}$$

$$0.450 \times 339,000 = 0.768 \times 198,000 \quad \text{check}$$

The stiffnesses and carry-over factors can be modified in accordance with Art. 14-3 and Fig. 14-6, thus:

	D		E (fixity $= 0$)
	0.0		1.0
K_{DE}	$+339,000$	$\xrightarrow{\ C_{DE}=0.450\ }$	$+153,000$
	$-117,000$	$\xleftarrow{\ C_{ED}=0.768\ }$	$-153,000$
K'_{DE}	$+222,000$		0

$$C'_{DE} = \frac{M_{ED}}{M_{DE}} = \frac{0}{222,000} = 0$$

DISTRIBUTION. The distribution factors are computed as usual. But each member has two stiffnesses, one for each end, so care must be taken to use the

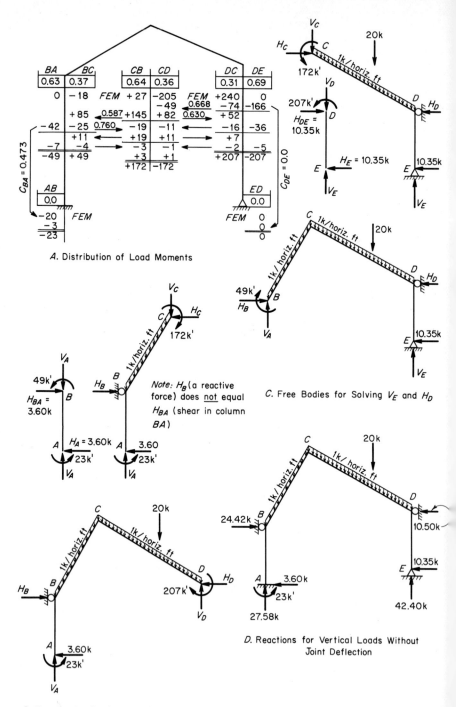

BA	BC		CB	CD		DC	DE
0.63	0.37		0.64	0.36		0.31	0.69
0	−18	FEM	+27	−205	FEM	+240	0
				−49	0.668	−74	−166
	+85	0.587	+145	+82	0.630	+52	
−42	−25	0.760	−19	−11	←	−16	−36
	+11	←	+19	+11	→	+7	
−7	−4		−3	−1	←	−2	−5
−49	+49		+3	+1		+207	−207
			+172	−172			

$C_{BA} = 0.473$

AB	
0.0	
−20	FEM
−3	
−23	

ED	
0.0	
FEM	0
	0
	0

$C_{DE} = 0.0$

A. Distribution of Load Moments

V_A 49k'

$H_{BA} = 3.60k$ H_B B

$H_A = 3.60k$ A A 3.60

23k' 23k'

V_A V_A

V_C

H_C C

172k'

Note: H_B (a reactive force) does not equal H_{BA} (shear in column BA)

B. Free Bodies for Solving V_A and H_B

V_C 20k

H_C C

172k' D H_D

V_D

207k' D H_D

$H_{DE} = 10.35k$ E

$H_E = 10.35k$ E 10.35k

V_E V_E

49k' B

H_B

V_A

C. Free Bodies for Solving V_E and H_D

20k

D H_D

E 10.35k

V_E

H_B B

H_B B

A 3.60k

23k'

V_A

C

20k

207k' D H_D

V_D

A 3.60k

23k'

V_A

24.42k B

A 3.60k

23k'

27.58k

C

20k

D

10.50k

E 10.35k

42.40k

D. Reactions for Vertical Loads Without Joint Deflection

Fig. 14–14. Analysis of gabled frame for intrapanel loads only.

290

correct one. For example, at joint B the distribution factor for member BA is

$$D_{BA} = \frac{K_{BA}}{K_{BA} + K_{BC}} = \frac{246{,}000}{246{,}000 + 145{,}000} = 0.63$$

The other distribution factors are computed similarly, always by using the stiffness at the joint where the distribution factor is wanted.

Great care must be taken to use the proper carry-over factors, which are shown with their arrows in Fig. 14–13A and in Figs. 14–14, 14–15, and 14–16.

MOMENTS WITHOUT JOINT DEFLECTION. The frame is first analyzed without joint translation by introducing false reactions at B and D. With these false reactions preventing joint translation, the only fixed-end moments are those produced by the vertical loads. These are distributed in Fig. 14–14A.

FALSE REACTIONS. The solution of the false reactions requires a fairly complex system of free bodies and equations. There are unknown horizontal forces at A, B, D, and E, and unknown vertical forces at A and E.

The unknown horizontal forces at A and E are quickly solved by using free bodies of each column. Taking moments about B of free body AB (Fig. 14–14B), we have

$$\Sigma M_B = 0 = -49 \text{ kip-ft} - 23 \text{ kip-ft} + 20H_A$$
$$H_A = 3.60 \text{ kips left}$$

Similarly, from free body DE (Fig. 14–14C), we have

$$H_E = 10.35 \text{ kips left}$$

There are still four[7] unknowns: V_A, V_E, H_B, and H_D. Every useful free body will contain at least two unknowns; the trick is to pick free bodies and equations that do not contain more.

From free body ABC (Fig. 14–14B) we have

$$\Sigma M_C = 0 = +172 \text{ kip-ft} - 23 \text{ kip-ft} - (1 \text{ kip/ft})15 \text{ ft}$$
$$\times \frac{15}{2} + 3.6 \text{ kips} \times 45 \text{ ft} - 25H_B + 15V_A$$

from which

$$15V_A - 25H_B + 198.5 = 0$$

From free body $ABCD$ (Fig. 14–14B) we have

$$\Sigma M_D = 0 = +207 \text{ kip-ft} - 23 \text{ kip-ft} - 20 \text{ kips} \times 14 \text{ ft} - (1 \text{ kip/ft})50 \text{ ft} \times \frac{50 \text{ ft}}{2}$$
$$+ 3.60 \text{ kips} \times 25 \text{ ft} - 5H_B + 50V_A$$

from which

$$50V_A - 5H_B - 1256 = 0$$

[7] Note that H_{BA} (Fig. 14–14B) is not equal to H_B, the false reaction at B. There are shear and thrust in member BC which also contribute to H_B.

Solving these two equations simultaneously yields:

$$V_A = 27.58 \text{ kips up}$$
$$H_B = 24.42 \text{ kips right}$$

The false reaction at D is found in the same manner. From a free body of column DE (Fig. 14–14C) we have

$$\Sigma M_D = 0 = -207 \text{ kip-ft} + 20H_E$$
$$H_E = 10.35 \text{ kips left}$$

Then from free body CDE we have

$$\Sigma M_C = 0 = -172 \text{ kip-ft} + (1 \text{ kip/ft})35 \text{ ft} \times \frac{35 \text{ ft}}{2} + 20 \text{ kips} \times 21 \text{ ft}$$
$$+ 10.35 \text{ kips} \times 40 \text{ ft} + 20H_D - 35V_E$$

from which

$$20H_D - 35V_E + 1274.5 = 0$$

And from free body $BCDE$ we have

$$\Sigma M_B = 0 = +49 \text{ kip-ft} + (1 \text{ kip/ft})50 \text{ ft} \times \frac{50 \text{ ft}}{2} + 20 \text{ kips} \times 36 \text{ ft} + 10.35 \text{ kips}$$
$$\times 15 \text{ ft} - 5H_D - 50V_E$$

from which

$$5H_D + 50V_E - 2174.25 = 0$$

Solving these last two equations simultaneously, we find

$$V_E = 42.40 \text{ kips up}$$
$$H_D = 10.50 \text{ kips left}$$

All the forces are shown in Fig. 14–14D. They should always be checked. The following are not absolute checks, but they will often disclose errors if there are any:

$$\Sigma H = -3.60 + 24.42 - 10.50 - 10.35 = +24.42 - 24.45 \cong 0 \qquad \text{check}$$
$$\Sigma V = 27.58 - (1 \text{ kip/ft})50 \text{ ft} - 20 + 42.40 = +69.98 - 70.00 \cong 0 \quad \text{check}$$

This solution for the false reactions is perfectly general and applies to any gabled frame—even to multiple frames. It is assumed that the reader has now mastered the procedure, so it will not be described again.

If the two knees, B and D, were at the same elevation, the simultaneous equations could be avoided. First, solve H_A by using free body AB. Second, solve for V_A by using free body $ABCD$ and taking moments about D. V_A is the only unknown in the equation because the line of action of H_B passes through D, and therefore H_B has no moment. Then V_E and H_D are found in the same manner as V_A and H_B.

JOINT DEFLECTION. As shown in preceding examples, the false reactions can be eliminated by permitting the proper amount of deflection to occur at each false reaction. But, of course, the amount of deflection is unknown, so the deflections are estimated, fixed-end moments are determined and distributed, and the reactive forces are computed. Then the estimated deflections are corrected by the ratio of the false reactions to the reactive forces.

Since there are two false reactions, there are two independent deflections—just as in the two-story frame of Art. 14–2. There are two methods of deflecting the structure. One method is to let the structure sway to one side, both knees (at B and D) moving an equal distance so that the upper part of the frame is not distorted. Next, the knees are permitted to spread, each knee moving outward an equal distance, making the peak move down. The proper combination of sidesway and spreading can produce any desired deflection at one knee together with any desired deflection at the other.

The second method of deflecting the structure is to let each knee deflect separately. The other knee is kept from deflecting so that the peak is forced to move instead. This method is adapted to the solution of multiple spans whereas the former is not. Therefore this second method is illustrated now.

DEFLECTION OF LEFT KNEE. The left knee is displaced to the left by an arbitrary estimated amount, BB' in Fig. 14–15A. Since the members cannot change in length, this forces C to move to C', and the structure distorts as shown by the dashed lines in Fig. 14–15A. Except for member DE, each member distorts in such a way that either end is displaced relative to the opposite end as follows: $BB' = \Delta_{AB}$, $C''C' = \Delta_{BC}$, and $CC' = \Delta_{CD}$, thus inducing fixed-end moments in AB, BC, and CD, respectively.

To determine the relationship between Δ_{AB}, Δ_{BC}, and Δ_{CD}, imagine member BC moved parallel to itself to $B'C''$. For the frame to be rejoined at the peak, C'' must swing through an arc of radius BC to C', and C must swing through an arc of radius CD to C'. These displacements are small compared to the size of the frame, so the arcs can be considered straight lines perpendicular to their respective members, as shown by the heavy solid lines in Fig. 14–15A. The relative values are best determined by a Williot diagram. Consider Figs. 14–15A and 14–15B together. Using a suitable scale, lay off OB''' equal and parallel to BB'. Draw OC'''' parallel to CC', and draw $B'''C''''$ parallel to $C''C'$. Note that OB''' is perpendicular to column AB, that OC'''' is perpendicular to rafter DC, and that $B'''C''''$ is perpendicular to rafter BC. In summary, we have[8]

$$OB''' \equiv BB' \equiv \Delta_{AB}$$

$$B'''C'''' \equiv C''C' \equiv \Delta_{BC}$$

$$OC'''' \equiv CC' \equiv \Delta_{CD}$$

[8] The symbol $\equiv$ means equal and parallel.

Note that the Williot diagram shows the true movement of each joint from its original position. The point B moves left, as shown by its position left of the origin. Point C moves down and to the left, as shown by its relation to the origin.

The fixed-end moments are found by the formula developed in Fig. 13–1:

$$M_{AB} = \frac{-\Delta_{AB}}{L} K_{AB}(1 + C_{AB})$$

where the minus sign indicates that moments are negative if the member is deflected in a clockwise direction. Assuming $\Delta_{AB} = 0.010$ ft; then from Fig. 14–15B we find

$$\Delta_{BC} = 0.0087 \text{ ft} \quad \text{and} \quad \Delta_{CD} = 0.0052 \text{ ft}$$

Therefore the fixed-end moments are

$$M_{AB} = \frac{+0.010}{20} \times 184,000(1 + 0.632) = +150 \text{ kip-ft}$$

$$M_{BA} = \frac{+0.010}{20} \times 246,000(1 + 0.473) = +181 \text{ kip-ft}$$

$$M_{BC} = \frac{-0.0087}{29.1} \times 145,000(1 + 0.760) = -76 \text{ kip-ft}$$

$$M_{CB} = \frac{-0.0087}{29.1} \times 188,000(1 + 0.587) = -89 \text{ kip-ft}$$

$$M_{CD} = \frac{+0.0052}{40.3} \times 106,000(1 + 0.630) = +22 \text{ kip-ft}$$

$$M_{DC} = \frac{+0.0052}{40.3} \times 100,000(1 + 0.668) = +22 \text{ kip-ft}$$

$$M_{DE} = M_{ED} = 0 \quad \text{because } DE \text{ is not deflected}$$

These moments are distributed in Fig. 14–15C. Because the false reactions are computed in exactly the same way as before, it seems unnecessary to repeat the computations again. The results, shown in Fig. 14–15D, should, however, be verified by the student.

DEFLECTION OF RIGHT KNEE. As with the left knee, the right knee is displaced some arbitrary amount, for example, 0.01 ft. The elastic curves are shown by the dashed lines in Fig. 14–16A. Notice that the Williot diagram, Fig. 14–16B, is exactly the same as the Williot diagram for the left knee, Fig. 14–15B.

The fixed-end moments for members BC and CD are the same as those for

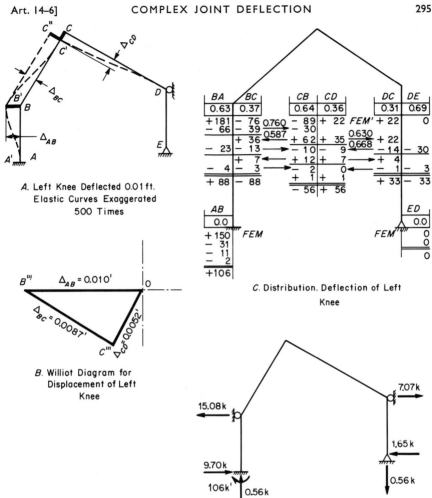

A. Left Knee Deflected 0.01 ft.
Elastic Curves Exaggerated
500 Times

B. Williot Diagram for
Displacement of Left
Knee

C. Distribution. Deflection of Left
Knee

D. Reactions for Deflection of Left
Knee

Fig. 14–15. Analysis of gabled frame for displacement of left knee.

deflection of the left knee. The unmodified fixed-end moments of member DE are found by using the *unmodified* stiffnesses and carry-over factors:

$$M_{DE} = \frac{-\Delta_{DE}}{L} K_{DE}(1 + C_{DE})$$

$$= \frac{-0.01}{20} \times 339,000(1 + 0.450) = -246 \text{ kip-ft}$$

$$M_{ED} = \frac{-0.01}{20} \times 198,000(1 + 0.768) = -175 \text{ kip-ft}$$

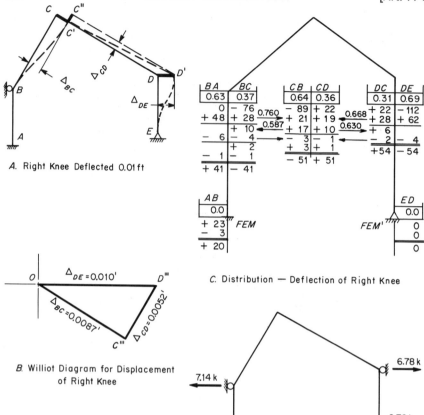

A. Right Knee Deflected 0.01 ft

B A	BC		CB	CD		DC	DE
0.63	0.37		0.64	0.36		0.31	0.69
0	− 76	0.760	− 89	+ 22	0.668	+ 22	− 112
+ 48	+ 28		+ 21	+ 19		+ 28	+ 62
	+ 10	0.587	+ 17	+ 10	0.630	+ 6	
− 6	− 4		− 3	− 1		− 2	− 4
	+ 2		+ 3	+ 1		+54	−54
− 1	− 1		− 51	+ 51			
+ 41	− 41						

AB		ED
0.0		0.0
+ 23 FEM		FEM′ 0
− 3		0
+ 20		0

C. Distribution — Deflection of Right Knee

B. Williot Diagram for Displacement of Right Knee

D. Reactions for Deflection of Right Knee

Fig. 14–16. Analysis of gabled frame for displacement of right knee.

These fixed-end moments must be modified as follows if the shortcut approach is to be used:

	D		E (fixity $= 0$)
M	-246		-175
	$+134 \longleftarrow$	$^{0.768}$	$+175$
M'	-112		0	(modified fixed-end moments)

The moments are distributed in Fig. 14–16C. The false reactions are then computed, and are shown in Fig. 14–16D.

TOTAL MOMENTS. The total moments are those due to intrapanel loads plus the corrected moments due to deflection of the left knee plus the corrected moments due to the deflection of the right knee.

As with the two-story frame of Art. 14–2, the two unknown deflections can be found by means of two simultaneous equations. Calling the correct pro-

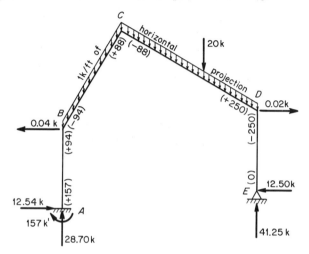

Fig. 14–17. Total moments, loads, and reactions for gabled frame.

portion of the deflection of the left knee x and the correct proportion of the deflection of the right knee y, we have

$$\text{False reaction at } B = 0 = 24.42 - 15.08x - 7.14y$$

$$\text{False reaction at } D = 0 = -10.50 + 7.07x + 6.78y$$

from which

$$x = 1.75$$
$$y = -0.28$$

The corrected deflection of the left knee is, then,

$$\Delta_B = 0.01 \times 1.75 = 0.0175 \text{ ft}$$

and the corrected deflection of the right knee is

$$\Delta_D = 0.01(-0.28) = -0.0028 \text{ ft}$$

to the left instead of to the right because the sign is negative.

The total moments due to the vertical loads plus the corrected moments due to the deflections of each knee are shown in Fig. 14–17 together with the reactive forces. All the reactive forces were found by the same method as explained under *False reactions*. This provides a check on the accuracy of the solution (although it is not an absolute check) and it is useful for finding blunders. If any mistake has been made in finding reactive forces in Figs. 14–14D, 14–15D, or 14–16D, or if a mistake has been made in combining total moments, it will become apparent here. Neither the student nor the practicing engineer should ever omit it.

14–7. Multiple-gabled Frames. Gabled frames are often used in sawtooth roof construction for factory buildings. Although they have many advantages, their analysis is tedious because of the many knee deflections and the resulting simultaneous equations. Fortunately, sufficient accuracy for a practical solution can be obtained by analyzing only the three bays at each end of a long series of gabled frames. The end bays are the most highly stressed, so a solution for them provides ample safety for the intermediate bays.

Two bays or three bays are treated just like the single bay of Art. 14–6. The knees are usually at the same elevation, so that simultaneous equations can be avoided in the solution of the false reactions if the proper free bodies are chosen in the correct order.

15

CHECKS

15–1. Need for Checks. Some method of checking the solution of important problems is highly desirable. A good method should be reasonably quick, it should be independent of the method by which the problem was originally solved, and it should be certain. It is not sufficient simply to review the solution, because if a mistake has been made, it is likely that the same mistake will be made again. A method that closely approaches these desirable qualities is the moment area method for making elastic checks. In conjunction with static checks, Eqs. 1–1, 1–2, and 1–3 ($\Sigma M = 0$, $\Sigma H = 0$, $\Sigma V = 0$) applied to a free body of the frame and to any portion of the frame, it is virtually certain. It is completely independent of the moment distribution solution. Not only is it reasonably quick but also it affords a good idea of the accuracy of the solution.

As presented in Part II, the moment area method is not always fast. That is because there are usually many unknowns, a great many moment diagrams, and often several simultaneous equations. But when used for checking a solution, there are no unknowns, no simultaneous equations, and not so many moment diagrams. Using the known moments obtained from the moment distribution solution, the moment area equations are used to find whether or not ΔX, ΔY, and $\Delta\theta$ are truly zero, or truly any other quantity they are supposed to be.

An elastic check, whether made by moment area or by any other method, is not enough; the solution must check statically as well. It is quite possible to find that an incorrect solution will check statically or that it will check elastically, but *a wrong solution cannot check both statically and elastically.* Both the static and elastic checks must be complete. It is not unusual for a wrong answer to meet all but one check, so *incomplete checks are equivalent to no checks at all.*

Checks for frames consisting of prismatic members are presented in Arts. 15–2 and 15–3. Formulas for non-prismatic members are given in Art. 15–4, and checks for a frame consisting of non-prismatic members are presented in Art. 15–5. A sound working knowledge of Part II is prerequisite to an understanding of this chapter.

15–2. Checks for a Single-Story Frame. The frame of Art. 13–4 is a good example for illustrating both static and elastic checks. The dimensions, loads, and total moments from Fig. 13–7B are repeated in Fig. 15–1A.

Example 15–2A. Static Checks. The static checks consist of finding all the reactive forces by making use of all the final end moments obtained through the moment distribution process; then the three equations of static equilibrium are used to see if the frame as a whole is truly in equilibrium. Table 15–1 indicates the steps in detail, the final checks being steps 7, 8, and 9.

Example 15–2B. Elastic Checks. The elastic checks consist of writing as many moment area equations as would be required for a solution by moment

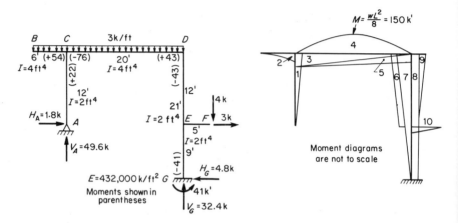

A. Dimensions, Loads, Total Moments, and Reactions   B. Moment Diagrams

Fig. 15–1. Static and elastic checks. Single-story frame.

area. This frame is statically indeterminate to two degrees, so two equations are required. Just as in the example of Art. 6–4, the easiest equations to apply are Eqs. 4–21 and 4–20:

$$\Delta X_A = 0 = \sum_A^G \bar{y} A_{MD/EI} + \sum \theta y + X = \sum_A^G \bar{y} A_{MD/EI} + 0 + 0$$

$$\Delta Y_A = 0 = \sum_A^G \bar{x} A_{MD/EI} + \sum \theta x + Y = \sum_A^G \bar{x} A_{MD/EI} + 0 + 0$$

Of course, the hinged joint at A implies $\Delta\theta_A \neq 0$, so that Eq. 4–22 is useless here.

All the moment diagrams are shown in Fig. 15–1B. They are plotted either by cantilever parts or by simple beam parts, whichever results in the fewer and simpler diagrams. In the example, cantilever parts are simpler for all members except CD. Note that there are somewhat fewer moment area diagrams than are required for a solution by moment area. (See Arts. 6–1 and 6–4.)

More important than the number of diagrams is their simplicity. All the maximum moments either are found directly from the moment distribution

TABLE 15–1

Static Checks for Single-Story Frame

Step	Quantity Wanted	Free Body	Equations	Value of Force, kips
1	H_A	AC	$\Sigma M_C = 0 = +22$ kip-ft $- 12H_A$	1.8 right
2	H_G	$DEFG$	$\Sigma M_D = 0 = -43$ kip-ft $- 41$ kip-ft $- 3$ kips $\times 12$ ft $+ 4$ kips $\times 5$ ft $+ 21H_G$	4.8 left
3	V_{CD}	CD	$\Sigma M_D = 0 = +43$ kip-ft $- 76$ kip-ft $- (3$ kips/ft$)20$ ft $\times 10$ ft $+ 20V_{CD}$	31.6 up
4	V_A	BCA	$\Sigma V = 0 = -(3$ kip/ft$)6$ ft $- 31.6$ $+ V_A$ (31.6 is V_{CD})	49.6 up
5	V_{DC}	CD	$\Sigma M_C = 0 = -76$ kip-ft $+ 43$ kip-ft $+ (3$ kips/ft$)20$ ft $\times 10$ ft $- 20V_{DC}$	28.4 up
6	V_G	$DEFG$	$\Sigma V = 0 = -28.4 - 4$ kips $+ V_G$ (28.4 is V_{DC})	32.4 up
7	check	$ABCDEFG$	$\Sigma H = 0 = +1.8$ kips $+ 3$ kips $- 4.8$ kips $= +4.8$ kips $- 4.8$ kips $= 0$	check
8	check	$ABCDEFG$	$\Sigma V = 0 = -(3$ kips/ft$)26$ ft $- 4$ kips $+ 49.6$ kips $+ 32.4$ kips $= -82$ kips $+ 82$ kips $= 0$	check
9	check	$ABCDEFG$	$\Sigma M_G = 0 = +49.6$ kips $\times 20$ ft $+ 1.8$ kips $\times 9$ ft $- (3$ kips/ft$)26$ ft $\times \dfrac{26}{2}$ ft $+ 4$ kips $\times 5$ ft $+ 3$ kips $\times 9$ ft $- 41$ kip-ft $= 1055.2$ $- 1055 \simeq 0$	check

process or can be quickly calculated from the reactions. From the known shape, length, and maximum ordinate, the moment areas are quickly computed and divided by EI to obtain the $A_{MD/EI}$ values shown in Table 15–2.

In this example the moment diagrams inside the frame are arbitrarily termed positive.[1] Values of x and y are termed positive to the right and upward respectively. Moment diagram numbers 2 and 10 must be omitted because the angle changes they cause do not affect the deflection of point A.[2]

The final checks show errors of 0.7 percent and 0.6 percent. In consideration of the fact that (1) moments were carried only to kip-ft, (2) that the total moments are only about 30 kip-ft, and (3) that an error of 2 kip-ft could occur in the moment distribution process, the errors in these checks are negligible.

[1] See Fig. 6–3 and discussion.
[2] See Art. 6–1.

TABLE 15–2
Elastic Checks for Single-Story Frame

Moment Diagram	Maximum Moment, kip-ft	Moment Area			$\bar{y}$	$\bar{x}$	$\Delta X_A = 0$		$\Delta Y_A = 0$	
		Length, ft	Area	$A_{MD/EI}$			$+\bar{y}A_{MD/EI}$	$-\bar{y}A_{MD/EI}$	$+\bar{x}A_{MD/EI}$	$-\bar{x}A_{MD/EI}$
1	22	12	+132	0.000153	+8	0	0.00122	—	0	—
2	54	6	omit				omit	—	omit	—
3	76	20	+760	0.001158	+12	+6.67	0.00528	—	0.00294	0.01158
4	150	20	−2000	0.000249	+12	+10	—	0.01390	—	—
5	43	20	+430	0.000278	+12	+13.33	0.00299	—	0.00332	—
6	4 × 5 = 20	12	+240	0.001225	+6	+20	0.00166	—	0.00556	—
7	4.8 × 21 = 100.8	21	+1058.4	0.000997	+5	+20	0.00613	—	0.02450	—
8	41	21	−861	0.000250	+1.5	+20	—	0.00150	—	0.01995
9	3 × 12 = 36	12	−216		+8	+20	omit	0.00200	omit	0.00500
10	4 × 5 = 20	5	omit							—
							0.01728	0.01740	0.03632	0.03653
							error = 0.7 percent		error = 0.6 percent	
								error = 0.7 percent		error = 0.6 percent

Although we used absolute values of $A_{MD/EI}$ in Table 15–2, it is not always necessary to do so. Relative values would be sufficient for the check above. It should be unnecessary to add that the relative moments of inertia would have to be included in the relative $A_{MD/EI}$ terms. If absolute deflections are wanted, absolute values of $A_{MD/EI}$ must be used.

15–3. Checks for a Two-Story Frame. To illustrate static and elastic checks on multi-story frames, the frame of Art. 14–2 will be checked. Loads, dimensions, and final moments from Fig. 14–5C are shown in Fig. 15–2A. Originally, EI values for the frame were not given, but they can be computed from the given stiffnesses. For example, the columns have stiffnesses of 12,000 kip-ft. Therefore

$$K = \frac{4EI}{L} \quad \text{or} \quad EI = \frac{KL}{4}$$

$$EI = \frac{KL}{4} = \frac{12,000 \times 16}{4} = 48,000$$

The other values of EI are computed accordingly.

Example 15–3A. *Static Checks.* The first step is to determine the shears in the columns, and from these shears the horizontal forces at B and C. These were found in Fig. 14–5C to be 6.9 kips and 3.2 kips, respectively, as reported and discussed in Art. 14–2. Next, shears at each end of each beam are found, and from these the axial forces in each of the columns can be found. The static checks consist of applying the three equations of statics to a free body of the entire frame and again to a free body of the upper story ($BCDE$ cut just above beam BE) only.

This is perfectly straightforward, and the checks for the upper story and those for the whole frame are quite similar to those detailed in Table 15–1, Art. 15–2. The reader will consequently be spared the details. The poorest check is the horizontal force at point C, which is 3.2 kips instead of the 3.0 kips it is supposed to be. If the column shears in Figs. 14–2 to 14–4 were calculated to three (instead of two) places, the second digits of the forces at B and C would be exact.

It may be desirable to add that the column extensions AH and FG in Fig. 15–2B have nothing whatever to do with the static checks. The static checks are concerned only with the real frame shown by the solid lines.

Example 15–3B. *Elastic Checks.* The partially fixed column bases cannot be handled easily by moment area because the rotations are unknown and, consequently, troublesome. But as discussed in Art. 13–5, the partially fixed ends can be replaced with a knife-edge or roller support, and the column can be extended far enough to a fixed support so that the distribution factors for the true columns (AB and FE) at their bases (A and F) are 25 percent.[3] These extensions are shown by dotted lines in Fig. 15–2B. The moment diagrams for the extensions can be determined mentally. For example, the final moment AH must be equal and opposite to moment AB because $\Sigma M = 0$ and the roller reaction at A can absorb no moment.

The final moment HA must be $\frac{1}{2}$ of moment AH because the carry-over factor is $\frac{1}{2}$. Since M_{AH} is 37 kip-ft, it follows that M_{HA} is $\frac{1}{2} \times 37 = 19$ kip-ft. These are the results that would be obtained if moment distribution were applied to the entire frame including the column extensions AH and FG.

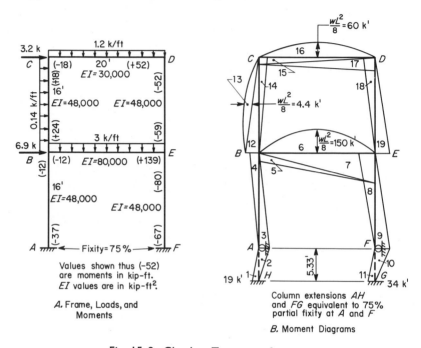

A. Frame, Loads, and Moments

Values shown thus (–52) are moments in kip-ft. EI values are in kip-ft².

B. Moment Diagrams

Column extensions AH and FG equivalent to 75% partial fixity at A and F

Fig. 15–2. Checks. Two-story frame.

In the same way M_{FG} is 67 and M_{GF} is $\frac{1}{2} \times 67 = 34$ kip-ft. Now, with these moments known, the rotations at A and F can be computed by moment area.

The frame is statically indeterminate to six degrees, so it must be checked with six equations. If we consider the column extensions AH and FG to be part of the frame, it is statically indeterminate to eight degrees: three unknowns at H, three at G, one at A, one at F, and three in the upper story. However, two equations can be checked mentally as follows:

$$\Delta X_A = 0 = \sum_A^H \bar{y} A_{MD/EI}$$

and

$$\Delta X_F = 0 = \sum_F^G \bar{y} A_{MD/EI}$$

[3] Review Art. 13–5 if this is not clear.

That these equations check perfectly ought to be obvious from consideration of moment diagrams 1 and 2 for ΔX_A and diagrams 10 and 11 for ΔX_F. This leaves, then, six (of the original eight) equations to be solved.

Three of the remaining six equations can be set up as $\Delta X_G = 0$, $\Delta Y_G = 0$, and $\Delta \theta_G = 0$, following elastic curve $HABEFG$ (the lower story only) by using only the moment diagrams lying along those members. Three more equations may be set up as $\Delta X_G = 0$, $\Delta Y_G = 0$, and $\Delta \theta_G = 0$, this time following elastic curve $HABCDEFG$ (omitting the middle beam) by using only those moment diagrams lying along those members. In this way six equations are obtained in which, at one time or another, all the moment diagrams are utilized.

An alternative procedure is to set up the three equations following the elastic curve of the lower story only, then set up three more equations following the elastic curve of only the upper story—that is, $BCDEB$—by using only the moment diagrams lying on those members. For simplicity, the absolute deflection of some convenient point such as B may be ignored and, instead, the deflections and rotation of member BC at point B with respect to member BE at point B can be set equal to zero. This must, of course, be true if joint B is rigid. Using moment diagrams along members $BCDEB$, the equations are, then,

$$\text{Relative } \Delta X_B = 0 = \sum_B^B \bar{y} A_{MD/EI}$$

$$\text{Relative } \Delta Y_B = 0 = \sum_B^B \bar{x} A_{MD/EI}$$

$$\text{Relative } \Delta \theta_B = 0 = \sum_B^B A_{MD/EI}$$

Another way of arriving at the same equations ultimately is to write moment area equations for absolute deflection:

$$\Delta X_B = \sum_B^B \bar{y} A_{MD/EI} + y_B \theta_B + X_B \tag{4--21}$$

Now the second term of the right side is zero because y_B is zero, and ΔX_B is, in this instance, equal to X_B. Subtracting ΔX_B from the left side and X_B from the right side, we have

$$0 = \sum_B^B \bar{y} A_{MD/EI}$$

as above. The other two equations can be developed in the same way.

Neither procedure of checking the frame (upper story only versus entire outer frame) has particular advantages. Because they are different, and in order to be as general as possible, the checks on the upper story are presented in Table 15–5.

TABLE 15–3
Moment Areas

Moment Diagram	Shape Coefficient, C	Maximum Moment, M, kip-ft	Length, L, ft	Area, CML	EI	$A_{MD/EI}$ Inside +	Outside −
1	½	19	5.33	51	48,000		0.00106
2	½	37	5.33	99	48,000	0.00205	
3	½	37	16	296	48,000	0.00616	
4	½	12	16	96	48,000		0.00200
5	½	12	20	120	80,000	0.00150	
6	⅔	150	20	2000	80,000		0.02500
7	½	139	20	1390	80,000	0.01738	
8	½	80	16	640	48,000	0.01333	
9	½	67	16	536	48,000		0.01117
10	½	67	5.33	178	48,000		0.00371
11	½	34	5.33	91	48,000	0.00190	
12	½	24	16	192	48,000		0.00400
13	⅔	4.4	16	47	48,000		0.00098
14	½	18	16	144	48,000	0.00300	
15	½	18	20	180	30,000	0.00600	
16	⅔	60	20	800	30,000		0.02666
17	½	52	20	520	30,000	0.01733	
18	½	52	16	416	48,000	0.00866	
19	½	59	16	472	48,000		0.00983

TABLE 15–4
Elastic Checks for Lower Story
(Elastic curve $HABEFG$. Origin of axes at H)

Moment Diagram	$\Delta\theta_H = 0 = \sum_H^G A_{MD/EI}$ $+A_{MD/EI}$	$-A_{MD/EI}$	Centroids $\bar{y}$	$\bar{x}$	$\Delta X_H = 0 = \sum_H^G \bar{y}A_{MD/EI}$ $+\bar{y}A_{MD/EI}$	$-\bar{y}A_{MD/EI}$	$\Delta Y_H = 0 = \sum_H^G \bar{x}A_{MD/EI}$ $+\bar{x}A_{MD/EI}$	$-\bar{x}A_{MD/EI}$
1		0.00106	1.78	0		0.00189		
2	0.00205		3.55	0	0.00727			
3	0.00616		10.67	0	0.06573			
4		0.00200	16.00	0		0.03200		
5	0.00150		21.33	6.67	0.03200		0.01001	
6		0.02500	21.33	10		0.53325		0.25000
7	0.01738		21.33	13.33	0.37077		0.23168	
8	0.01333		16.00	20	0.21328		0.26660	
9		0.01117	10.67	20		0.11918		0.22340
10		0.00371	3.55	20		0.01317		0.07420
11	0.00190		1.78	20	0.00338		0.03800	
	0.04232	0.04294			0.69243	0.69949	0.54629	0.54760
	error = 1.5 percent				error = 1.0 percent		error = 0.2 percent	

A considerable portion of this labor can be avoided by doing as much of this mentally as possible and writing only the answers. For example, $A_{MD/EI}$ for any moment diagram can be computed on the slide rule with nothing written except the answer, which is most conveniently written in the moment diagram. Values in Tables 15–3 and 15–4 can be similarly computed, the answers only being recorded in two columns. In this way, the static and elastic checks take about half the time required for the original solution by moment

TABLE 15–5

Elastic Checks for Upper Story

(Elastic curve $BCDEB$. Origin of axes at B) *

Moment Diagram	Relative $\Delta\theta_B = 0$ $0 = \sum\limits_{B}^{B} A_{MD/EI}$		Centroids		Relative $\Delta X_B = 0$ $0 = \sum\limits_{B}^{B} \bar{y}A_{MD/EI}$		Relative $\Delta Y_B = 0$ $0 = \sum\limits_{B}^{B} \bar{x}A_{MD/EI}$	
	$+A_{MD/EI}$	$-A_{MD/EI}$	$\bar{y}$	$\bar{x}$	$+\bar{y}A_{MD/EI}$	$-\bar{y}A_{MD/EI}$	$+\bar{x}A_{MD/EI}$	$-\bar{x}A_{MD/EI}$
12		0.00400	5.33	0		0.02132		
13		0.00098	8	0		0.00784		
14	0.00300		10.67	0	0.03201			
15	0.00600		16	6.67	0.09600		0.04002	
16		0.02666	16	10		0.42656		0.26660
17	0.01733		16	13.33	0.27728		0.23100	
18	0.00866		10.67	20	0.09240		0.17320	
19		0.00983	5.33	20		0.05239		0.19660
7		0.01738	0	13.33				0.23168
6	0.02500		0	10			0.25000	
5		0.00150	0	6.67				0.01000
	0.05999	0.05937			0.49769	0.50811	0.69422	0.70488
	error = 1.0 percent				error = 2.1 percent		error = 1.5 percent	

* Note that the signs of moment diagrams 5, 6, and 7 must be changed from those of Tables 15–3 and 15–4, because those that were outside for the lower story are inside for the upper story.

distribution. Even this amount of time can be reduced by using as many shortcuts as possible, for example, comparative values rather than absolute values for moment areas, centroidal distances, etc.

15–4. Elastic Checks for Non-prismatic Members.

A method has been developed[4] for finding areas and centroids of moment diagrams for non-prismatic members that is easier and very much faster than either the use of integral calculus (Art. 4–4) or the method of dividing the moment diagrams into segments (Art. 6–6). The equations are developed from the same constants of stiffnesses, carry-over factors, and fixed-end moments that are necessary to moment distribution. No additional constants are necessary for the elastic checks. In a way this is unfortunate, because if a mistake has been made in any constant, it will not be discovered by the elastic check. The only way to avoid such mistakes is to be extremely careful when determining these constants.

[4] By Professor Bruce Jameyson, University of California.

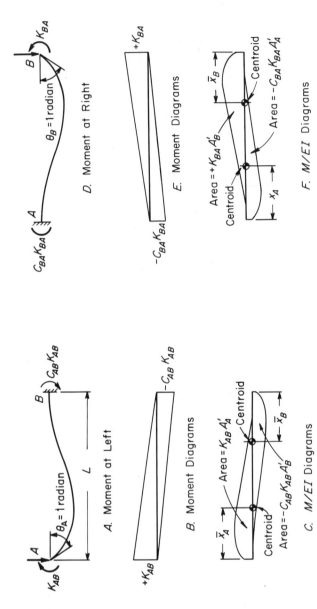

Fig. 15-3. Areas of M/EI diagrams for end moments in unsymmetrical, non-prismatic members.

DEVELOPMENT OF FORMULAS FOR END MOMENTS. In Fig. 15–3, two loading conditions are shown for an unsymmetrical non-prismatic member AB, one for a moment K_{AB} (the stiffness) applied at the left and one for a moment K_{BA} applied at the right. Moment diagrams and MD/EI areas are shown for the two loading conditions. Let A'_A be the MD/EI area for a *unit* moment at A and A'_B be the MD/EI area for a *unit* moment at B. Writing the moment area equation (Eq. 4–22) for change of slope for a moment equal to K_{AB} applied at point A, we have

$$\theta_A = 1 = \sum_A^B A_{MD/EI} + \sum \theta = \sum_A^B A_{MD/EI} + 0 = +K_{AB}A'_A - C_{AB}K_{AB}A'_B$$

and for the moment applied at B,

$$\theta_B = 1 = \sum_B^A A_{MD/EI} + \sum \theta = \sum_B^A A_{MD/EI} + 0 = K_{BA}A'_B - C_{BA}K_{BA}A'_A$$

Solving the above equations simultaneously for A'_A and A'_B gives

$$A'_A = \frac{1 + C_{BA}}{K_{AB}(1 - C_{AB}C_{BA})} \quad \text{and} \quad A'_B = \frac{1 + C_{AB}}{K_{BA}(1 - C_{AB}C_{BA})}$$

For any moment other than unity, the areas become

$$A_A = M_{AB}A'_A = \frac{M_{AB}}{K_{AB}}\left(\frac{1 + C_{BA}}{1 - C_{AB}C_{BA}}\right) \tag{15–1}$$

$$A_B = M_{BA}A'_B = \frac{M_{BA}}{K_{BA}}\left(\frac{1 + C_{AB}}{1 - C_{AB}C_{BA}}\right)$$

Writing the moment area equation (Eq. 4–20) for deflection at A, and again for deflection at B, we have

$$\Delta Y_A = 0 = \sum_A^B \bar{x}A_{MD/EI} + \sum \theta x + Y = \sum_A^B \bar{x}A_{MD/EI} + 0 + 0$$

$$= K_{AB}A'_A\bar{x}_A - C_{AB}K_{AB}A'_B(L - \bar{x}_B)$$

$$\Delta Y_B = 0 = \sum_B^A \bar{x}A_{MD/EI} + \sum \theta x + Y = \sum_B^A \bar{x}A_{MD/EI} + 0 + 0$$

$$= K_{BA}A'_B\bar{x}_B - C_{BA}K_{BA}A'_A(L - \bar{x}_A)$$

Solving these equations simultaneously yields

$$\bar{x}_A = L\frac{C_{AB}(A'_B/A'_A) - C_{AB}C_{BA}}{1 - C_{AB}C_{BA}}$$

$$\bar{x}_B = L\frac{C_{BA}(A'_A/A'_B) - C_{AB}C_{BA}}{1 - C_{AB}C_{BA}}$$

Remembering that $K_{AB}C_{AB} = K_{BA}C_{BA}$ and solving for A'_B/A'_A, results in

$$\frac{A'_B}{A'_A} = \frac{(1 + C_{AB})/[K_{BA}(1 - C_{AB}C_{BA})]}{(1 + C_{BA})/[K_{AB}(1 - C_{AB}C_{BA})]} = \frac{K_{AB}}{K_{BA}}\left(\frac{1 + C_{AB}}{1 + C_{BA}}\right)$$

$$= \frac{C_{BA}}{C_{AB}}\left(\frac{1 + C_{AB}}{1 + C_{BA}}\right)$$

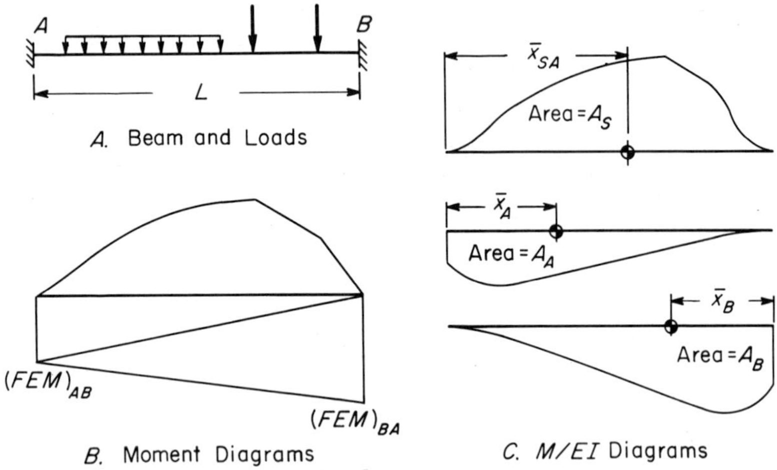

A. Beam and Loads

B. Moment Diagrams

C. M/EI Diagrams

Fig. 15–4. Areas of M/EI diagrams for loads on unsymmetrical, non-prismatic members.

Substituting this expression into the formula for $\bar{x}_A$, and its reciprocal into the formula for $\bar{x}_B$, and simplifying, we find,

$$\bar{x}_A = L\,\frac{C_{AB}}{1 + C_{BA}} \qquad (15\text{–}2)$$

$$\bar{x}_B = L\,\frac{C_{AB}}{1 + C_{AB}}$$

DEVELOPMENT OF FORMULAS FOR INTRAPANEL LOADS. Intrapanel loads of any type are shown in Fig. 15–4A. These produce fixed-end moments $(FEM)_{AB}$ and $(FEM)_{BA}$, which are, in this example, called negative (because they produce compression in the lower fibers) to correspond with moment area sign convention. The moment diagrams are shown in simple beam parts in Fig. 15–4B and the M/EI diagrams, in Fig. 15–4C. Writing the moment area equation (Eq. 4–22) for change of slope at A, we have

$$\Delta\theta_A = 0 = \sum_A^B A_{MD/EI} + \sum 0 = \sum_A^B A_{MD/EI} + 0 = A_s + A_A + A_B$$

in which the signs of A_A and A_B are internally negative because of the negative $(FEM)_{AB}$ and $(FEM)_{BA}$. Substituting the above-developed expressions for A_A and A_B gives

$$A_s = -A_A - A_B = \frac{-(FEM)_{AB}}{K_{AB}}\left(\frac{1 + C_{BA}}{1 - C_{AB}C_{BA}}\right) - \frac{(FEM)_{BA}}{K_{BA}}\left(\frac{1 + C_{AB}}{1 - C_{AB}C_{BA}}\right)$$

$$(15\text{–}3)$$

Writing the moment area equation (Eq. 4–20) for deflection at A, gives

$$\Delta Y_A = 0 = \sum_A^B \bar{x}A_{MD/EI} + \sum \theta x + Y = \sum_A^B \bar{x}A_{MD/EI} + 0 + 0$$

$$= A_s \bar{x}_{sA} + A_A \bar{x}_A + A_B(L - \bar{x}_B)$$

Substituting the values for A_s, A_A, A_B, $\bar{x}_A$, and $\bar{x}_B$, and simplifying, we find

$$\bar{x}_{sA} = L \frac{(FEM)_{AB}C_{AB} + (FEM)_{BA}}{(FEM)_{AB}[(C_{AB}/C_{BA}) + C_{AB}] + (FEM)_{BA}(1 + C_{AB})} \quad (15\text{–}4)$$

These formulas are summarized in Table 15–6. Note carefully the sign convention explained at the bottom of the table.

15–5. Checks for a Gabled Frame. The static checks consist of writing the Eqs. 1–1, 1–2, and 1–3 ($\Sigma M = 0$, $\Sigma H = 0$, and $\Sigma V = 0$) for the

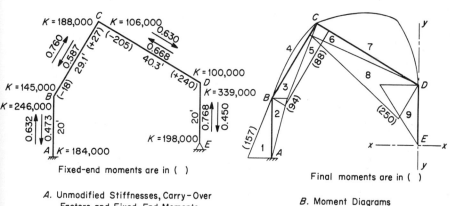

A. Unmodified Stiffnesses, Carry-Over Factors, and Fixed-End Moments

B. Moment Diagrams

Fig. 15–5. Elastic checks for gabled frame.

forces acting on the frame as shown in Fig. 14–17. In this example the static errors are less than 1 percent.

Example 15–5. *Elastic Checks.* The moment diagrams are plotted in simple beam parts in Fig. 15–5B. The frame is statically indeterminate to two degrees, so at least two equations are needed for checks. The easiest two to apply are $\Delta X_E = 0$ and $\Delta Y_E = 0$, so the axes are located through point E, and all centroidal distances are calculated from these axes.

TABLE 15-6
Areas and Centroids of M/EI Diagrams

Description	Simple Beam Subjected to Any End Moment	Simple Beam Subjected to Any Loading
Loading condition		
Moment diagram		
M/EI diagram (actual shape depends on variation of I)	Centroid Area $= A_A$	Centroid Area $= A_s$

Formulas for unsymmetrical non-prismatic members:

$$A_A = \frac{M_{AB}}{K_{AB}}\left(\frac{1+C_{BA}}{1-C_{AB}C_{BA}}\right) \quad (15\text{-}1)$$

$$\bar{x}_A = L\frac{C_{BA}}{1+C_{BA}} \quad (15\text{-}2)$$

$$A_s = \frac{-(FEM)_{AB}}{K_{AB}}\left(\frac{1+C_{BA}}{1-C_{AB}C_{BA}}\right) - \frac{(FEM)_{BA}}{K_{BA}}\left(\frac{1+C_{AB}}{1-C_{AB}C_{BA}}\right) \quad (15\text{-}3)$$

$$\bar{x}_{sA} = L\frac{(FEM)_{AB}C_{AB} + (FEM)_{BA}}{(FEM)_{AB}(C_{AB}|C_{BA}) + C_{AB}] + (FEM)_{BA}(1+C_{AB})} \quad (15\text{-}4)$$

For symmetrical non-prismatic members, formulas reduce to:

$$A_A = \frac{M_{AB}}{K}\frac{1}{1-C} \quad (15\text{-}5)$$

$$\bar{x}_A = L\frac{C}{1+C} \quad (15\text{-}6)$$

$$A_s = \frac{-(FEM)_{AB} - (FEM)_{BA}}{K(1-C)} \quad (15\text{-}7)$$

$$\bar{x}_A = L\frac{C(FEM)_{AB} + (FEM)_{BA}}{[(FEM)_{AB} + (FEM)_{BA}](1+C)} \quad (15\text{-}8)$$

For symmetrical prismatic members, formulas reduce to:

$$A_A = \frac{2M_{AB}}{K} \quad (15\text{-}9)$$

$$\bar{x}_A = \frac{L}{3} \quad (15\text{-}10)$$

$$A_s = \frac{-2[(FEM)_{AB} + (FEM)_{BA}]}{K} \quad (15\text{-}11)$$

$$\bar{x}_A = L\frac{(FEM)_{AB} + 2(FEM)_{BA}}{3[(FEM)_{AB} + (FEM)_{BA}]} \quad (15\text{-}12)$$

Sign convention: the signs of K and C are always positive. For FEM, use the sign convention of moment area, in which moments are positive if they create compression in the upper fibers of the member. Change the signs of the MD/EI areas as necessary to make them conform to the moment area equations used for the elastic checks.

To illustrate the use of the formulas of Table 15–6, the MD/EI areas and centroids for a few representative diagrams are computed in the following. The MD/EI area for diagram 6 is from Eq. 15–1,

$$A_6 = \frac{M_{CD}}{K_{CD}}\left(\frac{1+C_{DC}}{1-C_{DC}C_{CD}}\right) = \frac{88}{106{,}000}\left(\frac{1+0.668}{1-0.668\times 0.630}\right) = 0.00239$$

and the centroid is, from Eq. 15–2

$$\bar{x}_C = L\frac{C_{DC}}{1+C_{DC}} = 40.3\frac{0.668}{1.668} = 16.13 \text{ ft from } C$$

TABLE 15–7

Elastic Checks for Gabled Frame

Diagram	MD/EI Area	Centroids Along Centerline from End of Member	From Coordinate Axes $\bar{y}$	$\bar{x}$	$\Delta X_E = 0$ $+\bar{y}A_{MD/EI}$	$-\bar{y}A_{MD/EI}$	$\Delta Y_E = 0$ $+\bar{x}A_{MD/EI}$	$-\bar{x}A_{MD/EI}$
1	+0.00180	$\bar{x}_A = 6.41$	1.41	50.00	0.0025		0.0900	
2	−0.00089	$\bar{x}_B = 7.75$	2.25	50.00		0.0020		0.0445
3	−0.00186	$\bar{x}_B = 10.78$	24.26	44.44		0.0451		0.0826
4	+0.00081	$\bar{x}_B = 14.02$	27.04	42.76	0.0219		0.0346	
5	−0.00149	$\bar{x}_C = 12.56$	29.22	41.48		0.0436		0.0618
6	−0.00239	$\bar{x}_C = 16.13$	31.98	20.97		0.0765		0.0502
7	+0.01232	$\bar{x}_C = 20.80$	29.67	16.92	0.3655		0.2088	
8	−0.00704	$\bar{x}_E = 15.58$	27.74	13.54		0.1952		0.0953
9	−0.00197	$\bar{x}_D = 8.69$	11.31	0.0		0.0225	0.0	
					0.3899	0.3849	0.3334	0.3344
					error = 1.3 percent		error = 0.3 percent	

The MD/EI area for diagram 7 is computed from Eq. 15–3 by considering that both $(FEM)_{CD}$ and $(FEM)_{DC}$ are negative because they produce compression on the bottom fibers:

$$A_7 = -\frac{(FEM)_{CD}}{K_{CD}}\left(\frac{1+C_{DC}}{1-C_{DC}C_{CD}}\right) - \frac{(FEM)_{DC}}{K_{DC}}\left(\frac{1+C_{CD}}{1-C_{CD}C_{DC}}\right)$$

$$= \frac{-(-205)}{106{,}000}\left(\frac{1+0.668}{1-0.668\times 0.630}\right) - \frac{-240}{100{,}000}\left(\frac{1+0.630}{1-0.630\times 0.668}\right)$$

$$= +0.00557 + 0.00675 = +0.01232$$

and the centroid is, from Eq. 15–4,

$$\bar{x}_C = L\frac{(FEM)_{CD}C_{CD}+(FEM)_{DC}}{(FEM)_{CD}[(C_{CD}/C_{DC})+C_{CD}]+(FEM)_{DC}(1+C_{CD})}$$

$$= 40.3\frac{-205\times 0.630-240}{-205[(0.630/0.668)+0.630]-240(1+0.630)} = 20.80 \text{ ft}$$

The area and centroid of diagram 9 must be computed by using the unmodified constants. The formulas were developed for unmodified constants, so they are not valid for the modified ones. Then too, modified stiffness is not really true stiffness at all, in a strict sense, but a mixture of stiffness together with some of the moment distribution.

The MD/EI area of diagram 9 is, from Eq. 15–1,

$$A_9 = \frac{M_{DE}}{K_{DE}}\left(\frac{1 + C_{ED}}{1 - C_{ED}C_{DE}}\right) = \frac{250}{339,000}\left(\frac{1 + 0.768}{1 - 0.768 \times 0.450}\right) = 0.00199$$

and the centroid is, from Eq. 15–2,

$$\bar{x}_D = L\,\frac{C_{ED}}{1 + C_{ED}} = 20\,\frac{0.768}{1.768} = 8.69 \text{ ft}$$

Elastic checks are shown in Table 15–7.

16

SPECIAL PROBLEMS

16–1. Trapezoidal Frames. Trapezoidal frames are sometimes used to support viaducts, large, high conveyors, and the like. The Vierendeel truss (Fig. 6–12*D*) is the most complex standard example of a trapezoidal frame. Because it can be solved by the following procedure, it may be likened to a trapezoidal frame of five stories.

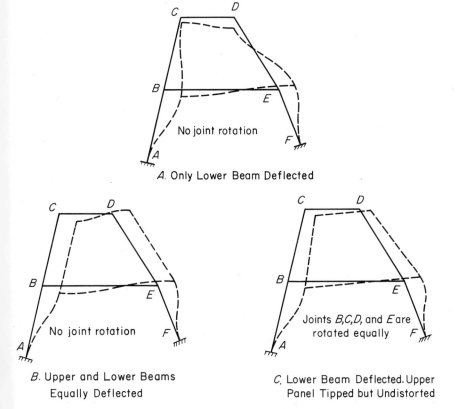

A. Only Lower Beam Deflected

B. Upper and Lower Beams
Equally Deflected

C. Lower Beam Deflected. Upper
Panel Tipped but Undistorted

Fig. 16–1. Joint deflection of trapezoidal frame.

315

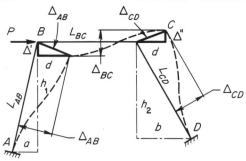

A. Deflection Without Joint Rotation

B. Deflection With Joint Rotation

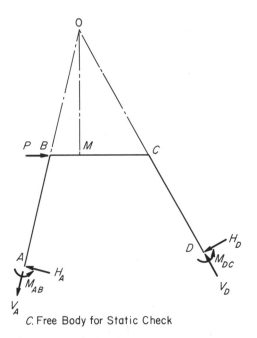

C. Free Body for Static Check

Fig. 16–2. Fixed-end moments in trapezoidal frame.

Like gabled frames, trapezoidal frames represent a type in which the deflection of one member causes dependent deflections and fixed-end moments in other members. Unfortunately, these dependent deflections often occur in most of the members, which makes the analysis complex and irksome. Now, it is not possible to limit deflections to one panel of a multi-story trapezoidal frame, but it is possible to confine curvature of members to one panel, which therefore limits fixed-end moments to one panel and certainly simplifies and shortens the work.

Several ways of deflecting the frame are shown in Fig. 16–1. When the lower beam is deflected and lateral deflection of the upper beam is prevented, as in Fig. 16–1*A*, note that every member is flexed. Note, too, that the upper beam is flexed if upper and lower beams are deflected equally as in Fig. 16–1*B*. However, none of the upper members is flexed if the lower beam is straightened as in Fig. 16–1*C*. To straighten the beam requires rotation of the joints *B* and *E*, which increases the fixed-end moments in the columns. The advantage of straightening the beam is that it is easier to compute this added moment than to compute the deformations in other members that do occur with any other system of deflecting the frame.

EQUATIONS FOR JOINT DEFLECTION WITHOUT ROTATION. In Fig. 16–2A the joints B and C are displaced, but there is no rotation of any joint. There are fixed-end moments at each end of every member, and from Fig. 13–1D the magnitude of any typical fixed-end moment is

$$M_{BC} = \frac{\Delta_{BC}}{L_{BC}} K_{BC}(1 + C_{BC})$$

and the other fixed-end moments are found similarly. However, the relationship between Δ_{AB}, Δ_{BC}, and Δ_{CD} must be known. This can be determined graphically from a Williot diagram as in Fig. 14–15B, or algebraically by the following development:

$$\text{Triangle } L_{AB}ah_1 \approx \text{triangle } d\,\Delta_{AB}\,\Delta'$$
$$\text{Triangle } L_{CD}bh_2 \approx \text{triangle } d\,\Delta_{CD}\,\Delta''$$

$$\frac{d}{h_1} = \frac{\Delta_{AB}}{L_{AB}} \quad \text{and} \quad \frac{d}{h_2} = \frac{\Delta_{CD}}{L_{CD}}$$

Solving each equation for d, and equating, gives

$$\frac{\Delta_{AB}}{L_{AB}} h_1 = \frac{\Delta_{CD}}{L_{CD}} h_2$$

or

$$\Delta_{CD} = \frac{L_{CD}}{L_{AB}}\frac{h_1}{h_2} \Delta_{AB}$$

Similarly

$$\frac{d}{h_1} = \frac{\Delta'}{a} \quad \text{and} \quad \frac{d}{h_2} = \frac{\Delta''}{b}$$

Solving for Δ' and Δ'', and adding, gives

$$\Delta_{BC} = \Delta' + \Delta'' = d\left(\frac{a}{h_1} + \frac{b}{h_2}\right)$$

and substituting for d,

$$d = \frac{\Delta_{AB}}{L_{AB}} h_1$$

yields

$$\Delta_{BC} = \frac{h_1 \Delta_{AB}}{L_{AB}}\left(\frac{a}{h_1} + \frac{b}{h_2}\right) = \frac{\Delta_{AB}}{L_{AB}}\left(a + b\frac{h_1}{h_2}\right) \tag{16–1}$$

Now, having all the deflections in terms of Δ_{AB}, we can find the fixed-end moments for any assumed value of Δ_{AB}. Or by solving for Δ_{AB} in terms of each fixed-end moment and equating all the expressions, the following relation between fixed-end moments can be obtained, dropping L_{AB}, which is common to all terms:

$$\frac{M_{AB}}{K_{AB}(1+C_{AB})} = \frac{M_{BA}}{K_{BA}(1+C_{BA})} = \frac{M_{BC}}{K_{BC}(1+C_{BC})} \times \frac{L_{BC}}{a+b(h_1/h_2)}$$

$$= \frac{M_{CB}}{K_{CB}(1+C_{CB})} \times \frac{L_{BC}}{a+b(h_1/h_2)} = \frac{M_{CD}}{K_{CD}(1+C_{CD})(h_1/h_3)}$$

$$= \frac{M_{DC}}{K_{DC}(1+C_{DC})(h_1/h_3)} \qquad (16\text{-}2)$$

Any fixed-end moment can be assumed, and the other fixed-end moments can be computed by means of Eq. 16-2.

These equations are best applied to one-story frames and to the upper story of multi-story frames. For all but the upper story of multi-story frames, it is better—as previously mentioned—to straighten the beam by rotating the joint so that distortions of the upper panels are eliminated.

EQUATIONS FOR JOINT ROTATION. In Fig. 16-2B, the solid line shows the structure in its deflected position without joint rotation. When the joints at B and C are rotated through the angle $\theta = \Delta_{BC}/L_{BC}$, the beam becomes straight and, since the joints are rigid, the columns must curve more sharply, as shown by the dashed lines. The additional rotation or curvature causes added moments in the columns. The additional moment in column BA at B is

$$M'_{BA} = K_{BA}\theta = K_{BA}\frac{\Delta_{BC}}{L_{BC}} = \frac{K_{BA}}{L_{BC}}\left[\frac{\Delta_{AB}}{L_{AB}}\left(a+b\frac{h_1}{h_2}\right)\right] \qquad (16\text{-}3)$$

Or by solving for Δ_{AB} in the formula for fixed-end moment,

$$M_{BA} = \frac{\Delta_{AB}}{L_{BA}}K_{BA}(1+C_{BA})$$

$$\Delta_{AB} = \frac{M_{BA}L_{BA}}{K_{BA}(1+C_{BA})}$$

By substituting for Δ_{AB} and simplifying, the additional moment is found to be

$$M'_{BA} = \frac{M_{BA}}{(1+C_{BA})L_{BC}}\left(a+b\frac{h_1}{h_2}\right)$$

When the top of the column rotates, some of the rotational moment M'_{BA} is carried over to the bottom of the column, causing an added moment M'_{AB} as follows:

$$M'_{AB} = M'_{BA}C_{BA} = \frac{M_{BA}C_{BA}}{(1+C_{BA})L_{BC}}\left(a+b\frac{h_1}{h_2}\right) \qquad (16\text{-}4)$$

In the same manner the top of the right column CD rotates, causing an additional moment at C of $M'_{CD} = K_{CD}\theta$, and some of the moment is carried over to D, causing an added moment of $M'_{DC} = K_{CD}\theta C_{CD}$. By substitution, the following equations can be developed:

$$M'_{CD} = \frac{K_{CD}\,\Delta_{AB}}{L_{BC}L_{AB}}\left(a + b\frac{h_1}{h_2}\right) = \frac{M_{CD}[a + b(h_1/h_2)]}{L_{BC}(1 + C_{CD})(h_1/h_2)} \qquad (16\text{–}5)$$

$$M'_{DC} = M'_{CD}C_{CD} = \frac{M_{CD}C_{CD}[a + b(h_1/h_2)]}{L_{BC}(1 + C_{CD})(h_1/h_2)} \qquad (16\text{–}6)$$

The starting fixed-end moments are

At AB	$M_{AB} + M'_{AB}$
At BA	$M_{BA} + M'_{BA}$
At CD	$M_{CD} + M'_{CD}$
At DC	$M_{DC} + M'_{DC}$

and there are no moments in member BC.

STATIC CHECKS. It is troublesome and time consuming to resolve the forces in trapezoidal frames into horizontal and vertical components. So rather than use the equations $\Sigma H = 0$ and $\Sigma V = 0$, it is simpler to use the equation $\Sigma M = 0$ in such a way as to obtain a check for the forces that are nearly horizontal or nearly vertical.

To use the equation $\Sigma H = 0$ for the free body of Fig. 16–2C, for example, it would be necessary to solve for V_A, H_A, V_D, and H_D, and then resolve all of them into horizontal components. It is much simpler, on the other hand, to solve only H_A and H_D, then project the centerlines of the columns to an intersection at point O, and finally to sum moments about point O thus:

$$\Sigma M_O = 0 = -P\overline{OM} - M_{AB} - M_{DC} + H_D\overline{OD} + H_A\overline{OA} \qquad (16\text{–}7)$$

This equation is sometimes called a "shear" equation since it can be used to solve for the force P, which is the total shear on the panel.

Vertical forces can be checked by summing moments about point B and then again about point C. Finally, the equilibrium of the entire frame may be checked by summing moments about point A and then again about point D.

The free body $ABCD$ is not the only one that can be used. Another useful free body can be formed by cutting the frame just below BC. It is necessary to be alert with respect to signs; the signs of forces and moments acting on the free body BC are opposite to those acting on free bodies of the columns.

16–2. Secondary Stresses in Trusses.
Trusses are usually analyzed as though the members were pin-connected at the joints. The old practice of using pins in the joints of bridges has fallen into disfavor, even for large

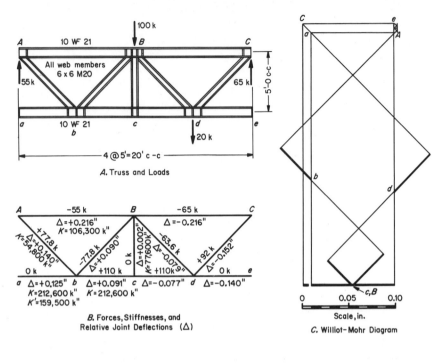

A. Truss and Loads

B. Forces, Stiffnesses, and
Relative Joint Deflections (Δ)

C. Williot-Mohr Diagram

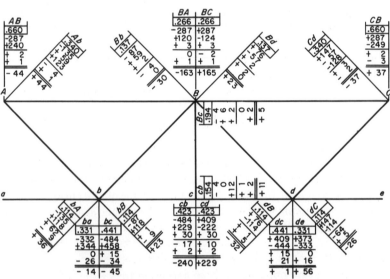

D. Distribution. Moments in Kip-Inches

Fig. 16–3. Secondary stresses in a truss.

bridges. So a pin-connected truss of any kind is rarely designed nowadays. The joints for most trusses are, instead, rigid, and to treat them as pin-connected joints results in errors on the unsafe side. Nevertheless, these errors are commonly ignored except for important trusses or trusses composed of short, heavy members.

Moment distribution is ideal for determining secondary stresses. The axial stresses are first found in the usual manner, assuming pin-connected joints. Then the deflections are determined for each joint. A convenient and quick method is the use of the Williot diagram.[1] Fixed-end moments for each member are determined from the known relative deflection of one end with respect to the other. These moments are distributed, and the bending stresses determined from the final moments are the secondary stresses.

In some cases, the bending moments so determined are large enough to affect seriously the axial stresses. If this is suspected, the false reactions at each joint can be computed from the bending moments, as follows. Compute the shear at the end of each member at a joint, and resolve the shears into horizontal and vertical components. The false reactions are equal and opposite to the resultant of these components. Forces equal and opposite to the false reactions are applied to the truss, a new Williot diagram is drawn, and moments due to these deflections are determined. The total secondary moments are equal to the first set of moments plus the second set. The process could be repeated until the desired accuracy is obtained, but it is not likely that more than two successive approximations would ever be needed.

Example 16–2. The truss in Fig. 16–3A is composed of wide-flange sections with the plane of the webs lying in the plane of the truss.[2] Diaphragms are sometimes needed in the upper and lower chords to support the flanges of the web members.

It is assumed that the truss is supported on knife edges or rollers at A, C, a, and e. Any other assumptions could have been made as easily. The forces in the members were found by assuming the joints to be pin-connected. The Williot-Mohr diagram in Fig. 16–3C was used to obtain the deflection of one end of each member with respect to its other end. Great care must be taken to insure that the Mohr diagram corrections are properly applied (although in this example the Mohr diagram is so tiny that a mistake would not be serious). It may well be desirable to eliminate the Mohr correction diagram by replotting the Williot diagram starting with the true position of two adjacent joints, thereby removing a fertile field for blunders.

The moments in the members cause shears, which in turn result in false reactions. For example, the false reaction at B necessary to resist the forces at B and c is 12 kips acting down. As the load at B is 100 kips, this represents an error of 12 percent. The error can be reduced by applying a force of 12 kips

---

[1] Chapter 17.
[2] This type of truss was pioneered by The Austin Company; it is very strong and astonishingly economical when mass-produced.

acting upward together with forces at the other joints to cancel the other false reactions. Then a new Williot diagram can be drawn and new moments can be determined, as previously outlined. Again we might expect errors of about 12 percent in the second analysis, but the error with respect to the original load of 100 kips would be only 12 percent of 12 percent, which would be less than 2 percent.

Some idea of the importance of the secondary stresses might be gained by comparing primary and secondary stresses. In the top chord, for example, the primary stress is:

$$s = \frac{P}{A} = \frac{65,000}{6.19} = 10,500 \text{ psi}$$

And at B, where the moment is 165 kip-in., the secondary stress is:

$$s = \frac{Mc}{I} = \frac{M}{S} = \frac{165,000}{21.5} = 7700 \text{ psi}$$

16–3. Mill Bents. The mill bent is a very specialized type of problem but a common one, nonetheless. Solutions presented in the literature usually take the form of complex equations, sometimes based on debatable assumptions and usually limited in scope and application.

In contrast, moment distribution admits any degree of refinement desired, allows any desirable assumptions to be easily made (such as degree of fixity of column bases), and is virtually unlimited in scope and applicability. Furthermore, it is easy to understand and quick to apply.

Typical wind forces are shown acting upon the mill bent of Fig. 16–4. The action of wind is quite uncertain, but for a structure of these proportions it is rational to assume that positive pressure acts on the windward side and negative pressure (suction) all over the roof and on the leeward side.[3] The wind loads are applied through purlins (roof beams) and girts (siding beams) to the bent. Light cranes are usually supported by column brackets such as those shown at B and H; heavy cranes are usually supported by another set of columns.

The columns for a structure such as this would consist of heavy steel wide-flange sections. The truss and the bracing would ordinarily consist of light angles. The columns can be considered to be infinitely stiff as compared with the individual truss members. Hence, the joints at D and F between the columns and the truss, and those at C and G between the columns and the knee braces, can be considered to be pin-connected joints (although the column itself is continuous at C and G). In spite of the comparative lightness of its individual members, the truss as a whole can be considered to be of infinite stiffness compared with the columns. With this assumption, the joints D, C, F, and G all deflect equally, as shown in Fig. 16–4B. Each

---

[3] "Wind Bracing in Steel Buildings," Fifth progress report of subcommittee No. 31, Committee on Steel of the Structural Division, *Proc. ASCE*, 62 (3): 397–412, March 1936.

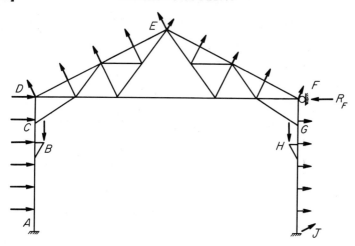

A. Mill Bent and Loads

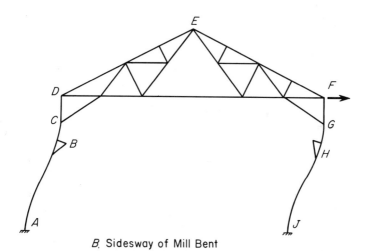

B. Sidesway of Mill Bent

Fig. 16–4. Analysis of mill bent.

column can then be considered rigidly supported at A (or any partial fixity may be assumed) and supported by knife edges at the knee brace and truss joints. When making the sidesway analysis, the knife edges at D and C and those at F and G are usually assumed to deflect equally.

The columns are first analyzed for intrapanel loads, either all acting at once or, preferably, each set of loads acting separately. Then the shears at the base of each column are found from free bodies of the lower portions of each column, CA and GJ. By resolving the horizontal components of all forces acting on the entire bent, the false reaction at F can be found. The analysis for sidesway is made by assuming a horizontal deflection of the truss, distributing the resulting fixed-end moments, and solving for the column shears and the deflecting force at F. This force and the moments are corrected (as in all other problems involving sidesway) and added to the moments caused by intrapanel loads. Finally, the forces exerted by the columns on the truss and knee braces are determined from free bodies of the entire columns, and these forces are included in the analysis of wind loads on the truss.

Greater refinements can be made. The true stiffnesses of all the members can be used, and the joints can be considered rigid. But such refinements are hardly warranted because the errors of the above approximate analysis are not large except in unusual problems.

Mill buildings are often continuously braced in the plane of the lower chord. In such cases, part of the wind load is carried by the knee braces and columns, and part is carried by the lower chord bracing into the end walls. The proportion carried by each system can be assumed on the basis of past experience, or the strain energy for a given deflection can be computed for each system, because the load carried by one system is proportional to the strain energy of that system.

16–4. Wind Stresses in Tall Buildings. For building frames more than three or four stories high, the exact solution of sidesway as explained in Arts. 14–1 and 14–2 is excessively cumbersome. Because of the uncertainties of wind or earthquake loads and the unknown but complex effect of curtain walls and other stiffening elements, a truly accurate analysis is apparently impossible. Therefore an approximate method is sufficient, provided the results are reasonable. Two well-known approximations are the cantilever[4] and portal[5] methods; these depend upon certain assumptions regarding the location of the points of contraflexure and the distribution of axial forces in the columns. A much more accurate method that is yet very fast is the K-percentage shortcut applied to moment distribution.

THE K-PERCENTAGE SHORTCUT. Rigorous analyses of tall buildings show that the joints in regular building frames deflect in nearly a straight line. The fixed-end moments for deflection are, for prismatic members, equal to $3\Delta K/2L$, and if straight-line joint deflection is assumed, the quantity Δ/L is constant for all stories, so the fixed-end moments are proportional to K or— even more simply—to I/L. Any fixed-end moments can be assumed, provided they are proportional to I/L in each story. They are then distributed and the column shears computed for each story. At any horizontal section the sum of the column shears must equal the sum of all the horizontal loads above the section. In each story the shears are corrected by a sidesway correction factor to make them equal to the horizontal loads acting above the

[4] A. H. Fuller and F. Kerekes, *Analysis and Design of Steel Structures* (New York: D. Van Nostrand Co., Inc., 1936), p. 460.
[5] *Ibid.*, p. 462.

story, and all the moments acting in that particular story are multiplied by that factor. If the sidesway correction factors are identical for all stories, it means that the joints truly do deflect in a straight line. If the sidesway correction factors for adjacent stories vary by, say, 10 percent, the final column moments could be in error by as much as 5 percent. The errors in the beams would be even less when the moments are computed as explained in Ex. 16–4A.

Theoretically, the correction of moments in one story adds moments to every story. But because the moments carried over and distributed into adjacent joints dissipate very quickly, the effect of a correction in one story has a negligible effect on all but the adjacent stories. Therefore the variation between sidesway correction factors for separated stories is not important; it is only necessary to compare factors for adjacent stories. If adjacent sidesway correction factors vary by less than 20 percent, the errors in the column moments are not likely to exceed 10 percent, which is sufficient accuracy for practical purposes.

If the adjacent sidesway correction factors vary too greatly, a second approximation may be made by either of two methods. The first method is easier to understand and use, but the second method is shorter. The first method consists of multiplying the original fixed-end moments by the sidesway correction factors to obtain a new set of fixed-end moments. Using these new fixed-end moments, the problem is worked all over again.

The second method consists of applying additional corrective fixed-end moments, which are then distributed and the results added to the moments from the first approximation. These corrective fixed-end moments are introduced primarily into those stories for which sidesway correction factors vary from the norm. The amount of corrective fixed-end moment required can be estimated by studying the variation between adjacent sidesway correction factors. This is easier to do than to explain. It is illustrated in Ex. 16–4B. This process can be repeated as many times as necessary to secure any desired accuracy.

Any kind of deflection curve—straight, curved, or irregular—can be assumed by starting with fixed-end moments proportional to $I\Delta/L^2$ instead of I/L. For irregular frames it may be better to estimate more exactly the relative deflections before beginning the distribution. Formulas for the proper relative deflections have been developed by Grinter,[6] but it is always possible to obtain any accuracy desired by introducing correction moments as explained above.

In very tall buildings the axial strains in the columns can produce secondary stresses of importance. They can be computed as a second approximation after the wind moments due to sidesway are determined. The axial forces are computed from statics. Then axial deformations are found, and

---

[6] Linton E. Grinter, *Theory of Modern Steel Structures*, Vol. II (rev. ed; New York: The Macmillan Co., 1949), p. 140.

fixed-end moments in the beams are determined from these deformations. These fixed-end moments are distributed in the usual manner.

Example 16–4A. First Approximation, K-percentage Shortcut. It is assumed that the joints of the frame in Fig. 16–5 deflect in a straight line. The relative I/L values for typical members are computed, using I in inch units (directly from the AISC Steel Construction Manual)[7] and L in feet. To obtain better

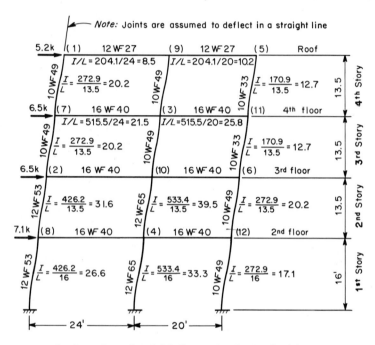

Fig. 16–5. Frame, loads, and relative I/L values. K-percentage shortcut.

values to work with, the I/L values of the columns are multiplied by ten to obtain fixed-end moments. The moments are distributed in Fig. 16–6, using Grinter's[8] style of recording. A regular system for distributing moments reduces chances for blunders. In this example the joints are balanced in the order indicated in parentheses in Fig. 16–5. By alternating the joints this way, some labor can be saved. In this example, carry-over moments of 4 kip-ft are ignored, which reduces the distribution to two or three cycles.

The shear in a story equals the sum of the column shears in that story. Since the column shear equals the end moments divided by the column length,

[7] *Steel Construction Manual of the American Institute of Steel Construction* (New York).
[8] Grinter, *op. cit.*, p. 138.

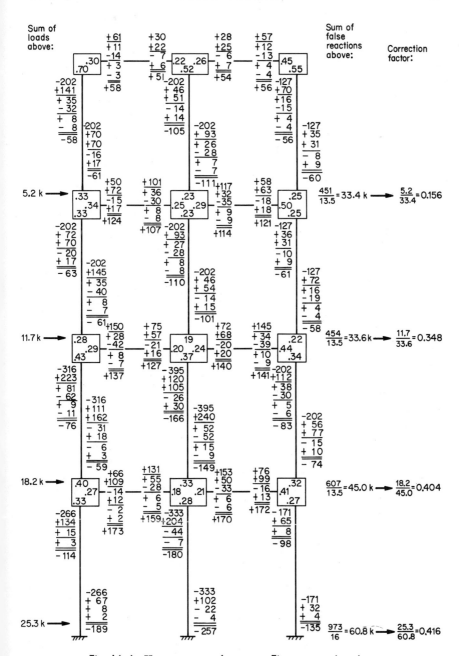

Fig. 16–6. K-percentage shortcut. First approximation.

the story shear equals the sum of all column moments in a story divided by the story height. The shears from top to bottom are, then:

4th story $(-58 \;\; -61 \; -105 \; -111 \; -56 \;\; -60)/13.5 = 33.4$ kips
3rd story $(-63 \;\; -61 \; -110 \; -101 \; -61 \;\; -58)/13.5 = 33.6$ kips
2nd story $(-76 \;\; -59 \; -166 \; -149 \; -83 \;\; -74)/13.5 = 45.0$ kips
1st story $(-114 \; -189 \; -180 \; -257 \; -98 \; -135)/16 \;\; = 60.8$ kips

without respect to signs.

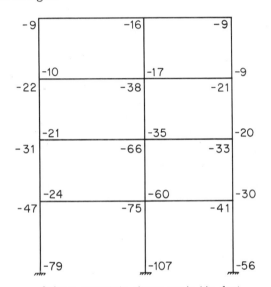

Column moments shown are in kip-feet

Fig. 16–7. Corrected moments from first approximation.

The true shears must equal the wind loads on the frame, which are from top to bottom for each story

4th story   5.2 kips
3rd story $5.2 + 6.5 = 11.7$ kips
2nd story $11.7 + 6.5 = 18.2$ kips
1st story $18.2 + 7.1 = 25.3$ kips

The correction factors are then

4th story $5.2/33.4 = 0.156$
3rd story $11.7/33.6 = 0.348$
2nd story $18.2/45.0 = 0.404$
1st story $25.3/60.8 = 0.416$

So the column moments in the corresponding stories are multiplied by these correction factors. The moments so corrected are shown in Fig. 16–7.

The sum of the beam and column moments at any joint must equal zero. At an exterior column, the moment in the beam equals the sum of the column moments. For example, at the left column on the fourth floor, the column moments are, from Fig. 16–7, -10 kip-ft and -22 kip-ft; the beam moment, then, is $+32$ kip-ft. At an interior column, the moments in the beams are distributed in proportion to the stiffnesses of the beam. For example, consider the interior joint on the fourth floor. The column moments are -17 kip-ft and -38 kip-ft, so the total beam moment is 55 kip-ft, of which

$$55 \times 25.8/47.3 = 30 \text{ kip-ft}$$

is distributed into the right beam and

$$55 \times 21.5/47.3 = 25 \text{ kip-ft}$$

is distributed into the left beam.

Example 16–4*B. Second Approximation, K-percentage Shortcut.* The second approximation is made to show the method and give an idea of the errors in the first (see Fig. 16–8). The corrective fixed-end moments are found by consideration of the sidesway correction factors as follows. The original moments in the fourth story were too large, as shown by the correction factor, which was small compared with correction factors in other stories. So the original moments should be reduced in the ratio of the adjacent correction factors. For example, the left-column fourth-story fixed-end moment of -202 kip-ft should have been about

$$(M) \frac{\text{Fourth-story correction factor}}{\text{Third-story correction factor}} = -202 \times \frac{0.156}{0.348} = -91 \text{ kip-ft}$$

The original fixed-end moment can be corrected to -91 kip-ft by adding a correcting fixed-end moment of $202 - 91 = +111$ kip-ft. In the third story, the left-column fixed-end moment should have been about

$$M = -202 \times \frac{0.348}{0.404} = -174 \text{ kip-ft}$$

And the original fixed-end moment can be corrected to -174 kip-ft by adding a correcting fixed-end moment of $202 - 174 = +28$ kip-ft.

These correcting fixed-end moments will result in a very adequate second approximation. However, such large fixed-end moments will cause large carry-over moments which, in turn, will upset the nicety of the solution. So a better approximation can be made by arbitrarily altering the correcting fixed-end moments somewhat. In a general way we can anticipate the effect of the balancing and carry-over moments as follows. When the large fourth-story moments are balanced, a good deal of moment will be carried over the third story, in effect reducing the third-story correcting fixed-end

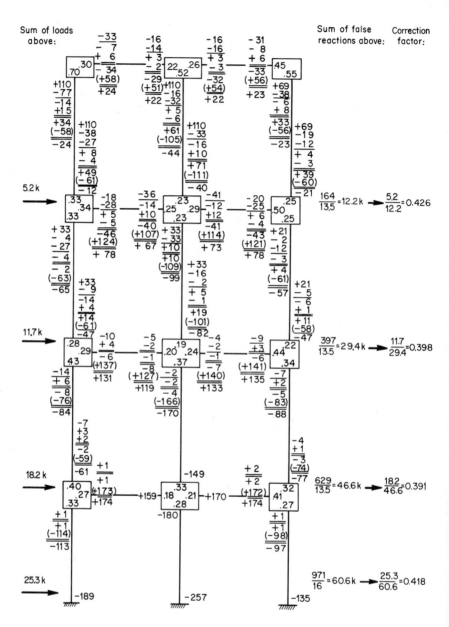

Moments in parentheses are total moments from Fig 16-5

The last moments are total moments for the second approximation

Fig. 16–8. K-percentage shortcut. Second approximation.

moments. So the third-story correcting moments should be increased. Considering the size of the correcting moments and the distribution and carry-over factors,[9] we might estimate that the third-story correcting fixed-end moments in the left column should be increased by about +5 kip-ft to a total of +33 kip-ft. In the same manner, carry-over moments from the third story to the fourth story will slightly reduce the correction of the fourth story. To compensate, suppose we increase the fourth-story correcting fixed-end

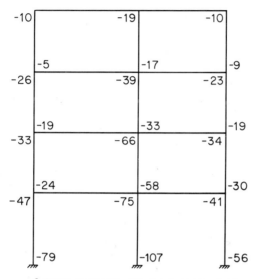

Column moments shown are in kip-feet

Fig. 16–9. Corrected moments from second approximation.

moments in the left column from +111 kip-ft to +113 kip-ft. But there is still one more consideration; when the correction in a story is very large, there is a tendency for the moments to overcompensate. To overcome this tendency, suppose we reduce the fourth-story fixed-end moment from +113 kip-ft to +110 kip-ft. (The end results show that it should have been reduced to about +105 kip-ft.) Of course, the correcting fixed-end moments in the other columns of each story must be proportional to their I/L values. For example, if the left column is to have a correcting fixed-end moment of 110 kip-ft, the right column must have a corresponding moment of 110 kip-ft × 12.7/20.2 = 69 kip-ft.

The results of the second approximation are excellent. They show a maximum variation in adjacent correction factors to be only 7 percent as compared with the original maximum of 76 percent. But note that the maximum difference between corresponding moments in Figs. 16–7 and 16–9

---

[9] Experience will develop the judgment to estimate the effects of these factors.

is only 5 kip-ft, an error of little importance even though the percentage error is high. For most practical purposes then, the second approximation is superfluous.

Grinter[10] showed that in a certain twenty-story building, the maximum error resulting from fixed-end moments proportional to column K values was only 7 percent, and the maximum variation of adjacent correction factors was 11 percent. The mean error in final moments appeared to be about 2 percent.

16–5. Other Shortcuts. The reader will note that only two shortcuts have been introduced in this chapter. The first using modified factors is almost universally used; the second, K-percentage, is a tremendous time saver. Neither is difficult to remember and neither differs much from basic moment distribution. They are explained herein partly for their practicality and partly to indicate the possibilities in shortcuts.

In general, the author believes shortcuts are better avoided. The basic approach is itself very fast, as compared with the classical methods such as moment area or virtual work, and, once learned, it is easy to remember. Except for the few mentioned below, most shortcuts do not save an appreciable amount of time, particularly in view of the fact that most structural engineers spend an inconsequential part of their time on analysis anyway. Unless one is continually engaged in analysis, the time saved by the shortcut is canceled by the time spent in reviewing or relearning it.

However, another worth-while shortcut deserves mention. It is a two-cycle method of moment distribution that yields maximum end moments and maximum and minimum center moments in continuous beams. It is particularly well adapted to the design of reinforced concrete buildings. It is fully explained in *Continuity of Concrete Building Frames*.[11]

A number of shortcuts have been proposed for sidesway corrections. In one group of these, sidesway moments are distributed along with moments due to vertical loads. In some, such as the Morris[12] method, shears are computed at the end of each cycle, and a new set of balancing fixed-end moments are introduced into the columns. An alternative procedure is to introduce an arbitrary estimated set of sidesway fixed-end moments either in every cycle or in random cycles to compensate sidesway.[13] Either method has the advantage that sidesway and load moments are distributed together, so the labor of distribution is reduced. But this advantage is reduced to some degree by the additional labor of checking shears each time sidesway correction is added. For regular frames, particularly symmetrical ones of equal story heights, these proposals are faster. For complex frames, the method

[10] Grinter, *op. cit.*, p. 137.

[11] Available upon request from the Portland Cement Association, 33 West Grand Avenue, Chicago 10, Ill., or from any branch office. Another valuable Portland Cement Association pamphlet, dealing with the distribution of horizontal loads in buildings, is *Analysis of Small Reinforced Concrete Buildings for Earthquake Forces*.

[12] C. T. Morris, "On Analysis of Continuous Frames," *Trans. ASCE*, 96: 66–69, 1932.

[13] Grinter, *op. cit.*, pp. 122–124.

presented herein (separate sidesway for each story) is faster. In practical office work it is advantageous to solve sidesway separately from the loads, partly because there may be several loading conditions and partly because design stresses for vertical loads are usually different from those due to vertical loads combined with the horizontal loads of wind or earthquake. For most practical problems, then, the Morris (and similar) methods are longer, not shorter. In conclusion, the over-all advantages of these shortcuts are dubious and the choice of a method is mostly a matter of personal preference.

There are many other shortcuts—some valuable, others not. After some experience and a thorough understanding of the basic principles, one can develop one's own shortcuts. More important than all the shortcuts, however, is accuracy—elimination of all blunders. There is no substitute for that.

Part V

OTHER METHODS

The purpose of this section is to introduce some other well-known methods of indeterminate structural analysis in order that the student may read the literature, understand the interrelationships of the methods, and appreciate their history and development. Limitations of space permit only well-known methods to be included. Except for Chapter 17, for which only Part I is a prerequisite, an understanding also of Parts II, III, and IV is, in general, prerequisite for Part V. This understanding means that the reader is quite proficient in structural analysis and such proficiency makes it easy to learn other methods. Consequently, much of the explanation in this section is terse, and these chapters are therefore short.

17

WILLIOT-MOHR DIAGRAM

17–1. Introduction. The Williot-Mohr diagram, partly introduced by Williot[1] in 1877 and completed by Mohr[2] ten years later, is an ingenious graphical solution for the deflections of trusses. It is simple, quick, and widely used. Furthermore, it is advantageous in that it yields the absolute movement of every panel point, that is, both vertical and horizontal components of the movements.

17–2. Williot Diagram. The first step in drawing the Williot diagram is to compute the change of length (δL) of each member in the truss due to loads acting on the truss, temperature effects, etc. The change of length due to loads is[3]

$$\delta L = \frac{FL}{AE} \tag{17-1}$$

where F is the total force acting on the member, L is its length, A is the cross-sectional area, and E is Young's modulus of elasticity. If all units are in terms of pounds and inches, both δL and the Williot diagram yield deflection in inches. But it is usually more convenient to express F in kips, L in feet, A in square inches, and E in kips per square inch. Then by dimensional analysis

$$\delta L = \frac{\text{kips} \times \text{feet}}{\text{inches}^2 \times \text{kips/inches}^2} = \text{feet}$$

So δL is in terms of feet. The change of length due to temperature is

$$\delta L = C\Delta TL \tag{17-2}$$

where C is the temperature coefficient per °F (0.0000065 for structural steel, half of this for wood, and twice this for aluminum), ΔT is the temperature change in °F, and L is the length.

Consider point B in Fig. 17–1 to be fixed in space as the point of intersection of members AB and BC. Such a point can move only if (1) point A

[1] Williot, "Notations practiques sur la statique graphique," *Annales Génie Civil*, 6: 601–621, 1877.
[2] Otto Mohr, "Über Geschwindigkeitspläne und Beschleunigungspläne," *Zivilingenieur*, 1887.
[3] See Art. 7–4 for derivation.

or C moves or (2) if member AB or BC suffers a change in length. If the new positions of points A and C are known to be A' and C' and the new lengths of members AB and BC are known to be $A'B_2$ and B_4C', the new location of point B can be determined by swinging arcs about points A' and C' as centers with the new lengths of the members as radii. The intersection of the arcs locates point B_5. But since the change in the lengths of members is seldom

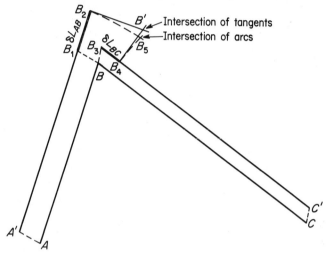

Fig. 17–1. Basis for Williot diagram.

greater than 1 in 1500, the movements are very small. Consequently, the procedure of swinging arcs can be replaced by erecting tangents at the ends of the radii. Thus the new position of point B becomes B' in Fig. 17–1.

Example 17–2. *Elementary Truss.* In the truss of Fig. 17–2A, the change of length of each member is indicated by plus (elongation) and minus (shortening). To obtain the deflection of each joint, consider point A (which does not move) to be the reference point and member AC (which does not rotate) to be the reference member. In order to be clearly visible, the changes of length are greatly exaggerated. This results in an unrealistically distorted truss in Fig. 17–2B.

To obtain sufficient accuracy in a drawing made to a reasonable scale, the truss itself can be omitted, leaving only the length changes and the tangents as shown in Fig. 17–2C, which is the Williot diagram. Note that point A is used as the reference point for measuring displacements of all joints of the truss. Since point A is fixed, all other fixed points coincide with it, and it becomes points B, C, and A' as well as the origin point O. Member AB is used as the reference (non-rotating) member, and since its direction does not change, the Williot diagram shows the true movements of the joints, B to B' and C to C'. The only use of the original truss in drawing Williot diagrams is

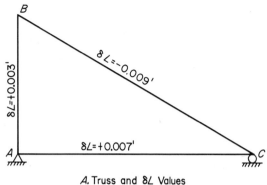

A. Truss and δL Values

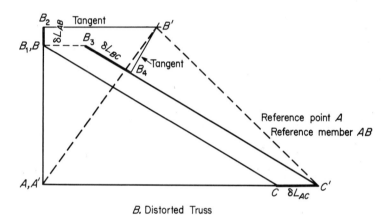

B. Distorted Truss

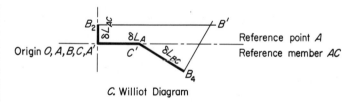

C. Williot Diagram

Fig. 17–2. Williot diagram for a simple truss.

in indicating the direction of the δL vectors and the tangents. The δL vectors are *always* parallel to the truss members, and the tangents are *always* perpendicular to both of them.

Without reference to Fig. 17–2*B*, the Williot diagram can be constructed as follows. Member AC lengthens; so with respect to point A, point C moves to the right and is so plotted. Member AB lengthens; so with respect to point A, point B' moves up (to B_2), then swings on an arc. Therefore, plot

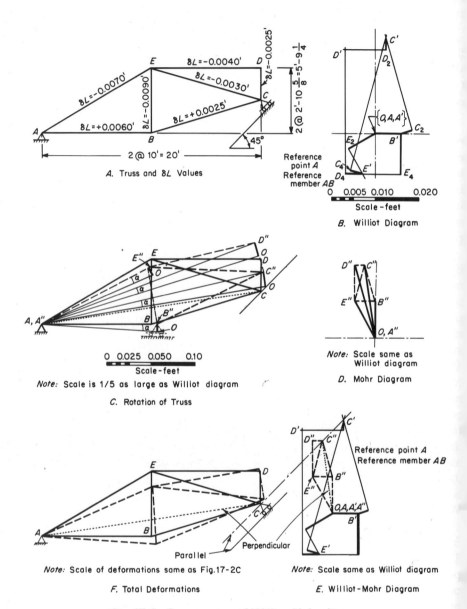

Fig. 17–3. Construction of Williot-Mohr diagram.

vector AB_2 up and erect a perpendicular tangent. Member BC shortens; so with respect to point C', point B' moves down to the right, then swings on an arc. Therefore, plot vector $C'B_4$ down to the right (and parallel to member BC), and erect a perpendicular tangent. The intersection of the two tangents (representing the arcs of swing) locates point B'.

17-3. Mohr Correction Diagram. Trusses usually rest on at least one fixed point, but frequently no member remains fixed in direction. To find the absolute deformations, it is necessary to (1) assume a reference member (which does not rotate), (2) construct the Williot diagram therefrom, and (3) correct for the rotation of the reference member.

Example 17-3. Figure 17-3A shows a truss, the members of which all rotate. In Fig. 17-3B, the Williot diagram is drawn by using point A as reference point and member AB as the reference member (which temporarily is assumed not to rotate). This is equivalent to assuming that the roller at C is moved to B and rolls on a horizontal surface, as shown by the dotted lines in Fig. 17-3C. The Williot diagram in Fig. 17-3B is constructed in a step-by-step process, each step being similar to that described for Fig. 17-2C. The points are located in the following order: A, B', E', C', and D'.

The deformed truss shown by the dashed lines in Fig. 17-3C is constructed by plotting the deflections of each panel point (B', C', D', E') from the origin of the Williot diagram. A smaller scale is used to avoid distorting the truss out of all resemblance to the original. The deflected positions of the panel points in Fig. 17-3C are termed A'', B'', C'', D'', and E''. Because reference member AB was assumed not to rotate, point C'' falls off the supporting surface. To reach its actual position, the distorted truss must be rotated about point A until point C'' falls on the supporting surface. The rotation required, termed α, equals arc $C''O$ divided by radius AC''. But again these movements are very small compared with the size of the truss, so radius AC'' can be approximated by radius AC and arc $C''O$ can be constructed as a tangent perpendicular to radius AC (not perpendicular to AC'' because the dashed lines show the truss distortions tremendously exaggerated—exaggerated 80 times, in fact). The movement of each panel point (shown by heavy lines labeled $B''O$, $C''O$, $D''O$, and $E''O$) must be added vectorially to the corresponding displacement (OB', OC', OD', and OE'), obtained from the Williot diagram, to give the total displacement.

The displacements $B''O$, $C''O$, $D''O$, and $E''O$ are plotted in Fig. 17-3D from a common origin O, using the same scale as that in the Williot diagram. The length of each vector equals the radius from the point in question to point A times angle α. Then, since each vector is both proportional and perpendicular to its radius, $A''B''C''D''E''$ determines a figure that is proportional to (and co-planar with) the original truss and perpendicular to it. This figure, shown by the dashed lines in Fig. 17-3D, is the Mohr correction diagram.

In practice the two diagrams are drawn in a single Williot-Mohr diagram, as shown in Fig. 17–3E. The size of the Mohr diagram can be determined by the fact that line $C''C'$ must be parallel to the surface supporting the rollers at C. Therefore point C'' is located at the intersection of a line through C' parallel to the supporting surface of the rollers and a line through the origin perpendicular to line AC.

The total displacement of any joint such as D, for example, is the vector sum of the displacement due to rotation (vector $D''O$) plus the displacement obtained from the Williot diagram (vector OD'). Since $D''O \leftrightarrow OD'$ equals $D''D'$, the total displacement of any panel point equals the distance measured from the point on the Mohr diagram to the corresponding point on the Williot diagram.

17–4. Practical Considerations. The limiting case in which a member does not change in length requires only the drawing of the tangent perpendicular to the member. If member CD in Fig. 17–3A did not change in length, then in Fig. 17–3B, D_2 would coincide with C' and tangent D_2D' accordingly would pass through C'.

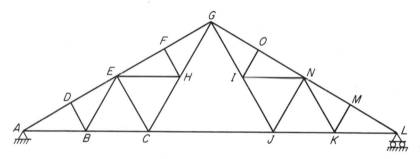

Fig. 17–4. Fink truss.

If the truss contains many members, the Williot diagram grows too large for the paper. In such instances it is wise to start the diagram by using a panel point and member near the middle of the truss for the reference point and reference member. Since such members rotate less than members near the end, the Mohr diagram and the Williot diagram are much smaller.

If the truss contains a great many panels, the Williot-Mohr diagram may be inaccurate since errors tend to accumulate. Then the deflection of one or two joints may be computed by virtual work, so the Williot-Mohr diagram can be corrected to correspond to accurately determined deflections. Any desired accuracy can be obtained by thus combining the two methods. The combination is relatively quick since the δL values computed for the Williot diagram are directly applicable to virtual work.

Trusses with subdivided panels can be solved in the manner described below for the Fink truss. Using any member on the left side of the truss for the reference member, the construction of the Williot diagram for panel points A through H in Fig. 17–4 is routine. The problem is to locate points I' and O'. First, locate points J' and N' by considering GJ and GN to be single members.

$$\delta L_{GJ} = \delta L_{GI} + \delta L_{IJ}$$

$$\delta L_{GN} = \delta L_{GO} + \delta L_{ON}$$

With the position of J' and N' established, points I' and O' can be located from them in the usual manner.

18

METHOD OF DEFLECTIONS

18–1. Introduction. The method of deflections is sometimes called the basic method, the method of superposition, the general method, or the method of consistent deflections. The structure is first cut back to a statically determinate one in the usual way—by the removal of one or more supports, for example. Then the deflections at the removed supports are computed by any method such as virtual work or moment area. Next, the deflections due to a concentrated load acting at one of the removed supports are calculated (again by any method desired—even a deflection formula, if an applicable one can be found). This process is repeated for a concentrated load acting in turn at each of the removed supports. Finally, the sum of the deflections at each support is equated to zero. The point of view is that at any redundant support, the structure does deflect due to loads and then—because of reactive forces—deflects an equal and opposite amount to yield a net deflection of zero.

In previous chapters we adopted the point of view that the deflection at a support was zero from first to last. But either point of view is valid. In fact the two are basically the same; only the procedure of calculation is different. Previously we used the principle of superposition before "computing" zero deflections, whereas in this chapter we compute deflections first, and then use the principle of superposition.

18–2. Maxwell's Theorem of Reciprocal Deflections. Maxwell's law (as it is usually called) was formulated by James Clerk Maxwell in 1864. It is a classic example of the widespread importance of a very simple fact. It can often be used to simplify structural analyses (especially when using the method of deflections), and it forms the basis for the use of "unloaded" models. With respect to any elastic structure whose deformations are small, it states: *The deflection of point A caused by a load acting at point B equals the deflection at point B caused by the same load acting at point A.*

To prove the theorem, compare the deflection at point A, Fig. 18–1A, with that at point B, Fig. 18–1B. The structure shown is a statically indeterminate elastic beam, but any other elastic structure would serve as well. To find the deflection at point A, apply a virtual load of 1 # at point A. Then apply the load P at point B and write the virtual work equation

$$1 \, \# \, \Delta_{AB} = \int_0^L \frac{m_A M_B}{EI} \, dx \qquad (8\text{–}1)$$

where Δ_{AB} means deflection at A due to load applied at B, m_A is the virtual moment for a virtual load of 1 $\#$ at A, and M_B is the real moment due to the load P acting at B. However, P is P times as great as 1, so M_B is P times as great as m_B, where m_B is the moment due to a 1-lb load. The above equation can then be expressed

$$1 \# \Delta_{AB} = \int_0^L \frac{m_A P m_B}{EI} \, dx$$

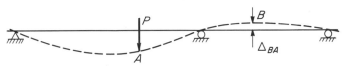

A. Deflection at A for Load at B

B. Equal Deflection at B for Same Load at A

Fig. 18–1. Proof of Maxwell's theorem.

Now apply the same load P to point A and find the resulting deflection at point B. From the explanation above,

$$1 \# \Delta_{BA} = \int_0^L \frac{m_A M_B}{EI} \, dx = \int_0^L \frac{m_B P m_A}{EI} \, dx$$

The identical integrals prove

$$\Delta_{AB} = \Delta_{BA} \tag{18–1}$$

which verifies the statement (1) that the deflection at point A due to a load acting at point B equals the deflection at point B due to the same load acting at point A. In the same manner it can be proved (2) that the rotation at point A due to a moment acting at point B equals the rotation at point B due to the same moment acting at point A, and (3) that the deflection at point A due to a moment applied at point B equals *numerically* the rotation at point B due to the application at point A of a load numerically equal to the moment originally applied at point B.

To forestall serious mistakes in the application of Maxwell's theorem, the following statements should be studied carefully: (1) The rotation at A due to a load applied at B does *not* equal the rotation at B due to the same load applied at A; (2) the deflection at A due to a moment applied at B does *not* equal the deflection at B due to the same moment applied at A.

18-3. Consistent Deflections. The principles set forth in Arts. 18-1 and 18-2 can be best illustrated by example.

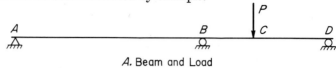

A. Beam and Load

B. Cut-Back Structure Showing Total Elastic Curve

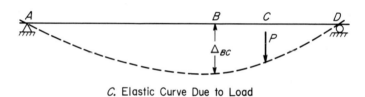

C. Elastic Curve Due to Load

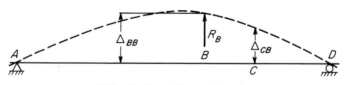

D. Elastic Curve Due to Reaction

Fig. 18-2. Consistent deflections. Beam with one redundant.

Example 18-3A. Beam with One Redundant. Let it be required to find the middle reaction of the beam in Fig. 18-2. One way to make the beam statically determinate is to remove a reaction and substitute an unknown force for it. Such a statically determinate beam is shown in Fig. 18-2*B*. Let

Δ_{BC} = deflection at B due to load P at C (Fig. 18-2*C*)

Δ_{BB} = deflection at B due to reaction R_B at B (Fig. 18-2*D*)

δ_{BC} = deflection at B due to a unit load at C

δ_{BB} = deflection at B due to a unit load at B

Since the total deflection at B is zero, we have

$$\Delta_{BB} = \Delta_{BC}$$

If the structure is elastic, deflections are proportional to load:

$$\Delta_{BB} = R_B \, \delta_{BB} \quad \text{and} \quad \Delta_{BC} = P_C \, \delta_{BC}$$

Substituting and solving for R_B yields

$$R_B = P_C \frac{\delta_{BC}}{\delta_{BB}} \tag{18–2}$$

By making use of Maxwell's theorem,

$$\delta_{BC} = \delta_{CB} \tag{18–1}$$

an alternative form is obtained:

$$R_B = P_C \frac{\delta_{CB}}{\delta_{BB}} \tag{18–3}$$

which has the advantage that deflections need to be found for only one position of the unit load, that is, for a unit load acting at point B. The fraction δ_{CB}/δ_{BB} can be multiplied by K/K, where K is a constant such that $K \, \delta_{BB}$ is a unit deflection. Let $K \, \delta_{CB}$ be called y_{CB}, the deflection at C due to a unit deflection at B. Then we have

$$R_B = P_C \frac{K\delta_{CB}}{K\delta_{BB}} = P_C \frac{y_{CB}}{1} = P_C y_{CB}$$

If more than one load acts on the structure, the equation can be generalized:

$$R_B = \sum Py \tag{18–4}$$

where y is the deflection at the point where the load is applied. The locus of y is, of course, the elastic curve, and from Eq. 18–4 it is by definition an influence line for R. The equivalence between the elastic curve and the influence line is sometimes called the Müller-Breslau principle.[1]

Example 18–3B. *Beam with Multiple Redundants.* A structure statically indeterminate to two degrees is shown in Fig. 18–3. The structure is made statically determinate by replacing two reactions with unknown forces. Deflection curves for the respective forces are shown in Figs. 18–3C, D, and E. Since the total deflections at points B and D are each zero, we have two equations which can be solved simultaneously for R_B and R_D:

$$\Delta_{BC} - \Delta_{BB} - \Delta_{BD} = 0$$
$$\Delta_{DC} - \Delta_{DD} - \Delta_{DB} = 0$$

[1] See Chapter 25.

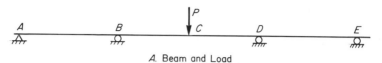

A. Beam and Load

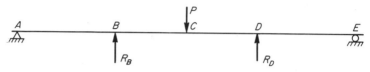

B. Cut-Back Structure and Loads

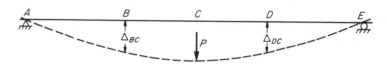

C. Elastic Curve Due to Load *P*

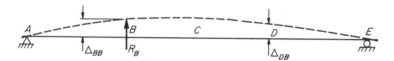

D. Elastic Curve Due to R_B

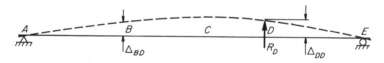

E. Elastic Curve Due to R_D

Fig. 18–3. Consistent deflections. Beam with more than one redundant.

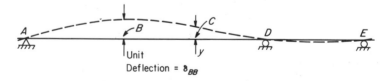

Fig. 18–4. Elastic curve for displacement at reaction and influence line for reaction.

from which

$$P_C \, \delta_{BC} = R_B \, \delta_{BB} + R_D \, \delta_{BD} \qquad (18\text{–}5A)$$

$$P_C \, \delta_{DC} = R_D \, \delta_{DD} + R_B \, \delta_{DB} \qquad (18\text{–}5B)$$

From Maxwell's theorem,

$$\delta_{BC} = \delta_{CB} \qquad \delta_{BD} = \delta_{DB} \qquad \delta_{DC} = \delta_{CD} \qquad \delta_{DB} = \delta_{BD} \qquad (18\text{–}1)$$

we have, therefore,

$$P_C \, \delta_{CB} = R_B \, \delta_{BB} + R_D \, \delta_{DB} \qquad (18\text{–}6A)$$

$$P_C \, \delta_{CD} = R_B \, \delta_{BD} + R_D \, \delta_{DD} \qquad (18\text{–}6B)$$

Note that these latter equations require only two elastic curves: those for 1-# loads at B and at D. The elastic curve in Fig. 18–3C is not required.

A simultaneous solution can be avoided by forcing one deflection in each of the above equations to be zero. If δ_{DB} is forced to be zero by replacing the reaction at D, the elastic curve looks like that in Fig. 18–4, and Eq. 18–6A reduces to Eq. 18–3:

$$R_B = P_C \frac{\delta_{CB}}{\delta_{BB}} \qquad (18\text{–}3)$$

For one or more loads, Eq. 18–3 can be altered into Eq. 18–4, as before, provided the deflection at the reaction is made unity.

$$R_B = \sum Py \qquad (18\text{–}4)$$

Thus by removing only one support and constructing an influence line for a unit deflection at that support, simultaneous solutions are avoided. This is not very difficult to do analytically, but it reaches the pinnacle of ease and perfection of conception with models. The subject is explored more fully in Chapter 25.

19

DOUBLE INTEGRATION

19–1. Introduction. The equation of the elastic curve of a beam was formulated in 1694 by James Bernoulli. Its application was greatly extended by Leonard Euler (1707–1783). Navier first used double integration in 1825 to solve statically indeterminate structures. The double-integration method has one advantage over others: it produces the equation of the elastic curve directly. But, of course, other methods can be forced to yield an equation of the elastic curve.

19–2. Theory. If a prismatic, elastic beam is subjected to pure bending (that is, if the shear is assumed to be negligible), the relation between the radius of curvature R of the neutral axis, the bending moment M, and Young's modulus of elasticity E is

$$\frac{1}{R} = \frac{M}{EI} \qquad \text{(B–3)}$$

as proved in Appendix B. From analytical geometry, the exact expression for curvature is

$$\frac{1}{R} = \frac{d^2y/dx^2}{[1 + (dy/dx)^2]^{3/2}}$$

where x and y are the coordinates of any point on the curve. By substitution we have

$$\frac{d^2y/dx^2}{[1 + (dy/dx)^2]^{3/2}} = \frac{M}{EI} \qquad \text{(19–1)}$$

The moment is expressed in terms of x measured along the neutral axis of the undeflected beam. The resulting equation solved for y is the equation of the elastic curve. However, Eq. 19–1 is very difficult to solve because of the complexity of the denominator on the left side. If the curvature is slight, $(dy/dx)^2$ is negligible and the denominator approaches unity,[1] resulting in the less formidable equation

$$\frac{d^2y}{dx^2} = \frac{M}{EI} \qquad \text{(19–2)}$$

---

[1] In moment area, this is analogous to assuming that the point of deflection moves along a tangent (AA_1, A_1A_2, etc., Fig. 4–1B) rather than along an arc.

Integrating Eq. 19-2 once gives dy/dx, which is the *slope* of the elastic curve. Integrating again yields y which is the *ordinate* of the elastic curve, which is to say, the equation of the elastic curve. If EI is constant and Eq. 19-2 is differentiated, we have (noting $dM/dx = V$, the shear)

$$\frac{d^3y}{dx^3} = \frac{d}{dx}\frac{d^2y}{dx^2} = \frac{d}{dx}\frac{M}{EI} = \frac{1}{EI}\frac{dM}{dx} = \frac{V}{EI}$$

Differentiating the above equation yields (since $dV/dx = w$)

$$\frac{d^4y}{dx^4} = \frac{d}{dx}\frac{V}{EI} = \frac{1}{EI}\frac{dV}{dx} = \frac{w}{EI}$$

Tabulating the above expressions expresses their relations more graphically[2]:

$$\frac{d^4y}{dx^4} = \frac{w}{EI}$$

$$\frac{d^3y}{dx^3} = \frac{V}{EI}$$

$$\frac{d^2y}{dx^2} = \frac{M}{EI} \tag{19-2}$$

$$\frac{dy}{dx} = \theta = \text{slope of elastic curve}$$

$$y = \text{deflection of elastic curve}$$

19-3. Applications and Comparisons. The application of double integration and comparison with moment area and virtual work are illustrated by the following examples.

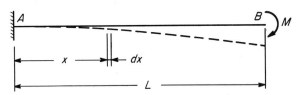

Fig. 19-1. Beam with constant moment.

Example 19-3A. *Double Integration.* The error involved in neglecting the term $(dy/dx)^2$ in Eq. 19-1 may be illustrated by calculating the equation of the elastic curve of the beam in Fig. 19-1. The moment is constant and is called M_O. Therefore, from Eq. 19-2, we have

$$\frac{d^2y}{dx^2} = \frac{M_O}{EI}$$

[2] For a more detailed derivation and discussion, see E. P. Popov, *Mechanics of Materials* (New York: Prentice-Hall, Inc., 1954), pp. 269-284.

Integrating gives

$$\frac{dy}{dx} = \theta = \int_0^x \frac{M_O\,dx}{EI} = \frac{M_O x}{EI} + C_1$$

The constant C_1 can be evaluated by recognizing that the slope is zero when x is zero:

$$\frac{dy}{dx} = 0 = \frac{M_O \times 0}{EI} + C_1$$

$$C_1 = 0$$

Integrating again gives

$$y = \int_0^x \frac{M_O x\,dx}{EI} = \frac{M_O x^2}{2EI} + C_2$$

But $y = 0$ when $x = 0$, and therefore C_2 is zero. Hence we find

$$y = \frac{M_O x^2}{2EI}$$

Now this is the equation of a parabola, but since the moment is constant, R is constant, and the equation should be that for an arc of a circle. The difference between the parabola and the circular arc is the error resulting from simplifying Eq. 19–1 to Eq. 19–2.

Example 19–3*B*. *Moment Area.* The equation of the elastic curve could also be found by moment area. By placing the axes through any general point O (origin), as in Fig. 19–2, we find

$$\Delta Y = \int \frac{Mx\,ds}{EI} + \sum x\theta + Y \qquad (4\text{–}14)$$

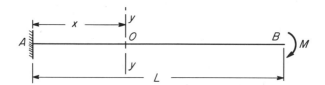

Fig. 19–2. Moment area for elastic curve.

In integrating between $x = 0$ and $x = x$, the second and third terms become zero.[3] The moment is M_O and ds becomes dx.

$$\Delta Y = \int_0^x \frac{M_O x\,dx}{EI} = \frac{M_O x^2}{2EI}$$

which is the equation of the elastic curve.

[3] Analogous to constants C_1 and C_2 becoming zero in the double-integration method.

Example 19–3*C*. *Virtual Work*. The equation of the elastic curve can also be found by virtual work by placing the virtual load at any general point *O*, as shown in Fig. 19–3. Then the deflection becomes from Eq. 8–1

$$1 \mathbin{\#} \Delta Y = \int_0^L \frac{Mm\,dx}{EI}$$

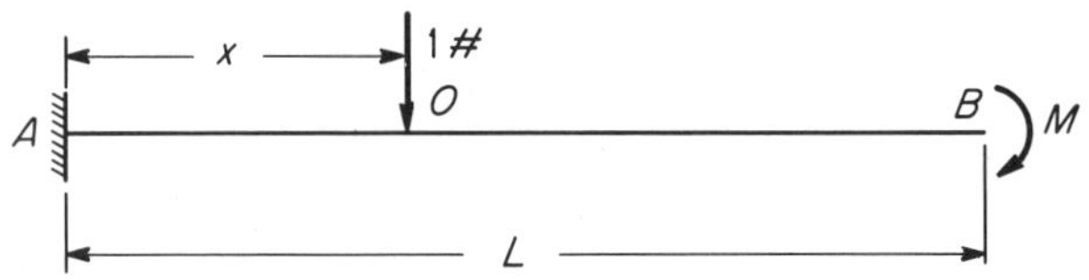

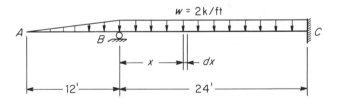

Fig. 19–3. Virtual work for elastic curve.

From *O* to *B*, $m = 0$, so we need to integrate only from *O* to *A*, that is, from $x = 0$ to $x = x$. The moment $M = M_O$ and $m = 1 \mathbin{\#} x$ or $x \mathbin{\#}$, so that we have

$$1 \mathbin{\#} \Delta Y = \int_0^x \frac{M_O x \mathbin{\#}\,dx}{EI}$$

or

$$\Delta Y = \frac{M_O x^2}{2EI}$$

as before.[4]

19–4. Indeterminate Structures. The solution of the redundant reaction of the beam of Fig. 19–4 illustrates the use of double integration applied to statically indeterminate structures.

Fig. 19–4. Statically indeterminate beam.

Example 19–4. The moment equation for portion *BC* can be obtained from Fig. 8–4*B*. It is

$$M = -12(x + 4) + V_B x - x^2$$

---

[4] The analogy to constants C_1 and C_2 lies in the facts that, since there is no slope at *A* ($C_1 = 0$) and no deflection at *A* ($C_2 = 0$), no constants need be added to the virtual work equation. An example of the necessity for adding constants to the virtual work equation is given in Ex. 8–3*B*.

Note the sign convention: moments producing compression in upper fibers are termed plus; those producing compression in lower fibers, minus. From Eq. 19–2 we have

$$\frac{d^2y}{dx^2} = \frac{M}{EI} = \frac{1}{EI}[-12(x+4) + V_Bx - x^2]$$

$$0 = \frac{dy}{dx} = \frac{1}{EI}\int_0^x [-12(x+4) + V_Bx - x^2]\,dx$$

$$= \frac{1}{EI}\left(-\frac{12x^2}{2} - 48x + \frac{V_Bx^2}{2} - \frac{x^3}{3}\right) + C_1$$

When $x = 24$, $dy/dx = 0$, enabling us to evaluate C_1 from

$$0 = \frac{1}{EI}\left[-6(24)^2 - 48 \times 24 + V_B\frac{(24)^2}{2} - \frac{(24)^3}{3}\right] + C_1$$

Hence we have

$$C_1 = \frac{(24)^2}{EI}\left(16 - \frac{V_B}{2}\right)$$

and

$$y = \frac{1}{EI}\int_0^x \left[-6x^2 - 48x + \frac{V_Bx^2}{2} - \frac{x^3}{3} + (24)^2\left(16 - \frac{V_B}{2}\right)\right]dx$$

Integrating, substituting, and rearranging terms result in

$$y = \frac{1}{EI}\left[-\frac{x^4}{12} + \left(\frac{V_B}{6} - 2\right)x^3 - 24x^2 + (24)^2\left(16 - \frac{V_B}{2}\right)x\right] + C_2$$

When $x = 0$, $y = 0$, and therefore $C_2 = 0$.

At $x = 24$, $y = 0$, which permits us to solve for V_B. Substituting gives

$$y = 0 = \frac{1}{EI}\left[-\frac{(24)^4}{12} + \left(\frac{V_B}{6} - 2\right)(24)^3 - 24(24)^2 + (24)^2\left(16 - \frac{V_B}{2}\right)24\right]$$

from which

$$V_B = +33$$

This agrees with the solutions by virtual work (Ex. 8–4) and by moment area (Ex. 5–2A), which should be studied for comparison with the work above.

To find the point of maximum deflection, set the derivative of y (with respect to x) equal to zero. Of course, we already have an expression for dy/dx, so it is necessary only to substitute the known values of C_1 and V_B:

$$\frac{dy}{dx} = 0 = \frac{1}{EI}\left[-6x^2 - 48x + \frac{33x^2}{2} - \frac{x^3}{3} + (24)^2\left(16 - \frac{33}{2}\right)\right]$$

This cubic equation is most readily solved by trial and error, yielding the value

$$x = 10.8$$

This value of x together with $V_B = 33$ and $C_2 = 0$ can be substituted into the equation of the elastic curve to yield the maximum deflection

$$y_{max} = \frac{1}{EI}\left[-\frac{(10.8)^4}{12} + \frac{7}{2}(10.8)^3 - 24(10.8)^2 - 288(10.8)\right]$$

$$y_{max} = -\frac{2635}{EI}$$

which is the same (within slide-rule accuracy) as the solution obtained by moment area (Ex. 5–2E). Note that the minus sign indicates a downward deflection.

20

ELASTIC WEIGHTS

20–1. Introduction. The elastic-weights method applied to beams is popularly called conjugate beam. It is sometimes called the bar-chain method when applied to trusses. It was developed by Müller-Breslau, a student of Otto Mohr, who extended some of Mohr's discoveries (as well as discoveries of others) into more useful forms for engineering analysis. The method is essentially an analogy for moment area (and in a somewhat broader sense, for virtual work, too). That is, the equations for moments and shears in an analogous (conjugate) beam are the same as the moment area equations for deflection and slope, respectively, in the real beam. Because the equations are the same and stem from the same root, either moment area or conjugate beam will accomplish the same results with the same effort. An advantage of the conjugate-beam method lies in the fact that terms such as $\sum \theta x$ and Y in the moment area equation (Eq. 4–20) are treated as reactions acting on the conjugate beam. This appeals to many engineers who are, of course, very skilled in computing reactions, moments, and shears.

20–2. Theory. Consider the cantilever beam of Fig. 20–1A to be subjected to any angle changes—θ_C and θ_D, for example. To find the deflection at any point such as B by the moment area method, the coordinate axes would be passed through point B. Then, from Eq. 4–20, we have

$$\Delta Y = \sum \bar{x} A_{MD/EI} + \sum x\theta + Y \qquad (4\text{--}20)$$

$$\Delta Y_B = \sum_B^E \bar{x} A_{MD/EI} + \sum_B^E x\theta + Y$$

The first and third terms equal zero, leaving

$$\Delta Y_B = \overline{BC}\theta_C + \overline{BD}\theta_D$$

From Eq. 4–22,

$$\Delta\theta = \sum A_{MD/EI} + \sum \theta \qquad (4\text{--}22)$$

$$\Delta\theta_B = 0 + \theta_C + \theta_D$$

Now consider the cantilever beam of Fig. 20–1B, which is turned end for end with respect to the beam in Fig. 20–1A. Thus it is reciprocally related to the real beam, which is to say, conjugate. If the angle changes θ_C and θ_D of the

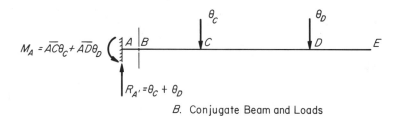

A. Real Beam and Angle Changes

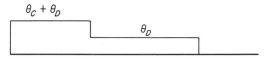

$M_A = \overline{AC}\theta_C + \overline{AD}\theta_D$

$R_{A'} = \theta_C + \theta_D$

B. Conjugate Beam and Loads

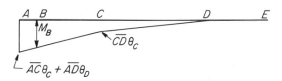

C. Shear Diagram for Conjugate Beam

D. Moment Diagram for Conjugate Beam

Fig. 20–1. Cantilever beam and its conjugate beam.

real beam are treated as loads, and if the conjugate beam is loaded with these angle changes, note that, by the principles of static equilibrium, the moment at point B is

$$M_B = \overline{BC}\theta_C + \overline{BD}\theta_D$$

which equals ΔY_B, the deflection at B. The shear in the conjugate beam is, by the principles of static equilibrium,

$$V_B = \theta_C + \theta_D$$

which equals $\Delta\theta_B$, the slope of the real beam.

The shear diagram and the moment diagram for the conjugate beam are shown in Figs. 20–1C and D. Note that the ordinate of the shear diagram numerically equals the slope of the real beam. The ordinate of the moment diagram equals the deflection of the real beam. Hence, the moment diagram of the conjugate beam is the *elastic curve* of the real beam.

The conjugate-beam principles also apply to a simply supported beam. Let the simple beam of Fig. 20–2A be subjected to any known angle changes,

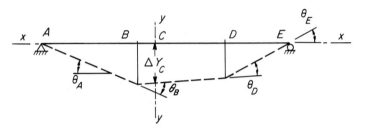

A. Simply Supported Beam and Angle Changes

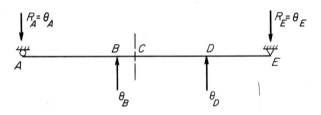

B. Conjugate Beam and Loads

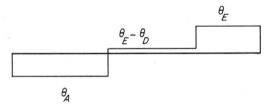

C. Shear Diagram for Conjugate Beam

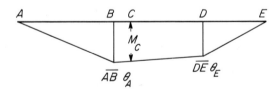

D Moment Diagram for Conjugate Beam

Fig. 20–2. Simple beam and its conjugate beam.

θ_C and θ_D, for example. To find the deflection or slope at any point such as point C by the moment area method, pass the coordinate axes through that point and write Eq. 4–20

$$\Delta Y = \sum \bar{x} A_{MD/EI} + \sum x\theta + Y \qquad (4\text{–}20)$$

$$\Delta Y_C = 0 + \sum_{C}^{E} x\theta + 0 = \overline{CE}\theta_E - \overline{CD}\theta_D$$

But θ_E would ordinarily be unknown, so it would have to be evaluated in terms of angle changes θ_C and θ_D. Since the deflection at point A is zero, θ_E can be evaluated from Eq. 4–20:

$$\Delta Y_A = \sum_{A}^{E} \bar{x} A_{MD/EI} + \sum_{A}^{E} x\theta + Y$$

$$\Delta Y_A = 0 = 0 - \overline{AB}\theta_B - \overline{AD}\theta_D + \overline{AE}\theta_E$$

$$\theta_E = \frac{\overline{AB}\theta_B + \overline{AD}\theta_D}{\overline{AE}}$$

By substitution, we find,

$$\Delta Y_C = \overline{CE}\frac{\overline{AB}\theta_B + \overline{AD}\theta_D}{\overline{AE}} - \overline{CD}\theta_D$$

The conjugate beam in Fig. 20–2B is shown simply supported at the ends and loaded with angle changes θ_B and θ_D acting upward. In moment area, the sign of an angle change is arbitrary. Correspondingly, the sign of a bending moment in a beam or a conjugate beam is arbitrary. To make the arbitrary moment diagram of the conjugate beam look like the elastic curve and not like a mirror image of it, it is necessary to treat angle changes concave upward as loads acting upward on the conjugate beam. (Note that in Fig. 20–1 the angle changes—concave down—were applied as loads acting down on the conjugate beam.) Then the moment in the conjugate beam at point C is

$$M_C = \overline{CE}R_E - \overline{CD}\theta_D$$

where R_E is the reaction at E. This reaction can be found by taking moments about point A:

$$\Sigma M_A = 0 = -\overline{AB}\theta_B - \overline{AD}\theta_D + \overline{AE}R_E$$

$$R_E = \frac{\overline{AB}\theta_B + \overline{AD}\theta_D}{\overline{AE}} = \theta_E$$

Substituting, we find

$$M_C = \overline{CE}\frac{\overline{AB}\theta_B + \overline{AD}\theta_D}{\overline{AE}} - \overline{CD}\theta_D$$

which is the same as the expression for ΔY_C and, therefore,

$$M_C = \Delta Y_C$$

That is, moment in the conjugate beam equals deflection of the real beam. The shear and moment diagrams for the conjugate beam are shown in Figs. 20–2C and D.

Now angle changes in real beams are equal to moment divided by EI. That is,

$$d\theta = \frac{M\,ds}{EI} \qquad (B\text{--}4)$$

Thus it follows that loading the conjugate beam with the angle changes of the real beam is synonymous with loading the conjugate beam with the MD/EI area ($A_{MD/EI}$) of the real beam.

20–3. Comparison of Real and Conjugate Beams. The preceding discussion as well as certain other conclusions resulting therefrom is summarized in Table 20–1.

TABLE 20–I

Comparison of Real and Conjugate Beams

Real Beam	Comparison	Conjugate Beam
Span	equals	span
Load	equals	—
Shear	equals	—
M/EI	equals	load intensity
MD/EI area ($A_{MD/EI}$)	equals	total load (for constant I)
Slope	equals	shear
Deflection	equals	moment
Fixed support	becomes	free end
Free end	becomes	fixed support
Simple exterior support	remains	simple exterior support
Simple interior support	becomes	free-floating hinge
Hinge	becomes	simple interior support

The last two lines in Table 20–1 can be deduced from logic. At an interior support the deflection in a real beam is zero, so the moment in its conjugate beam must also be zero. If a moment in a structure is known to be zero, a hinge can be introduced at that point without altering its behavior. Therefore the conjugate beam can be considered hinged at the point where the real beam rests upon an interior support. Slope in the real beam may have any value, so the shear in the conjugate beam must also have the same value. Since a hinge can transmit shear, the hinged conjugate beam can faithfully represent the real beam.

At a hinge in a real beam, the elastic curve usually breaks, forming an angle change and, in general, the hinge will probably deflect. The deflection indicates that a moment exists in the conjugate beam, and the sudden change in slope indicates a sudden change in shear. A sudden change in shear can result only from a concentrated load. A simple support of the conjugate beam meets these requirements. These deductions may be verified by comparing the algebraic expressions obtained from the conjugate beam with those obtained from moment area.

The comparison between real and conjugate beams is shown graphically in Fig. 20–3. If some conjugate beams seem to be unstable, their appearances are deceiving. Conjugate beams are always stable and always determinate,

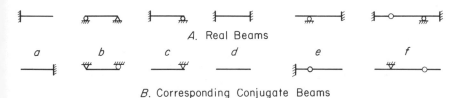

A. Real Beams

a b c d e f

B. Corresponding Conjugate Beams

Fig. 20–3. Relations between real and conjugate beams.

for it was upon such postulates that the idea was developed. Conjugate beams which appear to lack sufficient support are supported by distributed loads representing positive or negative (as the situation demands) MD/EI areas. For example, the conjugate of beam c in Fig. 20–3B is supported partly by the knife edge and partly by a distributed reaction consisting of the negative moment diagram of the real beam. The laws of static equilibrium apply to conjugate beams exactly as they apply to real beams, because the analogy was derived on the basis of static equilibrium.

20–4. Application to Beams. *Example* 20–4A. *Stiffness and Carry-over.* A prismatic beam is shown in Fig. 20–4A, subjected to a moment at A sufficient to rotate the beam 1 radian. Let us evaluate this moment (stiffness) and the ratio of the moment at the opposite end divided by M_A (carry-over factor). The free body of the beam is shown in Fig. 20–4B, the moment diagrams in Fig. 20–4C, and the loaded conjugate beam in Fig. 20–4D. Note the conjugate beam is supported at A by a downward reaction which is unity because the angle change at A is 1 radian (unity) concave downward. The fixed support at B in the real beam becomes a free end at B in the conjugate beam. Taking moments about A in the conjugate beam,

$$\Sigma M_A = 0 = \frac{L}{2}\frac{M_B}{EI}\frac{2L}{3} - \frac{L}{2}\frac{M_A}{EI}\frac{L}{3}$$

Multiplying by $6EI/L^2$ and solving the ratio M_B/M_A, we find

$$\text{Carry-over factor} = \frac{M_B}{M_A} = \frac{1}{2}$$

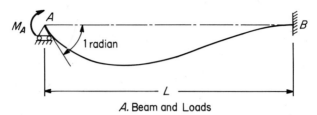

A. Beam and Loads

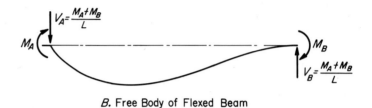

B. Free Body of Flexed Beam

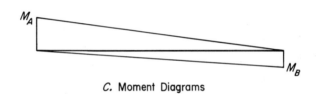

C. Moment Diagrams

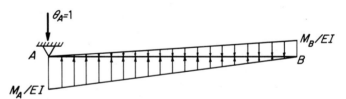

D. Conjugate Beam, Reactions, and Loads

Fig. 20–4. Stiffness of prismatic beam.

The stiffness can be obtained by taking moments about B or by summing vertical forces. The latter approach yields

$$\Sigma F_y = 0 = 1 + \frac{L}{2}\frac{M_B}{EI} - \frac{L}{2}\frac{M_A}{EI}$$

$$\text{Stiffness} = M_A = M_B + \frac{2EI}{L} = \frac{4EI}{L}$$

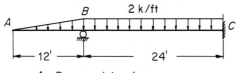

A. Beam and Loads

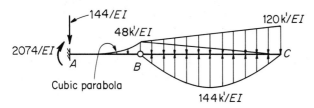

B. Conjugate Beam and Loads

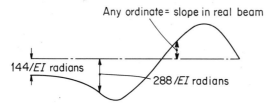

C. Shear Diagram for Conjugate Beam

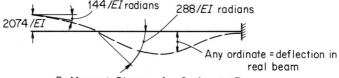

D. Moment Diagram for Conjugate Beam
and Elastic Curve of Real Beam

**Fig. 20–5. Statically indeterminate beam and its relations with
its conjugate beam.**

Example 20–4B. Indeterminate Beam. A more complex problem is illustrated in Fig. 20–5A. The conjugate beam and its loads, the MD/EI areas, are shown in Fig. 20–5B. The loads (like the moment diagrams of Fig. 5–4C) are applied in simple beam parts for easy computation. According to Table 20–1 and Fig. 20–3, the conjugate beam is seen to be free at C, hinged at B, and fixed at A. Since the conjugate beam is hinged at B its moment at B is zero. Dividing the trapezoidal load from B to C into, two triangles, as shown in Fig. 20–5B, and noting that, because of the hinge at B, the moment at B in the conjugate beam is zero, we have

$$M'_B = 0 = \frac{48}{EI} \times \frac{24}{2} \times \frac{24}{3} + \frac{M_C}{EI} \times \frac{24}{2} \times \frac{2}{3} \times 24 - \frac{144}{EI} \times \frac{2}{3} \times 24 \times \frac{24}{2}$$

$$M_C = 120 \text{ kip-ft}$$

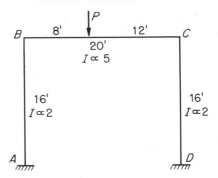

A. Frame and Load

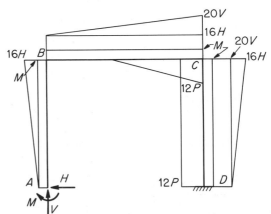

B. Cut-Back Structure, and Moment Diagrams

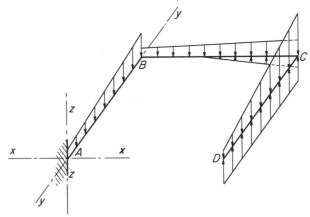

C. Conjugate Structure Loaded with *M/EI* Diagrams

Fig. 20-6. Conjugate frame.

Note that the equation for M'_B is the same as the moment area equation for ΔY_B from Table 5–6.

The ordinate of the shear diagram in Fig. 20–5C represents true slope. A positive ordinate indicates a slope that is upward to the right. The moment diagram of Fig. 20–5D is, of course, the elastic curve of the real beam, in which an ordinate downward indicates a downward deflection.

20–5. Frames. The method of elastic weights was extended by Kinney[1] in 1946 to include solutions for rigid frames. A typical example is shown in Fig. 20–6. The frame is first cut back to a statically determinate structure by cutting away the rigid support at point A and replacing it with three unknown reactions. The conjugate frame is laid out in the xy plane and the MD/EI areas are applied as loads parallel to the z axis. The ordinary principles of moments in three dimensions apply without modification to the moments in the conjugate frame, which are, of course, equal to deflection. Since the frame is fixed at point D, the moment area equations for movement at point A would reduce to

$$\Delta Y_A = \int_A^D \frac{xM\,ds}{EI} = \sum \bar{x} A_{MD/EI} \qquad (4\text{--}14,\ 4\text{--}20)$$

$$\Delta X_A = \int_A^D \frac{yM\,ds}{EI} = \sum \bar{y} A_{MD/EI} \qquad (4\text{--}15,\ 4\text{--}21)$$

$$\Delta\theta = \int_A^D \frac{M\,ds}{EI} = \sum A_{MD/EI} \qquad (4\text{--}16,\ 4\text{--}22)$$

But $\int_A^D xM\,ds/EI$ as applied to the conjugate frame in Fig. 20–6C is the bending moment M'_y about the yy axis (a moment acting in the xz plane), $\int_A^D yM\,ds/EI$ is the bending moment M'_x about the xx axis (a moment acting in the yz plane), and $\int_A^D M\,ds/EI$ is the vertical (z-component) shear V'_z in the conjugate frame at point A. Consequently Eqs. 4–20, 4–21, and 4–22 can be rewritten

$$M'_y = \sum \bar{x} A_{MD/EI} \qquad (20\text{--}1)$$

$$M'_x = \sum \bar{y} A_{MD/EI} \qquad (20\text{--}2)$$

$$V'_z = \sum A_{MD/EI} \qquad (20\text{--}3)$$

The simultaneous solution of Eqs. 20–1, 20–2, and 20–3 evaluates the unknown reactions H, V, and M. Deflections at any other point can now be found by means of the same equations. If the support at point A were a pin, the moment would be zero and the conjugate frame (just like a conjugate beam) would rest upon a knife edge at point A. The knife edge would furnish a vertical force equal to the rotation of the real frame.

---

[1] J. S. Kinney, *Indeterminate Structural Analysis* (Reading, Mass.: Addison-Wesley Publishing Co., Inc., 1957), pp. 143–162.

20–6. Trusses. As applied to trusses, the method of elastic weights is not different from that already described. All that is necessary is a means of converting the stresses in the members into angle changes, which can then be applied to a conjugate beam. A triangular element of a truss is shown in Fig. 20–7. Let

$$c = AM + MB = b \cos \alpha + a \cos \beta$$

The differential [since $d\,(uv) = u\,dv + v\,du$] is

$$dc = -b \sin \alpha\, d\alpha + \cos \alpha\, db - a \sin \beta\, d\beta + \cos \beta\, da$$
$$\sin \alpha = h/b \quad \text{and} \quad \sin \beta = h/a$$

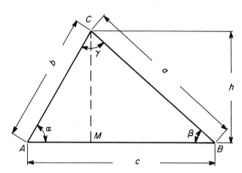

Fig. 20–7. Element of a truss.

Substitution gives

$$dc = -h\, d\alpha + \cos \alpha\, db - h\, d\beta + \cos \beta\, da$$
$$h(d\alpha + d\beta) = -dc + \cos \alpha\, db + \cos \beta\, da$$
$$\alpha + \beta + \gamma = 180° \quad \text{so} \quad d\alpha + d\beta + d\gamma = 0$$
$$h\, d\gamma = dc - \cos \alpha\, db - \cos \beta\, da$$

$$dc = \frac{F}{A}\frac{L}{E} = s_c \frac{c}{E} = s_c \frac{b \cos \alpha + a \cos \beta}{E}$$

$$db = s_b \frac{b}{E} \quad \text{and} \quad da = s_a \frac{a}{E}$$

Combining and multiplying by E/h, we have

$$E\, d\gamma = s_c \left(\frac{b}{h} \cos \alpha + \frac{a}{h} \cos \beta \right) - s_b \frac{b}{h} \cos \alpha - s_a \frac{a}{h} \cos \beta$$

$$E\, d\gamma = s_c (\cot \alpha + \cot \beta) - s_b \cot \alpha - s_a \cot \beta$$

Rearranging and expressing $d\gamma$ as $\Delta\gamma$ gives

$$E\, \Delta\gamma = (s_c - s_b) \cot \alpha + (s_c - s_a) \cot \beta \qquad (20\text{–}4A)$$

And in the same manner we have

$$E\,\Delta\alpha = (s_a - s_b)\cot\gamma$$
$$+ (s_a - s_c)\cot\beta \quad (20\text{--}4B)$$

$$E\,\Delta\beta = (s_b - s_a)\cot\gamma$$
$$+ (s_b - s_c)\cot\alpha \quad (20\text{--}4C)$$

A positive value indicates an increase in angle.

All the angle changes at any one point must be added algebraically to produce the total angle change, so θ_B at point B in Fig. 20–8A equals γ_1 plus γ_2. The deformed truss is shown in Fig. 20–8B and the upper chord is shown isolated in Fig. 20–8C with its angle changes to produce a bar chain. These angle changes, applied to the conjugate beam in Fig. 20–8D, produce bending moments which are equal to the vertical components of the deflection of the upper chord. The horizontal components of deflection may be found by adding vectorially the changes of length of each bar in the bar chain.

If a line of panel points is not initially straight (as, for example, line $AbcdE$), the approach must be modified. Along such a line the deflections result partly from (1) angle changes and partly from (2) the changes of length of the bar chain. That part of the deflection due only to angle changes can be computed by

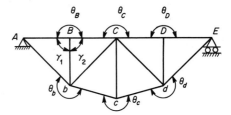

A. Truss and Angles

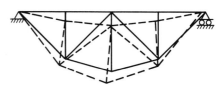

B. Deformed Truss

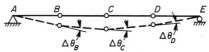

C. Upper Chord and Angle Changes

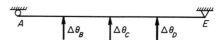

D. Conjugate Beam for Upper Chord

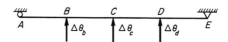

E. Conjugate Beam for Lower Chord

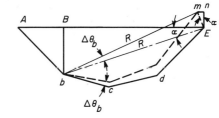

F. Single Angle Change at b

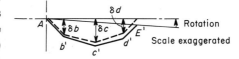

G. Vector Addition of Change in Length of Bar Chain $A\,bcd\,E$

Fig. 20–8. Conjugate beam applied to trusses.

368 OTHER METHODS [Art. 20-6

beam, as shown in Fig. 20–8E. Note that no error is introduced by making the
conjugate beam straight instead of curved. This can be proved by considering
a single angle change, as shown in Fig. 20–8F,

$$\overline{mE} = R \, \Delta\theta_b$$
$$\overline{nE} = \overline{mE} \cos \alpha = R \cos \alpha \, \Delta\theta_b$$
$$R \cos \alpha = \overline{BE}$$
$$nE = \Delta Y_E = \overline{BE} \, \Delta\theta_b$$

From the straight conjugate beam of Fig. 20–8E the deflection at E due only
to $\Delta\theta_b$ is

$$\Delta Y_E = \overline{BE} \, \Delta\theta_b$$

This identity proves that the conjugate beam can be straight.

The deflections due to changes of length of the bar chain can be determined graphically by plotting the length changes of each bar, as shown in
Fig. 20–8G. Unless the truss is symmetrically loaded, the last point on the
bar chain may be displaced vertically, as exemplified by point E'. Since
point E cannot be displaced vertically, the entire bar chain $Ab'c'd'E'$ must be
rotated as a rigid unit until point E' is level with A. The bar chain thus
formed (after rotation) is shown dashed in Fig. 20–8G, and the deflections are
indicated by δb, δc, and δd. When these deflections are added to those
obtained from the conjugate beam of Fig. 20–8E, the results equal the total
vertical deflections.

21

ELASTIC CENTER

21–1. Introduction. The elastic-center or neutral-point method was originated by Müller-Breslau and published in 1886.[1] It has an advantage over moment area and virtual work in that simultaneous equations are avoided. But they are avoided by an artifice which may, particularly for unsymmetrical rigid frames, be more time-consuming than the solution of simultaneous equations. However, it is faster if there are several load conditions to be analyzed, and it is more accurate than a method which involves simultaneous equations. That is, it is more accurate in the sense that significant numbers are not lost in the solution. An advantage is that the slide rule is usually sufficiently accurate for computations. Compared to moment area or virtual work, it is harder to understand and more susceptible to blunders.

21–2. Theory. The rigid frame of Fig. 21–1A is cut back to a statically determinate structure by the removal of a support. Let each portion of the rigid frame have an imaginary finite width equal to the reciprocal of EI, that is, a width equal to $1/EI$. The resulting frame is herein termed an "analogous" frame. The centerline of the analogous frame is congruent (coincident) with that of the real frame. The centroid of the elastic area ($\int ds/EI$) of the analogous frame is located at point O and is termed "elastic center" or "neutral point." Axes xx and yy are any convenient orthogonal axes through the elastic center. If the frame is unsymmetrical, as in this figure, the principal axes[2] $x'x'$ and $y'y'$ will be inclined at an angle α to the xx and yy axes. (Note that unsymmetrical loads do not cause rotation of principal axes; only an unsymmetrical frame can do that.)

Now imagine the free left end of the frame, point A, to be rigidly connected to a rigid bracket which is extended to point O, the elastic center, where it is anchored by reactions X_O, Y_O, and M_O. Since point A is fixed in the real

---

[1] H. F. B. Müller-Breslau, *Die neueren Methoden der Festigkeitslehre und der Statik der Baukonstruktionen* (Leipzig: Baumgartner, 1886).

[2] They need not be principal axes; conjugate axes will suffice. But most engineering students have studied principal axes in mechanics, whereas many students are unfamiliar with conjugate axes. Conjugate axes are any pair of axes for which the product of inertia is zero. Principal axes are the only conjugate axes which are perpendicular to each other. Principal axes are also the axes about which the moments of inertia are respectively the greatest and the least. An axis of symmetry is always a principal axis.

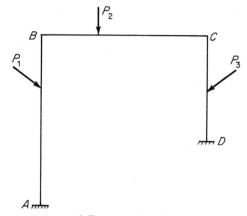

A. Frame and Loads

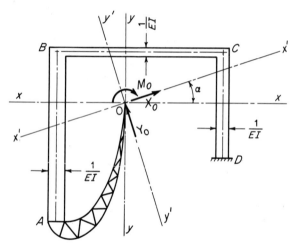

B. Cut-Back Structure (Analogous Frame), Rigid
Bracket, Principal Axes, and Elastic Center Reactions˙

Fig. 21–1. Elastic-center method.

frame, the bracket must be held immobile by these "bracket reactions" at
point O. The moment area equations are

$$\Delta Y = \int \frac{Mx\,ds}{EI} + \sum x\theta + Y \qquad (4\text{–}14)$$

$$\Delta X = \int \frac{My\,ds}{EI} + \sum y\theta + X \qquad (4\text{–}15)$$

$$\Delta \theta = \int \frac{M\,ds}{EI} + \sum \theta \qquad (4\text{–}16)$$

in which ΔY, ΔX, and $\Delta \theta$ each equal zero.[3] If we consider only those angle changes which are caused by moment,[4] all except the integral terms cancel, leaving only

$$0 = \int \frac{Mx \, ds}{EI}$$

$$0 = \int \frac{My \, ds}{EI}$$

$$0 = \int \frac{M \, ds}{EI}$$

The moment M is the total moment which can be divided into the following parts:

M_s = static moment (moment due to loads P_1, P_2, P_3, etc. acting on cut-back frame)
M_O = moment acting on the inelastic bracket
yX_O = moment due to force X_O on inelastic bracket
xY_O = moment due to force Y_O on inelastic bracket

Substituting these parts for the total moment in the above equations gives

$$0 = \int \frac{M_s x \, ds}{EI} + M_O \int \frac{x \, ds}{EI} + X_O \int \frac{xy \, ds}{EI} + Y_O \int \frac{x^2 \, ds}{EI} \quad (21\text{–}1A)$$

$$0 = \int \frac{M_s y \, ds}{EI} + M_O \int \frac{y \, ds}{EI} + X_O \int \frac{y^2 \, ds}{EI} + Y_O \int \frac{xy \, ds}{EI} \quad (21\text{–}2A)$$

$$0 = \int \frac{M_s \, ds}{EI} + M_O \int \frac{ds}{EI} + X_O \int \frac{y \, ds}{EI} + Y_O \int \frac{x \, ds}{EI} \quad (21\text{–}3A)$$

If $1/EI$ is the "width" of an analogous frame whose centerline dimensions are equal to those of the real frame, the terms in these equations referred to the principal axes are those shown in Table 21–1.

Substituting the terms of Table 21–1 for principal axes into Eqs. 21–1A, 21–2A, and 21–3A, we have

$$0 = M_{y'} + 0 + 0 + Y_O I_{y'} \quad (21\text{–}1B)$$
$$0 = M_{x'} + 0 + X_O I_{x'} + 0 \quad (21\text{–}2B)$$
$$0 = W + M_O A + 0 + 0 \quad (21\text{–}3B)$$

[3] If any of quantities ΔX, ΔY, or $\Delta \theta$ does not equal zero, the corresponding equation (Eq. 4–14, 4–15, or 4–16) is omitted. This causes no difficulty because fewer equations are needed if the number of redundant reactions is reduced.

[4] Certain finite angle changes can be included, as shown later, but this method lacks the flexibility of moment area, so frames which suffer finite angle changes and displacements (except at supports) are not, in general, adapted to this method.

TABLE 21–1
Summary of Properties of Elastic Area

Term	Definition	Symbol
$\displaystyle\int \frac{ds}{EI}$	elastic area of analogous frame	A
$\displaystyle\int \frac{x'\,ds}{EI}$	first moment* about $y'y'$ axis	$A\bar{x}' = 0$
$\displaystyle\int \frac{y'\,ds}{EI}$	first moment about $x'x'$ axis	$A\bar{y}' = 0$
$\displaystyle\int \frac{x'y'\,ds}{EI}$	product of inertia†	$P_{x'y'} = 0$
$\displaystyle\int \frac{(x')^2\,ds}{EI}$	moment of inertia about $y'y'$ axis	$I_{y'}$
$\displaystyle\int \frac{(y')^2\,ds}{EI}$	moment of inertia about $x'x'$ axis	$I_{x'}$
$\displaystyle\int \frac{M_s\,ds}{EI}$	moment weight ($M D_s/EI$ area caused by loads P)	W
$\displaystyle\int \frac{M_s x'\,ds}{EI}$	static moment of moment weight ($M D_s/EI$ area) about $y'y'$ axis $= W\bar{x}' = M_{y'}$	$M_{y'}$
$\displaystyle\int \frac{M_s y'\,ds}{EI}$	static moment of moment weight ($M D_s/EI$ area) about $x'x'$ axis $= W\bar{y}' = M_{x'}$	$M_{x'}$

* Since the width of the analogous frame is $1/EI$, $ds/EI = $ length $\times$ width $= dA$, a differential area. From mechanics $\int x\,dA$ is the first moment of the area. The first moment is zero about any centroidal axis.

† $\int (xy\,ds/EI) = \int xy\,dA = $ product of inertia. From mechanics, the product of inertia is zero for principal axes or for conjugate axes. Thus $\int (x'y'\,ds/EI)$ is zero because $x'x'$ and $y'y'$ are principal axes.

and solving for Y_O, X_O, and M_O without regard for signs (which can be determined later) gives

$$Y_O = \frac{M_{y'}}{I_{y'}} \tag{21–4}$$

$$X_O = \frac{M_{x'}}{I_{x'}} \tag{21–5}$$

$$M_O = \frac{W}{A} \tag{21–6}$$

The solution of simultaneous equations is avoided, because each reaction on the inelastic bracket (Y_O, X_O, and M_O) can be determined by a single equation. These reactions can be used to calculate moment, shear, and thrust at any point in the structure by means of the equations of static equilibrium (Eqs. 1–1, 1–2, and 1–3).

One of the distinctive features of the elastic center is this: if any one of the reactions Y_O, X_O, or M_O is the only load applied to the structure, the bracket will move only along the line of action of that reaction. For example, if X_O is the only force applied to the structure in Fig. 21–1B, the bracket will deflect along the $x'x'$ axis, but it will not rotate or deflect in the $y'y'$ direction. If M_O is the only load applied, the bracket will rotate about point O, but point O will not deflect. For proof, let X_O be the only force applied to the structure and solve for deflection normal to X_O by moment area:

$$\Delta Y = \int \frac{M x' \, ds}{EI} + \sum x'\theta + Y \qquad (4\text{–}14)$$

The total moment at any point is $y'X_O$. Substituting, we have

$$\Delta Y = X_O \int \frac{x'y' \, ds}{EI} + 0 + 0$$

But $\int x'y' \, ds/EI$ is the product of inertia which is zero for principal axes. Therefore we have

$$\Delta Y = 0$$

Nor will the bracket rotate when X_O is applied to it. Hence we have

$$\Delta\theta = \int \frac{M \, ds}{EI} + \sum \theta \qquad (4\text{–}16)$$

$$\Delta\theta = X_O \int \frac{y' \, ds}{EI} + 0$$

And since $\int y' \, ds/EI$ is the first moment of the elastic area about the $x'x'$ axis, it is zero because the $x'x'$ axis is also a centroidal axis. Therefore we have

$$\Delta\theta = 0$$

However, it does not follow that the bracket moves only in the direction of any load applied at point O. If a load on the bracket is not parallel to X_O or Y_O, the bracket will *not* deflect in the direction of the load. Furthermore, if the frame is supported by a hinge reaction, all of the bracket-reaction forces (except those with a line of action through the hinge) will cause the bracket to rotate.

21–3. Moments and Products of Inertia. The formulas for the moments and products of inertia which apply to the equations herein are the standard ones to be found in any text on mechanics. The necessary ones are summarized in Fig. 21–2. The direction of the principal axes can be found by the formula

$$\tan 2\alpha = \frac{2P_{xy}}{I_y - I_x} \tag{21-7}$$

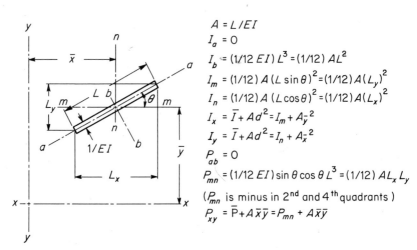

$$A = L/EI$$
$$I_a = 0$$
$$I_b = (1/12\ EI)\ L^3 = (1/12)\ AL^2$$
$$I_m = (1/12)\ A\ (L\sin\theta)^2 = (1/12)A(L_y)^2$$
$$I_n = (1/12)\ A\ (L\cos\theta)^2 = (1/12)A(L_x)^2$$
$$I_x = \bar{I} + Ad^2 = I_m + A\bar{y}^2$$
$$I_y = \bar{I} + Ad^2 = I_n + A\bar{x}^2$$
$$P_{ab} = 0$$
$$P_{mn} = (1/12\ EI)\sin\theta\cos\theta\ L^3 = (1/12)\ AL_x L_y$$
$$(P_{mn}\ \text{is minus in 2}^{\text{nd}}\ \text{and 4}^{\text{th}}\text{quadrants})$$
$$P_{xy} = \bar{P} + A\bar{x}\bar{y} = P_{mn} + A\bar{x}\bar{y}$$

Fig. 21–2. Formulas for moments and products of inertia.

where xx and yy are any centroidal axes. Angle α is measured counterclockwise from the xx axis to the $x'x'$ axis when it is positive and clockwise when negative. The principal moments of inertia are

$$I_{x'} = \frac{I_x + I_y}{2} + \frac{I_x - I_y}{2}\cos 2\alpha - P_{xy}\sin 2\alpha \tag{21-8A}$$

$$I_{y'} = \frac{I_x + I_y}{2} - \frac{I_x - I_y}{2}\cos 2\alpha + P_{xy}\sin 2\alpha \tag{21-8B}$$

where $x'x'$ and $y'y'$ are the principal axes. Adding Eqs. 21–5A and B, we find

$$I_{x'} + I_{y'} = I_x + I_y = \text{constant} \tag{21-9}$$

CENTROIDS. The formula for the distance to the centroid from any convenient axis is

$$\bar{y} = \frac{\sum A\bar{y}}{\sum A} \tag{21-10}$$

where A is $\int ds/EI$ or L/EI.

21–4. Applications to Rigid Frames. *Example 21–4A. Fixed Rigid Frame.* The frame of Fig. 21–3A is symmetrical, so the $y'y'$ axis is vertical and passes through the geometrical center. The $x'x'$ axis is located by taking

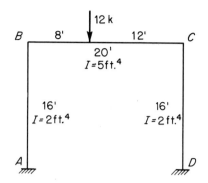

A. Frame and Load

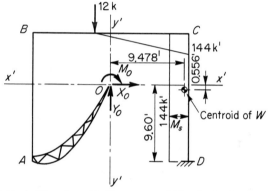

B. Cut-Back Structure, M_s Diagrams, and Elastic Center Reactions

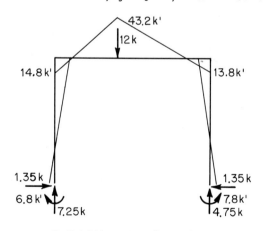

C. Total Moments and Reactions

Fig. 21–3. Fixed rigid frame. Elastic center.

moments about any convenient reference axis. Using a reference axis 8 ft above A and D, we have

$$\bar{y} = \frac{\sum A\bar{y}}{\sum A} = \frac{0.2 \times 20 \times 8}{(0.2 \times 20) + (0.5 \times 16 \times 2)} = 1.6 \text{ ft}$$

The elastic properties (listed in Table 21–1) are computed in Table 21–2.

TABLE 21–2

Frame Constants

Portion	Elastic Area $A = ds/EI$	Distance from $x'x'$ Axis $\bar{y}$	Distance from $y'y'$ Axis $\bar{x}$	Moments of Inertia	
				$I_{x'} = \bar{I} + A\bar{y}^2$ $\bar{I} = (A/12)L_y^2$	$I_{y'} = \bar{I} + A\bar{x}^2$ $\bar{I} = (A/12)L_x^2$
AB	$\frac{16}{2} = 8$	-1.60	-10	$\bar{I} = \frac{8}{12}(16)^2 = 170.5$ $A\bar{y}^2 = 8(1.6)^2 = 20.5$	$\bar{I} = \qquad 0$ $A\bar{x}^2 = 8(10)^2 = 800$
BC	$\frac{20}{5} = 4$	$+6.40$	0	$\bar{I} = \qquad 0$ $A\bar{y}^2 = 4(6.4)^2 = 164$	$\bar{I} = \frac{4}{12}(20)^2 = 133.3$ $A\bar{x}^2 = \qquad 0$
CD	$\frac{16}{2} = 8$	-1.60	$+10$	$\bar{I} = \frac{8}{12}(16)^2 = 170.5$ $A\bar{y}^2 = 8(1.6)^2 = 20.5$	$\bar{I} = \qquad 0$ $A\bar{x}^2 = \qquad 800$
	$A = 20$			$I_{x'} = \qquad 546.0$	$I_{y'} = \qquad 1{,}733.3$

Now we must evaluate W, $M_{x'}$, and $M_{y'}$. These are the areas and moments respectively of the moment diagram M_s, which is due only to the 12-kip vertical load. The calculations are found in Table 21–3.

TABLE 21–3

M_s Constants

Portion	Moment Weight $W = \int M_s \, ds/EI$	Distance from $x'x'$ Axis $\bar{y}$	Distance from $y'y'$ Axis $\bar{x}$	$W\bar{y} = M_{x'}$	$W\bar{x} = M_{y'}$
AB	0				
BC	$\frac{1}{2} \times \frac{144}{5} \times 12 = 172.8$	$+6.40$	$+6.0$	$+1{,}105$	$+1{,}036$
CD	$\frac{144}{2} \times 16 = 1{,}152.0$	-1.60	$+10.0$	$-1{,}843$	$+11{,}520$
	$W = 1{,}324.8$			$M_{x'} = -738$	$M_{y'} = 12{,}556$

The elastic center reactions are as follows:

$$Y_O = \frac{M_{y'}}{I_{y'}} = \frac{12{,}556}{1733.3} = 7.25 \text{ kips} \tag{21–4}$$

$$X_O = \frac{M_{x'}}{I_{x'}} = \frac{-738}{546} = -1.35 \text{ kips} \tag{21–5}$$

$$M_O = \frac{W}{A} = \frac{1324.8}{20} = 6.62 \text{ kip-ft} \tag{21–6}$$

Although rules for signs can be formulated, it is better to avoid rules and use reason. This is how: picture the deflection of the bracket at point O (elastic center) due only to M_s; then the direction of each elastic center reaction is clearly evident. From Fig. 21–3B, the $\int M_s ds/EI$ diagrams make the bracket at point O move down, left, and rotate counterclockwise. This can be checked by finding the centroid of W:

$$\bar{x} = \frac{M_{y'}}{W} = \frac{12{,}556}{1324.8} = 9.48 \text{ to the right of } O$$

$$\bar{y} = \frac{M_{x'}}{W} = \frac{-738}{1324.8} = -0.556 = 0.556 \text{ below } O$$

Now if all the angle changes due to P are concentrated at this point, the left portion of the frame rotates counterclockwise about this point, which makes the end of the bracket (point O) move down, left, and counterclockwise. Now each elastic center reaction produces movement only in the direction of that reaction. Thus Y_O must act upward to push point O up, X_O acts right to push it right, and M_O acts clockwise to rotate it clockwise.

Moments at any point in the frame are computed by the ordinary principles of static equilibrium. This frame is considered a cantilever fixed at point D and loaded with Y_O, X_O, M_O, and the 12-kip load. The calculations are quite straightforward, and the results are shown in Fig. 21–3C.

Example 21–4B. Pin-connected Frame. The same frame with pin connections at A and D is shown in Fig. 21–4A. The location of the principal axes can be determined by inspection. The elastic area of a hinge is infinite because its EI value is zero and $1/0 = \infty$. Thus the neutral point is—from symmetry—mid-way between points A and D. Since the total elastic area A is infinite, and the moment of inertia $I_{y'}$ is infinite, Eqs. 21–4 and 21–6 yield $Y_O = 0$ and $M_O = 0$ by inspection. But $I_{x'}$ is not infinite because at any finite value for y in the expression $\int (y')^2 ds/EI$, EI is finite. In other words, EI is zero only when y is zero. Therefore Eq. 21–5 will evaluate a finite reaction acting on the bracket.

The frame can be cut back by introducing rollers at A and extending the bracket from the *hinge* (not the member) at A to point O. This bracket cannot sustain Y_O or M_O, because it is unstable, but it can resist X_O. The calculations are shown in Table 21–4.

$$X_O = \frac{M_{x'}}{I_{x'}} = \frac{1842}{2390} = 0.772 \text{ kip right} \qquad (21\text{–}5)$$

Again, the direction of X_O is obtained by considering the movement of point O due to the 12-kip load only. It moves left, so X_O must act to the right.

Example 21–4C. One Column Pinned, One Fixed. The frame is shown in Fig. 21–5. The elastic area of a hinge is infinite so the centroid of the analogous rigid frame passes through point A. But the frame is now unsymmetrical so the principal axes must rotate. Note that values in Table 21–5

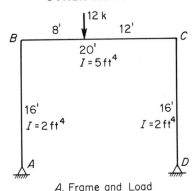

A. Frame and Load

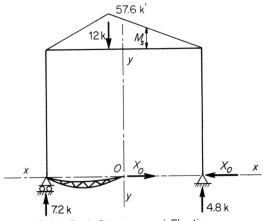

B. Cut-Back Structure and Elastic
Center and Reaction

Fig. 21–4. Pin-ended rigid frame. Elastic center.

refer to the vertical and horizontal (yy and xx) axes.

$$\tan 2\alpha = \frac{2P_{xy}}{I_y - I_x} = \frac{+2 \times 1920}{3733.3 - 2389} = +2.856 \tag{21–7}$$

$$2\alpha = 70.7° \qquad \cos 2\alpha = +0.3305 \qquad \sin 2\alpha = +0.9438$$

$$I_{x'} = \frac{I_x + I_y}{2} + \frac{I_x - I_y}{2}\cos 2\alpha - P_{xy}\sin 2\alpha \tag{21–8A}$$

$$= \frac{2389 + 3733}{2} + \frac{2389 - 3733}{2} \times 0.3305 - (+1920)(0.9438) = 1027$$

$$I_{y'} = I_x + I_y - I_{x'} \tag{21–9}$$

$$= 2389 + 3733 - 1027 = 5095$$

TABLE 21–4

Frame and M_s Constants

Portion	Distance from $x'x'$ Axis $\bar{y}$	Moment of Inertia $I_{x'} = \bar{I} + A\bar{y}^2$ $\bar{I} = L^3/12EI$		Moment Weight $W = \int M_s\, ds/EI$		Distance from $x'x'$ Axis $\bar{y}$	$W\bar{y} = M_{x'}$
AB	8	$\bar{I} = \dfrac{(16)^3}{12 \times 2} =$	171	0			
		$A\bar{y} = \tfrac{16}{2}(8)^2 =$	512				
BC	16	$\bar{I} =$	0	$\dfrac{1}{2} \times \dfrac{57.6}{5} \times 20 = 115.2$		16	1,842
		$A\bar{y} = \tfrac{20}{5}(16)^2 =$	1,024				
CD	8	$\bar{I} = \dfrac{(16)^3}{12 \times 2} =$	171	0			
		$A\bar{y} = \tfrac{16}{2}(8)^2 =$	512				
		$I_{x'} =$	2,390			$M_{x'} =$	$\overline{1,842}$

The magnitude and location of W was determined in Ex. 21–4A and, relative to xx and yy axes, is shown in Fig. 21–5B. The centroid of W relative to the principal axes is also shown in Fig. 21–5B to be $\bar{x}' = 21.10$ ft and $\bar{y}' = 3.87$ ft. Then

$$M_{y'} = W\bar{x}' = 1324.8 \times 21.10 = 27,950$$

$$M_{x'} = W\bar{y}' = 1324.8 \times 3.87 = 5130$$

$$Y_O = \frac{M_{y'}}{I_{y'}} = \frac{27,950}{5,095} = 5.49 \text{ kips} \qquad (21\text{–}4)$$

$$X_O = \frac{M_{x'}}{I_{x'}} = \frac{5130}{1027} = 5.00 \text{ kips} \qquad (21\text{–}5)$$

$$M_O = \frac{W}{A} = \frac{1324.8}{\infty} = 0 \qquad (21\text{–}6)$$

The forces Y_O and X_O act in the directions shown in Fig. 21–4B for the reasons explained for Ex. 21–4A. To find moments in the frame, these forces may be resolved into horizontal and vertical components, as shown in Fig. 21–5C.

21–5. Other Structures. The neutral-point method is not popular for the solution of rigid frames because it is not as quick nor as easy to use as moment distribution. It can also be used for beams just as it can for frames; but, again, it is not as popular as moment distribution, although it is quite often used for computing influence lines.

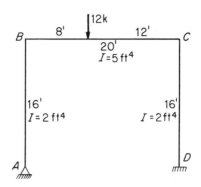

A. Frame and Load

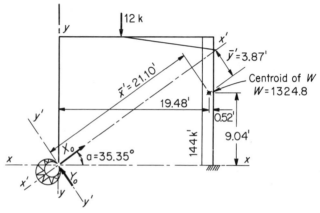

B. Cut-Back Structure and Principal Axes

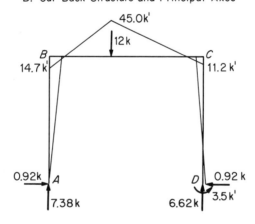

C. Reactions and Moment Diagrams

Fig. 21-5. Frame with pinned and fixed columns.

TABLE 21-5
Frame Constants

Portion	Elastic Area $A = \int ds/EI$	Distance from xx Axis $\bar{y}$	Distance from yy Axis $\bar{x}$	Product of Inertia $P_{xy} = \bar{P} + A\bar{x}\bar{y}$	$I_x = \bar{I} + A\bar{y}^2$ $\bar{I} = (A/12)L_y^2$	$I_y = \bar{I} + A\bar{x}^2$ $\bar{I} = (A/12)L_x^2$
Hinge at						
A	∞	0	0	$\bar{P} =$ 0	$\bar{I} =$ 0	$\bar{I} =$ 0
AB	$\frac{16}{2} = 8$	8	0	$\bar{P} =$ $A\bar{x}\bar{y} = 8 \times 8 \times 0 =$ 0	$\bar{I} = \frac{8}{12}(16)^2 = 170.5$ $A\bar{y}^2 = 8(8)^2 = 512$	$\bar{I} =$ 0 $A\bar{x}^2 =$ 0
BC	$\frac{20}{5} = 4$	16	10	$\bar{P} =$ 0 $A\bar{x}\bar{y} = 4 \times 16 \times 10 = +640$	$\bar{I} =$ 0 $A\bar{y}^2 = 4(16)^2 = 1{,}024$	$\bar{I} = \frac{4}{12}(20)^2 = 133.3$ $A\bar{x}^2 = 4(10)^2 = 400$
CD	$\frac{16}{2} = 8$	8	20	$\bar{P} =$ 0 $A\bar{x}\bar{y} = 8 \times 8 \times 20 = +1{,}280$	$\bar{I} = \frac{8}{12}(16)^2 = 170.5$ $A\bar{y}^2 = 8(8)^2 = 512$	$\bar{I} =$ 0 $A\bar{x}^2 = 8(20)^2 = 3{,}200$
	$A = \infty$			$P_{xy} =$ +1,920	$I_x =$ +2,389.0	$I_y =$ +3,733.3

The most significant use of the method is for the solution of arches and rings or rigid frames with curved members. Arches, particularly, are usually subject to several load conditions and, since the elastic properties of the arch are unaffected by the loads, the time spent in computing them may be saved many times over. For such structures, then, the neutral-point method may well be more satisfactory than moment area or virtual work.

22

THE COLUMN ANALOGY

22–1. Introduction. The column analogy was introduced by Cross[1] in 1930. Except for a superficial difference, it is essentially the elastic center method. The "superficial" difference makes column analogy slightly more convenient but, on the other hand, it makes the physical action of the structure more obscure. Professor Cross described it as a mechanical tool which is well adapted to a systematic routine that is accurate and rapid but not illuminating.

22–2. Theory. The equations for elastic center reactions are, from Art. 21–2,

$$Y_O = \frac{M_{y'}}{I_{y'}} \tag{21–4}$$

$$X_O = \frac{M_{x'}}{I_{x'}} \tag{21–5}$$

$$M_O = \frac{W}{A} \tag{21–6}$$

The moment at any general point in the rigid frame is the moment M_s due to loads acting on the cut-back structure and, in addition, the moments due to the elastic center reactions. However, the elastic center reactions act in opposition to the loads on the cut-back structure. That is, if the M_s moments produce a downward deflection of the bracket, the elastic center reaction must produce an equal and opposite deflection. Thus the total moment at any point can be expressed algebraically as

$$M = M_s - M_i = M_s - M_O - Y_O x' - X_O y' \tag{22–1}$$

where M_i is the moment caused by the elastic center reactions. Substituting the values for Y_O, X_O, and M_O from Eqs. 21–4, 21–5, and 21–6, we have

$$M_i = \frac{W}{A} + \frac{M_{y'}}{I_{y'}} x' + \frac{M_{x'}}{I_{x'}} y' \tag{22–2}$$

[1] Hardy Cross, *The Column Analogy* (University of Illinois, 1930), Engineering Experiment Station, Bulletin 215.

However Eq. 22–2 is also the equation[2] for axial stress in a short column loaded with an axial, eccentric weight W, so M_i equals stress at the base of the analogous column.

22–3. Application to Rigid Frames. *Example* 22–3. An example frame and its analogous column are shown in Fig. 22–1. Note that the cross-sectional area of the column is the elastic area of the analogous frame (see Fig. 21–1B). The length of the column is immaterial. The M_s diagram (which is W because $W = \int M_s \, ds/EI$) is applied to the top of the column as a load, so M_s itself is a stress. The reactive stresses at the bottom equal M_i, and they may be tension or compression.

The column analogy is supposed to be a method of routine, so a systematized sign convention is desirable, perhaps. Many conventions are possible, among them the following one:

x is positive right.

y is positive up.

Moments are positive when they produce tension on inner fibers in frames and lower fibers in beams.

Tensile stresses in the analogous column are positive.

M_s is applied as a stress at the top face of the analogous column. If positive, it must be tension and acts upward.

M_i is computed as a reactive stress acting at the base of the column. It is positive if tension and acts downward.

Whether the reactive stress (M_i) is tension or compression is evident by inspection if the centroid of W is located with respect to the principal axes.

The frame of Fig. 22–1 is symmetrical and the xx and yy axes are also principal ($x'x'$ and $y'y'$) axes. The primes are, then, superfluous for this example and are omitted. The elastic properties of the frame, computed in Ex. 21–4A, are summarized:

$$A = 20$$
$$I_x = 546$$
$$I_y = 1733.3$$
$$W = -1324.8$$

W acts at $x = +9.48$ and $y = -0.556$

$$M_x = -1324.8(-0.556) = +738$$
$$M_y = -1324.8(+9.48) = -12{,}556$$

[2] The equation for stress in a short column is usually given by

$$s = \pm \frac{W}{A} \pm \frac{M_y}{I_y} x \pm \frac{M_x}{I_x} y$$

but it should be understood that the formula $s = My/I$ is valid only when referred to principal axes (designated herein by primes). The general equation for any set of xx and yy axes is

$$s = \pm \frac{W}{A} \pm \frac{M_x I_y - M_y P_{xy}}{I_x I_y - (P_{xy})^2} y \pm \frac{M_y I_x - M_x P_{xy}}{I_y I_x - (P_{xy})^2} x$$

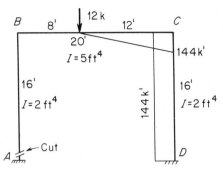

A. Cut-Back Structure and M_s
Diagrams

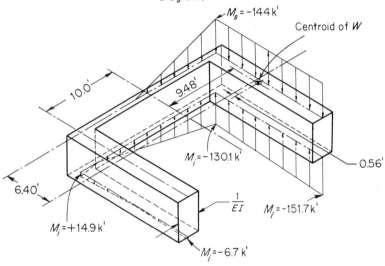

B. Analogous Column

Fig. 22–I. The column analogy.

Applying Eq. 22–2 at each corner of the frame and utilizing the sign convention explained above, we have the following:

At A,

$$M_i = \frac{W}{A} + \frac{M_y}{I_y} x + \frac{M_x}{I_x} y \qquad (22\text{–}2)$$

$$M_i = \frac{-1324.8}{20} + \frac{-12{,}556}{1733.3}(-10) + \frac{+738}{546}(-9.60) = -6.7 \text{ kip-ft}$$

At B,

$$M_i = \frac{-1324.8}{20} + \frac{-12{,}556}{1733.3}(-10) + \frac{+738}{546}(+6.40) = +14.9 \text{ kip-ft}$$

At C,
$$M_i = \frac{-1324.8}{20} + \frac{-12{,}556}{1733.3}(+10) + \frac{+738}{546}(+6.40) = -130.1 \text{ kip-ft}$$
At D,
$$M_i = \frac{-1324.8}{20} + \frac{-12{,}556}{1733.3}(+10) + \frac{+738}{546}(-9.60) = -151.7 \text{ kip-ft}$$

These values of M_i are plotted on the base of the column in Fig. 22–1B. The total moments are found from Eq. 22–1.

$$M = M_s - M_i \qquad (22\text{–}1)$$
$$M_A = 0 - (-6.7) = +6.7 \text{ kip-ft}$$
$$M_B = 0 - (+14.9) = -14.9 \text{ kip-ft}$$
$$M_C = -144 - (-130.1) = -13.9 \text{ kip-ft}$$
$$M_D = -144 - (-151.7) = +7.7 \text{ kip-ft}$$

Now the difference between the column analogy and the neutral-point method becomes evident. It lies in the concept of an analogous column instead of an analogous frame, and in the mental substitution of stresses on the analogous column for moments in the real frame. But the equations and the numbers which are substituted into them are precisely the same.

22–4. Other Structures. The column analogy is essentially a variation of the neutral-point method. Consequently, it is suitable for the same kind of problems as is the neutral-point method. It would follow from the discussion of Art. 21–5, then, that it can be used for beams, frames, arches, and rings. As applied to beams and rigid frames, it cannot compete in speed or ease with moment distribution. But it is well adapted for arches, rings, or rigid frames with curved members.

23

SLOPE DEFLECTION

23–1. Introduction. The earliest form of analysis based upon the deflection and slope of the ends of members in trusses or rigid frames was given in 1880 by Manderla.[1] In 1892 Mohr[2] used an improved version to determine secondary stresses in trusses. The modern form was presented in 1915 by Maney.[3] The method involves writing a series of simultaneous equations for the moments at each end of each member in terms of (1) fixed-end moments, (2) moments caused by rotation, and (3) moments caused by deflection. Thus it is essentially moment distribution reduced to equation form. Because slope deflection was developed first, many engineers prefer to think of moment distribution as the solution of the slope-deflection equations by successive approximation. That is true only in a broad sense, because moment distribution solves only part of the slope-deflection equation and that part is solved in terms of moment—not slope. The slope-deflection method was widely used prior to 1930. Since then its popularity has waned in favor of moment distribution, in spite of the fact that rapid methods for solving simultaneous equations are known.[4,5]

23–2. Theory. As shown in Part IV, the moments at the ends of a member result from (1) the fixed-end moment, (2) the rotation of each end, and (3) the deflection of one end with respect to the other.[6] The fixed-end moments are the same as those used in moment distribution and, to avoid confusion, we can assume the same sign convention, that is, clockwise moments acting upon a free body of the member are positive.

ROTATION. The moments due to rotation can be obtained from the stiffness and carry-over factors. The stiffness K is kEI/L, and is the moment

---

[1] Heinrich Manderla, "Die Berechnung der Sekundärspannungen," *Allgemeine Bauzeitung*, 45: 34, 1880.

[2] Otto Mohr, "Die Berechnung der Fachwerke mit starren Knotenverbindungen," *Zivilingenieur*, 38: 577, 1892.

[3] George A. Maney, *Studies in Engineering*, No. 1 (University of Minnesota, 1915).

[4] John B. Wilbur, "Successive Elimination of Unknowns in the Slope Deflection Method," *Trans. ASCE*, 102: 346–370, 1937.

[5] W. L. Schwalbe, Esq., "Simultaneous Equations in Mechanics Solved by Iteration," *Trans. ASCE*, 102: 939–969, 1937.

[6] In moment distribution we write the fixed-end moments, add the moments due to rotation (distribution and carry-over), and then add the moments due to deflection (or sidesway) obtained from a separate solution.

required to rotate one end of a member (whose opposite end is fixed) through 1 radian of angle. If the angle θ is less than 1 radian, the moment is $K(\theta/1$ radian), or $M = kEI\theta/L$. In Fig. 23–1A, the left end is rotated through angle θ_A by a moment which equals $k_{AB}EI\theta_A/L$, and part of this moment is carried over to the right end. If the left end now remains fixed in its rotated position while the right end is rotated, as shown in Fig. 23–1B, the moment at

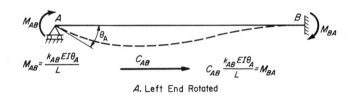

A. Left End Rotated

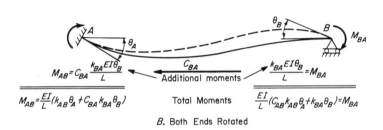

B. Both Ends Rotated

Fig. 23–1. End moments caused by rotation.

B is increased by $k_{BA}EI\theta_B/L$, and part of the moment, $C_{BA}k_{BA}EI\theta_B/L$, is carried over to the left end, producing a total moment

$$M_{AB} = \frac{EI}{L}(k_{AB}\theta_A + C_{BA}k_{BA}\theta_B) \qquad (23\text{--}1)$$

If the member is prismatic, k equals 4 and C equals $\frac{1}{2}$. Thus by substitution, we have

$$M_{AB} = \frac{EI}{L}(4\theta_A + 2\theta_B) = \frac{2EI}{L}(2\theta_A + \theta_B) \qquad (23\text{--}2A)$$

and similarly,

$$M_{BA} = \frac{2EI}{L}(2\theta_B + \theta_A) \qquad (23\text{--}2B)$$

The signs must be consistent: moments and angles are positive clockwise.

DEFLECTION. Moments for deflection of one end relative to the other end were evaluated in Fig. 13–1 to be

$$M_{AB} = -K_{AB}\frac{\Delta}{L}(1 + C_{AB}) = \frac{-k_{AB}EI\Delta}{L^2}(1 + C_{AB}) \qquad (23\text{--}3)$$

If the member is prismatic, Eq. 23–3 reduces to

$$M_{AB} = -\frac{6EI\Delta}{L^2} \tag{23-4}$$

The minus sign indicates a minus moment if the member as a whole rotates clockwise.

COMBINATION. By adding the moments due to (1) fixed ends, (2) rotation (Eq. 23–2), and (3) deflection (Eq. 23–4), and rearranging, the total moment at A is found to be

$$M_{AB} = \frac{2EI}{L}\left(2\theta_A + \theta_B - \frac{3\Delta}{L}\right) \pm (FEM)_{AB} \tag{23-5}$$

where $(FEM)_{AB}$ is, of course, the fixed-end moment. This is the slope-deflection equation for prismatic members. If the members are not prismatic, add moments from Eqs. 23–1 and 23–3 plus the fixed-end moment to obtain

$$M_{AB} = \frac{EI}{L}\left[k_{AB}\theta_A + C_{BA}k_{BA}\theta_B - \frac{k_{AB}\Delta}{L}(1 + C_{AB})\right] \pm (FEM)_{AB} \tag{23-6}$$

However, we have

$$C_{BA}k_{BA} = C_{AB}k_{AB}$$

from Maxwell's theorem of reciprocal deflections, so Eq. 23–6 can be expressed in a better form:

$$M_{AB} = \frac{k_{AB}EI}{L}\left[\theta_A + C_{AB}\theta_B - \frac{\Delta}{L}(1 + C_{AB})\right] \pm (FEM)_{AB} \tag{23-7}$$

This is the generalized slope-deflection equation. The values of k and C may be found in Appendix A. After k and C are evaluated, Eq. 23–7 is used just as easily (and in exactly the same way) as Eq. 23–5.

23–3. Application. The slope-deflection equations alone are not sufficient for an analysis because they have to do only with the elastic properties of the structure. It is also necessary to write the equations of static equilibrium and to solve all of them simultaneously. This is illustrated in the following example.

Example 23–3. The rigid frame in Fig. 23–2 illustrates all of the facets of slope deflection as applied to prismatic structures. By visualizing the elastic curve, we see that there can be no rotation at D, but there will be rotation at A, B, and C, and, finally, the horizontal deflection at B must equal that at C, so that $\Delta_{AB} = \Delta_{CD} = \Delta$. There are fixed-end moments only in member BC. These facts are kept in mind as we write slope-deflection equations for moment at each end of every member:

$$M_{AB} = \frac{2EI}{L}\left(2\theta_A + \theta_B - \frac{3\Delta}{L}\right) \pm (FEM)_{AB} \tag{23-5}$$

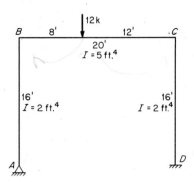

Fig. 23–2. Rigid frame.

Substituting all known values into the equation of each end of every member in turn, we have

$$M_{AB} = \frac{2E2}{16}\left(2\theta_A + \theta_B - \frac{3\Delta}{16}\right) + 0$$

$$M_{BA} = \frac{2E2}{16}\left(2\theta_B + \theta_A - \frac{3\Delta}{16}\right) + 0$$

$$(FEM)_{BC} = \frac{-Pab^2}{L^2} = \frac{-12 \times 8(12)^2}{(20)^2} = -34.56 \text{ kip-ft}$$

$$M_{BC} = \frac{2E5}{20}(2\theta_B + \theta_C - 0) - 34.56$$

$$(FEM)_{CB} = \frac{+Pa^2b}{L^2} = \frac{+12(8)^2 12}{(20)^2} = +23.04 \text{ kip-ft}$$

$$M_{CB} = \frac{2E5}{20}(2\theta_C + \theta_B - 0) + 23.04$$

$$M_{CD} = \frac{2E2}{16}\left(2\theta_C + 0 - \frac{3\Delta}{16}\right) + 0$$

$$M_{DC} = \frac{2E2}{16}\left(0 + \theta_C - \frac{3\Delta}{16}\right) + 0$$

These six slope-deflection equations contain ten unknowns: θ_A, θ_B, θ_C, Δ, M_{AB}, M_{BA}, M_{BC}, M_{CB}, M_{CD}, and M_{DC}. We can eliminate the unknown moments (M_{AB}, etc.) by substituting them into equations of static equilibrium. One such equation is

$$\Sigma H = 0 \qquad\qquad (1\text{--}2)$$

In a free-body diagram of the entire frame we see that the shears at the base of the columns must be equal and opposite.[7] Since shear at A equals $(M_{AB} + M_{BA})/L$ and shear at D equals $(M_{DC} + M_{CD})/L$, we have

$$\frac{M_{AB} + M_{BA}}{L} + \frac{M_{DC} + M_{CD}}{L} = 0$$

If all signs are assumed plus as above, the true sign of each moment will be automatically determined by the operation of algebra. Canceling L and substituting the slope-deflection equations for moment, we have

$$M_{AB} + M_{BA} + M_{DC} + M_{CD} = 0 = \frac{E}{4}\left(2\theta_A + \theta_B - \frac{3\Delta}{16}\right)$$

$$+ \frac{E}{4}\left(2\theta_B + \theta_A - \frac{3\Delta}{16}\right) + \frac{E}{4}\left(2\theta_C - \frac{3\Delta}{16}\right) + \frac{E}{4}\left(\theta_C - \frac{3\Delta}{16}\right)$$

Since the sum of moments at any joint must total zero, we have

$$M_{BA} + M_{BC} = 0 = \frac{E}{4}\left(2\theta_B + \theta_A - \frac{3\Delta}{16}\right) + \frac{E}{2}(2\theta_B + \theta_C) - 34.56$$

$$M_{CB} + M_{CD} = 0 = \frac{E}{2}(2\theta_C + \theta_B) + 23.04 + \frac{E}{4}\left(2\theta_C - \frac{3\Delta}{16}\right)$$

Finally the hinge at point A tells us that

$$M_{AB} = 0 = \frac{E}{4}\left(2\theta_A + \theta_B - \frac{3\Delta}{16}\right)$$

giving four equations with four unknowns: θ_A, θ_B, θ_C, and Δ. Solving the last equation for θ_A in terms of θ_B and Δ, we have

$$\theta_A = \frac{3\Delta}{32} - \frac{\theta_B}{2}$$

Substituting this into the other equations reduces the number of unknowns to three, which is somewhat more palatable. The resulting equations are

$$3\theta_B + 6\theta_C - \frac{15\Delta}{16} = 0$$

$$11\theta_B + 4\theta_C - \frac{3\Delta}{16} = 8 \times \frac{34.56}{E}$$

$$2\theta_B + 6\theta_C - \frac{3\Delta}{16} = -4 \times \frac{23.04}{E}$$

---

[7] This is the same principle used to correct sidesway moments in moment distribution.

from which (with slide-rule accuracy)

$$\theta_B = \frac{+34.6}{E}$$

$$\theta_C = \frac{-29.3}{E}$$

$$\frac{\Delta}{16} = \frac{-4.83}{E}$$

$$\theta_A = \frac{-24.5}{E}$$

Substituting these values into the slope-deflection equations for moment, we have

$$M_{AB} = \frac{4E}{16}\left[2\left(\frac{-24.5}{E}\right) + \frac{34.6}{E} - 3\left(\frac{4.83}{E}\right)\right] = 0.0$$

$$M_{BA} = \frac{4E}{16}\left[2\left(\frac{34.6}{E}\right) + \frac{-24.5}{E} - 3\left(\frac{-4.83}{E}\right)\right] = +14.8$$

$$M_{BC} = \frac{10E}{20}\left[2\left(\frac{34.6}{E}\right) + \frac{-29.3}{E}\right] - 34.56 = -14.6$$

$$M_{CB} = \frac{10E}{20}\left[2\left(\frac{-29.3}{E}\right) + \frac{34.6}{E}\right] + 23.04 = +11.0$$

$$M_{CD} = \frac{4E}{16}\left[2\left(\frac{-29.3}{E}\right) - 3\left(\frac{-4.83}{E}\right)\right] = -11.0$$

$$M_{DC} = \frac{4E}{16}\left[\frac{-29.3}{E} - 3\left(\frac{-4.83}{E}\right)\right] = -3.9$$

The sign of the answer indicates whether moments are clockwise (plus) or counterclockwise (minus), because all moments were assumed positive in the beginning.

24

CASTIGLIANO'S THEOREMS

24–I. Introduction. Castigliano's theorems have been of great importance in the past, and for practical structural analysis they are still highly esteemed by many. Some feel they constitute the only completely universal method of analysis (which is not exactly true because virtual work can solve any problem that can be solved by Castigliano's theorems); some feel that the difference between Castigliano's theorems and virtual work lies only in the order in which mathematical manipulations are made;[1] and still others think there is no difference at all because the two methods lead to exactly the same computations.[2] At least one authority[3] feels that there is a practical difference, that Castigliano's first theorem is a roundabout method and that his second theorem is a mathematical abstraction. Although opinion concerning the relation between virtual work and Castigliano's theorems is mixed, there seems to be universal agreement that the concept of virtual work is simpler and more straightforward.

Castigliano originally stated three theorems.[4] But the second is the converse of the first, so the first two are now called Castigliano's first theorem. In modern terminology it is stated: *The derivative of the total internal work with respect to any one load equals the deflection at the point of load in the direction of the load.* In equation form it is:

$$\frac{\partial W}{\partial P_1} = \Delta_1 \tag{24-1}$$

Castigliano called the third theorem a corollary of the second. It is now called the second theorem or, better, the principle of least work. It is stated: *An elastic structure will deform in such a manner that the internal work of deformation will be a minimum.* Actually the second theorem was discovered before the first. In 1818 Vène stated an incorrect principle which later led to

---

[1] Linton E. Grinter, *Theory of Modern Steel Structures*, Vol. II (rev. ed; New York: The Macmillan Co., 1949), p. 46.

[2] Carl L. Shermer, *Fundamentals of Statically Indeterminate Structures* (New York: The Ronald Press Co., 1957), p. 23.

[3] J. A. Van den Broek, *Elastic Energy Theory* (2d ed; New York: John Wiley & Sons, Inc., 1942), p. 225.

[4] E. S. Andrews, *Elastic Stresses in Structures*, transl. from Alberto Castigliano, *Théorème de l'équilibre des systèmes élastiques et ses applications* (London: Scott Greenwood and Son, 1919).

the theorem of least work. Cournot, Pagani, Mossotti, Dorna, and especially Manabrea investigated least work, but their proofs lacked exactness, so most authorities did not accept the theorem and some even published papers to show its fallacy. Castigliano first proved it rigorously in 1873, and in a thesis for a degree in engineering at Turin showed least work to be only a corollary of the "first" theorem.[5]

24-2. Real Work. If a load is gradually applied to an elastic structure, the work equals average force times distance moved in the direction of the force. This is expressed mathematically by Eq. 7–2,

$$W = \frac{F}{2}\,\Delta \tag{7-2}$$

In a member in a truss, the change in length of a member, Δ, is FL/AE. Substituting gives

$$W = \frac{F}{2}\frac{FL}{AE} = \frac{F^2 L}{2AE} \tag{24-2}$$

for a single member. For a truss composed of many members the work is

$$W = \Sigma \frac{F^2 L}{2AE} \tag{24-3}$$

Work is also equal to average moment times the angular rotation in radians, or

$$W = \frac{M}{2}\,d\theta$$

From Eq. B–4 we have,

$$d\theta = \frac{M\,ds}{EI} \tag{B-4}$$

Substituting gives

$$W = \frac{M}{2}\frac{M\,ds}{EI} = \frac{M^2\,ds}{2EI} \tag{24-4}$$

for a short (infinitesimal) length of beam. For an entire beam or rigid frame, the total internal work is

$$W = \int_0^L \frac{M^2\,ds}{2EI} \tag{24-5}$$

24-3. Proof of Castigliano's Theorems. If we take the partial derivative of the internal work with respect to some load P_1 on the structure, Eq. 24–5 becomes

$$\frac{\partial W}{\partial P_1} = \int_0^L \frac{2M(\partial M/\partial P_1)\,ds}{2EI} = \int_0^L \frac{M(\partial M/\partial P_1)\,ds}{EI} \tag{24-6}$$

[5] Alberto Castigliano, "Nuova teoria all'equilibrio dei sistemi elastici," *Trans. Acad. Sci.*, 11: 127–286, Turin, 1876.

The term $\partial M / \partial P_1$ means the ratio of a small change of moment with respect to a small change in P_1. If we let the small change in P_1 be U, a virtual load of infinitesimal magnitude, then we have

$$\frac{\partial M}{\partial P_1} = m \qquad (24\text{–}7)$$

where m is the virtual bending moment (a small change of moment) due to the virtual load U. Substituting into Eq. 24–6 gives

$$\frac{\partial W}{\partial P_1} = \int_0^L \frac{Mm\, ds}{EI} \qquad (24\text{–}8)$$

The right-hand term equals the deflection at the point where U—and therefore P_1—is applied. Consequently, we have

$$\frac{\partial W}{\partial P_1} = \Delta_1 \qquad (24\text{–}1)$$

If the deflection is wanted at some point between loads, it is necessary to place an imaginary load at that point. The imaginary load can approach zero, so that it in itself will cause no deflection. This is equivalent to the virtual load in the method of virtual work.

Castigliano's second theorem—least work—does not require rigorous proof. If we take the derivative of the internal work with respect to any reaction or any redundant force, we have

$$\frac{\partial W}{\partial R} = \Delta_R \qquad (24\text{–}1)$$

But because the reaction or redundant is fixed, $\Delta_R = 0$, so that we have

$$\frac{\partial W}{\partial R} = 0 \qquad (24\text{–}9)$$

When the derivative of a quantity with respect to another is equal to zero, either a maximum or a minimum exists. A bit of reflection shows that a maximum has no meaning.[6] Therefore Eq. 24–9 states that the internal work of deformation is a minimum and proves Castigliano's second theorem. It might also be stated as follows: *In an elastic structure, the reactions will develop such values as will render the internal work a minimum.*

In trusses, the forces in members depend upon the loads on the truss, so the partial derivative of W with respect to any load is, from Eq. 24–3,

$$\frac{\partial W}{\partial P_1} = \frac{2F(\partial F / \partial P_1)L}{2AE} \qquad (24\text{–}10)$$

---

[6] Because if the work increases indefinitely, the reaction must also increase indefinitely.

Just as $\partial M/\partial P_1 = m$, so $\partial F/\partial P_1 = u$, and Eq. 24–10 becomes

$$\frac{\partial W}{\partial P_1} = \sum \frac{FuL}{AE} \qquad (24\text{--}11)$$

showing that for trusses as well as for beams

$$\frac{\partial W}{\partial P_1} = \Delta_1 \qquad (24\text{--}1)$$

24–4. Applications. *Example* 24–4*A. Real Work.* If the loading is very simple, the deflection can be solved by the use of real work. Combining Eqs. 7–2 and 24–5, we have

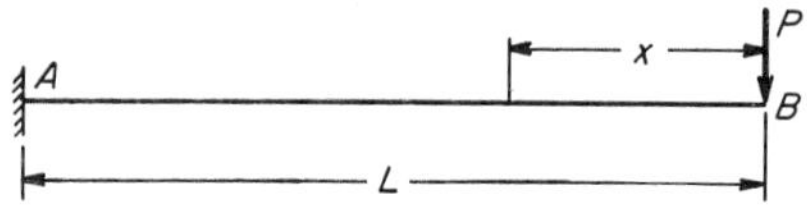

Fig. 24–1. Cantilever beam.

$$\frac{F}{2}\Delta = W = \int_0^L \frac{M^2\,ds}{EI} \qquad (7\text{--}2,\ 24\text{--}5)$$

A cantilever beam subjected to a single concentrated load is pictured in Fig. 24–1. The moment at any point is Px. Substituting gives

$$\frac{P}{2}\Delta = \int_0^L \frac{(Px)^2\,dx}{2EI} = \frac{P^2}{2EI}\int_0^L x^2\,dx = \frac{P^2}{2EI}\left[\frac{x^3}{3}\right]_0^L = \frac{P^2L^3}{2\times 3EI}$$

$$\Delta = \frac{PL^3}{3EI}$$

Example 24–4*B. Castigliano's Theorem.* Solving the same problem by Castigliano's theorem, we write

$$\frac{\partial W}{\partial P} = \Delta \qquad (24\text{--}1)$$

From the foregoing example, we have

$$W = \int_0^L \frac{M^2\,ds}{EI} = \frac{P^2L^3}{6EI}$$

Differentiating, we find the deflection

$$\Delta = \frac{\partial W}{\partial P} = \frac{2PL^3}{6EI} = \frac{PL^3}{3EI}$$

as before.

But instead of integrating the expression for M first and then differentiating, we can save work by differentiating first and then integrating; thus we have

$$W = \int_0^L \frac{P^2x^2\,dx}{2EI}$$

$$\Delta = \frac{\partial W}{\partial P} = \int_0^L \frac{2Px^2\,dx}{2EI}$$

Now integrate:

$$\Delta = \frac{P}{EI}\int_0^L x^2\,dx = \frac{P}{EI}\left[\frac{x^3}{3}\right]_0^L = \frac{PL^3}{3EI}$$

The saving in labor is not so apparent as it would be if the expression for M were more complicated.

Example 24–4C. Deflection of Unloaded Point. Using Castigliano's theorem, the deflection can only be obtained at a point of concentrated load. To find the deflection at an unloaded point (or a point at which only a distributed load is acting), it is necessary to introduce an imaginary concentrated load. This load is allowed to become zero, eventually, so that it does not affect the elastic curve of the structure.

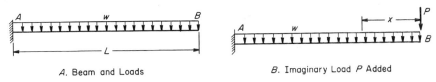

A. Beam and Loads   B. Imaginary Load P Added

Fig. 24–2. Deflection at a point without a concentrated load.

To find the end deflection of the uniformly loaded cantilever in Fig. 24–2A, apply load P at the free end, as shown in Fig. 24–2B. The moment is

$$M = \frac{wx^2}{2} + Px$$

so that the work is

$$W = \int_0^L \frac{M^2\,dx}{2EI} = \frac{1}{2EI}\int_0^L \left(\frac{wx^2}{2} + Px\right)^2 dx$$

$$= \frac{1}{2EI}\int_0^L \left(\frac{w^2x^4}{4} + \frac{2wx^2Px}{2} + P^2x^2\right) dx$$

$$= \frac{1}{2EI}\left(\frac{w^2L^5}{20} + \frac{wL^4P}{4} + \frac{P^2L^3}{3}\right)$$

Now differentiate:

$$\Delta = \frac{\partial W}{\partial P} = \frac{1}{2EI}\left(0 + \frac{wL^4}{4} + \frac{2PL^3}{3}\right)$$

Now let P vanish to zero. This yields

$$\Delta = \frac{wL^4}{8EI}$$

Again it would save some labor to differentiate first and integrate afterward.

$$W = \frac{1}{2EI}\int_0^L \left(\frac{wx^2}{2} + Px\right)^2 dx$$

The partial derivative of W with respect to P equals deflection

$$\Delta = \frac{\partial W}{\partial P} = \frac{1}{2EI} \int_0^L 2\left(\frac{wx^2}{2} + Px\right)(0 + x)\,dx$$

Having differentiated, we can let P equal zero and collect terms

$$\Delta = \frac{\partial W}{\partial P} = \frac{1}{EI} \int_0^L \frac{wx^3}{2}\,dx$$

Note that the above integral is exactly the one that would be obtained directly by virtual work, since the real moment would be $wx^2/2$ and the virtual moment would be $x \times 1 \#$. The accusation that Castigliano's theorem is roundabout is justified when either of the above procedures—the classical ones—is followed. Of course, from this point onward there is absolutely no difference between the two methods. The final step of the solution is

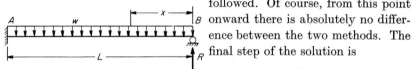

Fig. 24–3. Redundant beam.

$$\Delta = \frac{w}{2EI}\left[\frac{x^4}{4}\right]_0^L = \frac{wL^4}{8EI}$$

The parallelism between virtual work and Castigliano's theorem becomes even clearer if we use Eq. 24–6:

$$\frac{\partial W}{\partial P} = \int_0^L \frac{M(\partial M/\partial P)\,ds}{EI} \qquad (24\text{–}6)$$

$$M = \frac{wx^2}{2} + Px$$

$$\frac{\partial M}{\partial P} = 0 + x$$

Substituting into Eq. 24–6 and letting P vanish to zero, we have

$$\Delta = \frac{\partial W}{\partial P} = \frac{1}{EI} \int_0^L \left(\frac{wx^2}{2} + 0\right)(0 + x)\,dx = \frac{wL^4}{8EI}$$

So in this procedure there is no difference between Castigliano's theorem and virtual work except in original concept. Note that $\partial M/\partial P$ equals x, which would be equal to the value of m had the equation of virtual work been used for the solution.

Example 24–4D. Redundant Reaction. To illustrate the solution of a statically indeterminate structure by the method of least work, consider the beam of Fig. 24–3. The moment is

$$M = \frac{-wx^2}{2} + Rx$$

so that we have

$$\frac{\partial M}{\partial R} = 0 + x$$

$$\frac{\partial W}{\partial R} = 0 \tag{24–9}$$

$$\frac{\partial W}{\partial R} = \int_0^L \frac{M(\partial M/\partial R)\, ds}{EI} \tag{24–6}$$

Substituting gives

$$0 = \frac{1}{EI} \int_0^L \left(\frac{-wx^2}{2} + Rx \right)(0 + x)\, dx$$

$$0 = \frac{-wL^4}{2 \times 4} + \frac{RL^3}{3}$$

whence

$$R = \tfrac{3}{8}wL$$

Part VI

MODELS

A model is anything of a particular form, shape, size, quality, construction, etc., intended for imitation.[1] The thing imitated is the prototype. A structural engineer is usually concerned only with imitating the structural mechanics of the prototype in whole or in part and, since it is only structural mechanics that needs to be imitated, the model might look quite different from the prototype. For example, a soap bubble[2] can be used to determine shearing stress in a shaft, an analog computer[3] may be used to find forces in bridges or to analyze mechanical vibrations, and a time exposure of confetti in slowly moving water[4] may be used to find direction of principal stresses in a complex tension bar. Photoelastic models[5] are made of transparent plastics to the same shape as the prototype and, insofar as practical, they are loaded in the same manner. All of these are only an indication of the many types of models that are possible. Some have no physical resemblance at all to the prototype. In this part we shall be concerned only with structural models—those which look like structures (at least in the geometry of their centerlines) and which imitate the structural behavior of the prototype.

Structural models can be divided into two classes—unloaded models and loaded models. Unloaded models are those which are bent or displaced at

---

[1] Webster's definition.

[2] The soap film, chemically toughened, is stretched over an opening of the same geometrical shape as the shaft cross-section. When bulged by a minute air pressure, the bubble takes the shape of the stress function, and its transverse slope is proportional to the shearing stress in the shaft. The slope can be measured by reflected light or by plotting contours with a micrometer needle. The method has proved practical for finding shearing stresses in propeller blades and in non-circular shafts.

[3] The electric circuit of the computer is set up to be analogous to the mechanical action of the prototype. The physical components of the prototype are represented by voltages, impedances, etc., so that a galvanometer may read, for instance, deflection of the prototype in inches. The use of computers, both analog and digital, will undoubtedly increase.

[4] Streamlines in laminar flow are of the same shape as stress trajectories. A time exposure shows confetti as streaks parallel to the stress trajectories.

[5] In white, polarized light, rainbow patterns appear which enable shearing stresses to be accurately determined. Dark bands (isoclinics) also appear wherever principal strains are parallel to the axis of polarization. These two types of bands permit a complete and accurate determination of stress distribution all over the model. It is directly applicable to the prototype, provided the shape and loading of the model are faithful and all the prototype stresses are within the elastic limit.

certain points by definite amounts but which are not otherwise subjected to forces; it is in this sense that the models are "unloaded." Results are limited to reactions and internal forces, and these can be determined for the prototype with ease and comparative rapidity. The models may be made of wire, cardboard, or certain plastics. They are cheap and easily made, although some of the apparatus used to obtain accurate displacements may be expensive. Loaded models are those to which calculated loads are applied. Reactions, internal forces, strains, deflections, slopes, vibrations, etc., can be determined. It is possible for an "unloaded" wire model to become a "loaded" model if the proper forces are applied to it, but, in general, loaded models are comparatively expensive and many require specially designed instruments to measure reactions, slopes, and small movements.

Most people think of structural models as small replicas of the real structure. But models may be of any size—smaller or larger than their prototypes. Of course, structural models are usually small for economy and convenience. But if a great many identical prototypes (e.g., airplanes or transmission towers) are to be built, one of them may be exhaustively tested, and that particular prototype may be thought of as a full-sized model. The relative size of model and prototype (model scale ratio) affects the results. Unless the model scale ratio is unity, the model results usually cannot be applied directly to the prototype but must be corrected. For the solution of reactions and deflections the corrections are easily made, but corrections alone may be entirely inadequate if the model must be faithful to the prototype when the latter is stressed beyond the elastic limit (a reinforced concrete beam, for example), when buckling must be considered as well as stress and deflection (as in airplanes), or when the model must be completely faithful in other respects (such as density). For such problems, either the model must be full size or it must be designed to represent limited aspects of prototype behavior.

The use of a model to solve a problem may be dictated by any of three reasons: (1) A mathematical analysis may appear impossible or at least impractical, or it may not be possible to establish with certitude the assumptions necessary to begin an analysis; (2) even though a mathematical analysis is possible, a solution by model testing may be quicker or more economical; and (3) the importance of the project may make model study desirable as a check. The first reason might apply to the stress distribution in a member of irregular shape, the second to the solution of a complex rigid frame, and the third to a monumental bridge.

25

UNLOADED MODELS

25–1. Introduction. The use of unloaded models is essentially based upon Maxwell's law of reciprocal deflections, which appeared as a small part of a monumental paper[1] in 1864. The very brevity of his treatment obscured the importance of the principle, and it remained for Müller-Breslau to recognize its significance and to conclude that, in conjunction with the principle of superposition,[2] Maxwell's law results in the equivalence between influence lines and certain elastic curves. In recognition of the first formal[3] statement, this is often called the Müller-Breslau principle. Since then, significant contributions to the art of mechanical structural analysis (the use of models to obtain influence lines) have been made by Beggs, Bull, Gottschalk, Eney, and many others. Unloaded structural models have been extensively used since about 1925.

25–2. Theory. An influence line can be defined as follows: it is the graph for a function (reaction, moment, stress, etc.) so drawn that a load multiplied by the ordinate of the graph at the point of loading equals the value of the function due to that load. Suppose the function is a reaction. Then any load multiplied by the ordinate (at the point of application of the load) equals the reaction due to the load. Suppose the function happens to be moment at a certain point. Then a load multiplied by the influence-line ordinate (at the point of loading) equals the moment. If there are several loads on the structure, the function due to each load may be found and the results added algebraically. If there is a uniformly distributed load, the area under the influence line multiplied by the intensity of the load equals the function, or the distributed load can be replaced by a series of equivalent concentrated loads. If influence lines are known for a sufficient number of functions (reactions or internal forces, or both), the analysis for any structure, simple or statically indeterminate, is reduced to simple arithmetic—the multiplication of loads by influence-line ordinates.

The Müller-Breslau principle may be restated more accurately: If a unit displacement be made parallel to the direction of any function (reaction,

---

[1] James Clerk Maxwell, "On the Calculations of the Equilibrium and Stiffness of Frames," *Philosophical Magazine*, 27 (4): 294 ff., 1864.

[2] See Art. 18–3.

[3] Heinrich F. B. Müller-Breslau, *Die neueren Methoden der Festigkeitslehre und der Statik der Baukonstruktionen* (Leipzig: Baumgartner, 1886).

internal shear, axial force, moment, etc.) in an unloaded elastic structure, the resulting elastic curve is the influence line for that function. Thus the influence line for a reaction is made by displacing the structure—or, better, a model of it—a unit distance parallel to the reaction, as shown in Fig. 25–1. Its elastic curve is the influence line. The structure is said to be unloaded because there must be no forces physically applied to it other than those

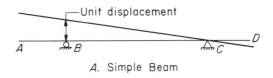

A. Simple Beam

B. Beam With One Redundant Reaction

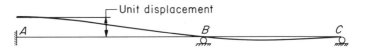

C. Beam With Two Redundant Reactions

Fig. 25–1. Influence lines for left reactions.

required to produce the unit displacement and the reactions required to prevent displacements at supports. In Fig. 25–1B where the left reaction is a roller support, note that the model is allowed to rotate freely as it is deflected. But in Fig. 25–1C where the left reaction is fixed, the displacement is made without rotation since the structure is not free to rotate at that point. Displacements and elastic curves must always be compatible with the kind of supports and with the structure itself.

The influence line for shear is produced by cutting a model of the structure, displacing one cut end a unit distance with respect to the other and parallel to it, and then permitting the cut ends to "float" into their position of equilibrium without external restraint, as shown in Fig. 25–2A. To produce an influence line for axial force or thrust, the cut ends are moved a unit distance apart and permitted to "float" into place, as shown in Fig. 25–2B. To obtain the influence line for moment, one cut face is rotated a unit amount (1 radian) with respect to the other, and the relatively rotated ends are permitted to "float" into their unrestrained position of equilibrium, as shown in Fig. 25–2C. Only one kind of relative deformation (angular, shear, or thrust) is permitted at a time. The other two types of relative deformation

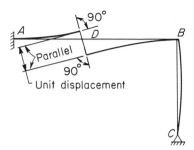

A. Influence Line for Shear at *D*

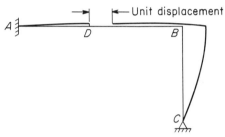

B. Influence Line for Thrust at *D*

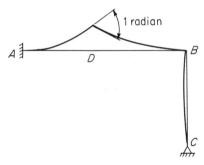

C. Influence Line for Moment at *D*

Fig. 25–2. Influence lines for internal forces.

are prevented. It is interesting to note that in statically determinate structures the elastic "curves" are not curved at all but straight (as shown in Fig. 25–1*A*, for example), and that such structures are not stressed by the unit displacement. On the other hand, statically indeterminate structures are always stressed by the unit displacement and the elastic curves are truly curved.

PROOF. To demonstrate the validity of the Müller-Breslau principle, consider the statically indeterminate structure of Fig. 25–3*A* which is loaded (for

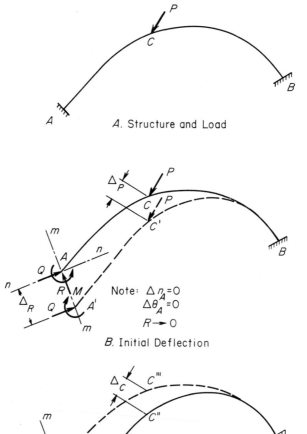

A. Structure and Load

B. Initial Deflection

C. Final Deflection

Fig. 25–3. Proof of Müller-Breslau principle.

the purpose of illustration only) with a single force P. Let it be required to determine the reaction component along axis mm. In Fig. 25–3B, let the reaction component R parallel to the mm axis relax to zero, permitting the deflection Δ_R to take place at point A and Δ_P to take place at point C, where load P is applied. As load P remains constant during this movement, the external work done by it is force times distance or $P\Delta_P$. This work is positive since the force moves in the sense of its application. The external work done by R is *average* force times distance and, because the structure is elastic, the average force is $R/2$. The work it does is $\frac{1}{2}R\Delta_R$, and it is minus because the force moves opposite to its sense of application. None of the other reactions does any work because there are no movements in their directions. The internal work done on the structure is positive because stresses result in strains of the same sign. From the principle of conservation of energy, external work (W_E) must equal internal work (W'_I):

$$W_E = P\Delta_P - \tfrac{1}{2}R\Delta_R = W'_I \qquad (25\text{–}1)$$

Now hold point A fixed and remove load P. The structure is now unloaded except for the reactions necessary to hold point A in its deflected position at point A'. The reaction R is now reversed in the sense shown in Fig. 25–3B. Let point A' move to point A by gradually relaxing R (and all other reactions) to zero. The work done is

$$W_E = -\tfrac{1}{2}R\Delta_R = -W''_I \qquad (25\text{–}2)$$

The middle term is minus because the reaction moves opposite to the direction of its application. The internal work W''_I is minus because the strains taking place are opposite in sense to the stresses. From the principle of superposition, which states that the deflections, strains, and stresses caused by one load are independent of those caused by another load, it follows that the internal work W'_I done in Fig. 25–3B equals the internal work W''_I done in Fig. 25–3C. That is to say, when point A moves to point A', the internal work is the same regardless of what *constant* loads act upon the structure,[4] so that we have

$$W'_I = W''_I$$

Combining Eqs. 25–1 and 25–2, we have

$$P\Delta_P - \tfrac{1}{2}R\Delta_R = W'_I = W''_I = \tfrac{1}{2}R\Delta_R$$

Collecting terms and solving for R yields

$$R = P\frac{\Delta_P}{\Delta_R} \qquad (25\text{–}3)$$

[4] Having found the value of Δ_R, we could produce such a deflection with P removed (or with any number of other constant loads added to the structure) without changing the value of the internal work. It sometimes requires considerable thought to appreciate the significance and validity of the principle of superposition. It might help to reflect that the elastic curve for several loads can be obtained by adding the deflections for each load separately, that is, by superimposing elastic curves on top of one another. Now if P is added to the unloaded structure, it will form an elastic curve. If the structure is deflected Δ_R, another elastic curve is added, the final curve being the sum of the two. Thus the elastic curve due *only to* P before deflection of point A equals the elastic curve due *only to* P after point A moves to point A', and thus no internal work *due to* P *only* is done during the deflection of point A to A'. There is left, then, the internal work due *only* to the deflection Δ_R. Since Δ_R in Fig. 25–3B equals Δ_R in Fig. 25–3C, the numerical amount of internal work must be the same in each, so that $W'_I = W''_I$.

In accordance with the principle of superposition, Δ_P (in Fig. 25-3B) equals[5] Δ_C (in Fig. 25-3C), where Δ_C is measured parallel to load P but on the unloaded structure. Therefore Eq. 25-3 can be expressed as

$$R = P \frac{\Delta_C}{\Delta_R} \qquad (25-4)$$

If there are a number of loads, the reaction due to each can be calculated and the results added algebraically. This leads to Eq. 25-5:

$$R = \frac{\sum Py}{\Delta_R} \qquad (25-5)$$

where y, like Δ_C, is the component of deflection of the load point measured parallel to the load. If Δ_R is made unity, Eq. 25-5 becomes synonymous with Eq. 18-4,

$$R = \sum Py \qquad (18-4)$$

Thus the elastic curve of an unloaded structure (such as that in Fig. 25-3C) becomes an influence line.

In much the same manner the proof can be extended to include moments as well as forces. Let the structure in Fig. 25-4A be loaded with the force P. Now let the moment M relax to zero by permitting the structure to rotate freely at point A. The external work done by P is plus $P\Delta_P$, by M is minus $\frac{1}{2}M\theta_M$ (since the average moment is $\frac{1}{2}M$), and by the internal fibers is W'_I. The external work must equal internal work:

$$W_E = P\Delta_P - \tfrac{1}{2}M\theta_M = W'_I \qquad (25-6)$$

Again remove load P but hold point A fixed. This requires an equal and opposite value of M to be applied at point A. Now let the structure rotate back to its original position by gradually relaxing M to zero. The work done is

$$W_E = -\tfrac{1}{2}M\theta_M = -W''_I \qquad (25-7)$$

Since W'_I equals W''_I for the same reasons previously explained, we have by combining Eqs. 25-5 and 25-6,

$$W_E = P\Delta_P - \tfrac{1}{2}M\theta_M = \tfrac{1}{2}M\theta_M$$

$$M = P \frac{\Delta_P}{\theta_M} \qquad (25-8)$$

However, the ordinates can be measured on the unloaded structure because Δ_P (Fig. 25-4A) equals Δ_C (Fig. 25-4B) for the same reasons as previously given, so that we have

$$M = P \frac{\Delta_C}{\theta_M} \qquad (25-9)$$

---

[5] The reasons in footnote 4 are also valid here. Curve AB in Fig. 25-3B is an elastic curve due to load P. Curve $A'B$ is the elastic curve due to P and Δ_R combined. The difference is a curve due only to Δ_R and, since Fig. 25-3C shows a curve due only to Δ_R, it follows that $\Delta_P = \Delta_C$.

The value of θ_M must be measured in radians, and Δ_C is measured in feet (or inches if moment in inch units is wanted). If Δ_C is measured by the scale used to construct the model, that is, in terms of prototype feet rather than model feet, the scale relation between model and prototype is automatically included, and thus the model results can be applied without further correction

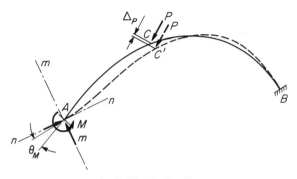

A. Initial Deflection

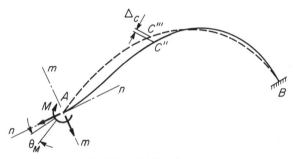

B. Final Deflection

Fig. 25–4. Müller-Breslau principle applied to moments.

to the prototype. If there are several loads, the effect of each can be determined separately and the results added to produce Eq. 25–10:

$$M = \frac{\sum Py}{\theta_M} \qquad (25\text{–}10)$$

If θ_M is made unity (1 radian), Eq. 25–10 reduces to Eq. 18–4:

$$M = \sum Py \qquad (18\text{–}4)$$

Of course, a rotation of 1 radian would produce considerable geometric distortion and the strain in most model materials would probably exceed the elastic limit, so such rotations are usually not physically applied to models.

Unit rotations can be applied mathematically, however. Distortions are eliminated simply by ignoring them in the mathematical expression for deflection.

To prove the validity of the Müller-Breslau principle applied to internal forces, the structure is cut in two at the point where the internal force is wanted. Then a differential displacement is produced (as in Fig. 25–2) and the work is evaluated exactly as before, which again leads to Eqs. 25–5 and 25–10. The only new concept involved is that, when one cut face is displaced relative to the other, the work done by the forces at the cut faces equals either force multiplied by its movement with respect to the other cut face.

The above proof is offered for two reasons: (1) It does not require a knowledge of previous chapters, and (2) it does require assimilation of considerable structural mechanics for a real understanding. A proof apparently more rigorous is found in Art. 18–3. But in a profound sense it is not more rigorous—just more mathematical. The philosophy underlying this proof is just as valid and, perhaps, even more enlightening.

25–3. Splines. Models of simple or continuous prismatic beams can be made of any spline that is elastic, uniformly flexible, and straight. Straight splines are not easy to find, but, fortunately, splines that are not quite straight can be used if their tendency to rotate is prevented and if ordinates are measured between neutral and deflected positions of the spline (and not between a straight line and the deflected spline). Wood, wire,[6] and even light steel bars, for large models, can be used. No manufacture and no calibration is involved. Any spline can be selected to represent the beam. A light one can be held between push-pins for supports. A larger one can be held by nails. No special equipment is required beyond pencil (or better, pen and ink), paper, a plank or drawing board, push-pins[7] or nails, an engineer's scale, and the spline itself. It is surprising that, with care, such simple equipment can produce good engineering results. Of course, influence lines for continuous beams can be so easily obtained by computation that the use of a spline for engineering work is limited. However, it is an excellent introduction to model study because its manipulation is directly applicable to the more advanced model methods.

Example 25–3A. Influence Lines for Reactions. A continuous beam is shown in Fig. 25–5A, together with several live loads to illustrate the calculation of reactions. A model was made of a 3/32-in.-diameter brazing rod to a scale of 1 in. equals 1 prototype ft. As the rod was not very straight, a short elbow was formed at the left end to keep it from rotating during displacement.

[6] Semi-hard brass drill rod is best but often hard to find. Steel drill rod is good. Oxyacetylene brazing rod and welding rod are readily available in 3-ft lengths. Even coiled wire is suitable if it can be straightened. The best way to straighten wire is to stretch it beyond the yield point.

[7] Push-pins (size No. 1) are available at stationery stores.

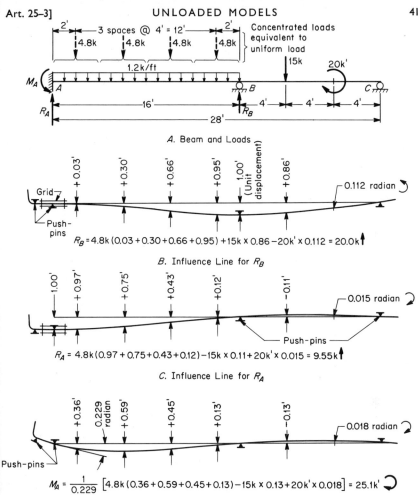

A. Beam and Loads

$R_B = 4.8k (0.03 + 0.30 + 0.66 + 0.95) + 15k \times 0.86 - 20k' \times 0.112 = 20.0k$

B. Influence Line for R_B

$R_A = 4.8k (0.97 + 0.75 + 0.43 + 0.12) - 15k \times 0.11 + 20k' \times 0.015 = 9.55k$

C. Influence Line for R_A

$M_A = \dfrac{1}{0.229} \left[4.8k (0.36 + 0.59 + 0.45 + 0.13) - 15k \times 0.13 + 20k' \times 0.018 \right] = 25.1k'$

D. Influence Line for M_A

Fig. 25–5. Influence lines for reactions.

The influence line for the middle support is shown in Fig. 25–5B. The wire was displaced 1 in. at the center reaction because a displacement much less than 1 in. is not so accurately measured, and a displacement of much more than 1 in. might overstrain the wire. Some other convenient displacement, such as 2 centimeters, would do just as well. Note that the left reaction was held fixed by bending the wire slightly upward and holding it with a push-pin placed at the left of the reaction, thus keeping it tangent to its original position. The grid ruled at the left reaction is an aid to estimating the tangency of the wire. At all other reactions the wire was permitted to rotate without restraint. This treatment of reactions corresponds exactly to the prototype, in which the left reaction is fixed and the others are free to rotate.

The influence line can be traced with pencil or, better, with a ruling pen, but neither can be allowed to press against the wire. A good way is to hold the pencil or pen loosely by its very top. To avoid parallax, keep the pencil in the plane tangent to the wire and perpendicular to the paper.

Influence-line ordinates are measured between a tracing of the wire before displacement and another tracing after displacement. Ordinates are not measured from a straight base line to the traced elastic curve because such measurements do not cancel the initial crookedness of the wire, and the resulting errors can be very large. The ordinates in Fig. 25–5B are given in terms of prototype feet at the points where load is applied. Note that the uniform load is approximated by four equivalent concentrated loads of 4.8 kips each. The deflections were estimated to the nearest 0.01 in. with an ordinary engineer's scale. But it is preferable to estimate measurements to the nearest 0.002 in. by using a strong magnifying glass and a scale graduated in hundredths of inches.

The sign of the reaction for any load can be determined by examination of the development leading to Eq. 25–5. Note that all the terms in Eq. 25–5 are positive, and that in Fig. 25–3B (which forms the basis for Eq. 25–5) the work of the reaction (negative) is opposite in sign to that of the load (positive). So if the spline moves in the direction of the load, the reaction acts opposite to the direction of displacement at the reaction point, and vice versa. For example, in Fig. 25–5B, the reaction point is moved down, and the spline moves in the direction of the 15-kip load, so the reaction acts opposite to the displacement of the reaction point, which means it acts upward. The spline rotates in the *opposite* direction to the applied moment, so the reaction for it acts in the direction of the displacement—downward.

The influence line for the left vertical reaction is shown in Fig. 25–5C. Note that no rotation is permitted at point A. To find the moment at the left reaction, the spline is rotated (but not otherwise displaced), as shown in Fig. 25–5D. Physically, a unit rotation (1 radian) would overstrain the wire and also result in excessive geometrical distortion, so any convenient rotation is used instead, and the amount is carefully measured afterward. All of the deflections are measured in prototype feet, so no further corrections need be applied for the model scale ratio.

Example 25–3B. Influence Lines for Internal Forces. Influence lines for internal forces—shear and axial force (thrust)—and internal moment can be obtained by cutting the spline at the point where the force is wanted and introducing a differential displacement in the direction of the force. An influence line for shear is shown in Fig. 25–6B. Note that the cut ends are displaced laterally, and are permitted to rotate freely, but they are not permitted to rotate or move axially *with respect to each other*. An influence line for moment is shown in Fig. 25–6C. Note that one cut end is rotated 0.25 radian relative to the other.

Although it is possible to join the cut ends with a soldered joint, it is not very practical, and some sort of device to produce these movements is almost a necessity. The device (called the Sanks deformeter[8]) used for these influence lines is shown in Fig. 25–8. It consists of a small piece of aluminum plate into which vee grooves have been milled in a pattern that permits

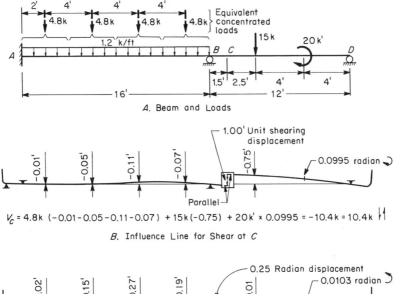

$V_c = 4.8k \ (-0.01 - 0.05 - 0.11 - 0.07) + 15k(-0.75) + 20k' \times 0.0995 = -10.4k = 10.4k$

B. Influence Line for Shear at C

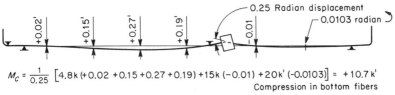

$M_c = \dfrac{1}{0.25} \left[4.8k(+0.02 + 0.15 + 0.27 + 0.19) + 15k(-0.01) + 20k'(-0.0103)\right] = +10.7k'$

Compression in bottom fibers

C. Influence Line for Moment at C

Fig. 25–6. Influence lines for internal functions.

deformation in shear, thrust, and moment. The wires are clamped into the grooves by a piece of plastic held with four small screws. Light, inexpensive, and accurate, it is very simple to use. It not only illustrates all the principles involved with the more expensive deformeters but also produces results comparable to those obtained by other deformeters, and is suitable for practical analysis of beams, rigid frames, and arches.

The sign of the internal forces follows the same principles as are explained for reactions: the work of deformation must be opposite in sign to the work of the loads. That is, if the spline moves in the direction of the load, the internal force (or moment) acts opposite to the direction of differential

[8] R. L. Sanks, "Quick, Inexpensive and Accurate Wire Models," *Civil Engineering*, 30 (4): 71–75, April, 1960.

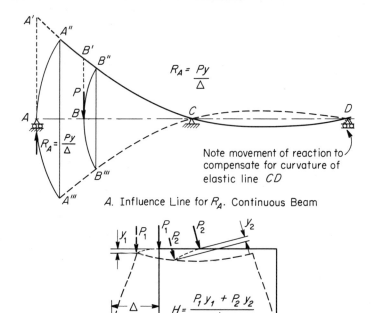

$$R_A = \frac{Py}{\Delta}$$

$$R_A = \frac{Py}{\Delta}$$

Note movement of reaction to compensate for curvature of elastic line *CD*

A. Influence Line for R_A. Continuous Beam

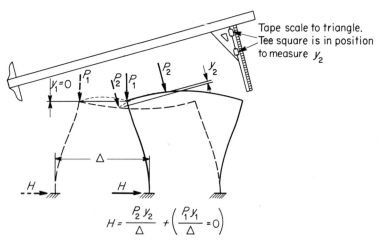

$$H = \frac{P_1 y_1 + P_2 y_2}{\Delta}$$

B. Influence Line for H. Deformation in Only One Direction

Tape scale to triangle. Tee square is in position to measure y_2

$$H = \frac{P_2 y_2}{\Delta} + \left(\frac{P_1 y_1}{\Delta} = 0 \right)$$

C. Influence Line for H. Equal and Opposite Deformations Cancel Geometric Distortion

Fig. 25–7. Geometrical distortion.

displacement, and vice versa. Calculations for shear and moment together with the proper signs are shown in Fig. 25–6.

25–4. Error. Certain errors are inherent in mechanical analysis. Some of them are inelasticity of model material, error in fabrication, error in measurement, and geometrical distortion. With care these errors can be reduced to acceptable standards, but they cannot be entirely eliminated.

Inelasticity can be reduced by using essentially elastic materials and by being careful not to strain them beyond the elastic limit. Practically, one can simply observe whether a certain deflection creates permanent set—then, if it does, use lesser deflections for the mechanical analysis.

Error in fabrication can take an infinite variety of forms—from unwanted variations in modulus of elasticity to the physical representation of actual joints with soldered gussets. Common sense must prevail. No firm rules can be given nor can all exigencies be covered. Use good grade materials. If you suspect non-uniformity, make tests. For example, some materials, such as cardboard, have a definite grain, and the modulus in one direction can be different from that in another. The error can be eliminated by a slight, compensating change in the width of members in a rigid frame or by making the frame of parallel-cut strips with glued joints. If a knee joint in a gabled frame is massive, make a correspondingly massive model joint. If it is compact, make a small joint. When using wire, get a great many different sizes that differ but little, so the relative flexibilities of different members can be closely approximated. If flexibility is to be varied by means of stiffeners, use several short ones rather than a few long ones. In cutting cardboard or plastic to calculated widths, be satisfied only with superior workmanship. A deformeter essentially increases the stiffness of a model member nearly to infinity within the clamp. This disturbance can cause appreciable errors. It can be minimized by using short clamps or by making the model members long. In general, not more than about 5 or 6 percent of the span length should be enclosed within the clamps.

Because the models must be physically displaced far enough to permit accurate measurements, a certain amount of geometrical distortion may occur. Distortion may be minimized by proper techniques. In Fig. 25–7A the beam is displaced by half the span length at point A. Should the displacement be measured (1) from A to A' and B to B', or (2) along the arc from A to A'' and from B to B'', or (3) along the vertical projection from A to A'' and from B to B''? The first is quite incorrect because additional fibers (those from A'' to A') are stressed, which changes the internal work and invalidates the proof in Art. 25–2. The second method is too cumbersome. The last method is not strictly correct, but the error produced in the reaction at A— even with this large displacement—does not exceed 2 percent. It should be noted that the right support must move slightly left so that *even reactions must always be applied to the same point on the model.*

However, if P is not vertical, it has a horizontal component which, when multiplied by the horizontal component of deflection at B, would change the reaction at A. But we know this cannot be true because all horizontal loads must be resisted by the knife-edge support at C. Therefore the roller supports at A and D cannot be affected by horizontal loads. The discrepancy is geometrical distortion. This kind of geometrical distortion can be eliminated if point A is displaced an equal and opposite amount to point A''', which in turn produces the elastic curve shown by the broken line. By measuring Δ directly from A''' to A'' and y directly from B''' to B'', most of the geometrical distortion is eliminated. The ordinates, being twice as great, can be measured with more accuracy.

Another illustration of the elimination of geometrical distortion is shown by Figs. 25-7B and 25-7C. According to the model, load P_1 does produce a reaction H equal to $P_1 y_1/\Delta$ in Fig. 25-7B. This is, of course, untrue, because P_1 should produce only a vertical (upward) reaction at A. In Fig. 25-7C, where the displacements are equal and opposite, the ordinate y_1 becomes zero and the error is eliminated. Equal and opposite displacements are always to be preferred. Another advantage of equal and opposite displacements is that the deformations can be reduced without loss of measuring accuracy, which reduces the errors due to geometrical distortion still more. For example, if point A in the beam of Fig. 25-7A were displaced only one-quarter of the span length one way and an equal amount the other way, the error would be reduced to a fraction of 1 percent.

Friction is devastating. In appreciable amounts it causes staggering errors and it must be essentially eliminated at all costs. It is always a problem for splines and wire models which are supported directly on the drawing paper. But it can be reduced (1) by filing gusset and stiffener plates smooth on the contact surface, and then vibrating the drawing board or pushing the model from side to side, gradually forcing it into its mean at-rest position; or (2) by raising the drawing board to a vertical position (or just past the vertical) so that the model falls away from the drawing board and thus is subject only to the force of gravity. If these measures do not suffice—and they may not if the model is a tall, rigid frame made heavy by stiffener plates—the model must be supported on glass plates separated by steel balls. Balls should be $\frac{1}{8}$ to $\frac{1}{4}$ in. in diameter, and can be prevented from rolling out of position by small rings. (Double-depression microscope slides are ideal because the troublesome rings are then unnecessary.) Wide models such as those made of cardboard or plastic may tend to buckle, and this must be prevented by placing weights upon the model over the balls. Even supporting the model on balls may not eliminate all the friction, so a check for friction should always be made by pushing the model gently from side to side and noting whether it always returns to the same position.

Errors are inherent in all measurements, but the amount of error can be reduced by proper and careful methods. For measurements of splines, a preliminary measurement with a scale divided into tenths of inches (which can be estimated to hundredths) can be refined with a check measurement using a scale graduated into fifty parts per inch. But a strong magnifying glass and a scale divided into hundredths of inches is better because it can be read to the nearest 0.002 in. This refinement is likely to be nullified if it is used on tracings of influence lines. To be effective, such a scale should be used on targets glued directly on the model. One method of keeping the scale properly aligned is pictured in Fig. 25–7C. To avoid parallax, set the targets so the scale can actually touch them, and keep the eye directly above the target.

In spite of geometrical distortion and all the other sources of error, the accuracy that can be obtained with such simple devices as splines and wire models is surprising. For example, the error in each of the three reactions in Fig. 25–5 is less than 1 percent. In Fig. 25–6, the errors are 1 percent for V_C and 3 percent for M_C. This accuracy is unusually good for traced influence lines, and luck no doubt played a part, since, for example, a change of 0.01 in. in any measurement between A and B in Fig. 25–6C changes the error by 2 percent. But with care, errors of 5 percent or less are the rule. Care must be re-emphasized. It means more than caution. It means the recognition of influencing factors and the delicacy to circumvent them. Model study is not a practical tool for the thick-witted or heavy-handed.

25–5. Wire Models. Wire models for rigid frames were proposed by Bull[9] in 1927. Except for calibrating the wires and soldering the joints, the wire model is as simple to make and to use as is the spline. The same techniques are employed and the same accuracy is obtained, which means that it is entirely feasible to obtain answers that are sufficiently accurate for structural design. Because deformations are large, the techniques, although similar, need not be so refined, and beginners are likely to obtain greater accuracy with wire models than with other types which utilize more sensitive equipment and methods.

The use of a wire model often provides a quicker solution than can be obtained mathematically. Arches, rings, and complex rigid frames, especially when subjected to several load combinations, are examples. But one of the most important purposes, certainly, is as an aid to acquiring a true structural sense. All of the theory and much of the manipulation and practice that is required for the more sophisticated model methods can be learned from wire models. Furthermore, wire models, like splines, are unique in that deflections are so large that the shape of the influence lines is unmistakable. An hour spent manipulating wire models is worth several hours of any other activity in absorbing the structural behavior of continuous beams and rigid frames.

---

[9] Anders Bull, "Brass Wire Models Used to Solve Indeterminate Structures," *Engineering News-Record*, 99: 920–922, 1927.

A

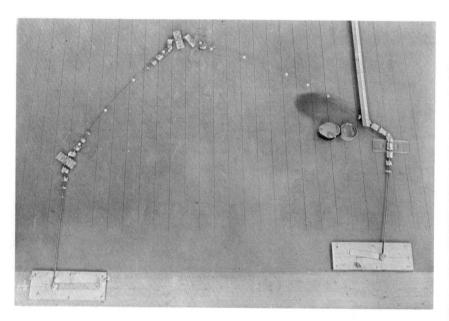

B

Fig. 25–8. Gusset, stiffener, and reaction plates in a wire model.
A. Model of rigid frame of Fig. 14–13A.   B. Deformeter and joint detail.

MATERIALS. Rigid frames usually consist of members with different flexibilities, so their model counterparts must match these different flexibilities. Consequently, wires must be obtained in many diameters which differ very little. Brass drill rod,[10] in drill gages and in fractional sizes from about 0.042 in. to 0.100 in., is usually best. Steel drill rod, also available in fractional sizes and in drill gages, is nearly as good and more universally obtainable. By using soldering acid, steel can be soldered almost as easily as brass. Gas welding and brazing rods available in 3-ft lengths and in diameters of $\frac{1}{16}$, $\frac{3}{32}$, and $\frac{1}{8}$ in. provide a wide range of six different flexibilities. By soldering short stiffener plates to the wire at suitable intervals, any desired flexibility can be produced which, considering their availability from welding shops and suppliers, may make welding and brazing rod the most useful of all. They must be used with care, however, because their flexibilities vary greatly on different axes and even—to some degree—from point to point.

Gusset and stiffener plates should be very thin; a tin can is as good as anything. Reaction or foundation plates are better made of heavier material. Galvanized iron, or sheet brass from 26 to 24 gage is about right. Properly made gusset, stiffener, and reaction plates are shown in Fig. 25–8. Note that a properly soldered joint is very short (0.2 in. of each wire buried in solder is plenty), and the wire is completely enclosed within a solder[11] "bubble."

For soldering the model, a large (2 ft × 2 ft) piece of asbestos-cement board is helpful, for unless the wires, gussets, and stiffeners are firmly held (by tape), the joints are not so easily made. Soldering can be done with an alcohol torch, but an electric iron is handier. A large, soft drawing board into which the push-pins can be stabbed, an engineer's scale divided into fiftieths (or better, hundredths) of an inch, electrician's pliers, and tin snips complete the essential equipment. Drawing ink in several bright colors and a ruling pen are desirable (although not necessary) for drawing the influence lines.

CALIBRATION. To represent the prototype faithfully, an unloaded model must meet only two requirements: (1) Its centerline must be geometrically similar to that of the prototype and (2) the relative EI values of its members must correspond to those of the prototype. The only satisfactory method of calibrating EI is one based on the deflection of the wire. Measurement of the diameter is of no value because, for one thing, it cannot account for variations of modulus of elasticity. The wire can be deflected as a simple beam or as a cantilever beam. It can be done in an elaborate device using mercury switches or contact indicator lights, or it can be done by using two push-pins for supports and any sort of weight, as shown in Fig. 25–9. The latter gives

---

[10] Obtainable from T. E. Conklin Brass and Copper Co., Inc., 54–60 Lafayette Street, New York 13, New York.

[11] Lead solders creep excessively. The only satisfactory solders known to the author are 10 percent silver to 90 percent tin, and 15 percent silver to 85 percent tin. They can be obtained from United Welding Service Co., Box 564, Franklin, Pa.

satisfactory results with suitable technique. The deflection must be large enough to measure accurately (at least 0.25 in.) but not large enough to produce significant geometric distortion (for this setup not over about 6 percent of the total length). Care must be used to ensure no friction. The weight must hang freely and the wire must slip easily on the push-pins. Friction can be detected by gently causing more, then less, deflection of the wire. Friction can usually be eliminated by tapping the board in which the push-pins are set or by otherwise causing vibration. If it cannot be essentially eliminated, mark the two extreme positions of the wire at rest and split the difference.

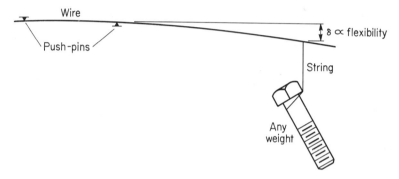

Fig. 25–9. Simple wire-calibrating device.

Use great care to avoid parallax and to place the weight in the same position for each wire tested. Finally, if the wire is not round, mark the wire so that it can be rotated to the same axis for which it was calibrated.

Flexibility is proportional to deflection, and both are inversely proportional to EI, so relative flexibility is an inverse measure of EI. To produce suitable deflections, it is often necessary to use two or more different weights for calibration. Then the relative flexibilities can be expressed as

$$f = \frac{\delta}{W} \tag{25–9}$$

where f is the relative flexibility, W is the weight, and δ is the deflection. The units in which W and δ are measured make no difference, provided they are the same for all wires tested.

If there are three or more different moments of inertia in the prototype, a trial-and-error selection of the proper wires is awkward. A better way to select wires is first to calibrate them and plot their relative flexibilities as points on 2- or 3-cycle logarithm paper. Cut a narrow strip of the log paper and plot points corresponding to the relative flexibilities of the prototype. Slide the strip across the log paper until the required relative flexibilities best match with the calibrated relative flexibilities. Such an elementary "slide rule" is shown in Fig. 25–10. In this figure it is assumed that relative moments of inertia in the prototype are 2, 3, and 5, so the relative flexibilities are respectively 0.5, 0.33, and 0.2. These points are plotted on the upper strip of log paper. Several steel drill rods were calibrated to yield flexibilities of 0.14, 0.19, 0.26, 0.31, 0.36, 0.38, 0.41, 0.42, 0.48, 0.56, 0.78, 0.89, and 1.30, and these are plotted as points a to m on the lower strip in Fig. 25–10. Note that wires bdi match the requirements closely. Other possibilities (which could be seen by sliding to the right a tracing of the upper strip) are dik, ejl, and jlm, but these are not as good.

If a suitable combination of wires is not found, more wires must be calibrated. There may be sufficient variation between wires of one nominal

Fig. 25–10. "Slide rule" for wire selection.

size (particularly if the wires are welding or brazing rod) so that, if every wire is calibrated, a suitable combination can be found. The flexibility of wire (particularly welding and brazing rod) often varies on different axes—sometimes as much as 10 percent. A few moments spent in draw-filing two opposite flat surfaces can produce large variations in flexibility. Then the wire can be rotated to the proper position to produce exactly the flexibility desired. However, a better method is to solder a series of stiffener plates at evenly spaced intervals along the wire. A varying flexibility (as for a haunch or a tapered member) can be modeled by varying the length of the stiffeners to correspond to the flexibility at each station. When flexibility is plotted against percent of bare wire, the result is a straight line on log-log paper. Such a plot,[12] made from wires carefully calibrated first, then stiffened with soldered plates and recalibrated, permits one to reproduce faithfully any flexibility desired, including the varying flexibility associated with haunches or tapered members.

MODEL MAKING. Lay out the centerlines of the model on the asbestos-cement board. Select the calibrated wires and cut them to the proper lengths (lengths of 8 to 20 in. are about right) with the pliers. Fasten them to the asbestos-cement board with Scotch drafting tape. Cut the gussets, stiffeners (if any), and reaction plates, and slip them under the wires. Heat the wires first, then apply acid and solder. Drill holes with a No. 58 drill for push-pins. File or sand the under side of gussets and reaction plates smooth to minimize friction, or mount the model on glass plates separated by balls.

[12] R. L. Sanks, *op. cit.*

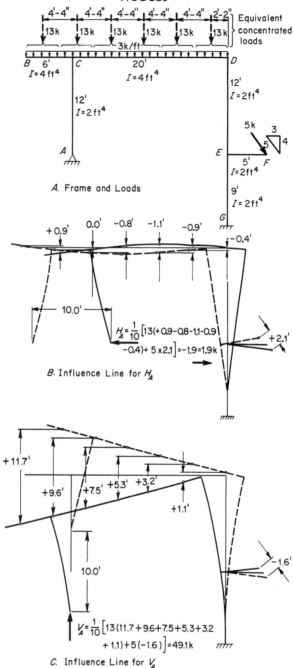

A. Frame and Loads

B. Influence Line for H_A

C. Influence Line for V_A

Fig. 25–11. Influence lines for a rigid frame.

Example 25–5. *Influence Lines.* Influence lines for the reactions are shown for a rigid frame in Fig. 25–11. Although the deflections are very large, the effects of geometrical distortion are small because ordinates are measured from the dashed line representing one deflection to the solid line representing an equal and opposite deflection. Note that deflections are not measured along the line of action of the load. They are measured parallel to the load but always from a load point to the same point on the deflected structure. Note, too, how the model is supported in the same manner as the prototype— right reaction fixed, left reaction pinned. Compare the solution in Fig. 25–11 with that of Ex. 9–2*A*.

25–6. Paper and Plastic Models. Models of paper or plastic have two advantages over wire models: (1) The more versatile and somewhat more accurate Beggs or Eney deformeters can be used, and (2) these models are better adapted to represent non-prismatic members. Paper models can be made from double- or triple-weight Bristol board. It is elastic, easily glued, and readily cut with a thin-bladed pocket knife or razor blade. It is universally available[13] and cheap. However, inaccuracies in cutting can hardly be rectified, and it does have some grain, so that its modulus varies somewhat in different directions.

Cellulose acetate[14] appears to be the best plastic. It can be obtained in large sheets of uniform thickness. The thickness should be 0.08 to 0.10 in. It can be cut with a coping saw or, better, with a jig saw. With a file it is not difficult to dress the width to within 0.002 or 0.003 in. In this it has a distinct advantage over paper. Since moment of inertia varies as the cube of the width, a small error in width creates a large error in moment of inertia. For example, an error of 2 percent in width (0.01 in. in $\frac{1}{2}$ in.) becomes an error of 6 percent in moment of inertia. It is elastic for any given time rate of loading. This limited type of elasticity is adequate, since it is deformation— not load—that is applied to the model.

BEGGS DEFORMETER. The oldest deformeter and the one which has been considered standard is the Beggs deformeter.[15,16] The principles of its operation are the same as those explained for wire models. The deformations are produced by using gage plugs of various diameters inserted between two bars, as shown in Fig. 25–12. Geometrical distortion is virtually non-existent because the movements are very small, only 0.05 in., but precision is obtained by finishing the gage plugs and their bearing surfaces to fantastically close tolerances—only plus or minus 1/100,000 in. Deformations are measured to an accuracy of about 1/10,000 in. with a filar microscope. Thus the expected

---

[13] At stationery stores.

[14] Celanese Corp. of America, 180 Madison Ave., New York 16, or Cellutone Co., 23 East 26th Street, New York, or Commercial Plastic and Supply Corp., 630 Broadway, New York 12. Specify clear, well-cured sheets especially selected for uniform thickness.

[15] George E. Beggs, "An Accurate Mechanical Solution of Statically Indeterminate Structures by the Use of Paper Models and Special Gages." *Proc. ACI*, 18: 58–82, 1922.

[16] Available from Soiltest, Inc., 4711 West North Avenue, Chicago, Ill.

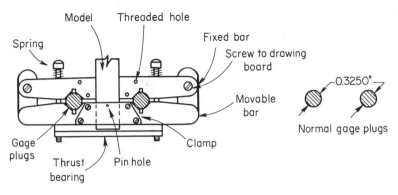

A. Deformeter and Normal Gage Plugs

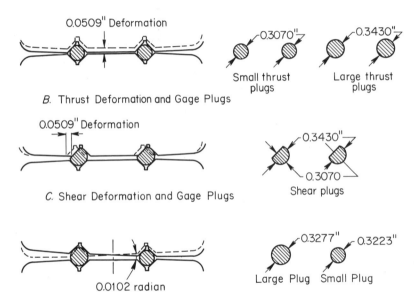

B. Thrust Deformation and Gage Plugs

C. Shear Deformation and Gage Plugs

D. Moment Deformation and Gage Plugs

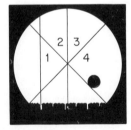

Indicator hair (3) shows position of measurement cross-hairs (2,4) relative to scale and center hair (1). Reading shown is 11483. The last three figures are read on a graduated drum.

E. Micrometer Cross-Hairs

Fig. 25-12. Beggs deformeter.

error of observation is only 1 in 500. Other errors are involved, of course, but an experienced and careful operator working in an atmosphere of constant temperature and humidity can consistently obtain superb results.

As it is shown in Fig. 25–12A, the instrument is a reaction gage. The fixed bar is screwed rigidly to a drawing board and the model is clamped to the

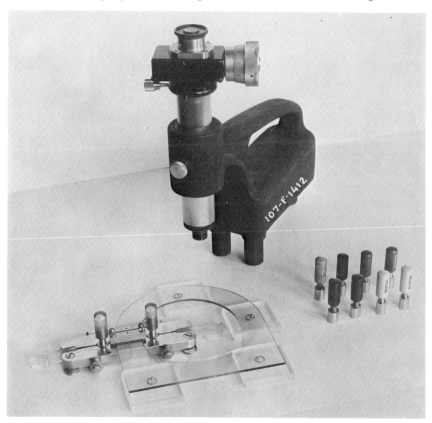

Fig. 25–13. Model of single-barrel conduit with Beggs deformeter. (Courtesy of U.S. Bureau of Reclamation.)

movable bar, which is positioned by any pair of gage plugs. When the deformeter is floated on steel balls and the model is cut in two, with each cut end clamped to one bar, it becomes an internal deformeter. The model itself is held down upon steel balls (rolling between glass plates) by small weights. The filar microscopes are oriented on targets of microscopic ink spots made with an atomizer or air brush. The sequence of operations is to orient the microscope over the target, read the microscope for both xx and yy axes, separate the deformeter bars with wedges, remove the plugs and insert new ones, and read the microscope again for both axes. The procedure is repeated

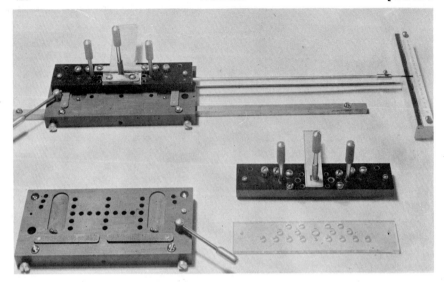

A

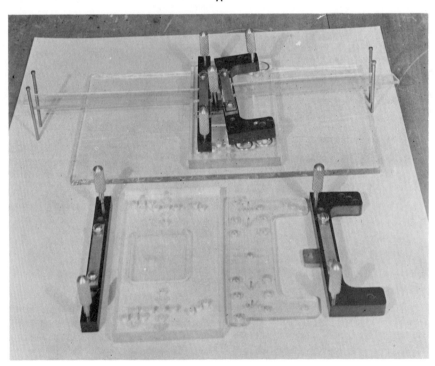

B

Fig. 25–14. Eney deformeter apparatus. A. Reaction gage. B. Internal gage.
(Courtesy of

for the three sets of plugs—shear, thrust, and moment. Then the microscope is moved to a new target and the whole process is repeated. A model with Beggs deformeters is shown in Fig. 25–13.

ENEY DEFORMETER. The Eney deformeter[17] was developed about 1935. Purchased,[18] it is less costly than the Beggs deformeter or, since it is not patented, it can be built by a skilled machinist. Displacements and rotations can be varied to suit the model. Movements are measured with a scale graduated to hundredths of inches. It can be read to the nearest 0.002 in. with a jeweler's eye loupe. If the largest displacement (2.00 in.) is used, the expected error of observation is about 1 in 1000. This tiny error is a bit misleading because other errors are involved, but nevertheless the Eney deformeter compares favorably with the Beggs deformeter in accuracy. Some of its other virtues are that it requires less skill to operate, is easier to align, and is faster, particularly for the intermittent user.

An Eney deformeter set up is shown in Fig. 25–14. Two types are used— one for an internal gage and a more massive one for a reaction gage. The scale is fastened to a holder that slides on, and can be locked to, a polished steel bar. The bar in turn is held by adjustable supports. The models are large. (A 24- by 30-in. drawing board is usually adequate only for the more compact models.) As with the Beggs deformeter, the model is held down upon steel balls by small weights. The larger movements tend to intensify buckling, but the tendency can be overcome by employing more balls, using them in pairs, and making the models narrow. Narrow members require more accuracy in construction, thus cellulose acetate is much better than paper as a model material.

[17] W. J. Eney, "A Large Displacement Deformeter Apparatus for Stress Analysis with Elastic Models," *Proc. Society for Experimental Stress Analysis*, VI (II): 84–93, 1948.

[18] Prof. W. J. Eney, Director, Fritz Eng. Lab., Lehigh University, Bethlehem, Pa.

C

C. Model with reaction gage (left) and internal gage (right).
William J. Eney.)

After a deformeter is deflected, the movement of every target is read by sliding the scale to each target in turn along the polished steel bar. After all targets are read, another deformation is produced and the targets read again. Eney prefers to clamp the model to the deformeters in neutral position, then to obtain the difference in ordinates between minimum and maximum deflections in order to eliminate lost motion. This requires four measurements of each target for every reaction component or internal force, but readings can be taken so quickly that it is still relatively fast.

OTHER DEFORMETERS. Other deformeters have been developed, including the R.P.I. deformeter,[19] the M.I.T. moment deformeter,[20] and the M.I.T. moment indicator.[21] Most of these are custom instruments and are not produced commercially. An interesting application of the use of plastic to build small deformeters for plastic models is described by Tse.[22] The deformeters, like Eney deformeters, utilize pins in tight-fitting holes to position the members. Separate deformeters are built for moment, shear, and thrust. Each is essentially a joint (made of the same plastic as the members) with the deformations built into them. A moment deformeter, for example, is built in the shape of a Y with three holes drilled on a suitable spacing along the centerline of each arm or leg. Using the Y as a template, matching holes are drilled in the member. After this the members can be keyed to the Y with short pieces of drill rod. Shifting one member from one arm to the other arm of the Y provides the equal and opposite deformations needed. Holes can be as large as one-third the width of the leg or member with little reduction in strength or moment of inertia. All the joints can be fabricated in a similar manner, thus making very large models practical. These can be placed directly on the floor. The large deformations make accurate results possible with the simplest of measuring methods. The deformeters can be built with only simple tools: hand drill, coping saw, and file, or better yet, drill press and jig saw.

25-7. Truss Models. The deflection of trusses is primarily caused by elastic changes in the member lengths. The amount of deflection caused by flexure in the members is very small and is usually neglected in mathematical analyses. A representative model, then, would be one composed of members which are pin-connected at the joints and which are axially stable enough to resist buckling yet axially springy enough to shorten or lengthen elastically with small forces. A practical type of model was introduced by Bull[23] in

[19] J. Sterling Kinney, *Indeterminate Structural Analysis* (Reading, Mass: Addison-Wesley Publishing Company, Inc., 1957), pp. 605–607.

[20] John B. Wilbur, *Structural Analysis Laboratory Research* (Cambridge, Mass: Publication from the Department of Civil and Sanitary Engineering, Massachusetts Institute of Technology, Ser. No. 65, December, 1938), pp. 7–17.

[21] *Ibid.*, pp. 37–47.

[22] K. F. Tse, "Practical Method of Analysing Structures Using Large Models," *Civil Engineering*, 51 (606): 1341–1344, London, December, 1956, and (607): 67–70, January, 1957.

[23] Anders Bull, "New Method of Mechanical Analysis for Trusses," *Civil Engineering*, 1 (3): 181–193, December, 1930.

1930. Axial springiness was obtained by using a yoke made of four leaves of 26-gage spring-brass sheet soldered to the member proper which was made of brass drill rod. But the yokes were hard to make and the soldered joints resulted in loss of elasticity. Eney[24] developed an improved yoke, shown in Fig. 25–15, by using threaded rod, machine screws, and fiber bushings. Such

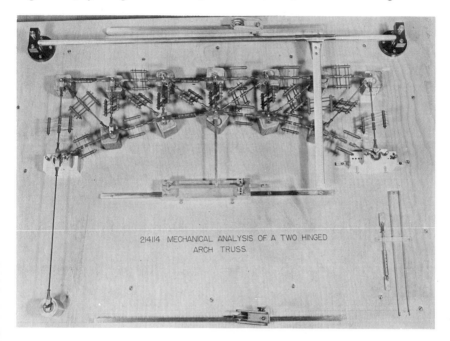

214114 MECHANICAL ANALYSIS OF A TWO HINGED
ARCH TRUSS

Fig. 25–15. Details of a model truss. (Courtesy of William J. Eney.)

an assembly is easy to make, can be used over and over again, is elastic, and similar yokes yield similar calibrations.

A model of the Holston bridge, constructed to a scale of 1 to 100, is shown in Fig. 25–16. The over-all accuracy of such models is excellent when they are carefully constructed so as to reduce play at joints to a minimum. Eney reported errors in influence lines obtained with this model[25] to be within 1 percent in spans adjacent to a displaced joint.

As with wire models, it is necessary only that the ratio of flexibility of the various members be reproduced. The flexibility of a truss member is

$$\delta L = \frac{FL}{AE}$$

[24] William J. Eney, "Studies of Continuous Bridge Trusses with Models," *Proc. Society for Experimental Stress Analysis*, VI (II): 94–105, 1948.
[25] *Ibid.*

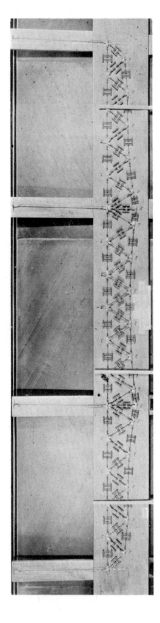

Fig. 25–16. Model of Holston bridge. (Courtesy of William J. Eney.)

The flexibility of a yoke is

$$\delta L = \frac{Fd^3}{EI} \tag{25–10}$$

where d is the bolt spacing, and I is the moment of inertia of the spring brass. However, the spring leaf is not fixed at the center of the bolt but, because of the physical size of the fiber bushing, at some distance from it. For this reason, Eq. 25–10 is quite inaccurate, and direct calibration is necessary. Equation 25–10 can be adjusted empirically by varying the exponent of d to fit the calibration.

Influence lines for individual members are constructed by producing a unit change of length in the member. Again, to reduce geometric distortion, a two-way movement is desirable, that is, first a contraction then an extension of the member.

26

LOADED MODELS

26-1. Similitude. The first general statement on similitude was made by Newton[1] in 1687, but the ideas of similitude were not applied successfully to engineering models for two centuries. Later contributions were made by Bertrand[2] in 1848, Routh[3] in 1897, Tolman[4] in 1914, Buckingham[5] in 1915, Groat[6] in 1918, Bridgman[7] in 1922, Chick[8] and Reynolds[9] in 1929, Weber[10] in 1930, Herrmann[11] in 1931, Farquharson et al.[12] in 1949, and others.

In a loose sense, similitude exists when there is some systematic relationship between a prototype and its model. In an exacting sense, similitude exists only when quantities such as stress, strain, force, velocity, etc., can be converted from model to prototype (and vice versa) by means of calculated reduction factors. The reduction factors may—and do—differ for different quantities. Similitude relations can be developed in several ways: (1) By a step-by-step reasoning process; (2) by a mathematical statement of the

[1] Sir Isaac Newton, *Principia*, Book II (1687), Theorem XXVI, Props. XXXII and XXXIII, and Corollaries 1 and 2.

[2] M. J. Bertrand, "Notes on the Principle of Similitude," *Journal de l'École Polytechnique*, 19 (32): 189–197, 1848.

[3] E. J. Routh, "The Principle of Similitude," "On Models," "Theory of Dimensions," *Dynamics of Rigid Bodies*, Part I (6th ed; New York: The Macmillan Co., 1897), pp. 292–296.

[4] R. C. Tolman, "The Principle of Similitude," *Physical Review*, Series 2, 3: 244ff., 1914.

[5] E. Buckingham, "Model Experiments and the Form of Empirical Equations," *Transactions, ASME*, 37: 263–296, 1915.

[6] B. F. Groat, "Ice Diversion, Hydraulic Models, and Hydraulic Similarity," *Transactions ASCE*, 82: 1139–1190, 1918.

[7] P. W. Bridgman, *Dimensional Analysis* (New Haven: Yale University Press, 1922).

[8] A. C. Chick, "Dimensional Analysis and the Principle of Similitude as Applied to Hydraulic Experiments with Models," in J. R. Freeman, *Hydraulic Laboratory Practice* (New York: ASME, 1929), Appendix 15, pp. 775–827.

[9] K. C. Reynolds, "Notes on the Laws of Hydraulic Similitude as Applied to Experiments with Models," in J. R. Freeman, *Hydraulic Laboratory Practice* (New York: ASME, 1929), Appendix 14, pp. 759–773.

[10] W. Weber, "The General Principles of Similitude in Physics and Their Relation to Dimensional Theory and the Science of Model Testing," *Jahrbuch der Schiffsbautechnischen Gesellschaft* Vol. 31 (Berlin: J. Springer, 1930).

[11] W. Herrmann, "The Conditions for Dynamic Similarity," *Verein Deutscher Ingenieure*, 75: 611–616, 1931.

[12] F. B. Farquharson, Frederick C. Smith, and George S. Vincent, *Aerodynamic Stability of Suspension Bridges* (University of Washington), Engineering Experiment Station, Bulletin No. 116, Part I, June, 1949; Part II, Oct., 1950; and Part III, June, 1952.

various influencing quantities in terms of their dimensional constants; and (3) by dimensional analysis. The first way is adapted only to a specific problem. The second is general, yet simple and straightforward, and it is the one explained herein. The third is the most rigorous, but it is complex and requires much study for complete understanding. It is the only one that can be used when there are influencing factors whose mathematical forms are unknown.

The necessary conditions for similitude can be stated by two propositions:

Proposition 1: The model must be geometrically similar to the prototype (geometrical similitude).

Proposition 2: The force reduction factor must be the same for all forces (mechanical similitude).

These two propositions are quite sufficient to ensure strict similarity, provided both model and prototype behave elastically. The first rule obviously requires that centerline dimensions be similar, but more, a strict interpretation leads to the conclusion that the geometry of the deflected structures also be similar, from which we conclude that strains in model and prototype must be equal. Such a stringent interpretation may be unnecessary if there are no secondary effects of distortion. The designer must decide whether that is so. It is not necessary to produce geometrical similarity in those dimensions that do not affect the behavior of model and prototype.

The second proposition means that the ratio of homologous forces in model and prototype must be constant regardless of whether the force is due to dead weight (gravitational force), to acceleration (inertial force), to strain (elastic force), or to force due to any other influence such as drag, friction, etc.

The symbols to be used are defined in the following. A subscript p indicates a prototype value. When no subscript is used, the symbol indicates a model value.

$$F = \text{force}$$
$$L = \text{length}$$
$$w = \text{unit weight}$$
$$g = \text{acceleration of gravity}$$
$$e = \text{strain (unit strain)}$$
$$E = \text{Young's modulus of elasticity}$$
$$t = \text{time}$$
$$C, C', c = \text{constants}$$
$$v = \text{velocity}$$
$$a = \text{acceleration}$$
$$n = L_p/L$$

Gravitational force is weight which equals volume times unit weight. Volume is cross-sectional area times length, and all lengths are proportional as a result of proposition 1. Therefore,

$$\frac{P_p}{F} = \frac{(\text{Area})_p}{\text{Area}} \times \frac{(\text{length})_p}{\text{length}} \times \frac{(\text{unit weight})_p}{\text{unit weight}} = \left(\frac{L_p}{L}\right)^3 \frac{w_p}{w} \qquad (26\text{–}1)$$

Inertial force is the product of mass and acceleration. Mass equals weight divided by the acceleration of gravity, and one expression for acceleration is length divided by time squared. Thus

$$\frac{F_p}{F} = \left[\frac{(\text{weight})_p/g_p}{\text{weight}/g}\right]\left[\frac{(\text{acceleration})_p}{\text{acceleration}}\right] = \left[\left(\frac{L_p}{L}\right)^3 \frac{w_p}{w}\frac{g}{g_p}\right]\left[\frac{L_p}{L}\left(\frac{t}{t_p}\right)^2\right]$$

$$= \left(\frac{L_p}{L}\right)^4 \frac{w_p g}{w g_p}\left(\frac{t}{t_p}\right)^2 \tag{26-2}$$

One expression for elastic force is stress times cross-sectional area. But stress equals strain times Young's modulus, and area is the product of two lengths, so

$$\frac{F_p}{F} = \frac{(\text{Area} \times \text{strain} \times \text{modulus})_p}{\text{Area} \times \text{strain} \times \text{modulus}} = \left(\frac{L_p}{L}\right)^2 \frac{e_p}{e}\frac{E_p}{E} \tag{26-3}$$

For generality we can include any other force simply as force X, so that

$$\frac{F_p}{F} = \frac{X_p}{X} \tag{26-4}$$

Proposition 2 requires that all force ratios be constant. Therefore, Eqs. 26–1, 26–2, 26–3, and 26–4 can be combined as follows:

$$\overset{(1)}{\frac{F_p}{F}} = \overset{(2)}{C} = \overset{(3)}{\left(\frac{L_p}{L}\right)^3 \frac{w_p}{w}} = \overset{(4)}{\left(\frac{L_p}{L}\right)^4 \frac{w_p}{w}\frac{g}{g_p}\left(\frac{t}{t_p}\right)^2} = \overset{(5)}{\left(\frac{L_p}{L}\right)^2 \frac{e_p}{e}\frac{E_p}{E}} = \overset{(6)}{\frac{X_p}{X}} \tag{26-5}$$

Note well that Eq. 26–5 actually consists of four equations. The acceleration of gravity cannot be varied (except under very unusual conditions) and, furthermore, strict interpretation of proposition 1 requires that the ratio of strains be unity; thus Eq. 26–5 is narrowed to

$$\overset{(1)}{\frac{F_p}{F}} = \overset{(2)}{C} = \overset{(3)}{\left(\frac{L_p}{L}\right)^3 \frac{w_p}{w}} = \overset{(4)}{\left(\frac{L_p}{L}\right)^4 \frac{w_p}{w}\left(\frac{t}{t_p}\right)^2} = \overset{(5)}{\left(\frac{L_p}{L}\right)^2 \frac{E_p}{E}} = \overset{(6)}{\frac{X_p}{X}} \tag{26-6}$$

from which all model scale reduction factors can be computed. Since there are actually four equations and six ratios ($F_p:F$, $L_p:L$, $w_p:w$, $t:t_p$, $E_p:E$, $X_p:X$), the choice of two ratios is left to the designer. Ordinarily we would select a certain value n for the length ratio $L_p:L$, in order to obtain a model size convenient for manipulation, large enough for accuracy, small enough for economy, and suitable in every way for the instruments with which we must measure it. Suitable model materials in a wide variety of elastic moduli do not exist, so perhaps our other choice is a definite ratio of Young's modulus, $E_p:E$. If we use the same material for both model and prototype, $E_p:E$ equals unity. Then the model scale reduction factors are computed as follows:

Length (arbitrary),

$$\frac{L_p}{L} = n \quad \text{or} \quad L_p:L = n{:}1$$

Young's modulus of elasticity (arbitrary)

$$\frac{E_p}{E} = 1 \qquad \text{or} \qquad E_p : E = 1 : 1$$

Force (solve terms 1 and 5, Eq. 26–6)

$$\frac{F_p}{F} = n^2 \qquad \text{or} \qquad F_p : F = n^2 : 1$$

Unit weight (solve terms 3 and 5, Eq. 26–6)

$$n^3 \frac{w_p}{w} = n^2 \qquad \text{or} \qquad w_p : w = 1 : n$$

Time (solve terms 4 and 5, Eq. 26–6)

$$n^4 \frac{1}{n} \left(\frac{t}{t_p}\right)^2 = n^2 \qquad \text{or} \qquad t_p : t = n : 1$$

Other terms can be derived. For example, one expression for moment of inertia is $I = bd^3/12$, where b is width and d is depth. Then

$$\frac{I_p}{I} = \frac{b_p d_p{}^3/12}{bd^3/12} = \frac{L_p}{L} \left(\frac{L_p}{L}\right)^3 = n^4 \qquad \text{or} \qquad I_p : I = n^4 : 1$$

For another example, velocity can be expressed as length divided by time. Thus

$$\frac{v_p}{v} = \frac{L_p}{L} \frac{t}{t_p}$$

from which

$$v_p : v = n : 1$$

Note that the scale reduction ratio for unit weight is $1 : n$. That is, the model material must be n times as heavy as the prototype material. This is usually impossible except within very narrow limits for n. However, it is usually feasible to add distributed weights to the model to produce the effect of increased density without changing the behavior of the model in any other way—such as increasing the moment of inertia.

This development for static forces can be extended to dynamic forces acting to produce, for example, free or forced vibration. Comparison of scale reduction factors with known equations of mechanics and with those obtained from dimensional analysis is further proof of the validity of this approach.

26–2. Loaded Model Design. The following discussion illustrates the application of similitude to practical model design. A model of the San Francisco-Oakland Suspension Bridge is chosen because its design, although straightforward, is yet complicated enough to illustrate the principles well.

Fig. 26–1. San Francisco-Oakland Bay Bridge. (Courtesy of California Division of Highways.)

The bridge itself, shown in Fig. 26–1, is still one of the great monuments of engineering, and the model, in its own way, was a milestone.

Three models were tested during the late planning stages of the bridge design, of which Model B was the one which most closely resembled the structure as constructed. This model had fixed-base "elastic" towers, stiffening trusses of variable moment of inertia, and a single suspension span with symmetrical side spans very nearly half as long as the main span. The following data were obtained from the study of Model B.[13]

    1. Stresses in the main cable.

    2. Moments in the stiffening truss at all critical points.

    3. Downward and upward deflections in the stiffening truss at mid-span in both main and side spans.

    4. Maximum changes of grade in the stiffening truss.

    5. Tower deflections.

    6. Lateral deflections in the stiffening truss and cable due to wind load in both main and side spans.

    7. Wind moments in stiffening truss.

    8. Horizontal reactions of the stiffening truss at towers and anchorages due to wind load.

    9. Change in direction of the main-span stiffening truss at towers due to wind load and full live load at normal temperature.

    10. Maximum longitudinal movement of main-span stiffening truss.

Considerations of available space, manufacture of parts to scale, cost, accuracy, convenience in conversion of results to prototype values, and previous experience led to the choice of a scale reduction factor of $n = 100$. However, a simple reduction of $n^2 = 10,000$ in cross-sectional area resulted in forces too great to be used with ease, so a further reduction in cross-sectional area was arbitrarily made by taking a longitudinal slice of the structure. A cross-section of the bridge is shown in Fig. 26–2A. The cables and trusses are first converted, as shown in Fig. 26–2B, to equivalent solid sections in which areas of cables are equal and moments of inertia of trusses are equal to those of the actual structure. (Cross-sectional area of trusses does not affect the behavior of the bridge, so that geometrical dissimilarity in this respect is permissible.) In Fig. 26–2C, all of the dimensions are reduced to model proportions by the factor n. But note that the section is truly inconvenient with main cables over ¼ in. in diameter and a solid stiffening "truss" more than 2 in. wide. In Fig. 26–2D, the circular members are transformed into equivalent ribbons which are as wide as the stiffening "truss." Cross-sectional areas of the ribbons are the same as those of the solid section of Fig. 26–2C, and the structural action is also the same. To reduce the cross-sectional area

[13] George E. Beggs, Raymond E. Davis, and Harmer E. Davis, "Tests on Structural Models of Proposed San Francisco-Oakland Suspension Bridge," *University of California Publications in Engineering*, 3 (2): pp. 59–166, November 1933. This is the source of Figs. 26–2 and 26–3 and Arts. 26–1 and 26–2.

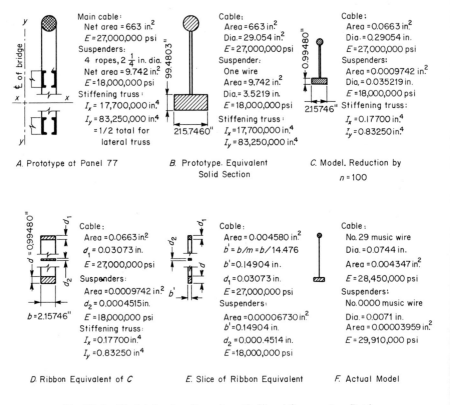

A. Prototype at Panel 77

B. Prototype. Equivalent Solid Section

C. Model. Reduction by $n = 100$

D. Ribbon Equivalent of C

E. Slice of Ribbon Equivalent

F. Actual Model

Fig. 26–2. Model B. San Francisco-Oakland Suspension Bridge.
(Source: University of California Press.)

to a size that would permit the use of commercially available wire, a vertical slice is taken, as shown in Fig. 26–2E. Again, structural action is not altered provided that forces are correspondingly reduced. The divisor, 14.476, is called m, the "slicing" factor.

The slicing factor was determined as follows. Minimum wire size for suspenders was No. 0000 (music-wire gage) for which

$$\text{diameter} = 0.0071 \text{ in.}$$

$$\text{area} = 0.00003959 \text{ in.}^2$$

$$E = 29,910,000 \text{ psi}$$

It is the elastic equivalent of a wire with $E_p = 18,000,000$ psi when it has an area of

$$A_1 = 0.00003959 \times \frac{29,910,000}{18,000,000} = 0.000065785 \text{ in.}^2$$

From this, it follows that m should be about

$$m = \frac{\text{ribbon area of suspender}}{\text{elastic equivalent area, } A_1} = \frac{0.0009742}{0.000065785} = 14.8088$$

The area of the main cable should be

$$\frac{\text{Ribbon area of main cable}}{m} = \frac{0.0663}{14.8088} = 0.0044707 \text{ in.}^2$$

But the nearest commercial wire was No. 29 with an area of 0.004347 in.^{2} and an E of 28,450,000 psi. It is elastically equivalent to a wire of $E_p = 27,000,000$ psi and an area of

$$A_2 = 0.00437 \times \frac{28,450,000}{27,000,000} = 0.004580 \text{ in.}^2$$

It was impossible to obtain commercial wire of exactly correct diameters for both suspenders and main cables, so a choice had to be made between maintaining similitude with main cable or with suspenders. There was no doubt. The main cables were the more important. Furthermore, the wire rope used for suspenders in the bridge was subject to some variation in properties which has but little effect on the bridge. The value of m, altered slightly to produce exact similitude between main cables, was

$$m = \frac{\text{ribbon area of cable}}{\text{elastic equivalent area, } A_2} = \frac{0.0663}{0.004580} = 14.476$$

The error thus introduced into the suspender area was only 2.2 percent.

With the introduction of the slicing factor, the model scale reduction factors are not the same as those derived in Art. 26–1. But the methods of Art. 26–1 are entirely valid and adequate for the re-evaluation. For geometrical similitude, the model scale reduction factors are as follows.

Length (arbitrarily chosen)

$$L_p : L = n : 1$$

Equivalent areas (arbitrarily chosen)

$$A_p : A = n^2 m : 1$$

Actual areas (computed above from equivalent areas)

$$A_p : A = n^2 m \frac{E}{E_p} : 1$$

Equivalent moments of inertia. From Art. 26–1, the model scale reduction factor is $n^4 : 1$. Moment of inertia is directly proportional to width, so for a slice $1/m$ as wide as the whole, the model scale reduction factor becomes

$$I_p : I = n^4 m : 1$$

Actual moments of inertia. Once again, model and prototype moduli of elasticity may differ, so by analogy[14] with areas the actual model scale reduction factor becomes

$$I_p:I = n^4m\frac{E}{E_p}:1$$

The model scale reduction factors for mechanical similitude are computed from Eq. 26–6, altered somewhat by the introduction of the slicing factor. In Eq. 26–1 volume is cross-sectional area times length, so the gravitational force ratio is written as

$$\frac{F_p}{F} = \frac{(\text{area})_p}{\text{area}} \times \frac{(\text{length})_p}{\text{length}} \times \frac{(\text{unit weight})_p}{\text{unit weight}}$$

Substituting $n^2mE/E_p:1$ for the ratio of actual areas, and noting that $L_p:L$ equals n, Eq. 26–1 is altered to

$$\frac{F_p}{F} = n^2m\frac{E}{E_p}\,n\frac{w_p}{w} = n^3m\frac{Ew_p}{E_pw} \tag{26–7}$$

Equation 26–2 for inertial force is altered only in the term for volume ratio. Noting $g:g_p$ is unity and $L_p:L$ is n,

$$\frac{F_p}{F} = n^2m\frac{E}{E_p}\,n\frac{w_p}{w}\,n\left(\frac{t}{t_p}\right)^2 = n^4m\frac{Ew_p}{E_pw}\left(\frac{t}{t_p}\right)^2 \tag{26–8}$$

Equation 26–3 is altered only in the term for the cross-sectional area ratio, which, with the slicing factor, is n^2mE/E_p. Strict geometrical similitude requires unit strains in model and prototype to be equal, particularly for large deflections such as those in a suspension bridge. Therefore Eq. 26–3 becomes

$$\frac{F_p}{F} = n^2m\frac{E}{E_p}\frac{1}{1}\frac{E_p}{E} = n^2m \tag{26–9}$$

Combining Eqs. 26–7, 26–8, and 26–9, we obtain

$$\frac{F_p}{F} = C = n^3m\frac{Ew_p}{E_pw} = n^4m\frac{Ew_p}{E_pw}\left(\frac{t}{t_p}\right)^2 = n^2m \tag{26–10}$$

The model scale reduction ratios are computed from Eq. 26–10 in exactly the same manner as those obtained from Eq. 26–6. In summary, they are:

Force $\qquad\qquad F_p:F = n^2m:1$

Unit weight $\qquad w_p:w = \dfrac{1}{n}\dfrac{E_p}{E}:1$

Time $\qquad\qquad t_p:t = n:1$

[14] An analogy does not *have* to be used. The equivalent moments of inertia can be computed in much the same way as were equivalent areas by making use of the fact that the stiffness of the actual model must be elastically equivalent to the stiffness of a theoretical one built of prototype steel.

Fig. 26–3. A model of the San Francisco-Oakland Suspension Bridge. (Courtesy of University of California Press.)

Other factors can be computed as follows:

Moment of force (equals force times length) $M_p:M = n^3m$

Unit stress (equals unit strain times modulus) $S_p:S = E_p:E$

One more set of dimensions requires careful consideration. Deflections caused by wind were required. Therefore, moments of inertia about the vertical axis as well as those about the horizontal axis had to be properly proportioned, and this was done simply by applying the model scale reduction factor for moment of inertia, $n^4mE/E_p:1$ to both axes. If we assume[15] (for the purpose of illustration only) that $E_p = 29,000,000$ psi and $E = 28,400,000$ psi,

$$n^4m \frac{E}{E_p} = (100)^4 14.476 \times \frac{28,400,000}{29,000,000} = 1.418 \times 10^9$$

The width b and the depth d of the model truss can then be computed by solving the following equations simultaneously:

$$I_x = \frac{17,700,000}{1.418 \times 10^9} = \frac{b^3d}{12}$$

$$I_y = \frac{83,250,000}{1.418 \times 10^9} = \frac{db^3}{12}$$

from which we find

$$d = 0.513$$

$$b = 1.111$$

In reality, a constant depth of 0.500 in. was used with widths varying from 0.930 to 1.195 in. The correspondence to the varying prototype values was actually very close. One of the models is shown in Fig. 26–3.

The results of this investigation were excellent. Comparison with theoretical results showed variations from 0 to 12 percent. Since the deflection theory is known to be slightly in error (due to the omission in basic equations of certain factors such as stretch of suspenders, variable moment of inertia of stiffening trusses, and resistance of towers to longitudinal bending), it seems safe to assume that these differences primarily represent errors in the deflection theory—not errors in the model tests.[16]

[15] These values are not given in the report by Beggs, Davis, and Davis.
[16] Ibid., p. 145.

27

COMPUTED INFLUENCE LINES

27–1. Introduction. The use of influence lines is often the best way to analyze a structure (such as a bridge) which is subjected to moving live loads. They offer two advantages over analyses for a series of fixed loads:

1. Once obtained, they permit very quick determination of stresses for different load conditions.
2. They indicate the portion of the structure that should be loaded to produce maximum stresses.

The second reason is less important than the first, since influence lines for a great many different structures have been constructed, and engineers generally know which portion must be loaded to produce maximum stresses.

Influence lines can be determined analytically by two methods: (1) A unit load can be placed at successive locations and for each location its influence on the desired stress can be obtained; and (2) the concept of influence lines as elastic curves can be utilized. The first may occasionally be the more rapid but, in general, it is unimaginative. A sensitive engineer might feel it lacks elegance. The second way consists of applying the methods of statically indeterminate structural analysis (for example, moment area, virtual work, moment distribution, neutral point) to calculate the elastic curves produced by imposed unit deformations (as embodied in Arts. 25–1 through 25–5). In other words, unit distortions are produced just as with wire models, but the elastic curves are obtained mathematically rather than mechanically. The term "mathematical models" might be applied to such a concept.

All of the methods explained in Parts II, III, IV, and V can be used to obtain the elastic curves. Moment distribution can be used only to a limited extent by finding rotations of the elastic curve at supports and joints. Nevertheless, the importance of the rotations overshadows the limitations so that moment distribution is quite often the most rapid solution.

27–2. Moment Area. *Example* 27–2. *Influence Line for Shear.* To construct an influence line for shear at the quarter-point of a fixed-ended beam, as shown in Fig. 27–1*A*, the beam is cut, and the cut ends are moved a unit distance apart by shearing forces, as shown in Fig. 27–1*B*. To produce shearing distortion only, moments are required to prevent relative rotation.

A. Beam Cut at Quarter Point

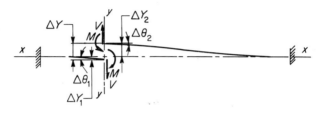

B. Deformed Beam

C. Moment Diagrams

Fig. 27–1. Influence line for shear.

The relation between M and V can be found by using Eq. 4–22:

$$\Delta\theta = \sum A_{MD/EI} + \sum \theta \qquad (4\text{–}22)$$
$$+EI\,\Delta\theta_1 = -4M - \tfrac{1}{2} \times 4V \times 4 = -4M - 8V$$
$$-EI\,\Delta\theta_2 = -12M + \tfrac{1}{2} \times 12V \times 12 = -12M + 72V$$

Signs must be carefully determined. $\Delta\theta_2$ is minus because the angle change as shown in Fig. 27–1B is concave downward—negative according to the convention already adopted for $\Delta\theta_1$. Relative rotation is zero, so we have

$$\Delta\theta_1 = \Delta\theta_2$$
$$-4M - 8V = +12M - 72V$$
$$M = 4V$$

Now each deflection can be found and added to produce the relative deflection. Let x be plus to the right and minus to the left. Then we have

$$\Delta Y = \sum \bar{x} A_{MD/EI} + \sum x\theta + Y \qquad (4\text{–}20)$$
$$EI\,\Delta Y_1 = -4M(-2) + \tfrac{1}{2}(-4V)4(-\tfrac{8}{3}) = +8M + 64V/3$$
$$EI\,\Delta Y_2 = -12M(+6) + \tfrac{1}{2}(+12V)12(+8) = -72M + 576$$
$$\Delta Y_1 + \Delta Y_2 = \Delta = 1 \qquad \text{and} \qquad M = 4V$$
$$8(4V) + \tfrac{64}{3}V - 72(4V) + 576V = EI$$
$$V = \frac{EI}{341.3}$$

A shearing distortion of unity is not actually required. Any distortion will do if Eq. 25–4 is used. A distortion of unity merely reduces Eq. 25–4 to Eq. 18–4. Instead of solving an unknown V, we might just as well assume a unit value for V and find ΔY.

$$\Delta Y = \Delta Y_1 + \Delta Y_2 = \frac{8(4V)}{EI} + \frac{64V}{3EI} - \frac{72(4V)}{EI} + \frac{576V}{EI} = \frac{341.3}{EI}$$

The calculation of ordinates for the elastic curve is now quite simple. A semi-graphical approach is explained by Shermer.[1]

27–3. Virtual Work. *Example 27–3A. Influence Line for Shear.* Difficulty with signs can be avoided by using virtual work. Using the

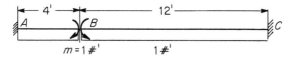

A. Relative Angular Deformation

B. Relative Linear Deformation

Fig. 27–2. Virtual forces and moment diagrams.

moment diagrams of Fig. 27–1C in conjunction with the virtual moment diagrams of Fig. 27–2 for relative rotation and relative shear, we find the sum of all the virtual work. Signs are automatic, provided the same convention is used for both real and virtual moments. We have

$$U \, \Delta\theta_{\text{relative}} = \sum \bar{m} A_{MD/EI} \qquad (8\text{–}4)$$

$$1 \, \#\text{-ft} \; \Delta\theta_{\text{relative}} = 0 = (-1 \, \#\text{-ft})(-4M) + (-1 \, \#\text{-ft})(-8V)$$
$$+ (-1 \, \#\text{-ft})(-12M) + (-1 \, \#\text{-ft})(+72V)$$

$$M = 4V$$

as before; and

$$U \Delta Y_{\text{relative}} = \sum \bar{m} A_{MD/EI} \qquad (8\text{–}3)$$

$$1 \, \# \; \Delta Y_{\text{relative}} = 1 \, \# = \frac{(-2 \, \#\text{-ft})(-4M)}{EI} + \frac{(-8/3 \, \#\text{-ft})(-8V)}{EI}$$
$$+ \frac{(+6 \, \#\text{-ft})(-12M)}{EI} + \frac{(+8 \, \#\text{-ft})(+72V)}{EI}$$

[1] Carl L. Shermer, *Fundamentals of Statically Indeterminate Structures* (New York: The Ronald Press Co., 1957), pp. 221–226.

Substituting $M = 4V$ gives

$$EI = 32V + \tfrac{64}{3}V - 288V + 576V$$

$$V = \frac{EI}{341.3}$$

as before.

Example 27–3B. Influence Line for Moment. The influence line for moment can be constructed in much the same way. The beam is cut, and

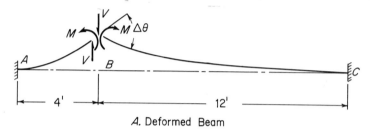

A. Deformed Beam

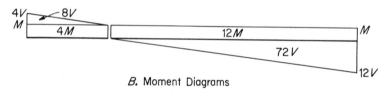

B. Moment Diagrams

Fig. 27–3. Influence line for moment.

moments are applied at the cut ends to produce a relative rotation. Since the moments must be equal and opposite to satisfy conditions for static equilibrium, the portion BC in Fig. 27–3 will deflect more because it is longer than portion AB. Therefore forces must also be applied to the cut ends to bring them together. These forces must be equal and opposite so that the juncture of cut ends can "float" without external restraint as would be done with a model.

The relative linear displacement is zero. Combining the moment diagrams of Fig. 27–3B with the virtual moment diagrams of Fig. 27–2B, we have

$$U \, \Delta Y_{\text{relative}} = \sum \bar{m}A_{MD/EI} \tag{8–3}$$

$$1 \,\#\, \Delta Y_{\text{relative}} = 0 = (-2\,\#\text{-ft})(+4M) + (-\tfrac{8}{3}\,\#\text{-ft})(+8V)$$
$$+ (+6\,\#\text{-ft})(+12M) + (+8\,\#\text{-ft})(-72V)$$
$$V = \tfrac{3}{28}M$$

The relative rotation between the cut ends is unity, so combining the moment diagrams of Fig. 27–3B with the virtual moment diagrams of Fig. 27–2A and setting V equal to $\frac{3}{28}M$, we have

$$U\,\Delta\theta_{\text{relative}} = \sum \bar{m}A_{MD/EI} \qquad (8\text{–}4)$$

$$1\,\#\text{-ft }\Delta\theta_{\text{relative}} = 1\,\#\text{-ft} = \frac{-1\,\#\text{-ft}}{EI}\times 4M + \frac{-1\,\#\text{-ft}}{EI}\times 8 \times \frac{3}{28}M$$

$$+ \frac{-1\,\#\text{-ft}}{EI}\times 12M + \frac{-1\,\#\text{-ft}}{EI}\left(-72 \times \frac{3M}{28}\right)$$

$$M = \frac{7EI}{64}$$

With M and V known, the ordinates of the influence line can be calculated easily, since each part of the beam can be treated separately as a simple cantilever loaded at the end with M and V.

27–4. Other Methods. Other methods can be used just as well. Double integration yields the equation of the elastic curve (influence line) directly and is often preferable for just that reason. The conjugate-beam method and the column analogy are popular. The elastic-center method is widely used because of the relation between the direction of forces and movements.[2,3] The computation of influence lines for beams and rigid frames that are statically indeterminate to many degrees is very tedious, and for such problems moment distribution can be used to advantage, as shown in the following article.

27–5. Influence Lines by Moment Distribution. There are two methods by which moment distribution can be used to construct influence lines: (1) Placing unit loads in successive locations and (2) constructing elastic curves. The first method can be quite tedious unless a shortcut is used. Every position of the unit load causes two fixed-end moments. These fixed-end moments must be computed for every new position of the load, it is true, but it is not necessary to distribute them every time. It is much quicker, instead, to distribute a single, unit, fixed-end moment (at one point only), and to obtain the function (reaction, shear, moment, etc., for which the influence line is constructed) in terms of that unit fixed-end moment. Now apply a unit load at some position and compute one of the fixed-end moments therefrom. The influence-line ordinate can be obtained directly by multiplying the known function for the unit fixed-end moment by the actual fixed-end moment. Repeat the procedure for the other fixed-end moment and add the

---

[2] *Ibid.*, pp. 233–235.

[3] Conde B. McCullough and Edward S. Thayer, *Elastic Arch Bridges* (New York: John Wiley & Sons, Inc., 1931).

results algebraically.[4] This simple type of shortcut can be used advantageously not only for influence lines but any time there are several different loading conditions in a moment distribution problem.

The second method is to introduce a unit distortion and construct the resulting elastic curve. The only purpose of the moment distribution is to obtain the rotations at the joints, which is done by adding all the *balancing moments only* and dividing by the stiffness, as explained in Art. 12–3. When the rotation at each end of a member is known, the elastic curve can be

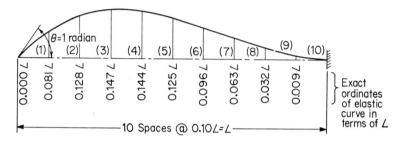

Fig. 27–4. Elastic curve of prismatic beam rotated 1 radian at one end.

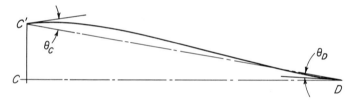

Fig. 27–5. Elastic curve due to deflection and rotation at both ends.

quickly constructed. Here, too, it saves time to determine the elastic curve for a unit rotation at one end of a member, as in Fig. 27–4. For any other rotation, such as 0.00023 radian, for example, the ordinates of Fig. 27–4 are multiplied by 0.00023. The equation of the elastic curve of a prismatic beam rotated 1 radian at one end, easily found by double integration, makes it simple to find the ordinate at any point. The equation is

$$y = \frac{x^3}{L^2} - \frac{2x^2}{L} + x \qquad (26\text{–}7)$$

where x is measured in terms of the span L from the rotated end. When both ends rotate, the elastic curves for the end rotations are simply added algebraically. If one end deflects, as in Fig. 27–5, the ordinates can be found as the sum of the ordinates for (1) the straight line $C'D$, (2) the elastic curve for the left end *rotated θ_C from the straight line $C'D$*, plus (3) the elastic curve for the right end *rotated θ_D from the straight line $C'D$*. Influence lines can thus be

[4] J. Sterling Kinney, *Indeterminate Structural Analysis* (Reading, Mass: Addison-Wesley Publishing Company, Inc., 1957), pp. 526–535.

easily and fairly rapidly assembled piece by piece from simple elastic curves. They can be plotted on graph paper to a large scale, and the plotted points can be connected with a french curve or a spline. The accuracy is good, provided enough points (ten are sufficient) are plotted for each span.

INTERNAL FORCES AND MOMENTS. Influence lines for shear and moment between supports are constructed nearly as easily as those for a reaction. To construct an influence line for moment at point C of the beam in Fig. 27–6,

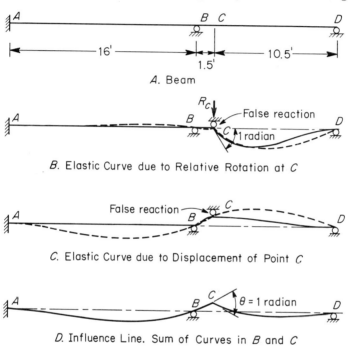

A. Beam

B. Elastic Curve due to Relative Rotation at C

C. Elastic Curve due to Displacement of Point C

D. Influence Line. Sum of Curves in B and C

Fig. 27–6. Influence line for M_C computed by moment distribution.

introduce a temporary or false reaction at point C and a unit angle change, as shown by the solid line in Fig. 27–6B. Note that the fixed-end moments are $M_{CD} = K_{CD}$ and $M_{DC} = K_{CD}C_{CD}$. Distribute the moments using *un-modified* stiffnesses and carry-over factors. This means you will have to balance joint D again and again. The rotation of any member at a joint is the sum only of the balancing moments divided by K. The beam now takes the shape shown by the dashed line in Fig. 27–6B. The false reaction is removed exactly as in a sidesway problem. Holding the joints fixed against rotation, deflect the false reaction some definite amount, as shown by the solid line in Fig. 27–6C, and compute the fixed-end moments. Distribute them, compute the force at the false reaction, and correct it to make it equal to R_C in Fig. 27–6B. The rotation of any member equals the thus *corrected* sum of balancing moments divided by K. Add the two curves (dashed lines in Figs. 27–6B and 27–6C corrected) together to obtain the curve in Fig. 27–6D. Note that the ordinates for any of these elastic curves can be computed (as previously explained) from the known end rotations and corrected deflections.

The influence line for shear is constructed in a similar manner by introducing a false reaction and a unit shearing distortion, as shown in Fig. 27–7A. There are fixed-end moments at CD and DC. These are distributed exactly as before, with the use of exactly the same distribution factors. The fact that

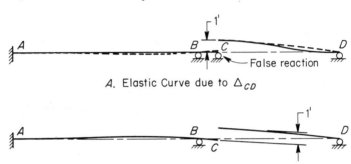

A. Elastic Curve due to Δ_{CD}

B. Influence Line. Sum of Fig. 27-7A and Fig. 27-6C Reduced

Fig. 27–7. Influence line for V_C computed by moment distribution.

the beam is cut and separated at point C does not change the distribution factors or the procedure. After the rotations have been found, the remainder of the work—removing the false reaction—is exactly the same as that given for Fig. 27–6C.

27–6. Complex Structures. The purpose of the following discussion is twofold: to extend the treatment of influence lines to more complex problems and to suggest—only suggest—the possibilities involved in using a combination of methods to shorten the work. These are vast subjects, and more than a glimpse is not intended. The methods encountered in this discussion are well adapted to this type of problem and give comparatively rapid solutions.

Example 27–6. *Tied Arch Truss.* A tied arch truss is shown in Fig. 27–8A. The influence line for any member can be solved by equations of static equilibrium if the influence lines for two reactions and the elastic tie are first constructed. There are three redundants, and various members and reactions can be chosen for the redundants. We shall consider R_A, R_B, and the elastic tie as redundants, leaving the cut-back structure shown in Fig. 27–8B. The steps in a solution by virtual work are as follows:

1. Apply a vertical 1-# virtual force at point A, and calculate the (now statically determinate) u forces in all members. The tie is cut and, therefore, receives no force. Then the forces due to R_A equal $R_A u_A = F_A$.

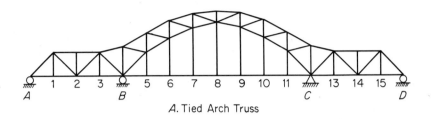

A. Tied Arch Truss

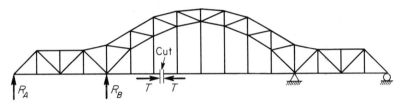

B. Cut-Back Structure and Redundant Forces

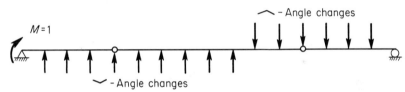

C. Conjugate Beam for Influence Line for R_A

D. Conjugate Beam for Influence Line for R_B

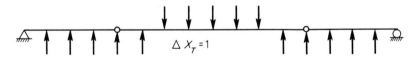

E. Conjugate Beam for Influence Line for T

Fig. 27–8. Influence lines for a complex truss.

2. Apply a vertical 1-# virtual force at point B and calculate the (now statically determinate) u forces in all members (except the tie, of course, which is cut). Then the forces due to R_B equal $R_B u_B = F_B$.

3. Apply equal and opposite 1-# u forces to the cut ends of the tie, creating a force of $1\#$ throughout the tie. Calculate the u forces in all the members. Then the forces due to the force T in the tie bar are $T u_T = F_T$.

4. The total force in any member is the force due to R_A plus that due to R_B plus that due to T, or

$$F = F_A + F_B + F_T = R_A u_A + R_B u_B + F_T u_T$$

To compute the influence line for R_A, use the expression

$$U\Delta = \sum u \frac{FL}{AE} \tag{7-6}$$

$$1 \# \Delta Y_A = 1 = \sum u_A \frac{FL}{AE}$$

where $F = R_A u_A + R_B u_B + F_T u_T$.

To solve the indeterminate forces, write as many elastic equations as redundants. Therefore,

$$1 \# \Delta Y_B = 0 = \sum u_B \frac{FL}{AE}$$

The cut faces of the elastic tie do not move relative to each other, so

$$1 \# \Delta X_T = 0 = \sum u_T \frac{FL}{AE}$$

These equations are solved for R_A, R_B, and T.

5. If there were more redundants, they would be cut, and a virtual force would be applied for each in turn, as in steps 1 through 3. The total force in any member would be

$$F = R_A u_A + R_B u_B + F_T u_T + \cdots + R_N u_N$$

In step 5, as many elastic equations are required as there are redundants, leading to the nth equation

$$\Delta N = 0 = \sum u_N \frac{(R_A u_A + R_B u_B + F_T u_T + \cdots + R_N u_N)L}{AE}$$

These equations are sufficient to evaluate R_A, R_B, T, $\cdots$, R_N.

6. The influence line for R_A may be computed by drawing a Williot-Mohr diagram, but it is inaccurate when there are so many members. It can be corrected by virtual work as explained in Art. 17-4, or it can be abandoned altogether in favor of the method of elastic weights. The elastic weights are applied to the conjugate beam in Fig. 27-8C. Note that the external simple supports remain so in the conjugate beam, the internal simple supports become hinges in the conjugate beam, and, since the left support deflects unity upward, there is a moment of unity applied to the conjugate beam. The elastic loads are the angle changes of the bottom chord determined either by algebra (Art. 20-6) or by small separate Williot diagrams of each joint. If the angle change is

concave upward, the elastic load is applied upward in the sign convention adopted here. The conjugate beam is, of course, determinate and its moment diagram is the influence line for R_A. As proved in Art. 20-6, there is no error introduced by making the conjugate beam straight instead of arched like the lower chord of the truss.

7. To obtain the influence line for R_B, write the elastic equations in the form

$$1 \# \Delta Y_A = 0 = \sum u_A \frac{FL}{AE}$$

$$1 \# \Delta Y_B = 1 = \sum u_B \frac{FL}{AE}$$

$$1 \# \Delta X_T = 0 = \sum u_T \frac{FL}{AE}$$

where $F = R_A u_A + R_B u_B + F_T u_T$. The equations are solved and the angle changes computed as before. The conjugate beam is shown in Fig. 27-8D. Because the deflection at B is unity, moments of unity must be applied to the conjugate beam.

8. To obtain the influence line for the force T in the elastic tie, write the elastic equations in the form

$$1 \# \Delta Y_A = 0 = \sum u_A \frac{FL}{AE}$$

$$1 \# \Delta Y_B = 0 = \sum u_B \frac{FL}{AE}$$

$$1 \# \Delta X_T = 1 = \sum u_T \frac{FL}{AE}$$

Again, $F = R_A u_A + R_B u_B + F_T u_T$. Again the angle changes are computed and applied to the conjugate beam, as shown in Fig. 27-8E. Note that the external supports remain simple ones, and the internal supports become hinges so that no moment (and, hence, no deflection in the actual structure) appears at the supports.

9. With influence lines known for the redundants, the reactions are quickly determined for any position of live load. Then the force in any member can be found from considerations of static equilibrium only. Therefore influence lines can be constructed for any member, with the use of principles of static equilibrium only (after influence lines for the redundants have been obtained).

10. It should be recognized that the conjugate beams in Fig. 27-8 could be shown differently. The simple support and the moment at point A in Fig. 27-8C could be replaced with a fixed support. When the conjugate beam is solved for moment at point A, the moment will be found to equal unity since the angle changes were computed for a unit deflection. This provides a check upon the accuracy of the computed angle changes.

In Fig. 27-8D the unit moment could be omitted. Then the beam would be continuous—not hinged—at point B since there is a unit deflection there. When the conjugate beam is solved for moment at point B, the moment will again be found to equal unity, since the angle changes were computed for a unit deflection at this point.

11. If there are only fixed loads applied to the structure, then it is not necessary to compute influence lines, and a direct determination of forces in all members is more quickly obtained by writing the elastic equations in the form

$$1 \mathbin{\#} \Delta Y_A = 0 = \sum u_A \frac{FL}{AE}$$

$$1 \mathbin{\#} \Delta Y_B = 0 = \sum u_B \frac{FL}{AE}$$

$$1 \mathbin{\#} \Delta X_T = 0 = \sum u_T \frac{FL}{AE}$$

If there are other redundants, write as many equations as there are redundants up to

$$1 \mathbin{\#} \Delta Y_N = 0 = \sum u_N \frac{FL}{AE}$$

where $F = R_A u_A + R_B u_B + F_T u_T + \cdots + R_N u_N$. The above equations are sufficient to determine stresses in all members. To find the deflection due to fixed loads, the Williot-Mohr diagram is usually sufficiently accurate if constructed to a large scale. Of course, it may be corrected by computing deflections at one or more points by virtual work. After the forces in all the members are obtained, the redundants may be disregarded in drawing a Williot-Mohr diagram or in computing a deflection by virtual work for the reasons explained in Arts. 7–7 and 8–10.

From a practical point of view, a shortcut is worth while. It results in the solution of only two (instead of three) simultaneous equations, and the tabulation is simpler. In step 4, instead of setting $\Delta Y_A = 1$, let $R_A = 1$. Then, since there are only two unknowns left, only two equations are needed to solve them.

$$1 \mathbin{\#} \Delta Y_B = 0 = \sum u_A \frac{(1 u_A + R_B u_B + F_T u_T)L}{AE}$$

$$1 \mathbin{\#} \Delta X_T = 0 = \sum u_T \frac{(1 u_A + R_B u_B + F_T u_T)L}{AE}$$

With R_B and F_T known, the deflection at point A as well as the deflections at all the other panel points can be computed by means of the conjugate beam. The influence line is obtained by dividing all the deflections by the deflection at point A. This is exactly equivalent to the use of Eq. 25–5.

$$R = \frac{\sum Py}{\Delta_R} \tag{25–5}$$

wherein the elastic curve ordinates y are divided by the deflection at reaction Δ_R.

APPENDIX

A

FRAME CONSTANTS

Nomenclature

a_A = ratio of length of haunch at end A to length of span

a_B = ratio of length of haunch at end B to length of span

b = ratio of distance from loading point to end A to length of span

b_1 = ratio of distance from loading point to end B to length of span

C_{AB} = carry-over factor of member AB at end A

C_{BA} = carry-over factor of member AB at end B

E = modulus of elasticity

h_A = depth of member at end A

h_B = depth of member at end B

h_c = depth of member at minimum section

I_c = moment of inertia of section of minimum depth

I_x = moment of inertia of any section distance x from A or x_1 from B

k_{AB} = stiffness factor of member AB at end A

$K_{AB} = \dfrac{k_{AB}EI_c}{L}$ = stiffness

k_{BA} = stiffness factor of member AB at end B

L = length of member

M_{AB} = fixed-end moment at end A of member AB for any type of loading; used to identify column of *FEM* coefficients in tables

M_{BA} = fixed-end moment at end B of member AB for any type of loading; used to identify column of *FEM* coefficients in tables

P = concentrated load

$r_A = (h_A - h_c)/h_c$ for rectangular cross-section at end A

$r_B = (h_B - h_c)/h_c$ for rectangular cross-section at end B

w = uniform load

W_A = weight of haunch per lin.ft right at end A

W_B = weight of haunch per lin.ft right at end B

x = distance from variable point to end A

x_1 = distance from variable point to end B

The use of the tables of constants is explained in Arts. 14–5 and 14–6. The derivation and use of the integral expressions is given in Art. 10–2. These tables are reproduced by permission from *Handbook of Frame Constants* published by Portland Cement Association.

Parabolic Haunches — Constant Width

TABLE 1

$a_A = 0.1$ a_B = variable $r_A = 0.4$ r_B = variable

Right Haunch		Carry-over Factors		Stiffness Factors		Unif. Load F.E.M. Coef. × vL^2		Concentrated Load F.E.M.—Coef. × PL, b =										Haunch Load at			
								0.1		0.3		0.5		0.7		0.9		Left Coef. × $W_A L^2$		Right Coef. × $W_B L^2$	
a_B	r_B	C_{AB}	C_{BA}	k_{AB}	k_{BA}	M_{AB}	M_{BA}	M_{AB}	M_{BA}	M_{AB}	M_{BA}	M_{AB}	M_{BA}	M_{AB}	M_{BA}	M_{AB}	M_{BA}	M_{AB}	M_{BA}	M_{AB}	M_{BA}
0.1	0.4	0.537	0.537	4.56	4.56	0.0873	0.0873	0.0869	0.0066	0.1583	0.0621	0.1313	0.1313	0.0621	0.1583	0.0066	0.0869	0.0008	0.0000	0.0000	0.0008
	0.6	0.549	0.536	4.60	4.72	0.0860	0.0898	0.0868	0.0069	0.1573	0.0640	0.1293	0.1354	0.0597	0.1630	0.0056	0.0888	0.0008	0.0000	0.0000	0.0008
	1.0	0.566	0.535	4.66	4.94	0.0841	0.0933	0.0866	0.0071	0.1557	0.0668	0.1262	0.1410	0.0563	0.1694	0.0043	0.0913	0.0008	0.0000	0.0000	0.0008
	1.5	0.580	0.534	4.71	5.12	0.0827	0.0964	0.0865	0.0074	0.1547	0.0691	0.1239	0.1459	0.0536	0.1750	0.0033	0.0934	0.0008	0.0000	0.0000	0.0008
	2.0	0.590	0.533	4.74	5.25	0.0817	0.0983	0.0864	0.0076	0.1539	0.0707	0.1223	0.1492	0.0517	0.1786	0.0026	0.0947	0.0008	0.0000	0.0000	0.0008
0.2	0.4	0.572	0.530	4.67	5.04	0.0845	0.0933	0.0866	0.0072	0.1558	0.0674	0.1263	0.1420	0.0568	0.1693	0.0058	0.0885	0.0008	0.0000	0.0002	0.0030
	0.6	0.598	0.528	4.75	5.38	0.0821	0.0981	0.0864	0.0077	0.1538	0.0715	0.1222	0.1503	0.0525	0.1782	0.0046	0.0909	0.0008	0.0000	0.0001	0.0031
	1.0	0.635	0.523	4.87	5.92	0.0786	0.1053	0.0861	0.0084	0.1508	0.0778	0.1162	0.1628	0.0460	0.1914	0.0030	0.0940	0.0008	0.0000	0.0001	0.0032
	1.5	0.667	0.519	4.98	6.39	0.0754	0.1119	0.0857	0.0090	0.1482	0.0828	0.1110	0.1737	0.0406	0.2027	0.0019	0.0961	0.0008	0.0000	0.0001	0.0032
	2.0	0.689	0.516	5.06	6.75	0.0737	0.1157	0.0856	0.0094	0.1464	0.0872	0.1074	0.1815	0.0369	0.2106	0.0013	0.0974	0.0008	0.0000	0.0001	0.0033
0.3	0.4	0.603	0.521	4.75	5.50	0.0827	0.0974	0.0864	0.0078	0.1538	0.0720	0.1226	0.1505	0.0537	0.1763	0.0057	0.0885	0.0008	0.0000	0.0005	0.0064
	0.6	0.642	0.515	4.87	6.08	0.0795	0.1041	0.0861	0.0085	0.1509	0.0782	0.1169	0.1627	0.0479	0.1883	0.0045	0.0910	0.0008	0.0000	0.0004	0.0066
	1.0	0.702	0.506	5.07	7.03	0.0746	0.1147	0.0856	0.0096	0.1463	0.0884	0.1079	0.1824	0.0392	0.2069	0.0029	0.0941	0.0008	0.0000	0.0003	0.0069
	1.5	0.755	0.498	5.25	7.95	0.0702	0.1242	0.0851	0.0107	0.1421	0.0978	0.0998	0.2005	0.0317	0.2233	0.0018	0.0963	0.0008	0.0000	0.0002	0.0071
	2.0	0.793	0.492	5.38	8.67	0.0673	0.1310	0.0847	0.0115	0.1390	0.1049	0.0939	0.2140	0.0265	0.2350	0.0012	0.0975	0.0008	0.0000	0.0001	0.0072
0.4	0.4	0.629	0.510	4.82	5.95	0.0816	0.0998	0.0862	0.0082	0.1524	0.0755	0.1201	0.1564	0.0519	0.1787	0.0058	0.0882	0.0008	0.0000	0.0012	0.0106
	0.6	0.681	0.500	4.97	6.78	0.0778	0.1080	0.0858	0.0091	0.1487	0.0838	0.1131	0.1720	0.0452	0.1921	0.0046	0.0905	0.0008	0.0000	0.0010	0.0111
	1.0	0.764	0.485	5.23	8.25	0.0718	0.1213	0.0851	0.0107	0.1426	0.0979	0.1016	0.1982	0.0358	0.2136	0.0030	0.0937	0.0008	0.0000	0.0007	0.0118
	1.5	0.842	0.472	5.49	9.79	0.0664	0.1339	0.0844	0.0124	0.1368	0.1121	0.0908	0.2238	0.0273	0.2330	0.0019	0.0959	0.0008	0.0000	0.0005	0.0121
	2.0	0.901	0.463	5.69	11.07	0.0625	0.1434	0.0839	0.0137	0.1322	0.1234	0.0827	0.2437	0.0217	0.2468	0.0013	0.0972	0.0008	0.0000	0.0004	0.0124
0.5	0.4	0.648	0.497	4.90	6.39	0.0809	0.1008	0.0860	0.0089	0.1519	0.0783	0.1188	0.1598	0.0511	0.1794	0.0060	0.0876	0.0008	0.0000	0.0023	0.0153
	0.6	0.711	0.481	5.05	7.46	0.0763	0.1099	0.0854	0.0100	0.1468	0.0881	0.1103	0.1779	0.0440	0.1938	0.0047	0.0900	0.0008	0.0000	0.0020	0.0160
	1.0	0.818	0.458	5.36	9.56	0.0698	0.1253	0.0846	0.0120	0.1398	0.1060	0.0971	0.2085	0.0340	0.2152	0.0031	0.0932	0.0008	0.0000	0.0017	0.0171
	1.5	0.922	0.443	5.73	11.92	0.0638	0.1402	0.0838	0.0140	0.1323	0.1251	0.0844	0.2408	0.0253	0.2351	0.0020	0.0955	0.0008	0.0000	0.0011	0.0181
	2.0	1.003	0.429	6.05	14.05	0.0590	0.1524	0.0831	0.0159	0.1263	0.1411	0.0745	0.2667	0.0195	0.2493	0.0014	0.0967	0.0008	0.0000	0.0008	0.0187

TABLE 2

		$a_A = 0.2$			a_B = variable								$r_A = 0.4$				r_B = variable		
0.1	0.4	0.530	0.572	5.04	4.67	0.0933	0.0845	0.0885	0.1693	0.0568	0.1420	0.1263	0.0674	0.1558	0.0072	0.0866	0.0030	0.0002	0.0008
	0.6	0.543	0.571	5.09	4.83	0.0919	0.0870	0.0884	0.1683	0.0587	0.1398	0.1303	0.0649	0.1605	0.0062	0.0886	0.0030	0.0002	0.0008
	1.0	0.560	0.570	5.15	5.06	0.0900	0.0905	0.0883	0.1669	0.0613	0.1367	0.1359	0.0613	0.1671	0.0047	0.0912	0.0030	0.0002	0.0008
	1.5	0.574	0.569	5.21	5.31	0.0884	0.0934	0.0882	0.1657	0.0634	0.1342	0.1406	0.0583	0.1725	0.0036	0.0933	0.0030	0.0002	0.0008
	2.0	0.583	0.568	5.25	5.39	0.0874	0.0953	0.0881	0.1649	0.0649	0.1325	0.1438	0.0563	0.1762	0.0029	0.0945	0.0030	0.0002	0.0008
0.2	0.4	0.565	0.565	5.16	5.16	0.0903	0.0903	0.0883	0.1668	0.0618	0.1367	0.1367	0.0618	0.1668	0.0063	0.0883	0.0030	0.0002	0.0030
	0.6	0.591	0.562	5.26	5.52	0.0878	0.0951	0.0881	0.1648	0.0657	0.1325	0.1449	0.0571	0.1757	0.0050	0.0907	0.0030	0.0001	0.0031
	1.0	0.627	0.558	5.40	6.08	0.0841	0.1022	0.0877	0.1618	0.0715	0.1261	0.1572	0.0502	0.1891	0.0033	0.0938	0.0030	0.0001	0.0032
	1.5	0.659	0.553	5.53	6.59	0.0810	0.1083	0.0875	0.1592	0.0767	0.1207	0.1630	0.0444	0.2005	0.0021	0.0960	0.0030	0.0001	0.0032
	2.0	0.681	0.550	5.62	6.96	0.0789	0.1125	0.0873	0.1573	0.0805	0.1168	0.1759	0.0404	0.2085	0.0014	0.0973	0.0030	0.0002	0.0033
0.3	0.4	0.596	0.555	5.26	5.64	0.0881	0.0943	0.0881	0.1648	0.0661	0.1329	0.1450	0.0585	0.1737	0.0062	0.0883	0.0030	0.0002	0.0064
	0.6	0.634	0.549	5.39	6.24	0.0851	0.1009	0.0877	0.1619	0.0719	0.1269	0.1571	0.0523	0.1858	0.0049	0.0907	0.0030	0.0002	0.0066
	1.0	0.693	0.539	5.64	7.25	0.0799	0.1113	0.0873	0.1573	0.0815	0.1174	0.1765	0.0429	0.2046	0.0032	0.0939	0.0030	0.0002	0.0068
	1.5	0.745	0.531	5.85	8.22	0.0753	0.1208	0.0868	0.1530	0.0905	0.1088	0.1944	0.0348	0.2213	0.0020	0.0961	0.0030	0.0002	0.0071
	2.0	0.783	0.525	6.01	8.98	0.0722	0.1275	0.0865	0.1499	0.0973	0.1025	0.2079	0.0292	0.2331	0.0013	0.0974	0.0030	0.0003	0.0072
0.4	0.4	0.622	0.543	5.34	6.11	0.0873	0.0967	0.0879	0.1634	0.0694	0.1303	0.1507	0.0566	0.1762	0.0063	0.0879	0.0030	0.0002	0.0106
	0.6	0.673	0.533	5.52	6.97	0.0833	0.1047	0.0875	0.1597	0.0771	0.1229	0.1661	0.0494	0.1900	0.0050	0.0903	0.0030	0.0002	0.0110
	1.0	0.755	0.517	5.84	8.52	0.0771	0.1178	0.0868	0.1536	0.0905	0.1108	0.1920	0.0393	0.2116	0.0033	0.0935	0.0030	0.0003	0.0118
	1.5	0.831	0.503	6.15	10.15	0.0713	0.1303	0.0862	0.1476	0.1039	0.0994	0.2174	0.0300	0.2311	0.0021	0.0958	0.0030	0.0003	0.0121
	2.0	0.889	0.493	6.39	11.51	0.0672	0.1396	0.0857	0.1430	0.1147	0.0906	0.2373	0.0237	0.2450	0.0014	0.0971	0.0030	0.0004	0.0124
0.5	0.4	0.640	0.527	5.40	6.58	0.0870	0.0978	0.0877	0.1627	0.0718	0.1286	0.1541	0.0556	0.1768	0.0065	0.0874	0.0030	0.0002	0.0153
	0.6	0.703	0.511	5.60	7.67	0.0823	0.1066	0.0871	0.1579	0.0810	0.1200	0.1718	0.0480	0.1915	0.0051	0.0897	0.0030	0.0002	0.0160
	1.0	0.807	0.488	5.97	9.85	0.0753	0.1214	0.0863	0.1506	0.0979	0.1061	0.2021	0.0371	0.2131	0.0034	0.0929	0.0030	0.0003	0.0171
	1.5	0.910	0.470	6.40	12.38	0.0686	0.1361	0.0855	0.1430	0.1160	0.0928	0.2341	0.0279	0.2326	0.0022	0.0953	0.0030	0.0003	0.0180
	2.0	0.989	0.456	6.74	14.65	0.0632	0.1483	0.0849	0.1369	0.1314	0.0819	0.2601	0.0213	0.2472	0.0015	0.0967	0.0029	0.0003	0.0186

Parabolic Haunches — Constant Width

TABLE 3

$a_A = 0.3$ $r_A = 0.4$ a_B = variable r_B = variable

Right Haunch		Carry-over Factors		Stiffness Factors		Unif. Load F.E.M. Coef. × wL^2		Conc. 0.1		Conc. 0.3		Conc. 0.5		Conc. 0.7		Conc. 0.9		Haunch Load Left Coef. × $W_A L^3$		Haunch Load Right Coef. × $W_B L^3$	
a_B	r_B	C_{AB}	C_{BA}	k_{AB}	k_{BA}	M_{AB}	M_{BA}	M_{AB}	M_{BA}	M_{AB}	M_{BA}	M_{AB}	M_{BA}	M_{AB}	M_{BA}	M_{AB}	M_{BA}	M_{AB}	M_{BA}	M_{AB}	M_{BA}
0.1	0.4	0.521	0.603	5.50	4.75	0.0974	0.0827	0.0885	0.0057	0.1763	0.0537	0.1505	0.1226	0.0720	0.1538	0.0078	0.0864	0.0064	0.0005	0.0000	0.0008
	0.6	0.533	0.602	5.56	4.92	0.0959	0.0851	0.0884	0.0059	0.1752	0.0554	0.1482	0.1265	0.0693	0.1585	0.0066	0.0884	0.0064	0.0005	0.0000	0.0008
	1.0	0.550	0.601	5.64	5.16	0.0939	0.0886	0.0883	0.0062	0.1738	0.0579	0.1450	0.1321	0.0654	0.1652	0.0050	0.0911	0.0064	0.0006	0.0000	0.0008
	1.5	0.564	0.600	5.70	5.36	0.0923	0.0915	0.0882	0.0064	0.1726	0.0600	0.1423	0.1368	0.0623	0.1707	0.0039	0.0931	0.0064	0.0006	0.0000	0.0008
	2.0	0.573	0.599	5.74	5.49	0.0912	0.0935	0.0881	0.0066	0.1718	0.0615	0.1405	0.1400	0.0602	0.1744	0.0031	0.0944	0.0064	0.0006	0.0000	0.0008
0.2	0.4	0.555	0.596	5.64	5.26	0.0943	0.0881	0.0883	0.0062	0.1737	0.0585	0.1450	0.1329	0.0661	0.1648	0.0068	0.0881	0.0064	0.0006	0.0002	0.0030
	0.6	0.580	0.593	5.76	5.63	0.0917	0.0931	0.0880	0.0066	0.1717	0.0622	0.1405	0.1409	0.0611	0.1738	0.0054	0.0905	0.0064	0.0006	0.0001	0.0031
	1.0	0.616	0.588	5.93	6.22	0.0877	0.1002	0.0877	0.0073	0.1686	0.0678	0.1339	0.1532	0.0537	0.1873	0.0035	0.0937	0.0063	0.0007	0.0001	0.0032
	1.5	0.647	0.583	6.07	6.74	0.0845	0.1064	0.0874	0.0078	0.1659	0.0728	0.1282	0.1639	0.0476	0.1988	0.0023	0.0959	0.0063	0.0007	0.0001	0.0032
	2.0	0.669	0.580	6.18	7.12	0.0823	0.1105	0.0872	0.0082	0.1640	0.0764	0.1241	0.1716	0.0433	0.2069	0.0015	0.0973	0.0063	0.0007	0.0000	0.0033
0.3	0.4	0.585	0.585	5.76	5.76	0.0923	0.0923	0.0880	0.0067	0.1717	0.0625	0.1410	0.1410	0.0625	0.1717	0.0067	0.0880	0.0064	0.0006	0.0006	0.0064
	0.6	0.623	0.578	5.92	6.38	0.0888	0.0989	0.0877	0.0073	0.1688	0.0682	0.1347	0.1529	0.0560	0.1839	0.0053	0.0905	0.0063	0.0007	0.0005	0.0066
	1.0	0.681	0.568	6.19	7.42	0.0834	0.1093	0.0872	0.0084	0.1640	0.0774	0.1248	0.1722	0.0460	0.2029	0.0034	0.0938	0.0063	0.0008	0.0003	0.0068
	1.5	0.732	0.559	6.44	8.43	0.0786	0.1187	0.0867	0.0093	0.1597	0.0861	0.1158	0.1901	0.0374	0.2197	0.0021	0.0960	0.0062	0.0009	0.0002	0.0071
	2.0	0.769	0.552	6.62	9.22	0.0753	0.1254	0.0863	0.0101	0.1565	0.0928	0.1092	0.2035	0.0313	0.2317	0.0014	0.0973	0.0062	0.0009	0.0002	0.0072
0.4	0.4	0.610	0.572	5.84	6.23	0.0911	0.0946	0.0879	0.0071	0.1703	0.0657	0.1383	0.1466	0.0607	0.1741	0.0068	0.0876	0.0063	0.0007	0.0015	0.0105
	0.6	0.660	0.561	6.06	7.13	0.0870	0.1026	0.0875	0.0079	0.1666	0.0732	0.1306	0.1618	0.0534	0.1882	0.0054	0.0901	0.0063	0.0007	0.0012	0.0110
	1.0	0.740	0.544	6.42	8.73	0.0805	0.1156	0.0867	0.0094	0.1603	0.0861	0.1180	0.1874	0.0422	0.2100	0.0035	0.0933	0.0062	0.0009	0.0008	0.0118
	1.5	0.815	0.530	6.78	10.43	0.0744	0.1280	0.0861	0.0109	0.1542	0.0992	0.1059	0.2129	0.0323	0.2296	0.0022	0.0957	0.0062	0.0010	0.0006	0.0121
	2.0	0.872	0.519	7.06	11.85	0.0701	0.1374	0.0855	0.0121	0.1494	0.1098	0.0969	0.2328	0.0255	0.2436	0.0015	0.0970	0.0061	0.0012	0.0005	0.0124
0.5	0.4	0.628	0.556	5.93	6.70	0.0904	0.0958	0.0877	0.0076	0.1696	0.0680	0.1366	0.1500	0.0594	0.1743	0.0070	0.0872	0.0063	0.0007	0.0027	0.0153
	0.6	0.690	0.540	6.15	7.83	0.0860	0.1046	0.0871	0.0088	0.1649	0.0769	0.1277	0.1674	0.0515	0.1896	0.0056	0.0895	0.0063	0.0008	0.0023	0.0160
	1.0	0.793	0.513	6.55	10.08	0.0786	0.1191	0.0863	0.0103	0.1576	0.0932	0.1132	0.1974	0.0400	0.2111	0.0037	0.0928	0.0062	0.0009	0.0018	0.0170
	1.5	0.894	0.496	7.06	12.70	0.0713	0.1339	0.0854	0.0125	0.1496	0.1108	0.0989	0.2294	0.0300	0.2312	0.0023	0.0951	0.0061	0.0011	0.0012	0.0180
	2.0	0.970	0.479	7.43	15.08	0.0660	0.1457	0.0847	0.0143	0.1433	0.1258	0.0879	0.2554	0.0231	0.2460	0.0016	0.0966	0.0060	0.0014	0.0009	0.0186

TABLE 4

		$a_A = 0.4$			a_B = variable									$r_A = 0.4$			r_B = variable				
0.1	0.4	0.510	0.629	5.95	4.81	0.0998	0.0816	0.0882	0.0058	0.1787	0.0519	0.1564	0.1201	0.0755	0.1524	0.0082	0.0862	0.0106	0.0012	0.0000	0.0008
	0.6	0.521	0.628	6.01	4.99	0.0984	0.0840	0.0881	0.0060	0.1781	0.0538	0.1540	0.1240	0.0727	0.1571	0.0070	0.0882	0.0106	0.0013	0.0000	0.0008
	1.0	0.538	0.627	6.10	5.23	0.0963	0.0875	0.0879	0.0063	0.1766	0.0563	0.1507	0.1296	0.0687	0.1638	0.0053	0.0910	0.0106	0.0013	0.0000	0.0008
	1.5	0.551	0.626	6.17	5.44	0.0945	0.0904	0.0878	0.0065	0.1754	0.0583	0.1480	0.1342	0.0654	0.1693	0.0041	0.0930	0.0105	0.0014	0.0000	0.0008
	2.0	0.560	0.625	6.22	5.58	0.0934	0.0923	0.0877	0.0067	0.1745	0.0598	0.1461	0.1373	0.0632	0.1730	0.0033	0.0944	0.0105	0.0014	0.0000	0.0008
0.2	0.4	0.543	0.622	6.11	5.34	0.0967	0.0873	0.0879	0.0063	0.1762	0.0566	0.1507	0.1303	0.0694	0.1634	0.0072	0.0879	0.0106	0.0014	0.0002	0.0030
	0.6	0.567	0.618	6.23	5.72	0.0939	0.0920	0.0876	0.0067	0.1744	0.0604	0.1462	0.1383	0.0642	0.1724	0.0057	0.0904	0.0105	0.0014	0.0002	0.0031
	1.0	0.603	0.613	6.42	6.32	0.0899	0.0990	0.0873	0.0074	0.1713	0.0660	0.1393	0.1505	0.0565	0.1860	0.0037	0.0936	0.0104	0.0016	0.0001	0.0032
	1.5	0.633	0.608	6.58	6.86	0.0865	0.1052	0.0870	0.0079	0.1685	0.0709	0.1333	0.1611	0.0500	0.1976	0.0024	0.0959	0.0104	0.0017	0.0001	0.0032
	2.0	0.654	0.604	6.70	7.25	0.0842	0.1094	0.0867	0.0083	0.1666	0.0745	0.1291	0.1688	0.0455	0.2057	0.0016	0.0972	0.0103	0.0018	0.0000	0.0033
0.3	0.4	0.572	0.610	6.23	5.84	0.0946	0.0911	0.0876	0.0068	0.1741	0.0607	0.1466	0.1383	0.0657	0.1703	0.0071	0.0879	0.0105	0.0015	0.0007	0.0063
	0.6	0.609	0.603	6.41	6.48	0.0910	0.0977	0.0873	0.0074	0.1715	0.0663	0.1402	0.1502	0.0589	0.1825	0.0056	0.0904	0.0104	0.0016	0.0005	0.0066
	1.0	0.666	0.592	6.71	7.55	0.0854	0.1081	0.0867	0.0085	0.1666	0.0754	0.1299	0.1693	0.0484	0.2016	0.0036	0.0937	0.0103	0.0018	0.0004	0.0068
	1.5	0.716	0.582	6.99	8.59	0.0803	0.1175	0.0862	0.0095	0.1622	0.0840	0.1205	0.1872	0.0394	0.2186	0.0023	0.0960	0.0102	0.0020	0.0002	0.0070
	2.0	0.752	0.575	7.20	9.41	0.0769	0.1242	0.0858	0.0103	0.1588	0.0906	0.1137	0.2006	0.0330	0.2307	0.0015	0.0973	0.0101	0.0022	0.0002	0.0072
0.4	0.4	0.596	0.596	6.32	6.32	0.0934	0.0934	0.0875	0.0072	0.1730	0.0639	0.1439	0.1439	0.0639	0.1725	0.0072	0.0875	0.0105	0.0015	0.0015	0.0105
	0.6	0.645	0.584	6.56	7.24	0.0891	0.1013	0.0870	0.0080	0.1692	0.0712	0.1359	0.1590	0.0562	0.1867	0.0057	0.0899	0.0104	0.0017	0.0013	0.0110
	1.0	0.723	0.567	6.96	8.89	0.0824	0.1143	0.0863	0.0095	0.1628	0.0839	0.1228	0.1843	0.0444	0.2087	0.0037	0.0932	0.0102	0.0020	0.0008	0.0117
	1.5	0.796	0.551	7.36	10.64	0.0761	0.1268	0.0855	0.0111	0.1566	0.0969	0.1104	0.2099	0.0341	0.2285	0.0024	0.0956	0.0101	0.0024	0.0007	0.0120
	2.0	0.852	0.540	7.67	12.11	0.0715	0.1362	0.0849	0.0124	0.1517	0.1073	0.1008	0.2298	0.0269	0.2426	0.0016	0.0970	0.0100	0.0026	0.0005	0.0124
0.5	0.4	0.614	0.581	6.40	6.78	0.0928	0.0945	0.0873	0.0076	0.1723	0.0660	0.1421	0.1472	0.0627	0.1725	0.0074	0.0870	0.0105	0.0016	0.0028	0.0152
	0.6	0.674	0.561	6.66	7.98	0.0880	0.1032	0.0867	0.0087	0.1678	0.0746	0.1329	0.1644	0.0550	0.1878	0.0059	0.0893	0.0104	0.0018	0.0024	0.0159
	1.0	0.774	0.537	7.17	10.30	0.0802	0.1178	0.0859	0.0105	0.1600	0.0906	0.1178	0.1946	0.0422	0.2097	0.0039	0.0927	0.0102	0.0022	0.0018	0.0169
	1.5	0.872	0.516	7.70	12.97	0.0729	0.1326	0.0849	0.0127	0.1521	0.1081	0.1027	0.2262	0.0320	0.2300	0.0025	0.0950	0.0100	0.0027	0.0014	0.0180
	2.0	0.947	0.499	8.08	15.40	0.0674	0.1443	0.0841	0.0145	0.1456	0.1229	0.0913	0.2522	0.0244	0.2448	0.0017	0.0965	0.0098	0.0031	0.0010	0.0186

Parabolic Haunches—Constant Width

TABLE 5

$a_A = 0.5$ | a_B = variable | $r_A = 0.4$ | r_B = variable

Right Haunch		Carry-over Factors		Stiffness Factors		Unif. Load F.E.M. Coef. × wL^2		Concentrated Load F.E.M.—Coef. × PL										Haunch Load at Left — F.E.M. Coef. × $W_A L^3$		Haunch Load at Right — F.E.M. Coef. × $W_B L^3$	
								b=0.1		b=0.3		b=0.5		b=0.7		b=0.9					
a_B	r_B	C_{AB}	C_{BA}	k_{AB}	k_{BA}	M_{AB}	M_{BA}	M_{AB}	M_{BA}	M_{AB}	M_{BA}	M_{AB}	M_{BA}	M_{AB}	M_{BA}	M_{AB}	M_{BA}	M_{AB}	M_{BA}	M_{AB}	M_{BA}
0.1	0.4	0.497	0.648	6.39	4.90	0.1008	0.0809	0.0876	0.0060	0.1794	0.0511	0.1598	0.1188	0.0783	0.1519	0.0089	0.0860	0.0153	0.0023	0.0000	0.0008
	0.6	0.508	0.647	6.42	5.02	0.0995	0.0834	0.0876	0.0061	0.1784	0.0531	0.1573	0.1223	0.0753	0.1564	0.0074	0.0880	0.0153	0.0025	0.0000	0.0008
	1.0	0.525	0.646	6.51	5.25	0.0972	0.0870	0.0875	0.0064	0.1769	0.0564	0.1542	0.1279	0.0713	0.1627	0.0056	0.0909	0.0152	0.0027	0.0000	0.0008
	1.5	0.538	0.645	6.59	5.47	0.0956	0.0900	0.0874	0.0066	0.1756	0.0582	0.1512	0.1324	0.0682	0.1682	0.0043	0.0929	0.0151	0.0029	0.0000	0.0008
	2.0	0.545	0.644	6.64	5.60	0.0943	0.0916	0.0873	0.0068	0.1745	0.0588	0.1493	0.1354	0.0663	0.1720	0.0035	0.0943	0.0151	0.0031	0.0000	0.0008
0.2	0.4	0.527	0.640	6.58	5.40	0.0978	0.0870	0.0874	0.0065	0.1768	0.0556	0.1541	0.1286	0.0718	0.1627	0.0077	0.0877	0.0153	0.0026	0.0002	0.0030
	0.6	0.552	0.636	6.69	5.77	0.0952	0.0914	0.0872	0.0068	0.1746	0.0595	0.1494	0.1366	0.0664	0.1717	0.0060	0.0902	0.0152	0.0028	0.0002	0.0031
	1.0	0.589	0.632	6.86	6.38	0.0911	0.0985	0.0869	0.0075	0.1713	0.0658	0.1425	0.1487	0.0585	0.1858	0.0039	0.0935	0.0150	0.0030	0.0001	0.0032
	1.5	0.617	0.626	7.04	6.93	0.0877	0.1045	0.0866	0.0080	0.1685	0.0706	0.1360	0.1593	0.0521	0.1971	0.0025	0.0958	0.0149	0.0033	0.0001	0.0032
	2.0	0.636	0.623	7.19	7.37	0.0852	0.1088	0.0863	0.0084	0.1669	0.0736	0.1317	0.1669	0.0470	0.2048	0.0017	0.0971	0.0148	0.0035	0.0001	0.0033
0.3	0.4	0.556	0.628	6.70	5.93	0.0958	0.0904	0.0872	0.0070	0.1743	0.0594	0.1500	0.1366	0.0680	0.1696	0.0076	0.0877	0.0153	0.0027	0.0007	0.0063
	0.6	0.593	0.620	6.88	6.55	0.0922	0.0973	0.0869	0.0075	0.1714	0.0653	0.1433	0.1485	0.0607	0.1820	0.0059	0.0902	0.0151	0.0030	0.0005	0.0066
	1.0	0.648	0.609	7.18	7.62	0.0867	0.1077	0.0862	0.0086	0.1667	0.0748	0.1329	0.1674	0.0501	0.2015	0.0038	0.0936	0.0149	0.0032	0.0004	0.0068
	1.5	0.694	0.600	7.46	8.65	0.0813	0.1170	0.0857	0.0097	0.1620	0.0834	0.1229	0.1853	0.0411	0.2181	0.0024	0.0959	0.0147	0.0036	0.0002	0.0070
	2.0	0.731	0.591	7.69	9.55	0.0778	0.1236	0.0853	0.0105	0.1585	0.0897	0.1158	0.1987	0.0341	0.2299	0.0016	0.0972	0.0145	0.0039	0.0002	0.0072
0.4	0.4	0.581	0.614	6.78	6.40	0.0945	0.0928	0.0870	0.0074	0.1725	0.0627	0.1472	0.1421	0.0660	0.1723	0.0076	0.0873	0.0152	0.0028	0.0016	0.0105
	0.6	0.628	0.602	7.03	7.33	0.0901	0.1008	0.0865	0.0082	0.1690	0.0703	0.1390	0.1573	0.0583	0.1862	0.0060	0.0897	0.0150	0.0032	0.0014	0.0109
	1.0	0.703	0.586	7.43	8.95	0.0834	0.1137	0.0858	0.0098	0.1627	0.0833	0.1255	0.1824	0.0461	0.2080	0.0039	0.0930	0.0148	0.0036	0.0009	0.0116
	1.5	0.771	0.568	7.85	10.80	0.0771	0.1262	0.0849	0.0113	0.1561	0.0959	0.1128	0.2080	0.0356	0.2280	0.0026	0.0955	0.0145	0.0042	0.0007	0.0120
	2.0	0.827	0.556	8.19	12.26	0.0723	0.1357	0.0843	0.0126	0.1512	0.1062	0.1026	0.2279	0.0276	0.2420	0.0017	0.0969	0.0142	0.0047	0.0005	0.0124
0.5	0.4	0.599	0.599	6.84	6.84	0.0937	0.0937	0.0866	0.0076	0.1718	0.0652	0.1451	0.1451	0.0652	0.1718	0.0076	0.0866	0.0150	0.0030	0.0030	0.0150
	0.6	0.656	0.581	7.14	8.07	0.0889	0.1023	0.0861	0.0087	0.1673	0.0739	0.1360	0.1622	0.0568	0.1861	0.0061	0.0892	0.0148	0.0035	0.0026	0.0158
	1.0	0.753	0.554	7.66	10.42	0.0811	0.1170	0.0853	0.0107	0.1595	0.0898	0.1205	0.1924	0.0442	0.2087	0.0040	0.0926	0.0145	0.0042	0.0020	0.0169
	1.5	0.849	0.531	8.21	13.15	0.0738	0.1319	0.0843	0.0128	0.1515	0.1070	0.1052	0.2239	0.0332	0.2293	0.0026	0.0949	0.0141	0.0050	0.0014	0.0179
	2.0	0.924	0.514	8.67	15.59	0.0682	0.1436	0.0835	0.0147	0.1449	0.1217	0.0933	0.2499	0.0256	0.2441	0.0018	0.0964	0.0138	0.0057	0.0011	0.0185

TABLE 6

		$a_A = 0.1$		a_B = variable										$r_A = 0.6$				r_B = variable				
0.1	0.4	0.536	0.549	4.72	4.60	0.0898	0.0860	0.0888	0.0056	0.1630	0.0597	0.1354	0.1293	0.0640	0.1573	0.0069	0.0868	0.0008	0.0000	0.0000	0.0008	0.0030
	0.6	0.548	0.548	4.76	4.76	0.0885	0.0885	0.0887	0.0058	0.1620	0.0616	0.1333	0.1333	0.0616	0.1620	0.0058	0.0887	0.0008	0.0000	0.0000	0.0008	0.0031
	1.0	0.566	0.547	4.82	4.98	0.0867	0.0921	0.0886	0.0062	0.1606	0.0643	0.1303	0.1390	0.0581	0.1686	0.0044	0.0913	0.0008	0.0000	0.0000	0.0008	0.0032
	1.5	0.580	0.546	4.87	5.17	0.0852	0.0950	0.0885	0.0063	0.1594	0.0665	0.1278	0.1437	0.0553	0.1740	0.0034	0.0933	0.0008	0.0000	0.0000	0.0008	0.0032
	2.0	0.589	0.545	4.90	5.30	0.0842	0.0969	0.0884	0.0065	0.1586	0.0681	0.1262	0.1470	0.0534	0.1777	0.0027	0.0946	0.0008	0.0000	0.0000	0.0008	0.0033
0.2	0.4	0.571	0.543	4.83	5.09	0.0870	0.0919	0.0886	0.0062	0.1605	0.0649	0.1303	0.1398	0.0587	0.1683	0.0060	0.0884	0.0008	0.0002	0.0000	0.0008	0.0064
	0.6	0.597	0.540	4.92	5.44	0.0846	0.0967	0.0884	0.0065	0.1585	0.0688	0.1261	0.1481	0.0542	0.1772	0.0047	0.0908	0.0008	0.0001	0.0000	0.0008	0.0066
	1.0	0.634	0.535	5.05	5.98	0.0810	0.1038	0.0881	0.0071	0.1555	0.0749	0.1200	0.1605	0.0476	0.1905	0.0031	0.0939	0.0008	0.0001	0.0000	0.0008	0.0069
	1.5	0.666	0.531	5.16	6.47	0.0780	0.1100	0.0878	0.0076	0.1529	0.0802	0.1147	0.1714	0.0420	0.2018	0.0020	0.0961	0.0008	0.0001	0.0000	0.0008	0.0071
	2.0	0.688	0.528	5.24	6.83	0.0760	0.1142	0.0877	0.0080	0.1511	0.0840	0.1110	0.1791	0.0382	0.2097	0.0013	0.0973	0.0008	0.0000	0.0000	0.0008	0.0072
0.3	0.4	0.602	0.533	4.92	5.56	0.0851	0.0959	0.0884	0.0066	0.1585	0.0693	0.1265	0.1482	0.0554	0.1752	0.0059	0.0884	0.0008	0.0005	0.0000	0.0008	0.0106
	0.6	0.641	0.527	5.05	6.14	0.0819	0.1026	0.0881	0.0072	0.1556	0.0753	0.1207	0.1604	0.0495	0.1873	0.0046	0.0909	0.0008	0.0004	0.0000	0.0008	0.0110
	1.0	0.701	0.518	5.25	7.11	0.0769	0.1131	0.0876	0.0082	0.1510	0.0852	0.1115	0.1799	0.0406	0.2060	0.0030	0.0940	0.0008	0.0003	0.0000	0.0008	0.0118
	1.5	0.754	0.509	5.44	8.05	0.0725	0.1226	0.0872	0.0091	0.1469	0.0944	0.1033	0.1980	0.0329	0.2225	0.0019	0.0962	0.0008	0.0002	0.0000	0.0008	0.0121
	2.0	0.792	0.504	5.59	8.79	0.0695	0.1293	0.0869	0.0098	0.1437	0.1014	0.0970	0.2115	0.0275	0.2342	0.0012	0.0975	0.0008	0.0001	0.0000	0.0008	0.0124
0.4	0.4	0.628	0.521	4.96	6.00	0.0840	0.0984	0.0882	0.0070	0.1571	0.0727	0.1240	0.1540	0.0538	0.1781	0.0060	0.0881	0.0008	0.0013	0.0000	0.0008	0.0153
	0.6	0.680	0.511	5.15	6.85	0.0803	0.1064	0.0879	0.0078	0.1535	0.0807	0.1168	0.1695	0.0472	0.1917	0.0047	0.0904	0.0008	0.0011	0.0000	0.0008	0.0159
	1.0	0.763	0.496	5.43	8.40	0.0742	0.1196	0.0873	0.0092	0.1474	0.0945	0.1052	0.1956	0.0371	0.2132	0.0031	0.0936	0.0008	0.0007	0.0000	0.0008	0.0170
	1.5	0.841	0.483	5.71	9.93	0.0687	0.1321	0.0867	0.0106	0.1415	0.1082	0.0941	0.2211	0.0283	0.2323	0.0020	0.0959	0.0008	0.0005	0.0000	0.0008	0.0180
	2.0	0.899	0.474	5.93	11.25	0.0647	0.1415	0.0862	0.0117	0.1370	0.1193	0.0857	0.2413	0.0223	0.2460	0.0013	0.0972	0.0008	0.0004	0.0000	0.0008	0.0187
0.5	0.4	0.647	0.508	5.02	6.42	0.0834	0.0995	0.0880	0.0074	0.1564	0.0753	0.1223	0.1573	0.0531	0.1784	0.0061	0.0876	0.0008	0.0025	0.0000	0.0008	
	0.6	0.710	0.494	5.23	7.55	0.0794	0.1086	0.0876	0.0084	0.1516	0.0850	0.1139	0.1753	0.0461	0.1929	0.0048	0.0900	0.0008	0.0022	0.0000	0.0008	
	1.0	0.817	0.471	5.57	9.67	0.0725	0.1236	0.0868	0.0102	0.1447	0.1024	0.1008	0.2059	0.0357	0.2140	0.0032	0.0932	0.0008	0.0018	0.0000	0.0008	
	1.5	0.920	0.452	5.97	12.10	0.0660	0.1384	0.0862	0.0121	0.1372	0.1210	0.0876	0.2377	0.0267	0.2343	0.0021	0.0955	0.0008	0.0012	0.0000	0.0008	
	2.0	1.001	0.439	6.30	14.25	0.0610	0.1498	0.0855	0.0136	0.1311	0.1368	0.0775	0.2640	0.0205	0.2486	0.0014	0.0967	0.0008	0.0009	0.0000	0.0008	

Parabolic Haunches—Constant Width

TABLE 7

$a_A = 0.2$ a_B = variable $r_A = 0.6$ r_B = variable

Right Haunch		Carry-over Factors		Stiffness Factors		Unif. Load F.E.M. Coef. × uL^2		Concentrated Load F.E.M.—Coef. × PL										Haunch Load at			
												b						Left F.E.M. Coef. × $W_A L^2$		Right F.E.M. Coef. × $W_B L^2$	
								0.1		0.3		0.5		0.7		0.9					
a_B	r_B	C_{AB}	C_{BA}	k_{AB}	k_{BA}	M_{AB}	M_{BA}	M_{AB}	M_{BA}	M_{AB}	M_{BA}	M_{AB}	M_{BA}	M_{AB}	M_{BA}	M_{AB}	M_{BA}	M_{AB}	M_{BA}	M_{AB}	M_{BA}
0.1	0.4	0.528	0.598	5.38	4.75	0.0981	0.0821	0.0909	0.0046	0.1782	0.0525	0.1503	0.1222	0.0715	0.1538	0.0077	0.0864	0.0031	0.0001	0.0000	0.0008
	0.6	0.540	0.597	5.44	4.92	0.0967	0.0846	0.0908	0.0047	0.1772	0.0542	0.1481	0.1261	0.0688	0.1585	0.0065	0.0884	0.0031	0.0001	0.0000	0.0008
	1.0	0.557	0.595	5.51	5.15	0.0947	0.0881	0.0907	0.0049	0.1756	0.0566	0.1449	0.1317	0.0650	0.1652	0.0050	0.0911	0.0031	0.0001	0.0000	0.0008
	1.5	0.570	0.594	5.58	5.35	0.0931	0.0909	0.0906	0.0051	0.1747	0.0587	0.1423	0.1364	0.0620	0.1706	0.0038	0.0931	0.0031	0.0001	0.0000	0.0008
	2.0	0.580	0.593	5.62	5.49	0.0920	0.0928	0.0905	0.0052	0.1739	0.0601	0.1405	0.1395	0.0599	0.1743	0.0031	0.0944	0.0031	0.0001	0.0000	0.0008
0.2	0.4	0.562	0.591	5.52	5.26	0.0951	0.0878	0.0907	0.0050	0.1757	0.0571	0.1449	0.1325	0.0657	0.1648	0.0067	0.0881	0.0031	0.0001	0.0002	0.0030
	0.6	0.587	0.587	5.63	5.63	0.0925	0.0925	0.0905	0.0053	0.1738	0.0607	0.1405	0.1405	0.0607	0.1738	0.0063	0.0905	0.0031	0.0001	0.0001	0.0031
	1.0	0.624	0.582	5.80	6.21	0.0887	0.0995	0.0902	0.0058	0.1708	0.0663	0.1339	0.1527	0.0535	0.1872	0.0036	0.0936	0.0031	0.0002	0.0001	0.0032
	1.5	0.655	0.578	5.94	6.74	0.0854	0.1056	0.0900	0.0063	0.1682	0.0711	0.1283	0.1634	0.0473	0.1987	0.0022	0.0959	0.0031	0.0002	0.0001	0.0032
	2.0	0.677	0.575	6.05	7.12	0.0833	0.1097	0.0898	0.0066	0.1664	0.0746	0.1243	0.1710	0.0431	0.2068	0.0015	0.0972	0.0031	0.0002	0.0000	0.0033
0.3	0.4	0.593	0.580	5.63	5.76	0.0931	0.0917	0.0905	0.0054	0.1738	0.0611	0.1409	0.1405	0.0622	0.1717	0.0066	0.0880	0.0031	0.0001	0.0006	0.0064
	0.6	0.631	0.573	5.80	6.38	0.0897	0.0982	0.0902	0.0059	0.1710	0.0666	0.1347	0.1524	0.0557	0.1838	0.0052	0.0905	0.0031	0.0002	0.0005	0.0066
	1.0	0.689	0.563	6.06	7.42	0.0844	0.1084	0.0898	0.0067	0.1664	0.0756	0.1249	0.1716	0.0458	0.2028	0.0034	0.0938	0.0031	0.0002	0.0003	0.0068
	1.5	0.741	0.554	6.31	8.43	0.0796	0.1178	0.0894	0.0075	0.1622	0.0841	0.1160	0.1895	0.0372	0.2196	0.0021	0.0960	0.0031	0.0002	0.0002	0.0071
	2.0	0.779	0.548	6.49	9.23	0.0764	0.1244	0.0891	0.0081	0.1590	0.0906	0.1095	0.2028	0.0312	0.2316	0.0014	0.0973	0.0030	0.0002	0.0002	0.0072
0.4	0.4	0.618	0.567	5.72	6.23	0.0920	0.0939	0.0904	0.0057	0.1724	0.0642	0.1383	0.1462	0.0604	0.1744	0.0067	0.0876	0.0031	0.0002	0.0014	0.0105
	0.6	0.669	0.556	5.93	7.13	0.0879	0.1018	0.0900	0.0064	0.1688	0.0715	0.1307	0.1613	0.0532	0.1881	0.0053	0.0901	0.0031	0.0002	0.0012	0.0109
	1.0	0.750	0.540	6.29	8.74	0.0815	0.1147	0.0895	0.0075	0.1628	0.0842	0.1182	0.1869	0.0420	0.2099	0.0035	0.0933	0.0031	0.0002	0.0008	0.0118
	1.5	0.826	0.526	6.64	10.44	0.0756	0.1270	0.0889	0.0087	0.1568	0.0968	0.1062	0.2121	0.0322	0.2295	0.0022	0.0957	0.0030	0.0002	0.0006	0.0121
	2.0	0.883	0.515	6.92	11.87	0.0713	0.1362	0.0885	0.0097	0.1522	0.1071	0.0971	0.2320	0.0254	0.2435	0.0015	0.0970	0.0030	0.0003	0.0005	0.0124
0.5	0.4	0.636	0.552	5.77	6.69	0.0914	0.0952	0.0902	0.0060	0.1717	0.0664	0.1366	0.1494	0.0595	0.1746	0.0068	0.0872	0.0031	0.0002	0.0028	0.0152
	0.6	0.697	0.538	6.03	7.85	0.0870	0.1040	0.0897	0.0069	0.1668	0.0753	0.1278	0.1668	0.0517	0.1896	0.0054	0.0897	0.0031	0.0002	0.0024	0.0159
	1.0	0.803	0.515	6.45	10.10	0.0795	0.1183	0.0892	0.0083	0.1600	0.0917	0.1136	0.1969	0.0404	0.2110	0.0036	0.0928	0.0030	0.0002	0.0018	0.0170
	1.5	0.904	0.493	6.96	12.72	0.0728	0.1330	0.0884	0.0100	0.1521	0.1088	0.0992	0.2282	0.0303	0.2314	0.0023	0.0952	0.0030	0.0003	0.0013	0.0179
	2.0	0.981	0.478	7.30	15.05	0.0678	0.1440	0.0878	0.0113	0.1461	0.1234	0.0879	0.2544	0.0235	0.2461	0.0016	0.0967	0.0030	0.0003	0.0010	0.0186

TABLE 8

$a_A = 0.3$ $a_B =$ variable $r_A = 0.6$ $r_B \doteq$ variable

		$a_A=0.3$																			
0.1	0.4	0.515	0.642	6.08	4.87	0.1041	0.0795	0.0910	0.1883	0.0045	0.0479	0.1627	0.1169	0.0782	0.1509	0.0085	0.0861	0.0066	0.0004	0.0000	0.0008
	0.6	0.527	0.641	6.14	5.05	0.1026	0.0819	0.0909	0.1873	0.0046	0.0495	0.1604	0.1207	0.0753	0.1556	0.0072	0.0881	0.0066	0.0004	0.0000	0.0008
	1.0	0.544	0.640	6.23	5.30	0.1005	0.0853	0.0907	0.1859	0.0048	0.0518	0.1570	0.1262	0.0712	0.1624	0.0055	0.0908	0.0066	0.0005	0.0000	0.0008
	1.5	0.557	0.638	6.31	5.51	0.0988	0.0882	0.0906	0.1847	0.0050	0.0537	0.1543	0.1307	0.0679	0.1679	0.0042	0.0930	0.0066	0.0005	0.0000	0.0008
	2.0	0.566	0.637	6.36	5.65	0.0977	0.0901	0.0905	0.1840	0.0051	0.0551	0.1524	0.1338	0.0656	0.1716	0.0034	0.0943	0.0066	0.0005	0.0000	0.0008
0.2	0.4	0.549	0.634	6.24	5.39	0.1009	0.0851	0.0907	0.1858	0.0049	0.0523	0.1571	0.1269	0.0719	0.1619	0.0074	0.0877	0.0066	0.0005	0.0002	0.0030
	0.6	0.573	0.631	6.38	5.80	0.0982	0.0897	0.0905	0.1838	0.0052	0.0557	0.1524	0.1347	0.0666	0.1710	0.0059	0.0902	0.0066	0.0005	0.0001	0.0031
	1.0	0.609	0.625	6.58	6.41	0.0942	0.0966	0.0902	0.1808	0.0057	0.0609	0.1455	0.1467	0.0587	0.1845	0.0039	0.0935	0.0065	0.0005	0.0001	0.0032
	1.5	0.639	0.620	6.76	6.97	0.0907	0.1027	0.0900	0.1782	0.0062	0.0655	0.1395	0.1573	0.0520	0.1962	0.0025	0.0954	0.0065	0.0006	0.0000	0.0032
	2.0	0.661	0.617	6.89	7.37	0.0884	0.1068	0.0898	0.1764	0.0065	0.0688	0.1353	0.1648	0.0474	0.2044	0.0016	0.0971	0.0065	0.0006	0.0000	0.0033
0.3	0.4	0.578	0.623	6.38	5.92	0.0989	0.0888	0.0905	0.1839	0.0053	0.0560	0.1529	0.1347	0.0682	0.1688	0.0073	0.0877	0.0066	0.0005	0.0007	0.0063
	0.6	0.615	0.615	6.58	6.58	0.0952	0.0952	0.0902	0.1810	0.0058	0.0612	0.1464	0.1464	0.0612	0.1810	0.0058	0.0902	0.0065	0.0006	0.0006	0.0065
	1.0	0.672	0.604	6.90	7.68	0.0896	0.1054	0.0898	0.1764	0.0066	0.0697	0.1360	0.1653	0.0505	0.2002	0.0038	0.0936	0.0065	0.0006	0.0004	0.0068
	1.5	0.723	0.595	7.20	8.75	0.0845	0.1147	0.0894	0.1721	0.0074	0.0778	0.1265	0.1830	0.0411	0.2172	0.0024	0.0959	0.0065	0.0007	0.0003	0.0070
	2.0	0.760	0.587	7.42	9.60	0.0810	0.1213	0.0891	0.1689	0.0080	0.0839	0.1196	0.1963	0.0345	0.2295	0.0016	0.0972	0.0064	0.0008	0.0002	0.0072
0.4	0.4	0.603	0.609	6.48	6.41	0.0977	0.0910	0.0904	0.1825	0.0056	0.0589	0.1502	0.1402	0.0663	0.1715	0.0074	0.0873	0.0066	0.0005	0.0016	0.0104
	0.6	0.652	0.597	6.74	7.36	0.0934	0.0987	0.0900	0.1789	0.0062	0.0657	0.1422	0.1550	0.0585	0.1852	0.0059	0.0898	0.0065	0.0006	0.0013	0.0109
	1.0	0.731	0.579	7.17	9.06	0.0866	0.1116	0.0894	0.1727	0.0074	0.0777	0.1289	0.1803	0.0463	0.2072	0.0039	0.0931	0.0065	0.0007	0.0009	0.0117
	1.5	0.805	0.563	7.61	10.87	0.0803	0.1237	0.0888	0.1657	0.0087	0.0898	0.1162	0.2053	0.0357	0.2271	0.0025	0.0955	0.0064	0.0008	0.0007	0.0120
	2.0	0.860	0.552	7.95	12.39	0.0756	0.1329	0.0883	0.1619	0.0097	0.0996	0.1064	0.2252	0.0282	0.2414	0.0017	0.0969	0.0064	0.0009	0.0005	0.0123
0.5	0.4	0.620	0.593	6.55	6.88	0.0973	0.0922	0.0902	0.1820	0.0059	0.0607	0.1485	0.1433	0.0653	0.1714	0.0075	0.0869	0.0066	0.0005	0.0030	0.0151
	0.6	0.680	0.577	6.85	8.07	0.0925	0.1007	0.0898	0.1774	0.0067	0.0690	0.1392	0.1603	0.0569	0.1866	0.0060	0.0894	0.0065	0.0006	0.0026	0.0158
	1.0	0.784	0.551	7.35	10.47	0.0848	0.1150	0.0890	0.1697	0.0082	0.0842	0.1241	0.1901	0.0446	0.2083	0.0040	0.0926	0.0064	0.0008	0.0020	0.0168
	1.5	0.880	0.528	7.96	13.22	0.0774	0.1292	0.0883	0.1622	0.0100	0.1007	0.1088	0.2212	0.0337	0.2288	0.0026	0.0950	0.0064	0.0009	0.0014	0.0178
	2.0	0.957	0.512	8.40	15.65	0.0716	0.1405	0.0875	0.1559	0.0114	0.1146	0.0966	0.2473	0.0261	0.2440	0.0018	0.0966	0.0063	0.0010	0.0011	0.0185

466 APPENDIX

Parabolic Haunches — Constant Width

TABLE 9

$a_A = 0.4 \qquad r_A = 0.6 \qquad a_B = \text{variable} \qquad r_R = \text{variable}$

Right Haunch a_J	r_B	C_{AB}	C_{BA}	k_{AB}	k_{BA}	Unif. M_{AB}	Unif. M_{BA}	b0.1 M_{AB}	b0.1 M_{BA_1}	b0.3 M_{AB}	b0.3 M_{BA}	b0.5 M_{AB}	b0.5 M_{BA}	b0.7 M_{AB}	b0.7 M_{BA}	b0.9 M_{AB}	b0.9 M_{BA}	Left M_{AB}	Left M_{BA}	Right M_{AB}	Right M_{BA}
0.1	0.4	0.500	0.681	6.78	4.97	0.1080	0.0778	0.0905	0.0046	0.1921	0.0452	0.1720	0.1131	0.0838	0.1487	0.0091	0.0858	0.0111	0.0010	0.0000	0.0008
	0.6	0.511	0.680	6.85	5.15	0.1064	0.0803	0.0904	0.0047	0.1917	0.0472	0.1695	0.1168	0.0807	0.1535	0.0078	0.0879	0.0110	0.0011	0.0000	0.0008
	1.0	0.528	0.678	6.96	5.41	0.1042	0.0836	0.0903	0.0049	0.1902	0.0496	0.1660	0.1223	0.0763	0.1602	0.0059	0.0907	0.0110	0.0011	0.0000	0.0008
	1.5	0.541	0.677	7.05	5.63	0.1024	0.0865	0.0902	0.0051	0.1890	0.0513	0.1631	0.1267	0.0724	0.1659	0.0045	0.0928	0.0110	0.0012	0.0000	0.0008
	2.0	0.550	0.676	7.11	5.78	0.1012	0.0884	0.0901	0.0053	0.1883	0.0526	0.1612	0.1298	0.0698	0.1695	0.0037	0.0942	0.0109	0.0012	0.0000	0.0008
0.2	0.4	0.533	0.673	6.97	5.52	0.1047	0.0833	0.0903	0.0050	0.1900	0.0494	0.1661	0.1229	0.0771	0.1597	0.0080	0.0875	0.0110	0.0011	0.0002	0.0030
	0.6	0.556	0.669	7.13	5.93	0.1018	0.0879	0.0901	0.0053	0.1881	0.0532	0.1613	0.1307	0.0715	0.1688	0.0064	0.0900	0.0109	0.0012	0.0002	0.0031
	1.0	0.591	0.663	7.36	6.57	0.0975	0.0949	0.0898	0.0058	0.1849	0.0584	0.1540	0.1426	0.0630	0.1825	0.0042	0.0934	0.0109	0.0013	0.0001	0.0032
	1.5	0.621	0.657	7.57	7.15	0.0938	0.1009	0.0895	0.0063	0.1823	0.0627	0.1477	0.1530	0.0556	0.1944	0.0027	0.0956	0.0108	0.0014	0.0001	0.0032
	2.0	0.641	0.654	7.72	7.58	0.0914	0.1050	0.0893	0.0067	0.1804	0.0660	0.1432	0.1605	0.0505	0.2026	0.0018	0.0971	0.0108	0.0015	0.0001	0.0033
0.3	0.4	0.561	0.660	7.13	6.06	0.1026	0.0870	0.0901	0.0054	0.1882	0.0534	0.1618	0.1306	0.0732	0.1666	0.0079	0.0875	0.0110	0.0012	0.0007	0.0063
	0.6	0.597	0.652	7.36	6.74	0.0987	0.0934	0.0898	0.0059	0.1852	0.0585	0.1550	0.1422	0.0657	0.1789	0.0062	0.0900	0.0109	0.0013	0.0006	0.0065
	1.0	0.652	0.640	7.73	7.88	0.0928	0.1035	0.0893	0.0068	0.1802	0.0669	0.1441	0.1609	0.0543	0.1982	0.0041	0.0934	0.0108	0.0015	0.0004	0.0068
	1.5	0.701	0.629	8.08	9.01	0.0874	0.1129	0.0888	0.0076	0.1760	0.0747	0.1341	0.1785	0.0441	0.2155	0.0026	0.0957	0.0107	0.0017	0.0003	0.0070
	2.0	0.737	0.621	8.34	9.89	0.0837	0.1195	0.0884	0.0082	0.1727	0.0807	0.1268	0.1918	0.0370	0.2280	0.0017	0.0972	0.0106	0.0019	0.0002	0.0072
0.4	0.4	0.584	0.645	7.24	6.56	0.1013	0.0891	0.0899	0.0057	0.1870	0.0562	0.1590	0.1359	0.0712	0.1692	0.0080	0.0870	0.0110	0.0013	0.0017	0.0104
	0.6	0.632	0.632	7.54	7.54	0.0968	0.0968	0.0895	0.0064	0.1831	0.0629	0.1506	0.1506	0.0629	0.1831	0.0064	0.0895	0.0108	0.0014	0.0014	0.0108
	1.0	0.708	0.612	8.04	9.30	0.0896	0.1095	0.0888	0.0076	0.1767	0.0749	0.1367	0.1756	0.0500	0.2049	0.0042	0.0929	0.0107	0.0017	0.0009	0.0117
	1.5	0.780	0.595	8.55	11.20	0.0829	0.1217	0.0882	0.0089	0.1705	0.0864	0.1233	0.2007	0.0385	0.2254	0.0027	0.0953	0.0105	0.0020	0.0007	0.0120
	2.0	0.833	0.583	8.95	12.79	0.0780	0.1310	0.0876	0.0100	0.1655	0.0961	0.1130	0.2205	0.0305	0.2399	0.0018	0.0968	0.0104	0.0022	0.0005	0.0123
0.5	0.4	0.602	0.628	7.33	7.03	0.1008	0.0901	0.0897	0.0060	0.1862	0.0583	0.1573	0.1390	0.0703	0.1690	0.0082	0.0865	0.0109	0.0014	0.0032	0.0150
	0.6	0.660	0.611	7.65	8.29	0.0956	0.0985	0.0892	0.0068	0.1813	0.0663	0.1475	0.1557	0.0618	0.1840	0.0065	0.0890	0.0108	0.0016	0.0027	0.0157
	1.0	0.759	0.583	8.28	10.80	0.0874	0.1128	0.0883	0.0084	0.1738	0.0809	0.1317	0.1853	0.0482	0.2061	0.0043	0.0924	0.0107	0.0019	0.0020	0.0167
	1.5	0.851	0.557	8.92	13.68	0.0796	0.1272	0.0875	0.0102	0.1657	0.0970	0.1155	0.2165	0.0364	0.2269	0.0028	0.0948	0.0104	0.0022	0.0016	0.0178
	2.0	0.926	0.541	9.48	16.30	0.0738	0.1388	0.0867	0.0118	0.1590	0.1105	0.1027	0.2425	0.0283	0.2420	0.0019	0.0964	0.0102	0.0025	0.0012	0.0185

$r_A = 0.6 \qquad r_R = \text{variable}$

TABLE 10

$a_A = 0.5$ $\quad$ a_B = variable $\quad$ $r_A = 0.6$ $\quad$ r_B = variable

0.1	0.4	0.481	0.711	5.05	7.46	0.1099	0.0763	0.0900	0.0047	0.1938	0.0440	0.1779	0.1103	0.0831	0.1468	0.0100	0.0854	0.0160	0.0020	0.0000	0.0008
	0.6	0.494	0.710	5.23	7.55	0.1086	0.0794	0.0900	0.0048	0.1929	0.0461	0.1753	0.1139	0.0850	0.1516	0.0084	0.0876	0.0159	0.0022	0.0000	0.0008
	1.0	0.509	0.709	5.48	7.65	0.1062	0.0825	0.0899	0.0050	0.1914	0.0488	0.1717	0.1194	0.0800	0.1584	0.0063	0.0905	0.0159	0.0023	0.0000	0.0008
	1.5	0.523	0.708	5.71	7.76	0.1045	0.0852	0.0898	0.0052	0.1899	0.0505	0.1686	0.1237	0.0766	0.1639	0.0048	0.0927	0.0158	0.0025	0.0000	0.0008
	2.0	0.530	0.708	5.85	7.85	0.1032	0.0874	0.0897	0.0054	0.1887	0.0510	0.1668	0.1268	0.0748	0.1680	0.0040	0.0941	0.0158	0.0026	0.0000	0.0008
0.2	0.4	0.511	0.703	5.60	7.67	0.1066	0.0823	0.0897	0.0051	0.1915	0.0480	0.1718	0.1200	0.0810	0.1579	0.0089	0.0871	0.0160	0.0022	0.0002	0.0030
	0.6	0.538	0.697	6.03	7.85	0.1040	0.0870	0.0897	0.0054	0.1896	0.0517	0.1668	0.1278	0.0753	0.1668	0.0069	0.0897	0.0159	0.0024	0.0002	0.0031
	1.0	0.571	0.693	6.65	8.10	0.0995	0.0939	0.0894	0.0059	0.1866	0.0573	0.1592	0.1397	0.0662	0.1808	0.0045	0.0932	0.0157	0.0026	0.0001	0.0032
	1.5	0.600	0.686	7.30	8.35	0.0959	0.0998	0.0890	0.0064	0.1835	0.0619	0.1526	0.1499	0.0589	0.1927	0.0029	0.0954	0.0156	0.0028	0.0001	0.0032
	2.0	0.618	0.684	7.71	8.55	0.0931	0.1040	0.0888	0.0068	0.1810	0.0641	0.1481	0.1575	0.0541	0.2013	0.0020	0.0970	0.0155	0.0029	0.0001	0.0033
0.3	0.4	0.540	0.690	6.15	7.83	0.1046	0.0860	0.0895	0.0056	0.1896	0.0515	0.1674	0.1277	0.0769	0.1649	0.0088	0.0871	0.0160	0.0023	0.0008	0.0063
	0.6	0.577	0.680	6.85	8.07	0.1007	0.0925	0.0894	0.0060	0.1866	0.0569	0.1603	0.1392	0.0690	0.1774	0.0067	0.0898	0.0158	0.0026	0.0006	0.0065
	1.0	0.630	0.669	8.00	8.50	0.0944	0.1024	0.0888	0.0069	0.1817	0.0655	0.1489	0.1578	0.0570	0.1967	0.0044	0.0932	0.0156	0.0028	0.0004	0.0068
	1.5	0.673	0.654	9.18	8.90	0.0892	0.1120	0.0882	0.0078	0.1769	0.0734	0.1385	0.1753	0.0467	0.2140	0.0028	0.0956	0.0154	0.0031	0.0003	0.0070
	2.0	0.708	0.649	10.10	9.22	0.0851	0.1183	0.0879	0.0084	0.1735	0.0788	0.1310	0.1887	0.0392	0.2266	0.0019	0.0971	0.0152	0.0033	0.0002	0.0072
0.4	0.4	0.561	0.674	6.66	7.98	0.1032	0.0880	0.0893	0.0059	0.1878	0.0550	0.1644	0.1329	0.0746	0.1678	0.0087	0.0867	0.0159	0.0024	0.0018	0.0104
	0.6	0.611	0.660	7.65	8.29	0.0985	0.0956	0.0890	0.0065	0.1840	0.0618	0.1557	0.1475	0.0663	0.1813	0.0068	0.0892	0.0157	0.0027	0.0016	0.0108
	1.0	0.681	0.639	9.43	8.85	0.0908	0.1083	0.0882	0.0077	0.1778	0.0732	0.1410	0.1724	0.0526	0.2039	0.0045	0.0926	0.0155	0.0031	0.0012	0.0115
	1.5	0.749	0.619	11.41	9.43	0.0843	0.1206	0.0876	0.0091	0.1711	0.0848	0.1275	0.1975	0.0409	0.2240	0.0030	0.0952	0.0152	0.0036	0.0009	0.0119
	2.0	0.800	0.607	13.10	9.90	0.0794	0.1300	0.0869	0.0103	0.1662	0.0943	0.1166	0.2173	0.0320	0.2387	0.0019	0.0967	0.0150	0.0039	0.0006	0.0123
0.5	0.4	0.581	0.657	7.14	8.07	0.1023	0.0889	0.0892	0.0061	0.1861	0.0568	0.1622	0.1360	0.0739	0.1673	0.0087	0.0861	0.0158	0.0026	0.0035	0.0148
	0.6	0.636	0.636	8.42	8.42	0.0972	0.0972	0.0887	0.0069	0.1816	0.0647	0.1525	0.1525	0.0647	0.1816	0.0069	0.0887	0.0156	0.0030	0.0030	0.0156
	1.0	0.730	0.606	10.96	9.12	0.0889	0.1115	0.0878	0.0086	0.1738	0.0791	0.1360	0.1820	0.0506	0.2045	0.0046	0.0922	0.0152	0.0036	0.0022	0.0167
	1.5	0.822	0.580	13.94	9.83	0.0810	0.1260	0.0869	0.0104	0.1658	0.0948	0.1195	0.2130	0.0383	0.2255	0.0031	0.0945	0.0148	0.0044	0.0016	0.0177
	2.0	0.894	0.562	16.62	10.45	0.0750	0.1376	0.0861	0.0120	0.1591	0.1084	0.1064	0.2388	0.0297	0.2408	0.0021	0.0961	0.0145	0.0050	0.0013	0.0184

Parabolic Haunches — Constant Width

TABLE 11

$a_A = 0.1$ a_B = variable $r_A = 1.0$ r_B = variable

Right Haunch		Carry-over Factors		Stiffness Factors		Unif. Load F.E.M. Coef. × wL^2		Concentrated Load F.E.M.—Coef. × PL										Haunch Load at			
								b										Left F.E.M. Coef. × $W_L L^2$		Right F.E.M. Coef. × $W_B L^2$	
								0.1		0.3		0.5		0.7		0.9					
a_B	r_B	C_{AB}	C_{BA}	k_{AB}	k_{BA}	M_{AB}	M_{BA}	M_{AB}	M_{BA}	M_{AB}	M_{BA}	M_{AB}	M_{BA}	M_{AB}	M_{BA}	M_{AB}	M_{BA}	M_{AB}	M_{BA}	M_{AB}	M_{BA}
0.1	0.4	0.535	0.566	4.94	4.66	0.0933	0.0841	0.0913	0.0043	0.1694	0.0563	0.1410	0.1262	0.0668	0.1557	0.0071	0.0866	0.0008	0.0000	0.0000	0.0008
	0.6	0.547	0.565	4.98	4.82	0.0921	0.0867	0.0913	0.0044	0.1686	0.0581	0.1390	0.1303	0.0643	0.1606	0.0062	0.0886	0.0008	0.0000	0.0000	0.0008
	1.0	0.564	0.564	5.05	5.05	0.0902	0.0902	0.0912	0.0046	0.1672	0.0607	0.1360	0.1360	0.0607	0.1672	0.0046	0.0912	0.0008	0.0000	0.0000	0.0008
	1.5	0.578	0.563	5.11	5.24	0.0886	0.0931	0.0912	0.0048	0.1661	0.0628	0.1335	0.1406	0.0578	0.1726	0.0034	0.0934	0.0008	0.0000	0.0000	0.0008
	2.0	0.588	0.562	5.14	5.38	0.0876	0.0950	0.0911	0.0049	0.1653	0.0643	0.1318	0.1438	0.0558	0.1763	0.0028	0.0946	0.0008	0.0000	0.0000	0.0008
0.2	0.4	0.570	0.560	5.06	5.15	0.0900	0.0900	0.0912	0.0047	0.1671	0.0613	0.1359	0.1367	0.0613	0.1669	0.0063	0.0883	0.0008	0.0000	0.0002	0.0030
	0.6	0.595	0.557	5.15	5.51	0.0881	0.0947	0.0911	0.0050	0.1652	0.0650	0.1317	0.1449	0.0566	0.1756	0.0049	0.0907	0.0008	0.0000	0.0001	0.0031
	1.0	0.633	0.552	5.30	6.07	0.0844	0.1018	0.0908	0.0054	0.1622	0.0708	0.1255	0.1572	0.0498	0.1892	0.0033	0.0938	0.0008	0.0000	0.0001	0.0032
	1.5	0.664	0.548	5.42	6.57	0.0813	0.1079	0.0906	0.0058	0.1597	0.0759	0.1200	0.1680	0.0440	0.2010	0.0021	0.0960	0.0008	0.0000	0.0001	0.0032
	2.0	0.686	0.545	5.51	6.94	0.0793	0.1121	0.0905	0.0061	0.1578	0.0796	0.1162	0.1757	0.0400	0.2085	0.0014	0.0973	0.0008	0.0000	0.0000	0.0033
0.3	0.4	0.601	0.550	5.16	5.64	0.0886	0.0939	0.0911	0.0050	0.1652	0.0654	0.1321	0.1450	0.0579	0.1738	0.0062	0.0883	0.0008	0.0000	0.0006	0.0064
	0.6	0.640	0.544	5.30	6.23	0.0853	0.1005	0.0908	0.0055	0.1624	0.0712	0.1262	0.1570	0.0518	0.1859	0.0048	0.0907	0.0008	0.0000	0.0005	0.0066
	1.0	0.699	0.534	5.52	7.23	0.0803	0.1108	0.0905	0.0063	0.1578	0.0806	0.1168	0.1764	0.0425	0.2047	0.0031	0.0939	0.0008	0.0000	0.0003	0.0069
	1.5	0.752	0.526	5.74	8.20	0.0758	0.1203	0.0901	0.0070	0.1538	0.0895	0.1083	0.1943	0.0345	0.2213	0.0020	0.0962	0.0008	0.0000	0.0002	0.0071
	2.0	0.790	0.520	5.89	8.96	0.0727	0.1269	0.0899	0.0075	0.1505	0.0960	0.1021	0.2077	0.0289	0.2332	0.0013	0.0974	0.0008	0.0000	0.0002	0.0072
0.4	0.4	0.627	0.538	5.23	6.10	0.0875	0.0963	0.0910	0.0053	0.1638	0.0687	0.1296	0.1507	0.0563	0.1766	0.0063	0.0879	0.0008	0.0000	0.0013	0.0106
	0.6	0.678	0.528	5.41	6.96	0.0836	0.1042	0.0907	0.0059	0.1602	0.0763	0.1223	0.1660	0.0496	0.1902	0.0049	0.0903	0.0008	0.0000	0.0011	0.0110
	1.0	0.761	0.512	5.72	8.51	0.0775	0.1172	0.0902	0.0070	0.1542	0.0895	0.1103	0.1919	0.0389	0.2118	0.0032	0.0935	0.0008	0.0000	0.0007	0.0118
	1.5	0.839	0.499	6.03	10.14	0.0719	0.1296	0.0897	0.0081	0.1484	0.1028	0.0990	0.2172	0.0298	0.2312	0.0021	0.0958	0.0008	0.0000	0.0006	0.0121
	2.0	0.897	0.489	6.27	11.50	0.0678	0.1388	0.0893	0.0090	0.1438	0.1134	0.0903	0.2371	0.0235	0.2449	0.0014	0.0971	0.0008	0.0000	0.0004	0.0124
0.5	0.4	0.646	0.525	5.25	6.51	0.0870	0.0972	0.0909	0.0056	0.1627	0.0713	0.1279	0.1542	0.0564	0.1769	0.0064	0.0875	0.0008	0.0000	0.0027	0.0152
	0.6	0.709	0.509	5.48	7.65	0.0825	0.1062	0.0905	0.0063	0.1584	0.0800	0.1194	0.1717	0.0488	0.1914	0.0050	0.0899	0.0008	0.0000	0.0023	0.0159
	1.0	0.816	0.489	5.88	9.84	0.0757	0.1215	0.0899	0.0077	0.1512	0.0975	0.1057	0.2023	0.0378	0.2129	0.0033	0.0931	0.0008	0.0000	0.0018	0.0170
	1.5	0.918	0.468	6.28	12.35	0.0692	0.1355	0.0893	0.0092	0.1436	0.1153	0.0925	0.2336	0.0284	0.2330	0.0022	0.0954	0.0008	0.0000	0.0012	0.0180
	2.0	0.999	0.453	6.60	14.60	0.0640	0.1470	0.0887	0.0104	0.1374	0.1304	0.0819	0.2593	0.0219	0.2474	0.0015	0.0967	0.0008	0.0000	0.0009	0.0187

TABLE 12

		$a_A = 0.2$		a_B = variable								$r_A = 1.0$					r_B = variable		
0.1	0.4	0.523	0.635	5.92	4.87	0.1053	0.0786	0.0940	0.0030	0.1914	0.0460	0.1628	0.0778	0.1508	0.0084	0.0861	0.0032	0.0001	0.0000	0.0008
	0.6	0.535	0.634	5.98	5.05	0.1038	0.0810	0.0939	0.0031	0.1905	0.0476	0.1605	0.0749	0.1555	0.0071	0.0881	0.0032	0.0001	0.0000	0.0008
	1.0	0.552	0.633	6.07	5.30	0.1018	0.0844	0.0938	0.0033	0.1892	0.0498	0.1572	0.0708	0.1622	0.0054	0.0908	0.0032	0.0001	0.0000	0.0008
	1.5	0.566	0.631	6.15	5.51	0.1001	0.0873	0.0938	0.0034	0.1881	0.0516	0.1545	0.0675	0.1677	0.0042	0.0929	0.0032	0.0001	0.0000	0.0008
	2.0	0.575	0.630	6.20	5.65	0.0990	0.0891	0.0937	0.0035	0.1873	0.0529	0.1526	0.0653	0.1715	0.0034	0.0943	0.0032	0.0001	0.0000	0.0008
0.2	0.4	0.558	0.627	6.08	5.40	0.1022	0.0841	0.0938	0.0033	0.1891	0.0502	0.1572	0.0715	0.1618	0.0073	0.0877	0.0032	0.0002	0.0002	0.0030
	0.6	0.582	0.624	6.21	5.80	0.0995	0.0887	0.0936	0.0036	0.1872	0.0535	0.1527	0.0663	0.1708	0.0058	0.0902	0.0032	0.0001	0.0002	0.0031
	1.0	0.619	0.619	6.41	6.41	0.0956	0.0956	0.0935	0.0038	0.1844	0.0584	0.1459	0.0584	0.1844	0.0038	0.0935	0.0032	0.0001	0.0001	0.0032
	1.5	0.649	0.614	6.59	6.97	0.0921	0.1015	0.0933	0.0041	0.1819	0.0628	0.1399	0.0518	0.1962	0.0025	0.0958	0.0032	0.0001	0.0001	0.0032
	2.0	0.671	0.611	6.71	7.38	0.0899	0.1056	0.0932	0.0044	0.1801	0.0660	0.1358	0.0472	0.2042	0.0017	0.0971	0.0032	0.0001	0.0000	0.0033
0.3	0.4	0.588	0.616	6.22	5.93	0.1002	0.0877	0.0937	0.0035	0.1873	0.0537	0.1532	0.0678	0.1686	0.0073	0.0877	0.0032	0.0001	0.0007	0.0063
	0.6	0.625	0.609	6.41	6.58	0.0966	0.0942	0.0935	0.0039	0.1845	0.0587	0.1467	0.0609	0.1808	0.0057	0.0902	0.0032	0.0001	0.0005	0.0065
	1.0	0.683	0.598	6.73	7.68	0.0911	0.1042	0.0932	0.0044	0.1801	0.0669	0.1365	0.0502	0.2000	0.0037	0.0936	0.0031	0.0001	0.0004	0.0068
	1.5	0.735	0.589	7.02	8.76	0.0862	0.1133	0.0929	0.0050	0.1760	0.0746	0.1272	0.0410	0.2170	0.0023	0.0959	0.0031	0.0001	0.0003	0.0070
	2.0	0.772	0.582	7.25	9.61	0.0827	0.1198	0.0927	0.0054	0.1730	0.0805	0.1203	0.0345	0.2293	0.0016	0.0972	0.0031	0.0001	0.0002	0.0072
0.4	0.4	0.613	0.603	6.32	6.42	0.0990	0.0899	0.0936	0.0037	0.1860	0.0565	0.1505	0.0660	0.1713	0.0074	0.0873	0.0032	0.0001	0.0016	0.0104
	0.6	0.663	0.591	6.57	7.36	0.0949	0.0975	0.0934	0.0042	0.1825	0.0630	0.1426	0.0584	0.1849	0.0058	0.0898	0.0032	0.0001	0.0013	0.0109
	1.0	0.743	0.574	7.00	9.07	0.0882	0.1100	0.0930	0.0050	0.1766	0.0745	0.1295	0.0462	0.2070	0.0039	0.0931	0.0031	0.0001	0.0008	0.0117
	1.5	0.818	0.558	7.43	10.89	0.0820	0.1220	0.0925	0.0058	0.1709	0.0861	0.1169	0.0356	0.2269	0.0025	0.0955	0.0031	0.0002	0.0007	0.0120
	2.0	0.875	0.548	7.78	12.43	0.0775	0.1311	0.0922	0.0065	0.1663	0.0955	0.1073	0.0282	0.2412	0.0017	0.0969	0.0031	0.0002	0.0005	0.0123
0.5	0.4	0.632	0.589	6.38	6.86	0.0985	0.0911	0.0935	0.0039	0.1858	0.0585	0.1487	0.0658	0.1713	0.0075	0.0869	0.0032	0.0001	0.0030	0.0150
	0.6	0.693	0.571	6.65	8.10	0.0939	0.0995	0.0932	0.0045	0.1808	0.0662	0.1397	0.0573	0.1866	0.0059	0.0894	0.0032	0.0001	0.0026	0.0157
	1.0	0.796	0.547	7.22	10.51	0.0865	0.1138	0.0928	0.0056	0.1740	0.0809	0.1245	0.0448	0.2079	0.0040	0.0926	0.0031	0.0001	0.0020	0.0168
	1.5	0.893	0.522	7.79	13.30	0.0793	0.1277	0.0922	0.0067	0.1665	0.0963	0.1095	0.0339	0.2285	0.0026	0.0950	0.0031	0.0002	0.0014	0.0178
	2.0	0.970	0.507	8.23	15.80	0.0736	0.1386	0.0917	0.0077	0.1604	0.1098	0.0978	0.0263	0.2435	0.0018	0.0966	0.0031	0.0002	0.0011	0.0185

Parabolic Haunches — Constant Width

TABLE 13

$a_A = 0.3$ a_B = variable $r_A = 1.0$ r_B = variable

Right Haunch a_B	r_B	Carry-over Factors C_{AB}	C_{BA}	Stiffness Factors k_{AB}	k_{BA}	Unif. Load F.E.M. Coef. × wL^3 M_{AB}	M_{BA}	Conc. b=0.1 M_{AB}	M_{BA}	b=0.3 M_{AB}	M_{BA}	b=0.5 M_{AB}	M_{BA}	b=0.7 M_{AB}	M_{BA}	b=0.9 M_{AB}	M_{BA}	Haunch Left Coef.×$W_A L^3$ M_{AB}	M_{BA}	Haunch Right Coef.×$W_B L^3$ M_{AB}	M_{BA}
0.1	0.4	0.506	0.702	7.03	5.07	0.1147	0.0746	0.0941	0.0029	0.2069	0.0392	0.1824	0.1079	0.0884	0.1463	0.0096	0.0856	0.0069	0.0003	0.0000	0.0008
	0.6	0.518	0.701	7.11	5.25	0.1131	0.0769	0.0940	0.0030	0.2060	0.0406	0.1799	0.1115	0.0852	0.1510	0.0082	0.0876	0.0069	0.0003	0.0000	0.0008
	1.0	0.534	0.699	7.23	5.52	0.1108	0.0803	0.0939	0.0031	0.2047	0.0425	0.1764	0.1168	0.0806	0.1578	0.0063	0.0905	0.0069	0.0003	0.0000	0.0008
	1.5	0.547	0.698	7.33	5.75	0.1090	0.0831	0.0938	0.0033	0.2036	0.0441	0.1735	0.1212	0.0770	0.1634	0.0048	0.0927	0.0068	0.0003	0.0000	0.0008
	2.0	0.556	0.697	7.40	5.91	0.1078	0.0849	0.0938	0.0033	0.2029	0.0453	0.1715	0.1242	0.0745	0.1672	0.0039	0.0941	0.0068	0.0003	0.0000	0.0008
0.2	0.4	0.539	0.693	7.25	5.64	0.1113	0.0799	0.0939	0.0032	0.2046	0.0429	0.1765	0.1174	0.0815	0.1573	0.0084	0.0873	0.0068	0.0003	0.0002	0.0030
	0.6	0.563	0.689	7.42	6.06	0.1084	0.0844	0.0938	0.0034	0.2028	0.0453	0.1716	0.1249	0.0756	0.1664	0.0067	0.0898	0.0068	0.0003	0.0002	0.0031
	1.0	0.598	0.683	7.68	6.73	0.1042	0.0911	0.0936	0.0037	0.2000	0.0502	0.1643	0.1365	0.0669	0.1801	0.0044	0.0932	0.0068	0.0004	0.0001	0.0031
	1.5	0.628	0.678	7.92	7.33	0.1004	0.0970	0.0934	0.0040	0.1975	0.0542	0.1579	0.1467	0.0594	0.1920	0.0029	0.0956	0.0068	0.0004	0.0001	0.0032
	2.0	0.649	0.674	8.08	7.77	0.0980	0.1010	0.0932	0.0042	0.1957	0.0571	0.1534	0.1541	0.0542	0.2003	0.0019	0.0970	0.0068	0.0004	0.0001	0.0032
0.3	0.4	0.568	0.681	7.42	6.19	0.1093	0.0834	0.0938	0.0034	0.2029	0.0460	0.1722	0.1248	0.0774	0.1640	0.0084	0.0872	0.0068	0.0003	0.0008	0.0063
	0.6	0.604	0.672	7.68	6.90	0.1054	0.0896	0.0936	0.0038	0.2002	0.0505	0.1653	0.1360	0.0697	0.1764	0.0066	0.0898	0.0068	0.0004	0.0006	0.0065
	1.0	0.660	0.660	8.10	8.10	0.0994	0.0994	0.0932	0.0043	0.1958	0.0578	0.1543	0.1543	0.0578	0.1958	0.0043	0.0932	0.0068	0.0004	0.0004	0.0068
	1.5	0.710	0.649	8.49	9.28	0.0940	0.1085	0.0929	0.0049	0.1917	0.0648	0.1442	0.1716	0.0473	0.2133	0.0027	0.0957	0.0067	0.0005	0.0003	0.0070
	2.0	0.745	0.642	8.79	10.22	0.0903	0.1149	0.0927	0.0053	0.1886	0.0702	0.1366	0.1846	0.0399	0.2259	0.0018	0.0971	0.0067	0.0005	0.0002	0.0071
0.4	0.4	0.592	0.666	7.55	6.71	0.1081	0.0854	0.0937	0.0036	0.2016	0.0484	0.1693	0.1299	0.0754	0.1666	0.0085	0.0867	0.0068	0.0004	0.0018	0.0103
	0.6	0.640	0.652	7.88	7.73	0.1035	0.0928	0.0934	0.0041	0.1982	0.0543	0.1609	0.1441	0.0669	0.1802	0.0068	0.0893	0.0068	0.0004	0.0015	0.0108
	1.0	0.717	0.632	8.45	9.58	0.0963	0.1050	0.0929	0.0049	0.1924	0.0646	0.1468	0.1685	0.0533	0.2027	0.0045	0.0927	0.0067	0.0006	0.0010	0.0116
	1.5	0.789	0.615	9.03	11.58	0.0896	0.1168	0.0925	0.0057	0.1866	0.0751	0.1332	0.1931	0.0413	0.2231	0.0029	0.0952	0.0067	0.0006	0.0008	0.0119
	2.0	0.843	0.603	9.50	13.28	0.0846	0.1258	0.0921	0.0064	0.1820	0.0838	0.1226	0.2127	0.0329	0.2379	0.0020	0.0967	0.0067	0.0007	0.0006	0.0123
0.5	0.4	0.609	0.648	7.62	7.18	0.1077	0.0867	0.0936	0.0038	0.2015	0.0501	0.1674	0.1329	0.0748	0.1667	0.0086	0.0862	0.0068	0.0004	0.0032	0.0149
	0.6	0.669	0.630	8.00	8.50	0.1024	0.0944	0.0932	0.0044	0.1967	0.0570	0.1578	0.1489	0.0655	0.1817	0.0069	0.0888	0.0068	0.0004	0.0028	0.0156
	1.0	0.766	0.603	8.74	11.12	0.0943	0.1085	0.0926	0.0055	0.1899	0.0703	0.1414	0.1779	0.0515	0.2036	0.0046	0.0922	0.0067	0.0006	0.0020	0.0167
	1.5	0.861	0.578	9.50	14.15	0.0863	0.1219	0.0920	0.0066	0.1821	0.0843	0.1251	0.2084	0.0392	0.2245	0.0030	0.0947	0.0067	0.0007	0.0016	0.0177
	2.0	0.938	0.560	10.15	16.90	0.0803	0.1329	0.0915	0.0076	0.1760	0.0968	0.1122	0.2339	0.0306	0.2399	0.0021	0.0963	0.0066	0.0008	0.0013	0.0184

TABLE 14

		$\alpha_A = 0.4$		α_B = variable						$r_A = 1.0$						r_B = variable			
0:1	0.4	0.485	0.764	8.25	5.23	0.1213	0.0937	0.0030	0.2136	0.1982	0.1016	0.0979	0.1426	0.0107	0.0851	0.0118	0.0000	0.0007	0.0008
	0.6	0.496	0.763	8.40	5.43	0.1196	0.0936	0.0031	0.2132	0.1956	0.1052	0.0945	0.1474	0.0092	0.0873	0.0118	0.0000	0.0007	0.0008
	1.0	0.512	0.761	8.51	5.72	0.1172	0.0935	0.0032	0.2118	0.1919	0.1103	0.0895	0.1542	0.0070	0.0902	0.0118	0.0000	0.0007	0.0008
	1.5	0.525	0.760	8.63	5.97	0.1152	0.0934	0.0034	0.2107	0.1888	0.1146	0.0855	0.1598	0.0054	0.0924	0.0117	0.0001	0.0008	0.0008
	2.0	0.533	0.758	8.72	6.13	0.1139	0.0933	0.0035	0.2099	0.1867	0.1175	0.0827	0.1637	0.0043	0.0939	0.0118	0.0001	0.0008	0.0008
0.2	0.4	0.517	0.755	8.52	5.84	0.1178	0.0935	0.0033	0.2116	0.1920	0.1108	0.0905	0.1536	0.0095	0.0868	0.0118	0.0007	0.0003	0.0030
	0.6	0.540	0.750	8.74	6.29	0.1147	0.0933	0.0035	0.2099	0.1869	0.1182	0.0842	0.1628	0.0075	0.0895	0.0118	0.0008	0.0002	0.0031
	1.0	0.574	0.743	9.07	7.00	0.1100	0.0931	0.0039	0.2070	0.1791	0.1295	0.0745	0.1766	0.0050	0.0930	0.0117	0.0008	0.0001	0.0031
	1.5	0.602	0.737	9.36	7.65	0.1060	0.0928	0.0042	0.2045	0.1723	0.1395	0.0662	0.1887	0.0032	0.0954	0.0117	0.0009	0.0001	0.0032
	2.0	0.622	0.733	9.58	8.13	0.1033	0.0927	0.0044	0.2026	0.1674	0.1468	0.0605	0.1972	0.0022	0.0969	0.0116	0.0010	0.0001	0.0032
0.3	0.4	0.544	0.740	8.73	6.42	0.1156	0.0933	0.0035	0.2100	0.1874	0.1180	0.0861	0.1603	0.0094	0.0867	0.0118	0.0009	0.0009	0.0062
	0.6	0.579	0.731	9.06	7.17	0.1116	0.0931	0.0039	0.2072	0.1803	0.1239	0.0777	0.1727	0.0074	0.0894	0.0117	0.0009	0.0007	0.0065
	1.0	0.632	0.717	9.58	8.45	0.1050	0.0927	0.0045	0.2027	0.1685	0.1468	0.0646	0.1924	0.0049	0.0929	0.0116	0.0010	0.0005	0.0068
	1.5	0.680	0.705	10.09	9.73	0.0991	0.0923	0.0051	0.1985	0.1577	0.1639	0.0530	0.2101	0.0031	0.0955	0.0115	0.0011	0.0003	0.0070
	2.0	0.714	0.696	10.47	10.74	0.0951	0.0920	0.0055	0.1953	0.1496	0.1769	0.0448	0.2231	0.0021	0.0969	0.0115	0.0012	0.0002	0.0071
0.4	0.4	0.567	0.723	8.89	6.96	0.1143	0.0932	0.0037	0.2087	0.1843	0.1228	0.0839	0.1628	0.0095	0.0863	0.0117	0.0008	0.0020	0.0102
	0.6	0.612	0.708	9.30	8.04	0.1095	0.0929	0.0042	0.2049	0.1756	0.1367	0.0749	0.1767	0.0076	0.0888	0.0117	0.0009	0.0017	0.0107
	1.0	0.686	0.686	10.02	10.02	0.1017	0.0924	0.0051	0.1992	0.1607	0.1607	0.0597	0.1992	0.0051	0.0924	0.0116	0.0011	0.0011	0.0116
	1.5	0.755	0.667	10.75	12.17	0.0944	0.0918	0.0060	0.1932	0.1460	0.1850	0.0465	0.2200	0.0033	0.0950	0.0114	0.0013	0.0009	0.0119
	2.0	0.807	0.653	11.34	14.01	0.0891	0.0914	0.0067	0.1884	0.1346	0.2045	0.0371	0.2352	0.0022	0.0965	0.0114	0.0015	0.0007	0.0122
0.5	0.4	0.586	0.703	8.95	7.43	0.1137	0.0930	0.0039	0.2080	0.1824	0.1255	0.0833	0.1627	0.0098	0.0858	0.0116	0.0009	0.0036	0.0148
	0.6	0.639	0.681	9.43	8.85	0.1083	0.0926	0.0045	0.2039	0.1724	0.1410	0.0732	0.1778	0.0077	0.0882	0.0115	0.0012	0.0031	0.0155
	1.0	0.731	0.653	10.37	11.62	0.0994	0.0920	0.0056	0.1965	0.1551	0.1726	0.0578	0.1999	0.0052	0.0918	0.0114	0.0013	0.0024	0.0165
	1.5	0.823	0.624	11.28	14.95	0.0911	0.0913	0.0068	0.1888	0.1374	0.1996	0.0441	0.2213	0.0034	0.0944	0.0112	0.0015	0.0018	0.0176
	2.0	0.895	0.606	12.10	17.90	0.0847	0.0907	0.0079	0.1823	0.1233	0.2251	0.0346	0.2371	0.0024	0.0960	0.0111	0.0018	0.0014	0.0183

Parabolic Haunches — Constant Width

TABLE 15

$a_A = 0.5 \qquad r_A = 1.0$

a_B = variable $\qquad r_B$ = variable

Right Haunch		Carry-over Factors		Stiffness Factors		Unif. Load F.E.M. Coef. × uL^2		Concentrated Load F.E.M.—Coef. × PL										Haunch Load at Left — F.E.M. Coef. × W_AL^2		Haunch Load at Right — F.E.M. Coef. × W_BL^2	
								b 0.1		0.3		0.5		0.7		0.9					
a_B	r_B	C_{AB}	C_{BA}	k_{AB}	k_{BA}	M_{AB}	M_{BA}	M_{AB}	M_{BA}	M_{AB}	M_{BA}	M_{AB}	M_{BA}	M_{AB}	M_{BA}	M_{AB}	M_{BA}	M_{AB}	M_{BA}	M_{AB}	M_{BA}
0.1	0.4	0.458	0.818	9.56	5.36	0.1253	0.0698	0.0932	0.0031	0.2152	0.0340	0.2085	0.0971	0.1060	0.1398	0.0120	0.0846	0.0171	0.0017	0.0000	0.0008
	0.6	0.471	0.817	9.67	5.57	0.1236	0.0725	0.0932	0.0032	0.2140	0.0357	0.2059	0.1008	0.1024	0.1447	0.0102	0.0870	0.0170	0.0018	0.0000	0.0008
	1.0	0.489	0.816	9.84	5.88	0.1215	0.0757	0.0931	0.0033	0.2129	0.0378	0.2023	0.1057	0.0975	0.1512	0.0077	0.0899	0.0170	0.0018	0.0000	0.0008
	1.5	0.499	0.814	10.00	6.11	0.1192	0.0787	0.0930	0.0035	0.2118	0.0392	0.1990	0.1099	0.0928	0.1571	0.0059	0.0922	0.0169	0.0019	0.0000	0.0008
	2.0	0.506	0.812	10.10	6.30	0.1175	0.0805	0.0928	0.0037	0.2115	0.0396	0.1968	0.1127	0.0900	0.1610	0.0047	0.0937	0.0168	0.0019	0.0000	0.0008
0.2	0.4	0.488	0.807	9.85	5.97	0.1214	0.0753	0.0929	0.0034	0.2131	0.0371	0.2021	0.1061	0.0979	0.1506	0.0105	0.0863	0.0171	0.0017	0.0003	0.0030
	0.6	0.515	0.803	10.10	6.45	0.1183	0.0795	0.0928	0.0036	0.2110	0.0404	0.1969	0.1136	0.0917	0.1600	0.0083	0.0892	0.0170	0.0018	0.0002	0.0030
	1.0	0.547	0.796	10.51	7.22	0.1138	0.0865	0.0926	0.0040	0.2079	0.0448	0.1890	0.1245	0.0809	0.1740	0.0056	0.0928	0.0168	0.0020	0.0001	0.0031
	1.5	0.571	0.786	10.90	7.90	0.1093	0.0922	0.0923	0.0043	0.2055	0.0485	0.1818	0.1344	0.0719	0.1862	0.0035	0.0951	0.0167	0.0021	0.0001	0.0032
	2.0	0.590	0.784	11.17	8.40	0.1063	0.0961	0.0922	0.0046	0.2041	0.0506	0.1764	0.1417	0.0661	0.1948	0.0025	0.0968	0.0166	0.0022	0.0001	0.0032
0.3	0.4	0.513	0.793	10.08	6.55	0.1191	0.0786	0.0928	0.0037	0.2111	0.0400	0.1974	0.1132	0.0932	0.1576	0.0103	0.0863	0.0170	0.0018	0.0009	0.0062
	0.6	0.551	0.784	10.47	7.35	0.1150	0.0848	0.0926	0.0040	0.2083	0.0446	0.1901	0.1241	0.0842	0.1697	0.0082	0.0890	0.0168	0.0020	0.0008	0.0064
	1.0	0.603	0.766	11.12	8.74	0.1085	0.0943	0.0922	0.0046	0.2036	0.0515	0.1779	0.1414	0.0703	0.1899	0.0055	0.0926	0.0167	0.0022	0.0005	0.0067
	1.5	0.642	0.751	11.74	10.08	0.1021	0.1036	0.0917	0.0053	0.1995	0.0581	0.1665	0.1583	0.0576	0.2079	0.0035	0.0953	0.0165	0.0024	0.0003	0.0069
	2.0	0.677	0.744	12.25	11.15	0.0977	0.1100	0.0914	0.0057	0.1965	0.0628	0.1578	0.1714	0.0485	0.2208	0.0024	0.0969	0.0163	0.0026	0.0003	0.0071
0.4	0.4	0.537	0.774	10.30	7.17	0.1178	0.0802	0.0927	0.0039	0.2097	0.0422	0.1946	0.1178	0.0906	0.1600	0.0105	0.0859	0.0169	0.0018	0.0022	0.0102
	0.6	0.583	0.759	10.80	8.28	0.1128	0.0874	0.0924	0.0043	0.2061	0.0482	0.1853	0.1317	0.0809	0.1738	0.0084	0.0883	0.0167	0.0020	0.0019	0.0107
	1.0	0.653	0.731	11.62	10.37	0.1050	0.0994	0.0918	0.0052	0.1999	0.0578	0.1698	0.1551	0.0652	0.1965	0.0056	0.0920	0.0165	0.0027	0.0013	0.0114
	1.5	0.717	0.710	12.50	12.60	0.0971	0.1117	0.0911	0.0062	0.1941	0.0677	0.1543	0.1792	0.0506	0.2178	0.0037	0.0948	0.0163	0.0027	0.0010	0.0118
	2.0	0.764	0.698	13.25	14.55	0.0915	0.1206	0.0907	0.0070	0.1894	0.0756	0.1420	0.1987	0.0403	0.2330	0.0024	0.0963	0.0161	0.0030	0.0008	0.0122
0.5	0.4	0.554	0.753	10.42	7.66	0.1170	0.0811	0.0926	0.0040	0.2087	0.0442	0.1924	0.1205	0.0898	0.1595	0.0107	0.0853	0.0169	0.0020	0.0042	0.0145
	0.6	0.606	0.730	10.96	9.12	0.1115	0.0889	0.0922	0.0046	0.2045	0.0506	0.1820	0.1360	0.0791	0.1738	0.0086	0.0878	0.0167	0.0022	0.0036	0.0152
	1.0	0.694	0.694	12.03	12.03	0.1025	0.1025	0.0915	0.0057	0.1970	0.0626	0.1639	0.1639	0.0626	0.1970	0.0057	0.0915	0.0164	0.0028	0.0028	0.0164
	1.5	0.781	0.664	13.12	15.47	0.0937	0.1163	0.0908	0.0070	0.1891	0.0759	0.1456	0.1939	0.0479	0.2187	0.0039	0.0940	0.0160	0.0034	0.0021	0.0174
	2.0	0.850	0.642	14.09	18.64	0.0870	0.1275	0.0901	0.0082	0.1825	0.0877	0.1307	0.2193	0.0376	0.2348	0.0027	0.0957	0.0157	0.0039	0.0016	0.0181

TABLE 16

$a_A = 0.1$ a_B = variable $r_A = 1.5$ a_B = variable

	0.4	0.534	0.580	5.12	4.71	0.0964	0.0827	0.0934	0.0033	0.1750	0.0536	0.1459	0.1239	0.0691	0.1547	0.0074	0.0865	0.0008	0.0000	0.0000	0.0008
	0.6	0.546	0.580	5.17	4.87	0.0950	0.0852	0.0933	0.0034	0.1740	0.0553	0.1437	0.1278	0.0665	0.1594	0.0063	0.0885	0.0008	0.0000	0.0000	0.0008
0.1	1.0	0.563	0.578	5.24	5.11	0.0931	0.0886	0.0934	0.0034	0.1726	0.0578	0.1406	0.1335	0.0628	0.1661	0.0048	0.0912	0.0008	0.0000	0.0000	0.0008
	1.5	0.577	0.577	5.30	5.30	0.0915	0.0915	0.0932	0.0037	0.1715	0.0599	0.1381	0.1381	0.0599	0.1715	0.0037	0.0932	0.0008	0.0000	0.0000	0.0008
	2.0	0.587	0.576	5.34	5.44	0.0905	0.0934	0.0931	0.0038	0.1707	0.0613	0.1364	0.1413	0.0578	0.1752	0.0030	0.0945	0.0008	0.0000	0.0000	0.0008
	0.4	0.569	0.574	5.25	5.21	0.0934	0.0884	0.0933	0.0036	0.1725	0.0583	0.1406	0.1342	0.0634	0.1657	0.0065	0.0882	0.0008	0.0000	0.0002	0.0030
	0.6	0.594	0.570	5.35	5.58	0.0909	0.0931	0.0931	0.0038	0.1706	0.0620	0.1364	0.1423	0.0587	0.1747	0.0051	0.0906	0.0008	0.0000	0.0001	0.0031
0.2	1.0	0.631	0.566	5.51	6.15	0.0873	0.1001	0.0929	0.0042	0.1677	0.0675	0.1300	0.1545	0.0516	0.1881	0.0034	0.0938	0.0008	0.0000	0.0001	0.0032
	1.5	0.663	0.562	5.64	6.66	0.0841	0.1061	0.0928	0.0045	0.1652	0.0724	0.1245	0.1652	0.0457	0.1995	0.0022	0.0960	0.0008	0.0000	0.0001	0.0032
	2.0	0.685	0.558	5.74	7.04	0.0820	0.1102	0.0927	0.0047	0.1634	0.0760	0.1206	0.1728	0.0416	0.2075	0.0015	0.0973	0.0008	0.0000	0.0000	0.0033
	0.4	0.600	0.564	5.36	5.70	0.0915	0.0923	0.0931	0.0039	0.1707	0.0623	0.1368	0.1423	0.0600	0.1726	0.0064	0.0882	0.0008	0.0000	0.0006	0.0064
	0.6	0.638	0.557	5.51	6.31	0.0882	0.0988	0.0930	0.0042	0.1679	0.0679	0.1307	0.1543	0.0537	0.1847	0.0050	0.0906	0.0008	0.0000	0.0005	0.0066
0.3	1.0	0.698	0.547	5.75	7.33	0.0831	0.1090	0.0927	0.0048	0.1634	0.0770	0.1212	0.1735	0.0441	0.2036	0.0033	0.0938	0.0008	0.0000	0.0003	0.0068
	1.5	0.750	0.539	5.98	8.33	0.0785	0.1183	0.0924	0.0054	0.1592	0.0855	0.1125	0.1913	0.0359	0.2203	0.0021	0.0961	0.0008	0.0000	0.0002	0.0071
	2.0	0.788	0.532	6.15	9.11	0.0753	0.1249	0.0922	0.0058	0.1562	0.0920	0.1062	0.2047	0.0301	0.2323	0.0014	0.0974	0.0008	0.0000	0.0002	0.0072
	0.4	0.626	0.551	5.44	6.17	0.0904	0.0945	0.0930	0.0041	0.1693	0.0654	0.1342	0.1480	0.0583	0.1754	0.0065	0.0878	0.0008	0.0000	0.0014	0.0105
	0.6	0.677	0.541	5.63	7.05	0.0865	0.1024	0.0928	0.0045	0.1659	0.0724	0.1267	0.1631	0.0513	0.1890	0.0051	0.0902	0.0008	0.0000	0.0012	0.0110
0.4	1.0	0.760	0.525	5.97	8.63	0.0803	0.1152	0.0924	0.0054	0.1598	0.0855	0.1146	0.1888	0.0405	0.2107	0.0034	0.0934	0.0008	0.0000	0.0008	0.0118
	1.5	0.837	0.511	6.30	10.31	0.0745	0.1274	0.0920	0.0062	0.1540	0.0983	0.1030	0.2141	0.0310	0.2302	0.0021	0.0957	0.0008	0.0000	0.0006	0.0121
	2.0	0.895	0.501	6.56	11.71	0.0704	0.1366	0.0917	0.0069	0.1495	0.1085	0.0941	0.2339	0.0245	0.2441	0.0014	0.0971	0.0008	0.0000	0.0004	0.0124
	0.4	0.645	0.538	5.47	6.59	0.0900	0.0956	0.0929	0.0043	0.1682	0.0682	0.1324	0.1512	0.0582	0.1756	0.0066	0.0874	0.0008	0.0000	0.0029	0.0151
	0.6	0.708	0.523	5.71	7.76	0.0852	0.1045	0.0927	0.0048	0.1639	0.0766	0.1237	0.1686	0.0505	0.1899	0.0052	0.0898	0.0008	0.0000	0.0025	0.0158
0.5	1.0	0.814	0.499	6.11	10.00	0.0787	0.1192	0.0922	0.0059	0.1571	0.0928	0.1099	0.1990	0.0392	0.2118	0.0035	0.0930	0.0008	0.0000	0.0019	0.0169
	1.5	0.915	0.481	6.57	12.55	0.0720	0.1336	0.0916	0.0070	0.1498	0.1100	0.0964	0.2304	0.0296	0.2313	0.0022	0.0953	0.0008	0.0000	0.0013	0.0179
	2.0	0.998	0.462	6.90	14.90	0.0670	0.1448	0.0912	0.0080	0.1428	0.1245	0.0857	0.2559	0.0228	0.2460	0.0015	0.0967	0.0008	0.0000	0.0010	0.0186

Parabolic Haunches — Constant Width

$a_A = 0.2$ a_B = variable **TABLE 17** $r_A = 1.5$ r_B = variable

Right Haunch		Carry-over Factors		Stiffness Factors		Unif. Load F.E.M. Coef. × wL^2		Concentrated Load F.E.M. — Coef. × PL, b										Haunch Load at			
								0.1		0.3		0.5		0.7		0.9		Left, Coef. × $W_A L^2$		Right, Coef. × $W_B L^2$	
e_B	r_B	C_{AB}	C_{BA}	k_{AB}	k_{BA}	M_{AB}	M_{BA}	M_{AB}	M_{BA}	M_{AB}	M_{BA}	M_{AB}	M_{BA}	M_{AB}	M_{BA}	M_{AB}	M_{BA}	M_{AB}	M_{BA}	M_{AB}	M_{BA}
0.1	0.4	0.519	0.667	6.39	4.98	0.1119	0.0754	0.0961	0.0019	0.2027	0.0406	0.1737	0.1110	0.0828	0.1482	0.0090	0.0857	0.0032	0.0001	0.0000	0.0008
	0.6	0.531	0.666	6.47	5.16	0.1100	0.0780	0.0961	0.0020	0.2018	0.0420	0.1714	0.1147	0.0802	0.1529	0.0076	0.0878	0.0032	0.0001	0.0000	0.0008
	1.0	0.548	0.664	6.57	5.42	0.1079	0.0813	0.0960	0.0021	0.2010	0.0440	0.1680	0.1200	0.0759	0.1597	0.0058	0.0906	0.0032	0.0001	0.0000	0.0008
	1.5	0.562	0.663	6.66	5.64	0.1061	0.0841	0.0960	0.0022	0.1995	0.0457	0.1652	0.1245	0.0724	0.1652	0.0045	0.0928	0.0032	0.0001	0.0000	0.0008
	2.0	0.571	0.662	6.72	5.80	0.1050	0.0859	0.0960	0.0022	0.1988	0.0469	0.1633	0.1276	0.0701	0.1690	0.0036	0.0942	0.0032	0.0001	0.0000	0.0008
0.2	0.4	0.553	0.659	6.59	5.53	0.1083	0.0810	0.0960	0.0021	0.2005	0.0444	0.1680	0.1207	0.0767	0.1592	0.0079	0.0875	0.0032	0.0001	0.0002	0.0030
	0.6	0.578	0.655	6.74	5.94	0.1056	0.0854	0.0959	0.0022	0.1987	0.0473	0.1634	0.1283	0.0711	0.1682	0.0063	0.0900	0.0032	0.0001	0.0002	0.0031
	1.0	0.614	0.649	6.97	6.59	0.1015	0.0921	0.0958	0.0025	0.1962	0.0518	0.1563	0.1399	0.0628	0.1819	0.0041	0.0933	0.0032	0.0001	0.0001	0.0032
	1.5	0.645	0.645	7.17	7.17	0.0980	0.0980	0.0957	0.0027	0.1936	0.0558	0.1502	0.1502	0.0558	0.1936	0.0027	0.0957	0.0032	0.0001	0.0001	0.0032
	2.0	0.666	0.641	7.32	7.60	0.0957	0.1020	0.0956	0.0028	0.1919	0.0587	0.1459	0.1576	0.0510	0.2019	0.0018	0.0971	0.0032	0.0001	0.0001	0.0033
0.3	0.4	0.583	0.647	6.74	6.07	0.1064	0.0845	0.0959	0.0023	0.1988	0.0476	0.1639	0.1282	0.0728	0.1659	0.0078	0.0874	0.0032	0.0001	0.0007	0.0063
	0.6	0.620	0.639	6.97	6.76	0.1027	0.0907	0.0954	0.0025	0.1962	0.0520	0.1573	0.1395	0.0655	0.1782	0.0062	0.0900	0.0032	0.0001	0.0006	0.0065
	1.0	0.678	0.628	7.33	7.92	0.0970	0.1004	0.0956	0.0029	0.1920	0.0594	0.1467	0.1579	0.0542	0.1975	0.0040	0.0934	0.0032	0.0001	0.0004	0.0068
	1.5	0.729	0.618	7.68	9.06	0.0919	0.1094	0.0954	0.0032	0.1881	0.0665	0.1370	0.1752	0.0443	0.2148	0.0025	0.0958	0.0032	0.0001	0.0003	0.0070
	2.0	0.766	0.611	7.94	9.96	0.0884	0.1158	0.0953	0.0035	0.1851	0.0718	0.1299	0.1883	0.0374	0.2273	0.0017	0.0971	0.0032	0.0001	0.0002	0.0072
0.4	0.4	0.608	0.633	6.86	6.58	0.1052	0.0865	0.0959	0.0024	0.1976	0.0500	0.1611	0.1333	0.0709	0.1685	0.0079	0.0870	0.0032	0.0001	0.0017	0.0104
	0.6	0.657	0.621	7.15	7.57	0.1009	0.0938	0.0956	0.0027	0.1944	0.0556	0.1530	0.1477	0.0627	0.1823	0.0063	0.0895	0.0032	0.0001	0.0014	0.0108
	1.0	0.737	0.602	7.65	9.36	0.0941	0.1060	0.0954	0.0032	0.1887	0.0662	0.1395	0.1723	0.0500	0.2045	0.0042	0.0928	0.0032	0.0001	0.0009	0.0117
	1.5	0.811	0.586	8.16	11.29	0.0877	0.1177	0.0951	0.0038	0.1831	0.0769	0.1265	0.1969	0.0387	0.2246	0.0027	0.0953	0.0032	0.0001	0.0007	0.0120
	2.0	0.867	0.575	8.57	12.93	0.0831	0.1266	0.0949	0.0042	0.1787	0.0855	0.1165	0.2164	0.0307	0.2392	0.0018	0.0968	0.0032	0.0001	0.0005	0.0123
0.5	0.4	0.626	0.617	6.93	7.04	0.1045	0.0877	0.0958	0.0025	0.1971	0.0521	0.1593	0.1360	0.0706	0.1685	0.0080	0.0866	0.0032	0.0001	0.0033	0.0149
	0.6	0.686	0.600	7.30	8.35	0.0998	0.0959	0.0954	0.0029	0.1927	0.0589	0.1499	0.1526	0.0619	0.1835	0.0064	0.0890	0.0032	0.0001	0.0028	0.0156
	1.0	0.786	0.571	7.90	10.90	0.0922	0.1093	0.0951	0.0035	0.1862	0.0719	0.1344	0.1818	0.0485	0.2055	0.0043	0.0923	0.0032	0.0001	0.0021	0.0167
	1.5	0.883	0.548	8.57	13.85	0.0849	0.1232	0.0948	0.0042	0.1791	0.0862	0.1191	0.2122	0.0372	0.2255	0.0028	0.0949	0.0032	0.0001	0.0016	0.0177
	2.0	0.963	0.529	9.15	16.60	0.0793	0.1340	0.0945	0.0049	0.1733	0.0987	0.1069	0.2375	0.0289	0.2407	0.0019	0.0965	0.0032	0.0001	0.0012	0.0184

TABLE 18 ($r_A = 1.5$)

		$a_A = 0.3$		a_B = variable						$r_A = 1.5$						r_B = variable				
0.1	0.4	0.498	0.755	7.95	5.25	0.1242	0.0702	0.0963	0.0018	0.2233	0.0317	0.2005	0.0998	0.1421	0.0107	0.0851	0.0071	0.0002	0.0000	0.0008
	0.6	0.509	0.754	8.05	5.44	0.1226	0.0725	0.0962	0.0019	0.2225	0.0329	0.1980	0.1033	0.1469	0.0091	0.0872	0.0071	0.0002	0.0000	0.0008
	1.0	0.526	0.752	8.20	5.74	0.1203	0.0758	0.0962	0.0020	0.2213	0.0345	0.1943	0.1083	0.1538	0.0070	0.0901	0.0071	0.0002	0.0000	0.0003
	1.5	0.539	0.750	8.33	5.98	0.1183	0.0785	0.0961	0.0021	0.2203	0.0359	0.1913	0.1125	0.1592	0.0054	0.0924	0.0071	0.0002	0.0000	0.0008
	2.0	0.548	0.749	8.41	6.15	0.1171	0.0802	0.0961	0.0021	0.2197	0.0369	0.1893	0.1154	0.1631	0.0043	0.0938	0.0070	0.0002	0.0000	0.0008
0.2	0.4	0.531	0.745	8.22	5.85	0.1208	0.0753	0.0961	0.0020	0.2213	0.0348	0.1944	0.1088	0.1530	0.0094	0.0868	0.0071	0.0002	0.0002	0.0030
	0.6	0.554	0.741	8.43	6.31	0.1178	0.0796	0.0960	0.0021	0.2196	0.0372	0.1895	0.1160	0.1622	0.0075	0.0894	0.0071	0.0002	0.0002	0.0031
	1.0	0.589	0.735	8.76	7.02	0.1133	0.0862	0.0959	0.0023	0.2170	0.0410	0.1819	0.1272	0.1760	0.0050	0.0929	0.0070	0.0003	0.0001	0.0031
	1.5	0.618	0.729	9.06	7.68	0.1094	0.0919	0.0958	0.0025	0.2148	0.0443	0.1752	0.1370	0.1881	0.0032	0.0954	0.0070	0.0003	0.0001	0.0032
	2.0	0.638	0.725	9.27	8.17	0.1069	0.0959	0.0957	0.0027	0.2132	0.0468	0.1705	0.1442	0.1966	0.0022	0.0968	0.0070	0.0003	0.0001	0.0032
0.3	0.4	0.559	0.732	8.43	6.44	0.1187	0.0786	0.0960	0.0021	0.2197	0.0374	0.1901	0.1158	0.1597	0.0093	0.0867	0.0071	0.0002	0.0009	0.0062
	0.6	0.595	0.723	8.75	7.20	0.1147	0.0845	0.0959	0.0024	0.2172	0.0411	0.1830	0.1265	0.1721	0.0074	0.0894	0.0070	0.0003	0.0007	0.0065
	1.0	0.649	0.710	9.28	8.49	0.1085	0.0940	0.0957	0.0027	0.2133	0.0473	0.1716	0.1442	0.1917	0.0049	0.0929	0.0070	0.0003	0.0005	0.0068
	1.5	0.698	0.698	9.78	9.78	0.1028	0.1028	0.0954	0.0031	0.2095	0.0533	0.1609	0.1609	0.2095	0.0031	0.0954	0.0070	0.0003	0.0003	0.0070
	2.0	0.733	0.690	10.17	10.81	0.0989	0.1091	0.0953	0.0034	0.2066	0.0579	0.1530	0.1737	0.2224	0.0021	0.0969	0.0070	0.0004	0.0002	0.0071
0.4	0.4	0.582	0.716	8.59	6.99	0.1175	0.0803	0.0960	0.0023	0.2186	0.0394	0.1872	0.1205	0.1622	0.0095	0.0862	0.0070	0.0002	0.0020	0.0102
	0.6	0.629	0.701	9.01	8.08	0.1129	0.0874	0.0957	0.0026	0.2155	0.0441	0.1785	0.1341	0.1760	0.0076	0.0888	0.0070	0.0003	0.0017	0.0107
	1.0	0.705	0.680	9.73	10.09	0.1054	0.0991	0.0955	0.0031	0.2101	0.0530	0.1639	0.1577	0.1985	0.0051	0.0923	0.0070	0.0003	0.0011	0.0115
	1.5	0.775	0.661	10.47	12.27	0.0983	0.1106	0.0951	0.0037	0.2048	0.0621	0.1495	0.1816	0.2192	0.0033	0.0949	0.0070	0.0004	0.0009	0.0119
	2.0	0.829	0.648	11.07	14.15	0.0932	0.1193	0.0949	0.0041	0.2005	0.0696	0.1383	0.2009	0.2345	0.0023	0.0965	0.0069	0.0004	0.0007	0.0122
0.5	0.4	0.600	0.694	8.65	7.46	0.1170	0.0813	0.0959	0.0024	0.2181	0.0411	0.1853	0.1229	0.1620	0.0097	0.0857	0.0070	0.0002	0.0036	0.0147
	0.6	0.654	0.673	9.18	8.90	0.1120	0.0892	0.0956	0.0028	0.2140	0.0467	0.1753	0.1385	0.1769	0.0078	0.0882	0.0070	0.0003	0.0031	0.0154
	1.0	0.751	0.642	10.08	11.74	0.1036	0.1021	0.0953	0.0035	0.2079	0.0576	0.1583	0.1665	0.1995	0.0053	0.0917	0.0069	0.0003	0.0024	0.0165
	1.5	0.843	0.616	11.07	15.12	0.0957	0.1158	0.0948	0.0042	0.2009	0.0699	0.1412	0.1961	0.2200	0.0035	0.0944	0.0069	0.0004	0.0018	0.0175
	2.0	0.920	0.598	11.90	18.20	0.0898	0.1263	0.0944	0.0048	0.1955	0.0807	0.1275	0.2212	0.2359	0.0025	0.0961	0.0068	0.0005	0.0014	0.0182

Parabolic Haunches — Constant Width

TABLE 19

$a_A = 0.4$ $\qquad$ $r_A = 1.5$ $\qquad$ $a_B = \text{variable}$ $\qquad$ $r_B = \text{variable}$

Right Haunch a_B	r_B	Carry-over Factors C_{AB}	C_{BA}	Stiffness Factors k_{AB}	k_{BA}	Unif. Load F.E.M. Coef. × wL^2 M_{AB}	M_{BA}	Conc. b=0.1 M_{AB}	M_{BA}	b=0.3 M_{AB}	M_{BA}	b=0.5 M_{AB}	M_{BA}	b=0.7 M_{AB}	M_{BA}	b=0.9 M_{AB}	M_{BA}	Haunch Left Coef × $W_A L^2$ M_{AB}	M_{BA}	Haunch Right Coef × $W_B L^2$ M_{AB}	M_{BA}
0.1	0.4	0.472	0.842	9.79	5.49	0.1339	0.0664	0.0959	0.0019	0.2330	0.0273	0.2238	0.0908	0.1368	0.1121	0.0124	0.0844	0.0121	0.0005	0.0000	0.0008
	0.6	0.483	0.841	9.93	5.71	0.1321	0.0687	0.0959	0.0020	0.2323	0.0283	0.2211	0.0941	0.1415	0.1082	0.0106	0.0867	0.0121	0.0005	0.0000	0.0008
	1.0	0.499	0.839	10.14	6.03	0.1296	0.0719	0.0958	0.0021	0.2312	0.0298	0.2172	0.0990	0.1484	0.1028	0.0081	0.0897	0.0121	0.0006	0.0000	0.0008
	1.5	0.511	0.837	10.31	6.30	0.1274	0.0745	0.0957	0.0021	0.2302	0.0310	0.2141	0.1030	0.1540	0.0983	0.0062	0.0920	0.0121	0.0006	0.0000	0.0008
	2.0	0.520	0.835	10.42	6.48	0.1260	0.0763	0.0957	0.0022	0.2295	0.0319	0.2119	0.1057	0.1579	0.0952	0.0050	0.0935	0.0121	0.0006	0.0000	0.0008
0.2	0.4	0.503	0.831	10.15	6.15	0.1303	0.0713	0.0958	0.0021	0.2311	0.0300	0.2174	0.0994	0.1476	0.1039	0.0110	0.0862	0.0121	0.0006	0.0003	0.0030
	0.6	0.526	0.826	10.44	6.64	0.1270	0.0756	0.0957	0.0022	0.2295	0.0322	0.2121	0.1062	0.1568	0.0968	0.0087	0.0889	0.0121	0.0006	0.0002	0.0030
	1.0	0.558	0.818	10.89	7.43	0.1220	0.0820	0.0955	0.0025	0.2269	0.0356	0.2040	0.1169	0.1709	0.0861	0.0058	0.0925	0.0120	0.0007	0.0002	0.0031
	1.5	0.586	0.811	11.29	8.16	0.1177	0.0877	0.0953	0.0027	0.2246	0.0387	0.1969	0.1265	0.1831	0.0769	0.0038	0.0951	0.0120	0.0007	0.0001	0.0032
	2.0	0.606	0.806	11.58	8.70	0.1149	0.0916	0.0952	0.0028	0.2229	0.0409	0.1918	0.1334	0.1918	0.0704	0.0026	0.0967	0.0119	0.0008	0.0001	0.0032
0.3	0.4	0.530	0.815	10.43	6.78	0.1280	0.0744	0.0957	0.0022	0.2296	0.0323	0.2129	0.1059	0.1542	0.0992	0.0109	0.0861	0.0121	0.0006	0.0010	0.0062
	0.6	0.563	0.805	10.87	7.61	0.1237	0.0803	0.0955	0.0025	0.2271	0.0357	0.2053	0.1162	0.1667	0.0898	0.0087	0.0888	0.0120	0.0007	0.0008	0.0064
	1.0	0.615	0.789	11.58	9.03	0.1168	0.0896	0.0952	0.0029	0.2231	0.0413	0.1931	0.1332	0.1866	0.0751	0.0057	0.0925	0.0119	0.0008	0.0006	0.0067
	1.5	0.661	0.775	12.27	10.47	0.1106	0.0983	0.0949	0.0033	0.2192	0.0468	0.1816	0.1495	0.2048	0.0621	0.0037	0.0951	0.0119	0.0009	0.0004	0.0070
	2.0	0.695	0.766	12.80	11.62	0.1062	0.1046	0.0947	0.0036	0.2163	0.0511	0.1730	0.1621	0.2181	0.0527	0.0025	0.0967	0.0118	0.0010	0.0003	0.0071
0.4	0.4	0.551	0.796	10.64	7.36	0.1268	0.0761	0.0956	0.0024	0.2285	0.0341	0.2099	0.1104	0.1566	0.0969	0.0111	0.0855	0.0120	0.0007	0.0024	0.0101
	0.6	0.595	0.780	11.20	8.55	0.1217	0.0829	0.0953	0.0027	0.2254	0.0385	0.2007	0.1233	0.1705	0.0864	0.0089	0.0882	0.0120	0.0007	0.0020	0.0105
	1.0	0.667	0.755	12.17	10.75	0.1136	0.0944	0.0950	0.0033	0.2200	0.0465	0.1850	0.1460	0.1932	0.0698	0.0060	0.0918	0.0119	0.0009	0.0013	0.0114
	1.5	0.733	0.733	13.18	13.18	0.1058	0.1058	0.0946	0.0039	0.2145	0.0548	0.1694	0.1694	0.2145	0.0548	0.0039	0.0946	0.0118	0.0011	0.0011	0.0118
	2.0	0.783	0.718	14.00	15.28	0.1001	0.1145	0.0942	0.0044	0.2100	0.0618	0.1571	0.1885	0.2302	0.0441	0.0027	0.0962	0.0117	0.0012	0.0008	0.0121
0.5	0.4	0.568	0.771	10.80	7.85	0.1262	0.0771	0.0955	0.0026	0.2280	0.0356	0.2080	0.1128	0.1561	0.0959	0.0113	0.0849	0.0120	0.0007	0.0042	0.0145
	0.6	0.619	0.749	11.41	9.43	0.1206	0.0843	0.0952	0.0030	0.2240	0.0409	0.1975	0.1275	0.1711	0.0848	0.0091	0.0876	0.0119	0.0009	0.0036	0.0152
	1.0	0.710	0.717	12.60	12.50	0.1117	0.0971	0.0948	0.0037	0.2178	0.0506	0.1792	0.1543	0.1941	0.0677	0.0062	0.0911	0.0118	0.0010	0.0027	0.0163
	1.5	0.797	0.683	13.92	16.23	0.1024	0.1108	0.0942	0.0045	0.2107	0.0619	0.1605	0.1832	0.2153	0.0523	0.0041	0.0940	0.0117	0.0012	0.0022	0.0173
	2.0	0.868	0.661	15.05	19.70	0.0961	0.1212	0.0937	0.0052	0.2047	0.0720	0.1452	0.2081	0.2316	0.0414	0.0029	0.0957	0.0116	0.0015	0.0016	0.0180

TABLE 20

$r_A = 1.5$ $r_B = $ variable $a_B = $ variable $a_A = 0.5$

		$a_A = 0.5$			a_B var.															
0.1	0.4	0.443	0.922	11.92	5.73	0.1402	0.0638	0.0955	0.0020	0.2351	0.2408	0.0253	0.0844	0.1251	0.1323	0.0141	0.0838	0.0181	0.0011	0.0000	0.0008
	0.6	0.452	0.920	12.10	5.97	0.1384	0.0600	0.0955	0.0021	0.2343	0.2377	0.0267	0.0876	0.1210	0.1372	0.0121	0.0862	0.0180	0.0012	0.0000	0.0008
	1.0	0.468	0.918	12.35	6.28	0.1355	0.0692	0.0954	0.0022	0.2330	0.2336	0.0284	0.0925	0.1153	0.1436	0.0092	0.0893	0.0180	0.0012	0.0000	0.0008
	1.5	0.481	0.915	12.55	6.57	0.1336	0.0720	0.0953	0.0022	0.2313	0.2304	0.0296	0.0964	0.1100	0.1498	0.0070	0.0916	0.0179	0.0013	0.0000	0.0008
	2.0	0.488	0.913	12.75	6.78	0.1317	0.0737	0.0953	0.0023	0.2304	0.2280	0.0300	0.0990	0.1068	0.1535	0.0056	0.0932	0.0178	0.0014	0.0000	0.0008
0.2	0.4	0.470	0.910	12.38	6.40	0.1361	0.0686	0.0953	0.0022	0.2326	0.2341	0.0279	0.0928	0.1160	0.1430	0.0125	0.0855	0.0180	0.0012	0.0003	0.0030
	0.6	0.493	0.904	12.72	6.96	0.1330	0.0728	0.0952	0.0023	0.2314	0.2282	0.0303	0.0992	0.1088	0.1521	0.0100	0.0884	0.0179	0.0013	0.0003	0.0030
	1.0	0.522	0.893	13.30	7.79	0.1277	0.0793	0.0950	0.0026	0.2285	0.2197	0.0339	0.1095	0.0963	0.1665	0.0067	0.0922	0.0178	0.0014	0.0002	0.0031
	1.5	0.548	0.883	13.85	8.57	0.1232	0.0849	0.0949	0.0028	0.2255	0.2120	0.0372	0.1191	0.0862	0.1791	0.0042	0.0948	0.0177	0.0016	0.0001	0.0032
	2.0	0.567	0.880	14.25	9.20	0.1195	0.0887	0.0947	0.0029	0.2236	0.2067	0.0389	0.1259	0.0792	0.1882	0.0030	0.0966	0.0176	0.0017	0.0001	0.0032
0.3	0.4	0.496	0.894	12.70	7.06	0.1339	0.0713	0.0951	0.0023	0.2312	0.2294	0.0300	0.0989	0.1108	0.1496	0.0125	0.0854	0.0180	0.0012	0.0011	0.0061
	0.6	0.528	0.880	13.22	7.96	0.1292	0.0774	0.0950	0.0026	0.2288	0.2212	0.0337	0.1088	0.1007	0.1622	0.0100	0.0883	0.0178	0.0014	0.0009	0.0064
	1.0	0.578	0.861	14.15	9.50	0.1219	0.0863	0.0947	0.0030	0.2245	0.2084	0.0392	0.1251	0.0843	0.1821	0.0066	0.0920	0.0177	0.0016	0.0007	0.0067
	1.5	0.616	0.843	15.12	11.07	0.1158	0.0957	0.0944	0.0035	0.2200	0.1961	0.0448	0.1412	0.0699	0.2009	0.0042	0.0948	0.0175	0.0018	0.0004	0.0069
	2.0	0.649	0.834	15.80	12.35	0.1103	0.1013	0.0941	0.0038	0.2172	0.1868	0.0487	0.1538	0.0595	0.2147	0.0029	0.0965	0.0174	0.0020	0.0003	0.0071
0.4	0.4	0.516	0.872	12.97	7.70	0.1326	0.0729	0.0950	0.0025	0.2300	0.2262	0.0320	0.1027	0.1081	0.1521	0.0127	0.0849	0.0180	0.0014	0.0027	0.0100
	0.6	0.557	0.851	13.68	8.92	0.1272	0.0796	0.0948	0.0028	0.2269	0.2165	0.0364	0.1155	0.0970	0.1657	0.0102	0.0875	0.0178	0.0016	0.0022	0.0104
	1.0	0.624	0.823	14.95	11.28	0.1185	0.0911	0.0944	0.0034	0.2213	0.1996	0.0441	0.1374	0.0785	0.1888	0.0068	0.0913	0.0176	0.0018	0.0015	0.0112
	1.5	0.683	0.797	16.23	13.92	0.1108	0.1024	0.0940	0.0041	0.2153	0.1832	0.0523	0.1605	0.0619	0.2107	0.0045	0.0942	0.0173	0.0022	0.0012	0.0117
	2.0	0.731	0.781	17.35	16.25	0.1040	0.1111	0.0935	0.0047	0.2106	0.1699	0.0592	0.1794	0.0499	0.2268	0.0031	0.0959	0.0171	0.0025	0.0009	0.0121
0.5	0.4	0.531	0.849	13.15	8.21	0.1319	0.0738	0.0949	0.0026	0.2293	0.2239	0.0332	0.1052	0.1070	0.1515	0.0128	0.0843	0.0179	0.0014	0.0050	0.0141
	0.6	0.580	0.822	13.94	9.83	0.1260	0.0810	0.0945	0.0031	0.2255	0.2130	0.0383	0.1195	0.0948	0.1658	0.0104	0.0869	0.0177	0.0016	0.0044	0.0148
	1.0	0.664	0.781	15.47	13.12	0.1163	0.0937	0.0940	0.0039	0.2187	0.1939	0.0479	0.1456	0.0759	0.1891	0.0070	0.0908	0.0174	0.0021	0.0034	0.0160
	1.5	0.747	0.747	17.13	17.13	0.1069	0.1069	0.0934	0.0048	0.2114	0.1741	0.0589	0.1741	0.0589	0.2114	0.0048	0.0934	0.0171	0.0025	0.0030	0.0171
	2.0	0.812	0.722	18.60	20.89	0.0995	0.1176	0.0928	0.0057	0.2052	0.1578	0.0687	0.1988	0.0466	0.2282	0.0034	0.0952	0.0168	0.0030	0.0020	0.0178

Parabolic Haunches — Constant Width

TABLE 21

$a_A = 0.1$ $\qquad$ $r_A = 2.0$ $\qquad$ α_B = variable $\qquad$ r_B = variable

Concentrated Load F.E.M.—Coef. × PL, at b = 0.1, 0.3, 0.5, 0.7, 0.9.
Unif. Load F.E.M. Coef. × wL^2. Haunch Load at Left: F.E.M. Coef. × $W_A L$; Right: F.E.M. Coef. × $W_B L$.

Right Haunch a_B	r_B	C_{AB}	C_{BA}	k_{AB}	k_{BA}	Unif M_{AB}	Unif M_{BA}	0.1 M_{AB}	0.1 M_{BA}	0.3 M_{AB}	0.3 M_{BA}	0.5 M_{AB}	0.5 M_{BA}	0.7 M_{AB}	0.7 M_{BA}	0.9 M_{AB}	0.9 M_{BA}	Left M_{AB}	Left M_{BA}	Right M_{AB}	Right M_{BA}
0.1	0.4	0.533	0.590	5.25	4.74	0.0983	0.0817	0.0947	0.0026	0.1786	0.0517	0.1492	0.1223	0.0707	0.1539	0.0076	0.0864	0.0008	0.0000	0.0000	0.0008
	0.6	0.545	0.589	5.30	4.90	0.0969	0.0842	0.0946	0.0027	0.1777	0.0534	0.1470	0.1262	0.0681	0.1586	0.0065	0.0884	0.0008	0.0000	0.0000	0.0008
	1.0	0.562	0.588	5.38	5.14	0.0950	0.0876	0.0946	0.0028	0.1763	0.0558	0.1438	0.1318	0.0643	0.1653	0.0049	0.0911	0.0008	0.0000	0.0000	0.0008
	1.5	0.576	0.587	5.44	5.34	0.0934	0.0905	0.0945	0.0030	0.1752	0.0578	0.1413	0.1364	0.0613	0.1707	0.0038	0.0931	0.0008	0.0000	0.0000	0.0008
	2.0	0.586	0.586	5.48	5.48	0.0924	0.0924	0.0945	0.0030	0.1744	0.0592	0.1395	0.1395	0.0592	0.1744	0.0030	0.0945	0.0008	0.0000	0.0000	0.0008
0.2	0.4	0.568	0.583	5.39	5.25	0.0953	0.0874	0.0945	0.0029	0.1762	0.0563	0.1438	0.1325	0.0649	0.1649	0.0066	0.0881	0.0008	0.0000	0.0000	0.0030
	0.6	0.593	0.580	5.49	5.62	0.0928	0.0920	0.0944	0.0031	0.1743	0.0599	0.1395	0.1405	0.0601	0.1739	0.0052	0.0905	0.0008	0.0000	0.0002	0.0031
	1.0	0.630	0.575	5.65	6.20	0.0891	0.0990	0.0943	0.0034	0.1715	0.0653	0.1331	0.1526	0.0529	0.1873	0.0035	0.0937	0.0008	0.0000	0.0001	0.0032
	1.5	0.662	0.571	5.80	6.72	0.0859	0.1050	0.0942	0.0036	0.1690	0.0701	0.1276	0.1633	0.0469	0.1988	0.0022	0.0960	0.0008	0.0000	0.0001	0.0032
	2.0	0.684	0.568	5.90	7.10	0.0838	0.1091	0.0941	0.0038	0.1672	0.0735	0.1235	0.1709	0.0426	0.2069	0.0015	0.0972	0.0008	0.0000	0.0001	0.0033
0.3	0.4	0.599	0.573	5.49	5.74	0.0935	0.0912	0.0944	0.0031	0.1744	0.0602	0.1400	0.1405	0.0615	0.1718	0.0066	0.0881	0.0008	0.0000	0.0006	0.0064
	0.6	0.637	0.566	5.65	6.36	0.0901	0.0977	0.0943	0.0034	0.1716	0.0656	0.1338	0.1524	0.0551	0.1840	0.0051	0.0905	0.0008	0.0000	0.0005	0.0066
	1.0	0.697	0.556	5.91	7.40	0.0849	0.1078	0.0941	0.0039	0.1672	0.0745	0.1242	0.1715	0.0453	0.2029	0.0033	0.0938	0.0008	0.0000	0.0003	0.0068
	1.5	0.749	0.548	6.15	8.41	0.0802	0.1171	0.0938	0.0043	0.1631	0.0828	0.1154	0.1893	0.0369	0.2197	0.0021	0.0961	0.0008	0.0000	0.0002	0.0070
	2.0	0.787	0.541	6.33	9.21	0.0771	0.1236	0.0937	0.0047	0.1600	0.0891	0.1089	0.2026	0.0309	0.2317	0.0014	0.0973	0.0008	0.0000	0.0002	0.0072
0.4	0.4	0.625	0.560	5.58	6.22	0.0923	0.0934	0.0944	0.0033	0.1730	0.0632	0.1373	0.1461	0.0598	0.1745	0.0067	0.0877	0.0008	0.0000	0.0014	0.0105
	0.6	0.676	0.550	5.78	7.11	0.0884	0.1012	0.0942	0.0037	0.1695	0.0698	0.1298	0.1612	0.0526	0.1883	0.0053	0.0901	0.0008	0.0000	0.0012	0.0109
	1.0	0.758	0.533	6.13	8.72	0.0821	0.1139	0.0939	0.0043	0.1637	0.0827	0.1175	0.1867	0.0415	0.2099	0.0035	0.0933	0.0008	0.0000	0.0008	0.0118
	1.5	0.835	0.520	6.48	10.42	0.0763	0.1260	0.0935	0.0050	0.1579	0.0952	0.1057	0.2119	0.0319	0.2295	0.0022	0.0957	0.0008	0.0000	0.0006	0.0121
	2.0	0.893	0.509	6.76	11.85	0.0721	0.1352	0.0933	0.0056	0.1534	0.1052	0.0968	0.2317	0.0252	0.2435	0.0015	0.0970	0.0008	0.0000	0.0004	0.0124
0.5	0.4	0.644	0.545	5.60	6.64	0.0916	0.0943	0.0943	0.0035	0.1720	0.0663	0.1354	0.1493	0.0588	0.1745	0.0068	0.0873	0.0008	0.0000	0.0031	0.0151
	0.6	0.708	0.530	5.85	7.85	0.0874	0.1032	0.0941	0.0040	0.1680	0.0748	0.1268	0.1668	0.0510	0.1887	0.0054	0.0897	0.0008	0.0000	0.0026	0.0158
	1.0	0.812	0.506	6.30	10.10	0.0805	0.1175	0.0937	0.0047	0.1610	0.0900	0.1127	0.1968	0.0396	0.2115	0.0037	0.0928	0.0008	0.0000	0.0019	0.0168
	1.5	0.913	0.488	6.78	12.75	0.0737	0.1317	0.0932	0.0056	0.1535	0.1068	0.0990	0.2280	0.0300	0.2304	0.0023	0.0953	0.0008	0.0000	0.0014	0.0178
	2.0	0.997	0.470	7.19	15.20	0.0684	0.1430	0.0929	0.0065	0.1472	0.1209	0.0885	0.2533	0.0232	0.2442	0.0016	0.0967	0.0008	0.0000	0.0011	0.0185

TABLE 22

$\alpha_A = 0.2$ α_B = variable $r_A = 2.0$ r_B = variable

	$\alpha_A = 0.2$																	
0.1	0.4	0.516	0.689	6.75	5.06	0.1157	0.0974	0.0013	0.2106	0.0369	0.1815	0.1074	0.0872	0.1464	0.0094	0.0856	0.0033	0.0000	0.0008
	0.6	0.528	0.688	6.83	5.24	0.1142	0.0973	0.0013	0.2097	0.0382	0.1791	0.1110	0.0840	0.1511	0.0080	0.0877	0.0033	0.0000	0.0008
	1.0	0.545	0.686	6.94	5.51	0.1120	0.0973	0.0014	0.2085	0.0400	0.1757	0.1162	0.0796	0.1578	0.0061	0.0905	0.0033	0.0000	0.0008
	1.5	0.558	0.685	7.04	5.74	0.1102	0.0973	0.0015	0.2075	0.0416	0.1728	0.1206	0.0760	0.1634	0.0047	0.0927	0.0033	0.0000	0.0008
	2.0	0.568	0.684	7.10	5.90	0.1091	0.0972	0.0015	0.2069	0.0426	0.1709	0.1235	0.0735	0.1672	0.0038	0.0941	0.0033	0.0000	0.0008
0.2	0.4	0.550	0.681	6.96	5.62	0.1125	0.0973	0.0014	0.2085	0.0404	0.1759	0.1168	0.0805	0.1573	0.0083	0.0873	0.0033	0.0002	0.0030
	0.6	0.575	0.677	7.12	6.05	0.1097	0.0972	0.0015	0.2068	0.0431	0.1710	0.1243	0.0746	0.1664	0.0066	0.0898	0.0033	0.0002	0.0031
	1.0	0.611	0.671	7.38	6.71	0.1056	0.0971	0.0017	0.2042	0.0472	0.1638	0.1358	0.0660	0.1801	0.0044	0.0932	0.0033	0.0001	0.0032
	1.5	0.641	0.666	7.60	7.32	0.1020	0.0971	0.0018	0.2019	0.0510	0.1576	0.1459	0.0587	0.1919	0.0028	0.0956	0.0033	0.0001	0.0032
	2.0	0.662	0.662	7.77	7.77	0.0996	0.0970	0.0019	0.2003	0.0536	0.1532	0.1532	0.0536	0.2003	0.0019	0.0970	0.0032	0.0001	0.0032
0.3	0.4	0.580	0.669	7.12	6.18	0.1105	0.0973	0.0015	0.2069	0.0433	0.1716	0.1241	0.0764	0.1640	0.0082	0.0872	0.0033	0.0007	0.0063
	0.6	0.617	0.661	7.37	6.89	0.1068	0.0971	0.0017	0.2044	0.0474	0.1648	0.1353	0.0688	0.1764	0.0065	0.0898	0.0033	0.0006	0.0065
	1.0	0.674	0.649	7.77	8.08	0.1010	0.0970	0.0019	0.2003	0.0542	0.1541	0.1534	0.0571	0.1957	0.0042	0.0932	0.0032	0.0004	0.0068
	1.5	0.725	0.638	8.17	9.27	0.0959	0.0968	0.0022	0.1966	0.0608	0.1442	0.1705	0.0468	0.2132	0.0027	0.0957	0.0032	0.0003	0.0070
	2.0	0.761	0.631	8.46	10.21	0.0922	0.0967	0.0024	0.1937	0.0658	0.1368	0.1835	0.0395	0.2258	0.0018	0.0971	0.0032	0.0002	0.0071
0.4	0.4	0.604	0.654	7.25	6.70	0.1094	0.0972	0.0016	0.2057	0.0455	0.1688	0.1291	0.0745	0.1666	0.0083	0.0867	0.0033	0.0000	0.0103
	0.6	0.654	0.641	7.58	7.72	0.1050	0.0971	0.0018	0.2026	0.0505	0.1605	0.1432	0.0660	0.1804	0.0067	0.0893	0.0033	0.0001	0.0108
	1.0	0.733	0.622	8.13	9.58	0.0981	0.0969	0.0022	0.1972	0.0605	0.1468	0.1674	0.0527	0.2026	0.0044	0.0927	0.0032	0.0001	0.0116
	1.5	0.806	0.606	8.70	11.58	0.0916	0.0967	0.0026	0.1918	0.0704	0.1334	0.1918	0.0409	0.2229	0.0028	0.0952	0.0032	0.0001	0.0119
	2.0	0.862	0.594	9.16	13.29	0.0868	0.0965	0.0029	0.1876	0.0785	0.1230	0.2112	0.0326	0.2377	0.0019	0.0967	0.0032	0.0001	0.0123
0.5	0.4	0.623	0.636	7.37	7.19	0.1088	0.0971	0.0017	0.2048	0.0470	0.1669	0.1317	0.0736	0.1669	0.0084	0.0863	0.0033	0.0035	0.0148
	0.6	0.684	0.618	7.71	8.55	0.1040	0.0970	0.0020	0.2013	0.0541	0.1575	0.1481	0.0641	0.1810	0.0068	0.0888	0.0033	0.0029	0.0155
	1.0	0.784	0.590	8.40	11.17	0.0961	0.0968	0.0025	0.1948	0.0661	0.1417	0.1764	0.0506	0.2041	0.0046	0.0922	0.0032	0.0022	0.0166
	1.5	0.880	0.567	9.20	14.25	0.0887	0.0966	0.0030	0.1882	0.0792	0.1259	0.2067	0.0389	0.2236	0.0029	0.0947	0.0032	0.0017	0.0176
	2.0	0.960	0.548	9.81	17.20	0.0827	0.0963	0.0034	0.1822	0.0908	0.1135	0.2315	0.0304	0.2384	0.0020	0.0963	0.0032	0.0013	0.0183

Parabolic Haunches — Constant Width

TABLE 23

$a_A = 0.3$ a_B = variable $r_A = 2.0$ r_B = variable

Right Haunch		Carry-over Factors		Stiffness Factors		Unif. Load F.E.M. Coef. × wL^2		Concentrated Load F.E.M. — Coef. × PL (b)										Haunch Load at			
								0.1		0.3		0.5		0.7		0.9		Left Coef.×$W_A L^2$		Right Coef.×$W_B L^2$	
a_B	r_B	C_{AB}	C_{BA}	k_{AB}	k_{BA}	M_{AB}	M_{BA}	M_{AB}	M_{BA}	M_{AB}	M_{BA}	M_{AB}	M_{BA}	M_{AB}	M_{BA}	M_{AB}	M_{BA}	M_{AB}	M_{BA}	M_{AB}	M_{BA}
0.1	0.4	0.492	0.793	8.67	5.38	0.1310	0.0673	0.0975	0.0012	0.2350	0.0265	0.2140	0.0939	0.1049	0.1390	0.0115	0.0847	0.0072	0.0001	0.0000	0.0008
	0.6	0.504	0.792	8.79	5.59	0.1293	0.0695	0.0975	0.0012	0.2342	0.0275	0.2115	0.0970	0.1014	0.1437	0.0098	0.0869	0.0072	0.0001	0.0000	0.0008
	1.0	0.520	0.790	8.96	5.89	0.1269	0.0727	0.0974	0.0013	0.2332	0.0289	0.2077	0.1021	0.0960	0.1505	0.0075	0.0899	0.0072	0.0002	0.0000	0.0008
	1.5	0.532	0.788	9.11	6.15	0.1249	0.0753	0.0974	0.0014	0.2323	0.0301	0.2047	0.1062	0.0920	0.1562	0.0058	0.0922	0.0072	0.0002	0.0000	0.0008
	2.0	0.541	0.787	9.21	6.33	0.1236	0.0771	0.0973	0.0014	0.2317	0.0309	0.2026	0.1089	0.0891	0.1600	0.0047	0.0937	0.0072	0.0002	0.0000	0.0008
0.2	0.4	0.525	0.783	8.98	6.01	0.1275	0.0722	0.0974	0.0013	0.2331	0.0292	0.2079	0.1025	0.0973	0.1499	0.0101	0.0865	0.0072	0.0002	0.0003	0.0030
	0.6	0.548	0.779	9.23	6.49	0.1244	0.0764	0.0973	0.0014	0.2316	0.0312	0.2028	0.1095	0.0906	0.1590	0.0081	0.0891	0.0072	0.0002	0.0002	0.0030
	1.0	0.582	0.772	9.61	7.25	0.1198	0.0827	0.0972	0.0016	0.2293	0.0345	0.1951	0.1203	0.0805	0.1730	0.0054	0.0927	0.0072	0.0002	0.0001	0.0031
	1.5	0.611	0.766	9.96	7.94	0.1158	0.0884	0.0971	0.0017	0.2273	0.0374	0.1883	0.1299	0.0718	0.1851	0.0035	0.0953	0.0072	0.0002	0.0001	0.0032
	2.0	0.631	0.761	10.21	8.46	0.1131	0.0922	0.0971	0.0018	0.2258	0.0395	0.1835	0.1368	0.0658	0.1937	0.0024	0.0967	0.0071	0.0002	0.0001	0.0032
0.3	0.4	0.552	0.769	9.22	6.62	0.1254	0.0753	0.0973	0.0014	0.2317	0.0313	0.2035	0.1092	0.0928	0.1565	0.0101	0.0863	0.0072	0.0002	0.0009	0.0062
	0.6	0.587	0.760	9.60	7.42	0.1213	0.0810	0.0972	0.0016	0.2295	0.0345	0.1963	0.1196	0.0839	0.1689	0.0080	0.0891	0.0072	0.0002	0.0008	0.0064
	1.0	0.642	0.745	10.22	8.79	0.1149	0.0903	0.0971	0.0018	0.2259	0.0399	0.1846	0.1366	0.0702	0.1886	0.0053	0.0927	0.0071	0.0002	0.0005	0.0067
	1.5	0.690	0.733	10.81	10.17	0.1091	0.0989	0.0969	0.0021	0.2224	0.0451	0.1737	0.1530	0.0579	0.2066	0.0034	0.0953	0.0071	0.0002	0.0004	0.0070
	2.0	0.724	0.724	11.27	11.27	0.1050	0.1050	0.0968	0.0023	0.2198	0.0491	0.1655	0.1655	0.0491	0.2198	0.0023	0.0968	0.0071	0.0003	0.0003	0.0071
0.4	0.4	0.575	0.752	9.41	7.20	0.1242	0.0769	0.0973	0.0015	0.2307	0.0330	0.2006	0.1137	0.0906	0.1588	0.0103	0.0858	0.0072	0.0002	0.0022	0.0101
	0.6	0.621	0.737	9.89	8.34	0.1195	0.0837	0.0972	0.0017	0.2280	0.0370	0.1918	0.1268	0.0807	0.1727	0.0082	0.0884	0.0072	0.0002	0.0019	0.0106
	1.0	0.696	0.714	10.74	10.47	0.1118	0.0951	0.0969	0.0021	0.2231	0.0448	0.1769	0.1496	0.0652	0.1953	0.0055	0.0920	0.0071	0.0002	0.0012	0.0115
	1.5	0.766	0.695	11.62	12.80	0.1046	0.1062	0.0967	0.0025	0.2181	0.0527	0.1621	0.1730	0.0511	0.2163	0.0036	0.0947	0.0071	0.0003	0.0010	0.0118
	2.0	0.818	0.681	12.34	14.82	0.0992	0.1147	0.0965	0.0028	0.2140	0.0592	0.1504	0.1919	0.0411	0.2318	0.0025	0.0963	0.0071	0.0003	0.0007	0.0122
0.5	0.4	0.591	0.731	9.55	7.69	0.1236	0.0778	0.0972	0.0016	0.2299	0.0341	0.1987	0.1158	0.0897	0.1585	0.0105	0.0853	0.0072	0.0002	0.0039	0.0145
	0.6	0.649	0.708	10.10	9.22	0.1183	0.0851	0.0971	0.0019	0.2266	0.0392	0.1887	0.1310	0.0788	0.1735	0.0084	0.0879	0.0072	0.0002	0.0033	0.0152
	1.0	0.744	0.677	11.15	12.25	0.1100	0.0977	0.0969	0.0024	0.2208	0.0485	0.1714	0.1578	0.0628	0.1965	0.0057	0.0914	0.0071	0.0003	0.0026	0.0163
	1.5	0.834	0.649	12.35	15.80	0.1013	0.1103	0.0965	0.0029	0.2147	0.0595	0.1538	0.1868	0.0487	0.2172	0.0038	0.0941	0.0071	0.0003	0.0020	0.0174
	2.0	0.910	0.629	13.35	19.20	0.0949	0.1208	0.0962	0.0033	0.2092	0.0689	0.1395	0.2112	0.0384	0.2328	0.0027	0.0958	0.0070	0.0004	0.0016	0.0181

TABLE 24

$a_A = 0.4$ a_B = variable $r_A = 2.0$ r_B = variable

0.1	0.4	0.463	0.901	11.07	5.69	0.1434	0.0625	0.0972	0.0013	0.2468	0.0217	0.2437	0.0827	0.1234	0.1322	0.0137	0.0839	0.0124	0.0004	0.0000	0.0008
	0.6	0.474	0.899	11.25	5.93	0.1415	0.0647	0.0972	0.0013	0.2460	0.0223	0.2413	0.0857	0.1193	0.1370	0.0117	0.0862	0.0124	0.0004	0.0000	0.0008
	1.0	0.489	0.897	11.50	6.27	0.1388	0.0678	0.0971	0.0014	0.2449	0.0235	0.2371	0.0903	0.1134	0.1438	0.0090	0.0893	0.0124	0.0004	0.0000	0.0008
	1.5	0.501	0.895	11.71	6.56	0.1366	0.0704	0.0971	0.0014	0.2441	0.0245	0.2339	0.0941	0.1085	0.1495	0.0069	0.0917	0.0124	0.0004	0.0000	0.0008
	2.0	0.509	0.893	11.85	6.76	0.1352	0.0721	0.0970	0.0015	0.2435	0.0252	0.2317	0.0968	0.1052	0.1534	0.0056	0.0933	0.0124	0.0004	0.0000	0.0008
0.2	0.4	0.493	0.889	11.51	6.39	0.1396	0.0672	0.0971	0.0014	0.2450	0.0237	0.2373	0.0906	0.1147	0.1430	0.0122	0.0857	0.0124	0.0004	0.0003	0.0030
	0.6	0.515	0.883	11.87	6.92	0.1362	0.0713	0.0970	0.0015	0.2435	0.0254	0.2320	0.0971	0.1071	0.1522	0.0097	0.0885	0.0124	0.0005	0.0003	0.0030
	1.0	0.548	0.875	12.43	7.78	0.1311	0.0775	0.0969	0.0017	0.2412	0.0282	0.2238	0.1073	0.0955	0.1663	0.0065	0.0922	0.0123	0.0005	0.0002	0.0031
	1.5	0.575	0.867	12.93	8.57	0.1266	0.0831	0.0968	0.0018	0.2392	0.0307	0.2164	0.1165	0.0855	0.1787	0.0042	0.0949	0.0123	0.0005	0.0001	0.0032
	2.0	0.594	0.862	13.29	9.16	0.1236	0.0868	0.0967	0.0019	0.2378	0.0326	0.2112	0.1230	0.0785	0.1876	0.0029	0.0965	0.0123	0.0006	0.0001	0.0032
0.3	0.4	0.519	0.872	11.85	7.06	0.1374	0.0701	0.0970	0.0015	0.2436	0.0255	0.2328	0.0969	0.1092	0.1494	0.0121	0.0855	0.0124	0.0005	0.0012	0.0061
	0.6	0.552	0.860	12.39	7.95	0.1329	0.0756	0.0969	0.0017	0.2414	0.0282	0.2252	0.1064	0.0996	0.1619	0.0097	0.0883	0.0123	0.0005	0.0009	0.0064
	1.0	0.603	0.843	13.28	9.50	0.1258	0.0846	0.0967	0.0020	0.2379	0.0329	0.2127	0.1226	0.0838	0.1820	0.0064	0.0921	0.0123	0.0006	0.0007	0.0067
	1.5	0.648	0.829	14.15	11.07	0.1193	0.0932	0.0965	0.0023	0.2345	0.0375	0.2009	0.1383	0.0696	0.2005	0.0041	0.0949	0.0122	0.0007	0.0004	0.0069
	2.0	0.681	0.818	14.82	12.34	0.1147	0.0992	0.0963	0.0025	0.2318	0.0411	0.1919	0.1504	0.0592	0.2140	0.0028	0.0965	0.0122	0.0007	0.0003	0.0071
0.4	0.4	0.540	0.852	12.11	7.67	0.1362	0.0715	0.0970	0.0016	0.2426	0.0269	0.2298	0.1008	0.1073	0.1517	0.0124	0.0849	0.0124	0.0005	0.0026	0.0100
	0.6	0.583	0.833	12.79	8.95	0.1310	0.0780	0.0968	0.0018	0.2399	0.0305	0.2205	0.1130	0.0961	0.1655	0.0100	0.0876	0.0123	0.0005	0.0022	0.0104
	1.0	0.653	0.807	14.01	11.34	0.1226	0.0891	0.0965	0.0022	0.2352	0.0371	0.2045	0.1346	0.0782	0.1884	0.0067	0.0914	0.0122	0.0007	0.0015	0.0114
	1.5	0.718	0.783	15.28	14.00	0.1145	0.1001	0.0962	0.0027	0.2302	0.0441	0.1885	0.1571	0.0618	0.2100	0.0044	0.0942	0.0121	0.0008	0.0012	0.0117
	2.0	0.767	0.767	16.34	16.34	0.1085	0.1085	0.0959	0.0031	0.2262	0.0500	0.1757	0.1757	0.0500	0.2262	0.0031	0.0959	0.0121	0.0009	0.0009	0.0121
0.5	0.4	0.556	0.827	12.20	8.19	0.1357	0.0723	0.0969	0.0017	0.2420	0.0276	0.2279	0.1026	0.1062	0.1512	0.0126	0.0843	0.0124	0.0005	0.0047	0.0142
	0.6	0.607	0.800	13.10	9.90	0.1300	0.0794	0.0967	0.0019	0.2387	0.0320	0.2173	0.1166	0.0943	0.1662	0.0103	0.0869	0.0123	0.0006	0.0039	0.0150
	1.0	0.698	0.764	14.55	13.05	0.1206	0.0915	0.0963	0.0024	0.2330	0.0403	0.1987	0.1420	0.0756	0.1894	0.0070	0.0907	0.0122	0.0008	0.0030	0.0161
	1.5	0.781	0.731	16.25	17.35	0.1111	0.1040	0.0959	0.0031	0.2268	0.0499	0.1794	0.1699	0.0592	0.2106	0.0047	0.0935	0.0121	0.0012	0.0025	0.0171
	2.0	0.851	0.707	17.65	21.20	0.1040	0.1142	0.0955	0.0037	0.2212	0.0584	0.1637	0.1940	0.0469	0.2275	0.0034	0.0953	0.0120	0.0011	0.0019	0.0178

Parabolic Haunches — Constant Width

TABLE 25

$a_A = 0.5 \qquad a_B = \text{variable} \qquad r_A = 2.0 \qquad r_B = \text{variable}$

Column groups: **Carry-over Factors** (C_{AB}, C_{BA}) · **Stiffness Factors** (k_{AB}, k_{BA}) · **Unif. Load F.E.M. Coef.** $\times\, wL^2$ (M_{AB}, M_{BA}) · **Concentrated Load F.E.M. — Coef.** $\times\, PL$ (at 0.1, 0.3, 0.5, 0.7, 0.9; each M_{AB}, M_{BA}) · **Haunch Load at** Left (Coef. $\times\, W_A L^2$) and Right (Coef. $\times\, W_B L^2$); each M_{AB}, M_{BA}.

a_B	r_B	C_{AB}	C_{BA}	k_{AB}	k_{BA}	Unif M_{AB}	Unif M_{BA}	0.1 M_{AB}	0.1 M_{BA}	0.3 M_{AB}	0.3 M_{BA}	0.5 M_{AB}	0.5 M_{BA}	0.7 M_{AB}	0.7 M_{BA}	0.9 M_{AB}	0.9 M_{BA}	Left M_{AB}	Left M_{BA}	Right M_{AB}	Right M_{BA}
0.1	0.4	0.439	1.003	14.05	6.05	0.1524	0.0590	0.0967	0.0014	0.2493	0.0195	0.2667	0.0745	0.1411	0.1263	0.0159	0.0831	0.0187	0.0008	0.0000	0.0008
	0.6	0.445	1.001	14.25	6.30	0.1498	0.0610	0.0967	0.0014	0.2486	0.0205	0.2640	0.0775	0.1368	0.1311	0.0136	0.0855	0.0187	0.0009	0.0000	0.0008
	1.0	0.453	0.999	14.60	6.60	0.1470	0.0640	0.0967	0.0015	0.2474	0.0219	0.2593	0.0819	0.1304	0.1374	0.0104	0.0887	0.0187	0.0010	0.0000	0.0008
	1.5	0.462	0.998	14.90	6.90	0.1448	0.0670	0.0965	0.0015	0.2460	0.0228	0.2559	0.0857	0.1245	0.1428	0.0080	0.0912	0.0186	0.0010	0.0000	0.0008
	2.0	0.470	0.997	15.20	7.19	0.1430	0.0684	0.0967	0.0016	0.2442	0.0232	0.2533	0.0885	0.1209	0.1472	0.0065	0.0929	0.0185	0.0011	0.0000	0.0008
0.2	0.4	0.456	0.989	14.65	6.74	0.1483	0.0632	0.0967	0.0015	0.2472	0.0213	0.2601	0.0819	0.1314	0.1369	0.0144	0.0849	0.0186	0.0009	0.0003	0.0029
	0.6	0.478	0.981	15.05	7.30	0.1440	0.0678	0.0967	0.0016	0.2461	0.0235	0.2544	0.0879	0.1234	0.1461	0.0113	0.0878	0.0186	0.0010	0.0003	0.0030
	1.0	0.507	0.970	15.80	8.23	0.1386	0.0736	0.0966	0.0018	0.2435	0.0263	0.2453	0.0978	0.1098	0.1604	0.0077	0.0917	0.0185	0.0011	0.0002	0.0031
	1.5	0.529	0.963	16.60	9.15	0.1340	0.0793	0.0966	0.0019	0.2407	0.0289	0.2375	0.1069	0.0987	0.1733	0.0049	0.0945	0.0184	0.0012	0.0001	0.0032
	2.0	0.548	0.960	17.20	9.81	0.1302	0.0827	0.0963	0.0020	0.2384	0.0304	0.2315	0.1135	0.0908	0.1822	0.0034	0.0963	0.0183	0.0013	0.0001	0.0032
0.3	0.4	0.479	0.970	15.08	7.43	0.1457	0.0660	0.0966	0.0016	0.2460	0.0231	0.2554	0.0879	0.1258	0.1433	0.0143	0.0847	0.0186	0.0009	0.0014	0.0060
	0.6	0.512	0.957	15.65	8.40	0.1405	0.0716	0.0966	0.0018	0.2440	0.0261	0.2473	0.0966	0.1146	0.1559	0.0114	0.0875	0.0185	0.0011	0.0010	0.0063
	1.0	0.560	0.938	16.90	10.15	0.1329	0.0803	0.0963	0.0021	0.2399	0.0306	0.2339	0.1122	0.0968	0.1760	0.0076	0.0915	0.0184	0.0013	0.0008	0.0066
	1.5	0.598	0.920	18.20	11.90	0.1263	0.0898	0.0961	0.0025	0.2359	0.0353	0.2212	0.1275	0.0807	0.1955	0.0048	0.0944	0.0182	0.0014	0.0005	0.0068
	2.0	0.629	0.910	19.20	13.35	0.1208	0.0949	0.0958	0.0027	0.2328	0.0384	0.2112	0.1395	0.0689	0.2092	0.0033	0.0962	0.0181	0.0016	0.0004	0.0070
0.4	0.4	0.499	0.947	15.40	8.08	0.1443	0.0674	0.0965	0.0017	0.2448	0.0244	0.2522	0.0913	0.1229	0.1456	0.0145	0.0841	0.0186	0.0010	0.0031	0.0098
	0.6	0.541	0.926	16.30	9.48	0.1388	0.0738	0.0964	0.0019	0.2420	0.0283	0.2425	0.1027	0.1105	0.1590	0.0118	0.0867	0.0185	0.0012	0.0025	0.0102
	1.0	0.606	0.895	17.90	12.10	0.1295	0.0847	0.0960	0.0024	0.2371	0.0346	0.2251	0.1233	0.0906	0.1823	0.0079	0.0907	0.0183	0.0014	0.0018	0.0111
	1.5	0.661	0.868	19.70	15.05	0.1212	0.0961	0.0957	0.0029	0.2316	0.0414	0.2081	0.1452	0.0720	0.2047	0.0052	0.0937	0.0180	0.0016	0.0015	0.0116
	2.0	0.707	0.851	21.20	17.65	0.1142	0.1040	0.0953	0.0034	0.2275	0.0469	0.1940	0.1637	0.0584	0.2212	0.0037	0.0955	0.0178	0.0019	0.0011	0.0120
0.5	0.4	0.513	0.924	15.59	8.67	0.1436	0.0682	0.0964	0.0018	0.2441	0.0256	0.2499	0.0933	0.1217	0.1449	0.0147	0.0835	0.0185	0.0011	0.0057	0.0138
	0.6	0.562	0.894	16.62	10.45	0.1376	0.0750	0.0961	0.0021	0.2408	0.0297	0.2388	0.1064	0.1084	0.1591	0.0120	0.0861	0.0184	0.0013	0.0050	0.0145
	1.0	0.642	0.850	18.64	14.09	0.1275	0.0870	0.0957	0.0027	0.2348	0.0376	0.2193	0.1307	0.0877	0.1825	0.0082	0.0901	0.0181	0.0016	0.0039	0.0157
	1.5	0.721	0.812	20.89	18.60	0.1176	0.0995	0.0952	0.0034	0.2282	0.0466	0.1988	0.1578	0.0687	0.2052	0.0057	0.0928	0.0178	0.0020	0.0030	0.0168
	2.0	0.784	0.784	22.83	22.83	0.1099	0.1099	0.0947	0.0040	0.2224	0.0549	0.1816	0.1816	0.0549	0.2224	0.0040	0.0947	0.0176	0.0023	0.0023	0.0176

TABLE 26

$a_A = 0$ | a_B = variable | $r_A = 0$ | r_B = variable

α_A		$a_A=0$		a_B = variable									$r_A=0$					r_B = variable			
0.1	0.4	0.539	0.498	4.44	4.10	0.0795	0.0914	0.0806	0.0100	0.1439	0.0696	0.1189	0.1378	0.0561	0.1614	0.0060	0.0872	0.0000	0.0000	0.0000	0.0008
	0.6	0.551	0.497	4.59	4.13	0.0782	0.0940	0.0804	0.0103	0.1429	0.0717	0.1169	0.1419	0.0539	0.1660	0.0051	0.0891	0.0000	0.0000	0.0000	0.0008
	1.0	0.569	0.496	4.79	4.18	0.0765	0.0976	0.0802	0.0107	0.1414	0.0747	0.1141	0.1478	0.0508	0.1726	0.0039	0.0917	0.0000	0.0000	0.0000	0.0008
	1.5	0.583	0.495	4.97	4.22	0.0751	0.1007	0.0800	0.0111	0.1402	0.0772	0.1119	0.1527	0.0483	0.1779	0.0030	0.0936	0.0000	0.0000	0.0000	0.0008
	2.0	0.593	0.494	5.09	4.24	0.0742	0.1026	0.0799	0.0113	0.1394	0.0790	0.1103	0.1560	0.0466	0.1816	0.0024	0.0948	0.0000	0.0000	0.0000	0.0008
0.2	0.4	0.575	0.492	4.89	4.19	0.0768	0.0975	0.0802	0.0108	0.1413	0.0754	0.1141	0.1487	0.0513	0.1724	0.0052	0.0888	0.0000	0.0000	0.0001	0.0030
	0.6	0.600	0.489	5.22	4.25	0.0745	0.1025	0.0799	0.0115	0.1393	0.0799	0.1103	0.1572	0.0472	0.1812	0.0041	0.0912	0.0000	0.0000	0.0001	0.0031
	1.0	0.638	0.485	5.72	4.35	0.0712	0.1098	0.0794	0.0125	0.1363	0.0867	0.1046	0.1699	0.0413	0.1943	0.0027	0.0942	0.0000	0.0000	0.0001	0.0032
	1.5	0.670	0.482	6.17	4.44	0.0684	0.1162	0.0791	0.0133	0.1337	0.0926	0.0997	0.1810	0.0364	0.2054	0.0017	0.0963	0.0000	0.0000	0.0000	0.0032
	2.0	0.692	0.479	6.50	4.50	0.0665	0.1205	0.0788	0.0140	0.1318	0.0968	0.0963	0.1889	0.0331	0.2132	0.0012	0.0975	0.0000	0.0000	0.0000	0.0033
0.3	0.4	0.606	0.483	5.33	4.25	0.0750	0.1018	0.0799	0.0116	0.1393	0.0804	0.1106	0.1574	0.0483	0.1793	0.0051	0.0889	0.0000	0.0000	0.0005	0.0064
	0.6	0.645	0.478	5.88	4.35	0.0720	0.1088	0.0794	0.0126	0.1364	0.0872	0.1052	0.1700	0.0430	0.1913	0.0040	0.0912	0.0000	0.0000	0.0004	0.0066
	1.0	0.705	0.469	6.77	4.51	0.0673	0.1196	0.0787	0.0142	0.1318	0.0982	0.0967	0.1899	0.0351	0.2097	0.0027	0.0942	0.0000	0.0000	0.0003	0.0069
	1.5	0.758	0.462	7.64	4.65	0.0633	0.1293	0.0781	0.0158	0.1276	0.1085	0.0892	0.2082	0.0283	0.2258	0.0016	0.0964	0.0000	0.0000	0.0002	0.0071
	2.0	0.797	0.456	8.30	4.75	0.0605	0.1362	0.0777	0.0169	0.1245	0.1161	0.0837	0.2218	0.0236	0.2372	0.0011	0.0976	0.0000	0.0000	0.0001	0.0072
0.4	0.4	0.632	0.473	5.76	4.31	0.0739	0.1045	0.0797	0.0122	0.1379	0.0844	0.1082	0.1636	0.0468	0.1823	0.0052	0.0885	0.0000	0.0000	0.0011	0.0107
	0.6	0.684	0.463	6.54	4.43	0.0703	0.1129	0.0791	0.0136	0.1342	0.0934	0.1016	0.1795	0.0409	0.1958	0.0041	0.0908	0.0000	0.0000	0.0009	0.0111
	1.0	0.768	0.450	7.93	4.64	0.0647	0.1260	0.0781	0.0159	0.1280	0.1086	0.0907	0.2060	0.0319	0.2169	0.0027	0.0939	0.0000	0.0000	0.0006	0.0119
	1.5	0.847	0.438	9.37	4.84	0.0596	0.1390	0.0773	0.0183	0.1223	0.1239	0.0808	0.2319	0.0242	0.2357	0.0017	0.0961	0.0000	0.0000	0.0005	0.0122
	2.0	0.905	0.429	10.55	5.00	0.0559	0.1491	0.0766	0.0201	0.1178	0.1359	0.0733	0.2519	0.0190	0.2489	0.0011	0.0973	0.0000	0.0000	0.0003	0.0125
0.5	0.4	0.653	0.461	6.16	4.34	0.0732	0.1058	0.0794	0.0127	0.1368	0.0873	0.1066	0.1672	0.0463	0.1823	0.0053	0.0877	0.0000	0.0000	0.0021	0.0155
	0.6	0.717	0.448	7.21	4.48	0.0693	0.1151	0.0788	0.0144	0.1325	0.0980	0.0991	0.1885	0.0399	0.1963	0.0042	0.0903	0.0000	0.0000	0.0018	0.0162
	1.0	0.824	0.428	9.12	4.75	0.0628	0.1310	0.0777	0.0174	0.1252	0.1173	0.0866	0.2171	0.0306	0.2181	0.0027	0.0933	0.0000	0.0000	0.0013	0.0173
	1.5	0.929	0.411	11.35	5.02	0.0571	0.1465	0.0765	0.0206	0.1179	0.1377	0.0748	0.2492	0.0227	0.2376	0.0018	0.0956	0.0000	0.0000	0.0010	0.0182
	2.0	1.013	0.399	13.29	5.23	0.0527	0.1586	0.0756	0.0234	0.1120	0.1547	0.0660	0.2750	0.0173	0.2514	0.0012	0.0969	0.0000	0.0000	0.0007	0.0188
0.75	0.4	0.679	0.431	6.97	4.42	0.0717	0.1059	0.0791	0.0133	0.1344	0.0902	0.1029	0.1681	0.0449	0.1792	0.0054	0.0870	0.0000	0.0000	0.0063	0.0283
	0.6	0.761	0.407	8.62	4.61	0.0672	0.1157	0.0783	0.0155	0.1291	0.1031	0.0941	0.1873	0.0386	0.1918	0.0044	0.0889	0.0000	0.0000	0.0057	0.0298
	1.0	0.912	0.373	12.13	4.96	0.0600	0.1331	0.0768	0.0198	0.1195	0.1287	0.0797	0.2217	0.0294	0.2119	0.0029	0.0917	0.0000	0.0000	0.0045	0.0325
	1.5	1.080	0.343	16.82	5.34	0.0524	0.1538	0.0751	0.0251	0.1095	0.1582	0.0660	0.2580	0.0218	0.2304	0.0020	0.0940	0.0000	0.0000	0.0035	0.0350
	2.0	1.229	0.322	21.69	5.68	0.0481	0.1668	0.0737	0.0301	0.1004	0.1854	0.0554	0.2882	0.0167	0.2438	0.0014	0.0954	0.0000	0.0000	0.0028	0.0367
1.00	0.4	0.673	0.410	7.55	4.59	0.0698	0.1045	0.0784	0.0134	0.1304	0.0903	0.0993	0.1652	0.0440	0.1755	0.0055	0.0861	0.0000	0.0000	0.0127	0.0394
	0.6	0.755	0.379	9.68	4.86	0.0648	0.1135	0.0772	0.0161	0.1234	0.1036	0.0896	0.1828	0.0377	0.1865	0.0044	0.0879	0.0000	0.0000	0.0113	0.0419
	1.0	0.910	0.334	14.62	5.36	0.0568	0.1301	0.0750	0.0211	0.1114	0.1292	0.0742	0.2138	0.0287	0.2040	0.0031	0.0903	0.0000	0.0000	0.0092	0.0461
	1.5	1.091	0.294	21.99	5.93	0.0492	0.1480	0.0725	0.0274	0.0991	0.1591	0.0603	0.2460	0.0214	0.2202	0.0022	0.0923	0.0000	0.0000	0.0074	0.0501
	2.0	1.260	0.266	30.58	6.45	0.0439	0.1622	0.0704	0.0339	0.0891	0.1868	0.0500	0.2727	0.0163	0.2318	0.0016	0.0938	0.0000	0.0000	0.0062	0.0533

Straight Haunches — Constant Width

TABLE 27

$a_A = 0.1$ $r_A = 0.4$ a_B = variable r_B = variable

Right Haunch		Carry-over Factors		Stiffness Factors		Unif. Load F.E.M. Coef. × vL^2		Concentrated Load F.E.M.—Coef. × PL										Haunch Load at			
								b										Left		Right	
								0.1		0.3		0.5		0.7		0.9		F.E.M. Coef. × $W_A L^3$		F.E.M. Coef. × $W_B L^3$	
a_B	r_B	C_{AB}	C_{BA}	k_{AB}	k_{BA}	M_{AB}	M_{BA}	M_{AB}	M_{BA}	M_{AB}	M_{BA}	M_{AB}	M_{BA}	M_{AB}	M_{BA}	M_{AB}	M_{BA}	M_{AB}	M_{BA}	M_{AB}	M_{BA}
0.1	0.4	0.552	0.552	4.83	4.83	0.0889	0.0889	0.0884	0.0060	0.1629	0.0617	0.1340	0.1340	0.0617	0.1629	0.0060	0.0884	0.0016	0.0000	0.0000	0.0016
	0.6	0.568	0.550	4.90	5.06	0.0871	0.0923	0.0883	0.0063	0.1615	0.0643	0.1310	0.1395	0.0583	0.1693	0.0048	0.0908	0.0016	0.0000	0.0000	0.0016
	1.0	0.591	0.548	4.98	5.37	0.0847	0.0969	0.0881	0.0067	0.1596	0.0679	0.1271	0.1472	0.0538	0.1780	0.0032	0.0938	0.0016	0.0001	0.0000	0.0016
	1.5	0.608	0.547	5.04	5.61	0.0828	0.1005	0.0880	0.0070	0.1582	0.0708	0.1241	0.1531	0.0504	0.1846	0.0021	0.0959	0.0016	0.0001	0.0000	0.0017
	2.0	0.619	0.546	5.08	5.77	0.0817	0.1027	0.0879	0.0071	0.1573	0.0725	0.1221	0.1569	0.0483	0.1888	0.0015	0.0971	0.0016	0.0001	0.0000	0.0017
0.2	0.4	0.601	0.540	4.99	5.55	0.0854	0.0963	0.0881	0.0070	0.1595	0.0689	0.1273	0.1483	0.0552	0.1766	0.0058	0.0889	0.0016	0.0000	0.0004	0.0059
	0.6	0.637	0.535	5.12	6.09	0.0821	0.1029	0.0878	0.0074	0.1567	0.0746	0.1215	0.1600	0.0492	0.1887	0.0044	0.0914	0.0016	0.0000	0.0003	0.0061
	1.0	0.689	0.528	5.31	6.92	0.0774	0.1126	0.0874	0.0083	0.1525	0.0833	0.1130	0.1776	0.0405	0.2066	0.0028	0.0946	0.0016	0.0001	0.0002	0.0063
	1.5	0.730	0.523	5.46	7.63	0.0736	0.1205	0.0870	0.0090	0.1491	0.0906	0.1060	0.1924	0.0335	0.2212	0.0016	0.0967	0.0016	0.0001	0.0001	0.0064
	2.0	0.757	0.519	5.57	8.12	0.0709	0.1258	0.0868	0.0095	0.1468	0.0956	0.1014	0.2022	0.0290	0.2307	0.0011	0.0979	0.0016	0.0001	0.0001	0.0065
0.3	0.4	0.642	0.523	5.10	6.26	0.0836	0.1003	0.0879	0.0075	0.1572	0.0745	0.1232	0.1580	0.0524	0.1820	0.0060	0.0883	0.0016	0.0000	0.0013	0.0122
	0.6	0.698	0.513	5.29	7.19	0.0794	0.1093	0.0875	0.0084	0.1533	0.0834	0.1153	0.1754	0.0449	0.1974	0.0047	0.0907	0.0016	0.0000	0.0011	0.0127
	1.0	0.784	0.499	5.60	8.79	0.0728	0.1237	0.0867	0.0100	0.1466	0.0981	0.1025	0.2036	0.0337	0.2216	0.0030	0.0940	0.0016	0.0001	0.0007	0.0134
	1.5	0.858	0.489	5.88	10.34	0.0671	0.1365	0.0861	0.0114	0.1407	0.1119	0.0910	0.2299	0.0246	0.2426	0.0019	0.0962	0.0016	0.0001	0.0005	0.0139
	2.0	0.909	0.481	6.09	11.50	0.0632	0.1455	0.0856	0.0125	0.1363	0.1222	0.0831	0.2487	0.0180	0.2567	0.0013	0.0976	0.0016	0.0001	0.0003	0.0143
0.4	0.4	0.673	0.503	5.17	6.91	0.0829	0.1016	0.0877	0.0078	0.1559	0.0780	0.1212	0.1626	0.0523	0.1802	0.0062	0.0872	0.0016	0.0000	0.0032	0.0196
	0.6	0.747	0.488	5.41	8.29	0.0782	0.1118	0.0872	0.0097	0.1510	0.0895	0.1118	0.1837	0.0449	0.1955	0.0050	0.0895	0.0016	0.0000	0.0027	0.0206
	1.0	0.870	0.466	5.83	10.90	0.0705	0.1295	0.0862	0.0113	0.1423	0.1104	0.0961	0.2207	0.0335	0.2198	0.0033	0.0927	0.0016	0.0001	0.0019	0.0222
	1.5	0.986	0.448	6.26	13.77	0.0633	0.1468	0.0853	0.0138	0.1337	0.1322	0.0808	0.2583	0.0238	0.2416	0.0022	0.0951	0.0016	0.0001	0.0013	0.0235
	2.0	1.071	0.437	6.60	16.17	0.0581	0.1599	0.0845	0.0157	0.1269	0.1497	0.0693	0.2876	0.0174	0.2566	0.0015	0.0966	0.0016	0.0001	0.0010	0.0243
0.5	0.4	0.691	0.483	5.22	7.46	0.0824	0.1099	0.0876	0.0081	0.1551	0.0795	0.1198	0.1623	0.0522	0.1764	0.0064	0.0863	0.0016	0.0000	0.0060	0.0274
	0.6	0.780	0.461	5.49	9.28	0.0776	0.1113	0.0870	0.0096	0.1496	0.0926	0.1100	0.1841	0.0450	0.1901	0.0052	0.0884	0.0016	0.0000	0.0052	0.0290
	1.0	0.938	0.430	5.99	13.08	0.0695	0.1302	0.0859	0.0125	0.1397	0.1181	0.0932	0.2243	0.0341	0.2127	0.0036	0.0914	0.0016	0.0001	0.0039	0.0315
	1.5	1.101	0.406	6.56	17.79	0.0616	0.1502	0.0846	0.0159	0.1289	0.1476	0.0762	0.2680	0.0249	0.2338	0.0025	0.0939	0.0016	0.0001	0.0029	0.0339
	2.0	1.230	0.390	7.05	22.23	0.0555	0.1667	0.0836	0.0190	0.1199	0.1737	0.0628	0.3046	0.0186	0.2491	0.0017	0.0954	0.0016	0.0001	0.0022	0.0357

TABLE 28

$\alpha_A = 0.2$ $\alpha_B = $ variable $r_A = 0.4$ $r_B = $ variable

0.1	0.4	0.540	0.601	5.55	4.99	0.0963	0.0854	0.0889	0.0058	0.1766	0.0552	0.1483	0.1273	0.0689	0.1595	0.0070	0.0881	0.0059	0.0040	0.0000	0.0016
	0.6	0.556	0.600	5.63	5.23	0.0944	0.0887	0.0887	0.0060	0.1752	0.0576	0.1452	0.1327	0.0652	0.1660	0.0054	0.0905	0.0059	0.0040	0.0000	0.0016
	1.0	0.579	0.597	5.74	5.56	0.0918	0.0934	0.0885	0.0064	0.1733	0.0610	0.1409	0.1403	0.0602	0.1748	0.0036	0.0936	0.0059	0.0040	0.0000	0.0016
	1.5	0.596	0.596	5.81	5.81	0.0898	0.0968	0.0883	0.0067	0.1718	0.0636	0.1377	0.1461	0.0564	0.1815	0.0024	0.0957	0.0059	0.0040	0.0000	0.0017
	2.0	0.606	0.595	5.87	5.98	0.0886	0.0990	0.0882	0.0068	0.1709	0.0653	0.1356	0.1497	0.0541	0.1857	0.0017	0.0970	0.0059	0.0040	0.0000	0.0017
0.2	0.4	0.588	0.588	5.75	5.75	0.0926	0.0926	0.0885	0.0065	0.1732	0.0618	0.1412	0.1412	0.0618	0.1732	0.0065	0.0885	0.0059	0.0040	0.0004	0.0059
	0.6	0.623	0.583	5.91	6.32	0.0891	0.0991	0.0892	0.0071	0.1704	0.0671	0.1350	0.1527	0.0552	0.1855	0.0050	0.0911	0.0058	0.0050	0.0003	0.0061
	1.0	0.674	0.575	6.15	7.20	0.0840	0.1087	0.0377	0.0079	0.1661	0.0752	0.1259	0.1701	0.0455	0.2037	0.0331	0.0944	0.0058	0.0050	0.0002	0.0063
	1.5	0.714	0.569	6.35	7.97	0.0799	0.1166	0.0373	0.0088	0.1626	0.0821	0.1183	0.1847	0.0377	0.2186	0.0019	0.0966	0.0058	0.0050	0.0001	0.0064
	2.0	0.741	0.565	6.49	8.50	0.0772	0.1218	0.0871	0.0092	0.1602	0.0867	0.1133	0.1945	0.0327	0.2283	0.0012	0.0978	0.0058	0.0050	0.0001	0.0065
0.3	0.4	0.628	0.570	5.89	6.49	0.0908	0.0964	0.0883	0.0071	0.1709	0.0669	0.1369	0.1506	0.0589	0.1785	0.0068	0.0878	0.0059	0.0050	0.0015	0.0121
	0.6	0.682	0.559	6.12	7.48	0.0862	0.1052	0.0878	0.0080	0.1670	0.0751	0.1284	0.1676	0.0507	0.1941	0.0053	0.0902	0.0058	0.0050	0.0012	0.0126
	1.0	0.766	0.543	6.52	9.19	0.0791	0.1194	0.0870	0.0096	0.1601	0.0889	0.1147	0.1955	0.0384	0.2185	0.0034	0.0935	0.0058	0.0050	0.0008	0.0133
	1.5	0.838	0.532	6.89	10.86	0.0729	0.1322	0.0863	0.0111	0.1540	0.1021	0.1022	0.2217	0.0282	0.2399	0.0022	0.0958	0.0057	0.0050	0.0007	0.0138
	2.0	0.888	0.524	7.15	12.13	0.0687	0.1412	0.0858	0.0122	0.1495	0.1117	0.0934	0.2406	0.0214	0.2543	0.0014	0.0972	0.0057	0.0050	0.0004	0.0142
0.4	0.4	0.657	0.549	5.97	7.16	0.0900	0.0975	0.0881	0.0075	0.1696	0.0701	0.1348	0.1549	0.0587	0.1766	0.0070	0.0867	0.0058	0.0050	0.0036	0.0194
	0.6	0.729	0.531	6.28	8.62	0.0850	0.1075	0.0875	0.0087	0.1646	0.0808	0.1248	0.1755	0.0505	0.1919	0.0056	0.0890	0.0058	0.0060	0.0030	0.0204
	1.0	0.849	0.507	6.81	11.41	0.0767	0.1248	0.0655	0.0110	0.1558	0.1004	0.1078	0.2121	0.0379	0.2165	0.0038	0.0923	0.0058	0.0070	0.0022	0.0221
	1.5	0.961	0.488	7.37	14.52	0.0690	0.1420	0.0854	0.0134	0.1468	0.1211	0.0912	0.2496	0.0271	0.2388	0.0025	0.0948	0.0057	0.0090	0.0015	0.0234
	2.0	1.044	0.475	7.81	17.15	0.0632	0.1551	0.0846	0.0154	0.1398	0.1379	0.0785	0.2792	0.0199	0.2544	0.0017	0.0964	0.0057	0.0100	0.0011	0.0242
0.5	0.4	0.674	0.526	6.03	7.72	0.0895	0.0968	0.0880	0.0077	0.1688	0.0715	0.1333	0.1546	0.0585	0.1728	0.0072	0.0858	0.0058	0.0050	0.0067	0.0270
	0.6	0.760	0.502	6.37	9.64	0.0844	0.1069	0.0873	0.0092	0.1633	0.0837	0.1228	0.1758	0.0506	0.1865	0.0059	0.0880	0.0058	0.0060	0.0058	0.0286
	1.0	0.913	0.468	7.01	13.67	0.0757	0.1253	0.0851	0.0121	0.1531	0.1075	0.1047	0.2154	0.0387	0.2092	0.0041	0.0910	0.0057	0.0080	0.0044	0.0311
	1.5	1.070	0.442	7.74	18.75	0.0672	0.1450	0.0848	0.0155	0.1420	0.1355	0.0863	0.2589	0.0284	0.2306	0.0028	0.0935	0.0056	0.0100	0.0033	0.0335
	2.0	1.194	0.424	8.37	23.57	0.0606	0.1614	0.0836	0.0187	0.1325	0.1606	0.0716	0.2957	0.0213	0.2463	0.0020	0.0952	0.0056	0.0130	0.0025	0.0353

Straight Haunches — Constant Width

TABLE 29

$a_A = 0.3$ $r_A = 0.4$ a_B = variable r_B = variable

Right Haunch		Carry-over Factors		Stiffness Factors		Unif. Load F.E.M. Coef. × wL^2		Concentrated Load F.E.M.—Coef. × PL										Haunch Load at			
								b										Left F.E.M. Coef. × $W_A \cdot L^2$		Right F.E.M. Coef. × $W_B \cdot L^2$	
								0.1		0.3		0.5		0.7		0.9					
a_B	r_B	C_{AB}	C_{BA}	k_{AB}	k_{BA}	M_{AB}	M_{BA}	M_{AB}	M_{BA}	M_{AB}	M_{BA}	M_{AB}	M_{BA}	M_{AB}	M_{BA}	M_{AB}	M_{BA}	M_{AB}	M_{BA}	M_{AB}	M_{BA}
0.1	0.4	0.523	0.642	6.26	5.10	0.1003	0.0836	0.0883	0.0060	0.1820	0.0524	0.1580	0.1232	0.0745	0.1572	0.0075	0.0879	0.0122	0.0013	0.0000	0.0016
	0.6	0.539	0.641	6.35	5.35	0.0983	0.0870	0.0881	0.0062	0.1803	0.0549	0.1546	0.1287	0.0704	0.1637	0.0059	0.0903	0.0122	0.0014	0.0000	0.0016
	1.0	0.561	0.638	6.48	5.69	0.0955	0.0916	0.0878	0.0066	0.1785	0.0582	0.1502	0.1361	0.0651	0.1727	0.0039	0.0934	0.0121	0.0015	0.0000	0.0016
	1.5	0.577	0.636	6.57	5.96	0.0934	0.0951	0.0876	0.0069	0.1771	0.0607	0.1468	0.1419	0.0610	0.1794	0.0026	0.0957	0.0121	0.0016	0.0000	0.0017
	2.0	0.587	0.635	6.63	6.14	0.0921	0.0973	0.0876	0.0070	0.1760	0.0624	0.1446	0.1454	0.0585	0.1837	0.0019	0.0969	0.0121	0.0016	0.0000	0.0017
0.2	0.4	0.570	0.628	6.49	5.89	0.0964	0.0908	0.0878	0.0068	0.1785	0.0589	0.1506	0.1369	0.0669	0.1709	0.0071	0.0883	0.0121	0.0015	0.0005	0.0059
	0.6	0.604	0.622	6.68	6.48	0.0927	0.0972	0.0875	0.0073	0.1754	0.0642	0.1439	0.1483	0.0598	0.1833	0.0055	0.0909	0.0120	0.0017	0.0004	0.0060
	1.0	0.653	0.614	6.96	7.41	0.0873	0.1068	0.0870	0.0081	0.1711	0.0722	0.1344	0.1656	0.0493	0.2018	0.0034	0.0942	0.0119	0.0019	0.0003	0.0062
	1.5	0.692	0.607	7.21	8.21	0.0829	0.1148	0.0866	0.0091	0.1674	0.0789	0.1263	0.1801	0.0409	0.2168	0.0021	0.0965	0.0118	0.0020	0.0002	0.0064
	2.0	0.717	0.603	7.37	8.77	0.0800	0.1200	0.0862	0.0096	0.1649	0.0835	0.1210	0.1900	0.0355	0.2267	0.0013	0.0978	0.0118	0.0021	0.0001	0.0065
0.3	0.4	0.608	0.608	6.65	6.65	0.0945	0.0945	0.0875	0.0073	0.1762	0.0640	0.1461	0.1461	0.0640	0.1762	0.0073	0.0875	0.0121	0.0016	0.0016	0.0121
	0.6	0.660	0.596	6.93	7.68	0.0897	0.1033	0.0870	0.0083	0.1719	0.0720	0.1371	0.1630	0.0553	0.1918	0.0058	0.0900	0.0120	0.0018	0.0013	0.0126
	1.0	0.741	0.579	7.40	9.47	0.0822	0.1175	0.0861	0.0100	0.1649	0.0856	0.1225	0.1909	0.0419	0.2164	0.0037	0.0934	0.0118	0.0022	0.0009	0.0133
	1.5	0.811	0.566	7.83	11.23	0.0755	0.1303	0.0854	0.0115	0.1584	0.0985	0.1093	0.2170	0.0306	0.2380	0.0024	0.0958	0.0116	0.0026	0.0006	0.0138
	2.0	0.859	0.557	8.15	12.57	0.0709	0.1394	0.0848	0.0127	0.1537	0.1080	0.0998	0.2360	0.0232	0.2527	0.0016	0.0972	0.0115	0.0028	0.0004	0.0142
0.4	0.4	0.635	0.585	6.75	7.33	0.0937	0.0956	0.0873	0.0078	0.1748	0.0671	0.1439	0.1504	0.0636	0.1742	0.0077	0.0864	0.0120	0.0017	0.0039	0.0193
	0.6	0.705	0.565	7.10	8.85	0.0884	0.1055	0.0868	0.0090	0.1696	0.0775	0.1333	0.1707	0.0547	0.1895	0.0061	0.0887	0.0118	0.0021	0.0033	0.0203
	1.0	0.820	0.539	7.73	11.76	0.0796	0.1227	0.0856	0.0113	0.1605	0.0967	0.1154	0.2071	0.0412	0.2144	0.0042	0.0921	0.0116	0.0025	0.0024	0.0219
	1.5	0.928	0.518	8.38	15.02	0.0714	0.1400	0.0843	0.0139	0.1510	0.1170	0.0978	0.2446	0.0295	0.2370	0.0027	0.0947	0.0114	0.0031	0.0017	0.0233
	2.0	1.007	0.504	8.91	17.77	0.0652	0.1533	0.0835	0.0160	0.1437	0.1338	0.0842	0.2745	0.0218	0.2529	0.0019	0.0963	0.0112	0.0035	0.0012	0.0241
0.5	0.4	0.650	0.561	6.81	7.90	0.0932	0.0949	0.0871	0.0080	0.1739	0.0684	0.1423	0.1501	0.0632	0.1704	0.0079	0.0855	0.0120	0.0018	0.0073	0.0267
	0.6	0.732	0.534	7.20	9.88	0.0877	0.1049	0.0866	0.0094	0.1683	0.0802	0.1310	0.1710	0.0547	0.1842	0.0064	0.0877	0.0118	0.0022	0.0063	0.0283
	1.0	0.878	0.497	7.95	14.05	0.0785	0.1232	0.0853	0.0124	0.1577	0.1024	0.1121	0.2104	0.0420	0.2071	0.0045	0.0908	0.0115	0.0028	0.0048	0.0309
	1.5	1.028	0.468	8.80	19.33	0.0695	0.1429	0.0836	0.0160	0.1462	0.1307	0.0926	0.2539	0.0308	0.2287	0.0030	0.0934	0.0112	0.0035	0.0036	0.0333
	2.0	1.147	0.449	9.54	24.37	0.0625	0.1594	0.0825	0.0193	0.1362	0.1561	0.0769	0.2908	0.0232	0.2447	0.0022	0.0950	0.0110	0.0042	0.0027	0.0352

TABLE 30

		$a_A = 0.4$				a_B = variable									$r_A = 0.4$						r_B = variable			
0.1	0.4	0.503	0.673	6.91	5.17	0.1016	0.0829	0.0872	0.0062	0.1802	0.0523	0.1626	0.1212	0.0780	0.1559	0.0078	0.0877	0.0196	0.0032	0.0000	0.0016			
	0.6	0.519	0.671	7.01	5.43	0.0994	0.0863	0.0870	0.0065	0.1787	0.0547	0.1592	0.1265	0.0738	0.1624	0.0062	0.0901	0.0195	0.0033	0.0000	0.0016			
	1.0	0.540	0.668	7.15	5.78	0.0965	0.0909	0.0867	0.0069	0.1766	0.0580	0.1545	0.1340	0.0682	0.1714	0.0042	0.0933	0.0194	0.0035	0.0000	0.0016			
	1.5	0.556	0.666	7.26	6.06	0.0943	0.0944	0.0865	0.0072	0.1750	0.0606	0.1509	0.1397	0.0639	0.1782	0.0028	0.0956	0.0193	0.0037	0.0000	0.0016			
	2.0	0.566	0.665	7.32	6.23	0.0929	0.0966	0.0864	0.0074	0.1740	0.0622	0.1487	0.1433	0.0612	0.1825	0.0020	0.0969	0.0193	0.0038	0.0000	0.0017			
0.2	0.4	0.549	0.657	7.16	5.97	0.0975	0.0900	0.0867	0.0070	0.1766	0.0587	0.1549	0.1348	0.0701	0.1696	0.0075	0.0881	0.0194	0.0036	0.0005	0.0058			
	0.6	0.581	0.651	7.37	6.59	0.0936	0.0965	0.0863	0.0077	0.1735	0.0639	0.1482	0.1461	0.0627	0.1821	0.0058	0.0907	0.0192	0.0040	0.0004	0.0060			
	1.0	0.629	0.641	7.69	7.54	0.0879	0.1061	0.0858	0.0086	0.1689	0.0719	0.1381	0.1634	0.0517	0.2006	0.0036	0.0941	0.0190	0.0044	0.0003	0.0062			
	1.5	0.667	0.634	7.96	8.37	0.0833	0.1141	0.0853	0.0095	0.1650	0.0787	0.1297	0.1779	0.0429	0.2158	0.0022	0.0964	0.0188	0.0048	0.0002	0.0064			
	2.0	0.692	0.629	8.14	8.94	0.0803	0.1195	0.0850	0.0101	0.1624	0.0833	0.1242	0.1878	0.0372	0.2258	0.0014	0.0977	0.0186	0.0051	0.0001	0.0065			
0.3	0.4	0.585	0.635	7.33	6.75	0.0956	0.0937	0.0864	0.0077	0.1742	0.0636	0.1504	0.1439	0.0671	0.1748	0.0078	0.0873	0.0193	0.0039	0.0017	0.0120			
	0.6	0.635	0.622	7.64	7.81	0.0905	0.1025	0.0859	0.0087	0.1699	0.0715	0.1412	0.1606	0.0580	0.1905	0.0061	0.0898	0.0190	0.0044	0.0014	0.0125			
	1.0	0.713	0.604	8.16	9.64	0.0826	0.1167	0.0849	0.0104	0.1626	0.0851	0.1260	0.1883	0.0440	0.2153	0.0040	0.0933	0.0186	0.0052	0.0009	0.0133			
	1.5	0.781	0.589	8.64	11.45	0.0757	0.1297	0.0841	0.0120	0.1558	0.0981	0.1123	0.2146	0.0321	0.2370	0.0025	0.0958	0.0181	0.0060	0.0006	0.0138			
	2.0	0.827	0.580	8.99	12.83	0.0709	0.1389	0.0834	0.0133	0.1508	0.1077	0.1026	0.2338	0.0242	0.2519	0.0017	0.0972	0.0179	0.0066	0.0004	0.0142			
0.4	0.4	0.610	0.610	7.44	7.44	0.0947	0.0947	0.0862	0.0081	0.1729	0.0666	0.1481	0.1481	0.0666	0.1729	0.0081	0.0862	0.0192	0.0041	0.0041	0.0192			
	0.6	0.677	0.589	7.82	8.98	0.0892	0.1046	0.0856	0.0094	0.1675	0.0769	0.1373	0.1683	0.0574	0.1882	0.0065	0.0886	0.0189	0.0047	0.0034	0.0202			
	1.0	0.787	0.560	8.51	11.96	0.0801	0.1219	0.0843	0.0119	0.1581	0.0960	0.1187	0.2046	0.0432	0.2133	0.0044	0.0920	0.0183	0.0059	0.0025	0.0218			
	1.5	0.891	0.537	9.22	15.30	0.0715	0.1392	0.0831	0.0145	0.1484	0.1164	0.1005	0.2422	0.0310	0.2361	0.0029	0.0946	0.0177	0.0072	0.0018	0.0232			
	2.0	0.968	0.522	9.79	18.15	0.0652	0.1525	0.0821	0.0167	0.1408	0.1330	0.0865	0.2722	0.0228	0.2521	0.0020	0.0962	0.0172	0.0082	0.0013	0.0241			
0.5	0.4	0.623	0.584	7.50	8.00	0.0941	0.0940	0.0861	0.0083	0.1720	0.0678	0.1463	0.1478	0.0661	0.1691	0.0083	0.0853	0.0191	0.0042	0.0076	0.0266			
	0.6	0.701	0.555	7.93	10.02	0.0884	0.1040	0.0854	0.0098	0.1661	0.0795	0.1348	0.1686	0.0572	0.1830	0.0067	0.0875	0.0188	0.0049	0.0065	0.0282			
	1.0	0.840	0.515	8.74	14.27	0.0789	0.1222	0.0840	0.0129	0.1553	0.1025	0.1151	0.2078	0.0437	0.2059	0.0047	0.0906	0.0181	0.0063	0.0050	0.0307			
	1.5	0.984	0.483	9.65	19.67	0.0696	0.1419	0.0824	0.0166	0.1436	0.1297	0.0950	0.2512	0.0321	0.2277	0.0032	0.0932	0.0174	0.0081	0.0037	0.0332			
	2.0	1.099	0.462	10.44	24.84	0.0624	0.1584	0.0810	0.0200	0.1336	0.1542	0.0789	0.2882	0.0242	0.2437	0.0023	0.0949	0.0167	0.0096	0.0028	0.0350			

Straight Haunches — Constant Width

TABLE 31

$a_A = 0.5$ a_B = variable $r_A = 0.4$ r_B = variable

Right Haunch a_B	r_B	Carry-over Factors C_{AB}	C_{BA}	Stiffness Factors k_{AB}	k_{BA}	Unif. Load F.E.M. Coef.× wL^2 M_{AB}	M_{BA}	b=0.1 M_{AB}	M_{BA}	b=0.3 M_{AB}	M_{BA}	b=0.5 M_{AB}	M_{BA}	b=0.7 M_{AB}	M_{BA}	b=0.9 M_{AB}	M_{BA}	Haunch Left Coef.× $W_A L^3$ M_{AB}	M_{BA}	Haunch Right Coef.× $W_B L^3$ M_{AB}	M_{BA}
0.1	0.4	0.483	0.691	7.46	5.22	0.1009	0.0863	0.0863	0.0064	0.1764	0.0522	0.1623	0.1198	0.1551	0.0795	0.0876	0.0081	0.0274	0.0000	0.0060	0.0016
	0.6	0.498	0.689	7.57	5.47	0.0987	0.0861	0.0861	0.0067	0.1748	0.0546	0.1589	0.1252	0.1616	0.0753	0.0901	0.0064	0.0272	0.0000	0.0063	0.0016
	1.0	0.519	0.686	7.72	5.83	0.0957	0.0858	0.0858	0.0071	0.1727	0.0579	0.1541	0.1326	0.1706	0.0650	0.0933	0.0043	0.0270	0.0000	0.0066	0.0016
	1.5	0.534	0.684	7.83	6.12	0.0935	0.0856	0.0856	0.0074	0.1711	0.0604	0.1504	0.1383	0.1774	0.0651	0.0955	0.0029	0.0268	0.0000	0.0069	0.0016
	2.0	0.544	0.683	7.90	6.30	0.0921	0.0855	0.0855	0.0076	0.1700	0.0621	0.1481	0.1420	0.1818	0.0623	0.0968	0.0020	0.0267	0.0000	0.0071	0.0017
0.2	0.4	0.526	0.674	7.72	6.03	0.0968	0.0858	0.0858	0.0072	0.1728	0.0585	0.1546	0.1333	0.1688	0.0715	0.0880	0.0077	0.0270	0.0005	0.0067	0.0058
	0.6	0.558	0.667	7.94	6.65	0.0928	0.0854	0.0854	0.0079	0.1696	0.0637	0.1478	0.1446	0.1813	0.0639	0.0906	0.0060	0.0267	0.0004	0.0073	0.0060
	1.0	0.604	0.657	8.28	7.62	0.0870	0.0849	0.0849	0.0089	0.1649	0.0717	0.1375	0.1618	0.1998	0.0527	0.0941	0.0037	0.0261	0.0003	0.0082	0.0062
	1.5	0.641	0.649	8.57	8.46	0.0823	0.0843	0.0843	0.0097	0.1610	0.0785	0.1290	0.1763	0.2151	0.0437	0.0964	0.0022	0.0257	0.0002	0.0090	0.0064
	2.0	0.665	0.644	8.76	9.05	0.0792	0.0840	0.0840	0.0103	0.1583	0.0831	0.1234	0.1861	0.2252	0.0378	0.0977	0.0015	0.0253	0.0001	0.0095	0.0065
0.3	0.4	0.561	0.650	7.90	6.81	0.0949	0.0855	0.0855	0.0079	0.1704	0.0632	0.1501	0.1423	0.1739	0.0684	0.0871	0.0080	0.0267	0.0018	0.0073	0.0120
	0.6	0.610	0.636	8.22	7.88	0.0898	0.0849	0.0849	0.0089	0.1660	0.0712	0.1408	0.1588	0.1896	0.0592	0.0897	0.0063	0.0262	0.0015	0.0082	0.0125
	1.0	0.686	0.616	8.76	9.75	0.0818	0.0840	0.0840	0.0107	0.1587	0.0846	0.1255	0.1864	0.2144	0.0449	0.0932	0.0041	0.0254	0.0010	0.0097	0.0133
	1.5	0.752	0.600	9.26	11.59	0.0748	0.0829	0.0829	0.0123	0.1520	0.0976	0.1118	0.2125	0.2362	0.0328	0.0958	0.0025	0.0246	0.0006	0.0112	0.0138
	2.0	0.797	0.590	9.63	13.00	0.0699	0.0824	0.0824	0.0136	0.1468	0.1071	0.1020	0.2316	0.2512	0.0248	0.0972	0.0017	0.0241	0.0004	0.0123	0.0142
0.4	0.4	0.584	0.623	8.00	7.50	0.0941	0.0853	0.0853	0.0083	0.1691	0.0661	0.1478	0.1463	0.1720	0.0678	0.0861	0.0083	0.0266	0.0042	0.0076	0.0191
	0.6	0.648	0.600	8.40	9.07	0.0884	0.0846	0.0846	0.0096	0.1636	0.0763	0.1370	0.1662	0.1873	0.0585	0.0885	0.0067	0.0260	0.0035	0.0087	0.0201
	1.0	0.755	0.569	9.11	12.10	0.0793	0.0834	0.0834	0.0121	0.1544	0.0950	0.1184	0.2022	0.2124	0.0440	0.0919	0.0045	0.0249	0.0025	0.0108	0.0217
	1.5	0.857	0.544	9.85	15.52	0.0707	0.0821	0.0821	0.0148	0.1448	0.1151	0.1002	0.2394	0.2353	0.0316	0.0945	0.0029	0.0238	0.0018	0.0131	0.0231
	2.0	0.933	0.528	10.43	18.43	0.0643	0.0811	0.0811	0.0170	0.1373	0.1315	0.0863	0.2692	0.2514	0.0232	0.0961	0.0020	0.0230	0.0013	0.0150	0.0240
0.5	0.4	0.595	0.595	8.07	8.07	0.0933	0.0852	0.0852	0.0085	0.1682	0.0672	0.1458	0.1458	0.1682	0.0672	0.0852	0.0085	0.0265	0.0077	0.0077	0.0265
	0.6	0.670	0.563	8.51	10.11	0.0875	0.0845	0.0845	0.0100	0.1623	0.0785	0.1344	0.1663	0.1820	0.0580	0.0874	0.0069	0.0258	0.0067	0.0090	0.0280
	1.0	0.804	0.519	9.33	14.44	0.0780	0.0830	0.0830	0.0131	0.1518	0.1009	0.1147	0.2047	0.2049	0.0442	0.0905	0.0048	0.0246	0.0053	0.0116	0.0305
	1.5	0.944	0.484	10.25	19.98	0.0688	0.0815	0.0815	0.0168	0.1403	0.1272	0.0948	0.2473	0.2266	0.0325	0.0931	0.0033	0.0233	0.0038	0.0145	0.0331
	2.0	1.058	0.462	11.05	25.34	0.0617	0.0801	0.0801	0.0203	0.1306	0.1511	0.0790	0.2839	0.2426	0.0245	0.0949	0.0023	0.0222	0.0029	0.0173	0.0348

TABLE 32

		$\alpha_A = 0.1$				α_B = variable								$r_A = 0.6$				r_B = variable			
0.1	0.4	0.550	0.568	5.06	4.90	0.0923	0.0908	0.0048	0.1693	0.0583	0.1395	0.1310	0.0643	0.1615	0.0063	0.0883	0.0016	0.0000	0.0000	0.0016
	0.6	0.567	0.567	5.12	5.12	0.0905	0.0906	0.0050	0.1679	0.0609	0.1366	0.1366	0.0609	0.1679	0.0050	0.0906	0.0016	0.0000	0.0000	0.0016
	1.0	0.590	0.565	5.21	5.44	0.0880	0.0951	0.0053	0.1660	0.0643	0.1325	0.1442	0.0562	0.1767	0.0034	0.0937	0.0016	0.0000	0.0000	0.0016
	1.5	0.607	0.564	5.28	5.69	0.086	0.0986	0.0055	0.1646	0.0670	0.1294	0.1500	0.0526	0.1833	0.0022	0.0958	0.0016	0.0000	0.0000	0.0016
	2.0	0.618	0.563	5.33	5.85	0.0850	0.1008	0.0057	0.1637	0.0687	0.1274	0.1537	0.0504	0.1875	0.0016	0.0970	0.0016	0.0001	0.0001	0.0017
0.2	0.4	0.600	0.556	5.23	5.63	0.0887	0.0905	0.0054	0.1660	0.0652	0.1327	0.1452	0.0576	0.1752	0.0060	0.0887	0.0016	0.0000	0.0004	0.0059
	0.6	0.636	0.551	5.37	6.18	0.0854	0.0902	0.0059	0.1632	0.0707	0.1269	0.1568	0.0514	0.1874	0.0046	0.0912	0.0016	0.0000	0.0003	0.0061
	1.0	0.687	0.544	5.57	7.03	0.0806	0.0899	0.0066	0.1590	0.0790	0.1181	0.1743	0.0423	0.2054	0.0029	0.0945	0.0016	0.0001	0.0002	0.0063
	1.5	0.728	0.539	5.75	7.77	0.0767	0.0896	0.0072	0.1556	0.0861	0.1109	0.1889	0.0351	0.2201	0.0017	0.0967	0.0016	0.0001	0.0001	0.0064
	2.0	0.755	0.535	5.86	8.28	0.0742	0.0894	0.0076	0.1533	0.0909	0.1062	0.1988	0.0304	0.2297	0.0011	0.0978	0.0016	0.0001	0.0001	0.0065
0.3	0.4	0.641	0.539	5.35	6.35	0.0870	0.0903	0.0059	0.1637	0.0704	0.1287	0.1546	0.0549	0.1803	0.0062	0.0881	0.0016	0.0000	0.0014	0.0122
	0.6	0.696	0.529	5.55	7.31	0.0826	0.0899	0.0066	0.1597	0.0790	0.1205	0.1718	0.0473	0.1958	0.0049	0.0906	0.0016	0.0000	0.0011	0.0127
	1.0	0.782	0.515	5.89	8.95	0.0759	0.0893	0.0079	0.1532	0.0931	0.1074	0.2000	0.0355	0.2203	0.0032	0.0938	0.0016	0.0001	0.0008	0.0134
	1.5	0.856	0.504	6.21	10.55	0.0701	0.0888	0.0091	0.1472	0.1066	0.0956	0.2260	0.0266	0.2416	0.0020	0.0960	0.0016	0.0001	0.0005	0.0139
	2.0	0.907	0.496	6.44	11.76	0.0661	0.0884	0.0100	0.1429	0.1165	0.0874	0.2451	0.0190	0.2558	0.0013	0.0973	0.0016	0.0001	0.0004	0.0143
0.4	0.4	0.671	0.519	5.43	7.01	0.0863	0.0901	0.0062	0.1624	0.0738	0.1265	0.1592	0.0547	0.1787	0.0065	0.0870	0.0016	0.0000	0.0033	0.0195
	0.6	0.745	0.503	5.69	8.42	0.0815	0.0897	0.0072	0.1575	0.0849	0.1170	0.1800	0.0470	0.1939	0.0052	0.0893	0.0016	0.0000	0.0028	0.0206
	1.0	0.868	0.480	6.15	11.11	0.0736	0.0889	0.0091	0.1489	0.1049	0.1008	0.2168	0.0352	0.2184	0.0035	0.0925	0.0016	0.0001	0.0020	0.0221
	1.5	0.983	0.463	6.63	14.09	0.0663	0.0881	0.0110	0.1403	0.1260	0.0851	0.2543	0.0251	0.2404	0.0023	0.0950	0.0016	0.0001	0.0014	0.0234
	2.0	1.068	0.451	7.01	16.59	0.0609	0.0875	0.0127	0.1335	0.1430	0.0732	0.2837	0.0184	0.2556	0.0016	0.0965	0.0016	0.0001	0.0010	0.0243
0.5	0.4	0.689	0.498	5.47	7.57	0.0858	0.0901	0.0064	0.1616	0.0753	0.1252	0.1589	0.0546	0.1748	0.0067	0.0861	0.0016	0.0000	0.0063	0.0272
	0.6	0.778	0.475	5.77	9.43	0.0809	0.0896	0.0076	0.1562	0.0878	0.1152	0.1803	0.0471	0.1886	0.0054	0.0882	0.0016	0.0000	0.0054	0.0288
	1.0	0.935	0.444	6.33	13.34	0.0727	0.0886	0.0100	0.1463	0.1122	0.0979	0.2201	0.0359	0.2112	0.0038	0.0912	0.0016	0.0001	0.0041	0.0313
	1.5	1.098	0.419	6.96	18.22	0.0647	0.0876	0.0128	0.1356	0.1407	0.0804	0.2637	0.0263	0.2324	0.0026	0.0937	0.0016	0.0001	0.0030	0.0337
	2.0	1.226	0.403	7.51	22.85	0.0584	0.0867	0.0154	0.1265	0.1661	0.0665	0.3003	0.0197	0.2478	0.0019	0.0953	0.0016	0.0001	0.0023	0.0355

Straight Haunches — Constant Width

TABLE 33

$\alpha_A = 0.2$ $r_A = 0.6$ $\alpha_B = \text{variable}$ $r_B = \text{variable}$

Right Haunch		Carry-over Factors		Stiffness Factors		Unif. Load F.E.M. Coef. × wL^2		Concentrated Load F.E.M.—Coef. × PL										Haunch Load at			
								0.1		0.3		0.5		0.7		0.9		Left Coef. × $W_A L^2$		Right Coef. × $W_B L^2$	
α_B	r_B	C_{AB}	C_{BA}	k_{AB}	k_{BA}	M_{AB}	M_{BA}	M_{AB}	M_{BA}	M_{AB}	M_{BA}	M_{AB}	M_{BA}	M_{AB}	M_{BA}	M_{AB}	M_{BA}	M_{AB}	M_{BA}	M_{AB}	M_{BA}
0.1	0.4	0.535	0.637	6.09	5.12	0.1029	0.0821	0.0914	0.0044	0.1887	0.0492	0.1600	0.1215	0.0746	0.1567	0.0074	0.0878	0.0061	0.0003	0.0000	0.0016
	0.6	0.551	0.636	6.18	5.37	0.1009	0.0854	0.0912	0.0046	0.1874	0.0514	0.1568	0.1269	0.0707	0.1632	0.0059	0.0902	0.0061	0.0003	0.0000	0.0016
	1.0	0.573	0.633	6.31	5.71	0.0982	0.0899	0.0911	0.0049	0.1856	0.0545	0.1524	0.1342	0.0654	0.1721	0.0040	0.0934	0.0061	0.0003	0.0000	0.0016
	1.5	0.590	0.631	6.40	5.98	0.0961	0.0934	0.0909	0.0051	0.1841	0.0569	0.1490	0.1399	0.0613	0.1789	0.0026	0.0956	0.0061	0.0003	0.0000	0.0016
	2.0	0.600	0.630	6.46	6.16	0.0948	0.0956	0.0909	0.0053	0.1832	0.0584	0.1468	0.1435	0.0588	0.1831	0.0019	0.0969	0.0061	0.0003	0.0000	0.0017
0.2	0.4	0.583	0.623	6.32	5.91	0.0991	0.0891	0.0911	0.0050	0.1855	0.0552	0.1527	0.1350	0.0671	0.1704	0.0071	0.0882	0.0061	0.0003	0.0005	0.0058
	0.6	0.618	0.618	6.51	6.51	0.0954	0.0954	0.0908	0.0055	0.1828	0.0600	0.1463	0.1463	0.0600	0.1828	0.0055	0.0908	0.0060	0.0004	0.0004	0.0060
	1.0	0.667	0.609	6.80	7.44	0.0901	0.1049	0.0904	0.0062	0.1787	0.0673	0.1367	0.1635	0.0497	0.2011	0.0034	0.0942	0.0060	0.0004	0.0002	0.0063
	1.5	0.707	0.603	7.04	8.26	0.0858	0.1127	0.0901	0.0068	0.1752	0.0736	0.1288	0.1778	0.0413	0.2163	0.0021	0.0965	0.0060	0.0005	0.0001	0.0064
	2.0	0.734	0.599	7.21	8.83	0.0830	0.1178	0.0899	0.0072	0.1729	0.0779	0.1235	0.1876	0.0358	0.2262	0.0013	0.0977	0.0060	0.0005	0.0001	0.0065
0.3	0.4	0.622	0.604	6.48	6.68	0.0972	0.0927	0.0909	0.0055	0.1833	0.0598	0.1483	0.1439	0.0642	0.1754	0.0073	0.0875	0.0060	0.0004	0.0017	0.0120
	0.6	0.676	0.592	6.77	7.72	0.0925	0.1013	0.0905	0.0063	0.1794	0.0672	0.1394	0.1606	0.0556	0.1910	0.0058	0.0901	0.0060	0.0004	0.0013	0.0126
	1.0	0.758	0.576	7.24	9.53	0.0851	0.1152	0.0898	0.0075	0.1729	0.0798	0.1250	0.1883	0.0422	0.2158	0.0038	0.0934	0.0060	0.0005	0.0009	0.0133
	1.5	0.830	0.563	7.68	11.32	0.0787	0.1278	0.0892	0.0086	0.1668	0.0919	0.1120	0.2141	0.0308	0.2376	0.0023	0.0957	0.0059	0.0006	0.0006	0.0138
	2.0	0.879	0.555	8.01	12.69	0.0741	0.1367	0.0887	0.0096	0.1624	0.1010	0.1026	0.2333	0.0230	0.2524	0.0016	0.0972	0.0059	0.0007	0.0004	0.0142
0.4	0.4	0.651	0.581	6.59	7.37	0.0965	0.0936	0.0907	0.0058	0.1821	0.0627	0.1461	0.1482	0.0639	0.1735	0.0077	0.0863	0.0060	0.0004	0.0040	0.0192
	0.6	0.722	0.563	6.94	8.91	0.0913	0.1033	0.0902	0.0068	0.1772	0.0724	0.1358	0.1682	0.0552	0.1888	0.0062	0.0887	0.0060	0.0005	0.0033	0.0202
	1.0	0.840	0.537	7.59	11.87	0.0828	0.1201	0.0894	0.0086	0.1685	0.0904	0.1180	0.2042	0.0417	0.2136	0.0042	0.0920	0.0060	0.0006	0.0024	0.0218
	1.5	0.951	0.517	8.26	15.20	0.0746	0.1369	0.0885	0.0105	0.1597	0.1097	0.1005	0.2416	0.0300	0.2363	0.0027	0.0946	0.0059	0.0007	0.0017	0.0232
	2.0	1.032	0.504	8.81	18.03	0.0686	0.1500	0.0877	0.0122	0.1526	0.1255	0.0869	0.2713	0.0221	0.2522	0.0019	0.0962	0.0059	0.0008	0.0012	0.0241
0.5	0.4	0.667	0.558	6.65	7.94	0.0960	0.0928	0.0906	0.0060	0.1813	0.0639	0.1446	0.1478	0.0637	0.1696	0.0079	0.0854	0.0060	0.0004	0.0073	0.0267
	0.6	0.752	0.532	7.05	9.96	0.0907	0.1026	0.0901	0.0071	0.1759	0.0750	0.1337	0.1684	0.0553	0.1833	0.0064	0.0876	0.0060	0.0004	0.0063	0.0282
	1.0	0.902	0.497	7.82	14.21	0.0818	0.1203	0.0891	0.0094	0.1659	0.0969	0.1148	0.2071	0.0426	0.2061	0.0045	0.0907	0.0059	0.0007	0.0049	0.0308
	1.5	1.056	0.469	8.71	19.63	0.0730	0.1394	0.0879	0.0122	0.1549	0.1229	0.0953	0.2502	0.0315	0.2277	0.0031	0.0933	0.0058	0.0008	0.0036	0.0332
	2.0	1.179	0.450	9.49	24.85	0.0660	0.1555	0.0869	0.0148	0.1454	0.1466	0.0796	0.2870	0.0238	0.2436	0.0023	0.0949	0.0058	0.0010	0.0028	0.0350

TABLE 34

		$a_A = 0.3$				$a_B = variable$					$r_A = 0.6$				$r_B = variable$			
0.1	0.4	0.513	0.698	7.19	5.29	0.1093	0.0907	0.0047	0.1974	0.0449	0.1153	0.0834	0.1533	0.0084	0.0875	0.0127	0.0011	0.0000	0.0016
	0.6	0.529	0.696	7.31	5.55	0.1072	0.0906	0.0049	0.1958	0.0473	0.1205	0.0790	0.1597	0.0066	0.0899	0.0127	0.0011	0.0000	0.0016
	1.0	0.550	0.694	7.47	5.92	0.1042	0.0903	0.0051	0.1938	0.0501	0.1277	0.0731	0.1687	0.0045	0.0932	0.0127	0.0011	0.0000	0.0016
	1.5	0.566	0.691	7.59	6.22	0.1019	0.0900	0.0054	0.1925	0.0524	0.1333	0.0686	0.1756	0.0030	0.0955	0.0127	0.0012	0.0000	0.0016
	2.0	0.576	0.690	7.67	6.40	0.1005	0.0900	0.0057	0.1916	0.0540	0.1368	0.0658	0.1799	0.0021	0.0968	0.0127	0.0012	0.0000	0.0017
0.2	0.4	0.559	0.682	7.48	6.12	0.1052	0.0902	0.0053	0.1941	0.0507	0.1284	0.0751	0.1670	0.0080	0.0878	0.0126	0.0012	0.0005	0.0058
	0.6	0.592	0.676	7.72	6.77	0.1013	0.0901	0.0058	0.1910	0.0556	0.1394	0.0672	0.1794	0.0063	0.0905	0.0126	0.0013	0.0004	0.0060
	1.0	0.640	0.666	8.09	7.77	0.0954	0.0895	0.0065	0.1868	0.0627	0.1564	0.0558	0.1980	0.0038	0.0940	0.0125	0.0015	0.0003	0.0062
	1.5	0.678	0.659	8.40	8.65	0.0907	0.0892	0.0072	0.1831	0.0683	0.1706	0.0464	0.2135	0.0024	0.0964	0.0123	0.0017	0.0002	0.0064
	2.0	0.703	0.654	8.61	9.26	0.0876	0.0888	0.0077	0.1807	0.0730	0.1804	0.0403	0.2237	0.0015	0.0976	0.0122	0.0018	0.0001	0.0065
0.3	0.4	0.596	0.660	7.68	6.93	0.1033	0.0900	0.0058	0.1918	0.0553	0.1371	0.0720	0.1719	0.0083	0.0870	0.0126	0.0013	0.0018	0.0120
	0.6	0.647	0.647	8.04	8.04	0.0982	0.0897	0.0066	0.1876	0.0625	0.1534	0.0625	0.1876	0.0066	0.0897	0.0125	0.0015	0.0015	0.0125
	1.0	0.726	0.629	8.64	9.98	0.0902	0.0888	0.0080	0.1807	0.0747	0.1808	0.0477	0.2126	0.0042	0.0931	0.0124	0.0018	0.0010	0.0132
	1.5	0.794	0.614	9.21	11.91	0.0831	0.0881	0.0092	0.1742	0.0865	0.2066	0.0350	0.2348	0.0027	0.0956	0.0122	0.0021	0.0007	0.0138
	2.0	0.841	0.605	9.63	13.40	0.0780	0.0875	0.0102	0.1695	0.0954	0.2257	0.0265	0.2500	0.0018	0.0971	0.0120	0.0023	0.0005	0.0142
0.4	0.4	0.622	0.635	7.81	7.64	0.1025	0.0898	0.0061	0.1905	0.0580	0.1412	0.0715	0.1695	0.0087	0.0859	0.0125	0.0014	0.0044	0.0190
	0.6	0.689	0.614	8.25	9.27	0.0969	0.0894	0.0072	0.1854	0.0673	0.1606	0.0620	0.1852	0.0070	0.0883	0.0123	0.0017	0.0037	0.0200
	1.0	0.801	0.585	9.06	12.42	0.0876	0.0884	0.0091	0.1763	0.0847	0.1962	0.0470	0.2103	0.0048	0.0917	0.0121	0.0021	0.0027	0.0216
	1.5	0.907	0.562	9.92	16.00	0.0789	0.0871	0.0111	0.1668	0.1032	0.2337	0.0340	0.2334	0.0031	0.0944	0.0119	0.0026	0.0020	0.0230
	2.0	0.984	0.547	10.61	19.07	0.0721	0.0863	0.0129	0.1595	0.1190	0.2637	0.0252	0.2498	0.0021	0.0960	0.0117	0.0030	0.0014	0.0239
0.5	0.4	0.636	0.610	7.88	8.22	0.1019	0.0898	0.0063	0.1896	0.0592	0.1408	0.0712	0.1660	0.0089	0.0849	0.0125	0.0015	0.0082	0.0262
	0.6	0.715	0.580	8.38	10.33	0.0962	0.0892	0.0075	0.1841	0.0696	0.1609	0.0619	0.1797	0.0072	0.0872	0.0123	0.0019	0.0071	0.0278
	1.0	0.857	0.540	9.34	14.82	0.0852	0.0862	0.0098	0.1736	0.0906	0.1991	0.0478	0.2027	0.0051	0.0903	0.0121	0.0023	0.0055	0.0304
	1.5	1.002	0.508	10.45	20.59	0.0770	0.0866	0.0129	0.1620	0.1153	0.2420	0.0355	0.2246	0.0035	0.0930	0.0118	0.0029	0.0041	0.0329
	2.0	1.117	0.488	11.43	26.18	0.0694	0.0854	0.0156	0.1520	0.1393	0.2791	0.0270	0.2409	0.0026	0.0946	0.0115	0.0036	0.0031	0.0347

Straight Haunches—Constant Width

Figure labels: $r_A h_c$, W_A, bL, P, h_c, W_B, $r_B h_c$, $a_A L$, L, $a_B L$, A, B

TABLE 35　　$a_A = 0.4$　　$a_B =$ variable　　$r_A = 0.6$　　$r_B =$ variable

Column groups: Right Haunch (a_B, r_B); Carry-over Factors (C_{AB}, C_{BA}); Stiffness Factors (k_{AB}, k_{BA}); Unif. Load F.E.M. Coef. × wL^2 (M_{AB}, M_{BA}); Concentrated Load F.E.M.—Coef. × PL for $b = 0.1, 0.3, 0.5, 0.7, 0.9$ (each M_{AB}, M_{BA}); Haunch Load at Left F.E.M. Coef. × $W_A L^2$ (M_{AB}, M_{BA}); Haunch Load at Right F.E.M. Coef. × $W_B L^2$ (M_{AB}, M_{BA}).

a_B	r_B	C_{AB}	C_{BA}	k_{AB}	k_{BA}	Unif M_{AB}	Unif M_{BA}	0.1 M_{AB}	0.1 M_{BA}	0.3 M_{AB}	0.3 M_{BA}	0.5 M_{AB}	0.5 M_{BA}	0.7 M_{AB}	0.7 M_{BA}	0.9 M_{AB}	0.9 M_{BA}	Left M_{AB}	Left M_{BA}	Right M_{AB}	Right M_{BA}
0.1	0.4	0.488	0.747	8.29	5.41	0.1118	0.0782	0.0895	0.0050	0.1955	0.0449	0.1837	0.1118	0.0895	0.1510	0.0091	0.0872	0.0206	0.0027	0.0000	0.0016
	0.6	0.503	0.745	8.42	5.69	0.1095	0.0815	0.0893	0.0052	0.1939	0.0470	0.1800	0.1170	0.0849	0.1575	0.0072	0.0897	0.0205	0.0028	0.0000	0.0016
	1.0	0.523	0.742	8.61	6.07	0.1063	0.0860	0.0890	0.0056	0.1918	0.0499	0.1749	0.1242	0.0785	0.1666	0.0049	0.0930	0.0206	0.0029	0.0000	0.0016
	1.5	0.539	0.740	8.76	6.38	0.1039	0.0895	0.0889	0.0058	0.1902	0.0522	0.1710	0.1298	0.0737	0.1735	0.0032	0.0953	0.0205	0.0031	0.0000	0.0016
	2.0	0.548	0.738	8.85	6.57	0.1024	0.0917	0.0887	0.0060	0.1892	0.0537	0.1686	0.1333	0.0706	0.1779	0.0023	0.0967	0.0205	0.0032	0.0000	0.0017
0.2	0.4	0.531	0.729	8.62	6.28	0.1075	0.0850	0.0890	0.0056	0.1919	0.0505	0.1755	0.1248	0.0808	0.1646	0.0087	0.0875	0.0204	0.0030	0.0006	0.0058
	0.6	0.563	0.722	8.91	6.94	0.1033	0.0913	0.0887	0.0062	0.1888	0.0552	0.1682	0.1358	0.0724	0.1772	0.0068	0.0902	0.0202	0.0033	0.0005	0.0060
	1.0	0.609	0.711	9.34	7.99	0.0971	0.1008	0.0881	0.0070	0.1841	0.0624	0.1573	0.1526	0.0601	0.1960	0.0042	0.0938	0.0200	0.0036	0.0003	0.0062
	1.5	0.645	0.703	9.71	8.91	0.0920	0.1087	0.0877	0.0077	0.1802	0.0686	0.1482	0.1669	0.0500	0.2117	0.0026	0.0962	0.0197	0.0041	0.0002	0.0064
	2.0	0.669	0.698	9.96	9.56	0.0886	0.1140	0.0874	0.0082	0.1775	0.0729	0.1420	0.1767	0.0434	0.2221	0.0017	0.0975	0.0196	0.0044	0.0001	0.0065
0.3	0.4	0.565	0.705	8.85	7.10	0.1055	0.0884	0.0887	0.0061	0.1895	0.0547	0.1707	0.1333	0.0775	0.1696	0.0090	0.0868	0.0203	0.0033	0.0021	0.0118
	0.6	0.614	0.689	9.27	8.25	0.1001	0.0969	0.0883	0.0070	0.1852	0.0620	0.1606	0.1495	0.0673	0.1854	0.0072	0.0894	0.0200	0.0037	0.0017	0.0123
	1.0	0.689	0.669	9.97	10.28	0.0915	0.1109	0.0874	0.0084	0.1779	0.0743	0.1444	0.1766	0.0515	0.2107	0.0047	0.0930	0.0196	0.0044	0.0011	0.0132
	1.5	0.755	0.652	10.63	12.30	0.0839	0.1236	0.0866	0.0098	0.1710	0.0862	0.1294	0.2026	0.0378	0.2332	0.0030	0.0955	0.0191	0.0052	0.0008	0.0138
	2.0	0.800	0.642	11.12	13.86	0.0786	0.1329	0.0860	0.0108	0.1659	0.0952	0.1183	0.2220	0.0286	0.2487	0.0019	0.0970	0.0189	0.0058	0.0005	0.0141
0.4	0.4	0.589	0.677	8.98	7.82	0.1046	0.0892	0.0886	0.0065	0.1882	0.0574	0.1683	0.1373	0.0769	0.1675	0.0094	0.0856	0.0202	0.0034	0.0047	0.0189
	0.6	0.653	0.653	9.50	9.50	0.0987	0.0987	0.0880	0.0076	0.1829	0.0667	0.1567	0.1567	0.0667	0.1829	0.0076	0.0880	0.0199	0.0040	0.0040	0.0199
	1.0	0.759	0.620	10.43	12.77	0.0889	0.1155	0.0868	0.0096	0.1734	0.0840	0.1366	0.1921	0.0507	0.2083	0.0052	0.0914	0.0193	0.0050	0.0029	0.0215
	1.5	0.859	0.594	11.41	16.50	0.0795	0.1325	0.0857	0.0119	0.1635	0.1027	0.1165	0.2295	0.0367	0.2317	0.0034	0.0942	0.0187	0.0062	0.0021	0.0229
	2.0	0.932	0.577	12.21	19.72	0.0723	0.1458	0.0848	0.0137	0.1557	0.1181	0.1007	0.2597	0.0269	0.2487	0.0022	0.0960	0.0182	0.0072	0.0015	0.0239
0.5	0.4	0.600	0.648	9.07	8.40	0.1039	0.0884	0.0885	0.0067	0.1873	0.0585	0.1662	0.1370	0.0763	0.1636	0.0096	0.0846	0.0201	0.0035	0.0087	0.0260
	0.6	0.674	0.615	9.64	10.57	0.0978	0.0979	0.0878	0.0079	0.1815	0.0688	0.1540	0.1569	0.0663	0.1776	0.0078	0.0869	0.0198	0.0041	0.0076	0.0275
	1.0	0.806	0.570	10.73	15.19	0.0876	0.1154	0.0865	0.0105	0.1707	0.0896	0.1327	0.1948	0.0511	0.2007	0.0055	0.0900	0.0191	0.0054	0.0059	0.0302
	1.5	0.943	0.534	11.96	21.16	0.0775	0.1345	0.0850	0.0136	0.1587	0.1145	0.1105	0.2376	0.0379	0.2228	0.0038	0.0927	0.0184	0.0070	0.0044	0.0327
	2.0	1.053	0.510	13.06	26.98	0.0697	0.1507	0.0837	0.0165	0.1484	0.1373	0.0927	0.2748	0.0288	0.2394	0.0028	0.0945	0.0178	0.0084	0.0033	0.0345

TABLE 36

		$a_A = 0.5$			a_B = variable										$r_A = 0.6$				r_B = variable		
0.1	0.4	0.461	0.780	9.28	5.49	0.1113	0.0776	0.0884	0.0052	0.1901	0.0450	0.1841	0.1100	0.0926	0.1496	0.0096	0.0870	0.0290	0.0052	0.0000	0.0016
	0.6	0.475	0.778	9.43	5.77	0.1089	0.0809	0.0882	0.0054	0.1886	0.0471	0.1803	0.1152	0.0878	0.1562	0.0076	0.0896	0.0288	0.0054	0.0000	0.0016
	1.0	0.495	0.774	9.65	6.17	0.1056	0.0854	0.0879	0.0058	0.1864	0.0501	0.1751	0.1223	0.0812	0.1653	0.0052	0.0929	0.0285	0.0058	0.0000	0.0016
	1.5	0.510	0.772	9.81	6.48	0.1031	0.0889	0.0877	0.0061	0.1847	0.0525	0.1711	0.1279	0.0761	0.1723	0.0034	0.0953	0.0284	0.0060	0.0000	0.0016
	2.0	0.519	0.770	9.91	6.68	0.1015	0.0911	0.0876	0.0062	0.1836	0.0540	0.1686	0.1314	0.0729	0.1767	0.0024	0.0966	0.0283	0.0062	0.0000	0.0017
0.2	0.4	0.502	0.760	9.64	6.37	0.1069	0.0844	0.0880	0.0059	0.1865	0.0506	0.1758	0.1228	0.0837	0.1633	0.0092	0.0873	0.0286	0.0058	0.0006	0.0058
	0.6	0.532	0.752	9.96	7.05	0.1026	0.0907	0.0876	0.0064	0.1833	0.0553	0.1684	0.1337	0.0750	0.1759	0.0071	0.0901	0.0282	0.0063	0.0005	0.0060
	1.0	0.576	0.740	10.43	8.13	0.0961	0.1002	0.0870	0.0073	0.1785	0.0626	0.1572	0.1504	0.0621	0.1948	0.0045	0.0937	0.0276	0.0072	0.0004	0.0062
	1.5	0.612	0.731	10.84	9.08	0.0908	0.1081	0.0865	0.0080	0.1744	0.0688	0.1478	0.1647	0.0516	0.2106	0.0027	0.0961	0.0272	0.0079	0.0002	0.0064
	2.0	0.635	0.724	11.11	9.74	0.0874	0.1134	0.0862	0.0085	0.1716	0.0731	0.1414	0.1745	0.0447	0.2211	0.0018	0.0975	0.0269	0.0083	0.0001	0.0065
0.3	0.4	0.534	0.732	9.88	7.20	0.1049	0.0877	0.0877	0.0064	0.1842	0.0547	0.1710	0.1310	0.0802	0.1683	0.0094	0.0866	0.0283	0.0063	0.0022	0.0118
	0.6	0.580	0.715	10.33	8.38	0.0993	0.0962	0.0872	0.0072	0.1797	0.0619	0.1609	0.1471	0.0696	0.1841	0.0075	0.0892	0.0278	0.0071	0.0019	0.0123
	1.0	0.653	0.692	11.09	10.46	0.0905	0.1101	0.0863	0.0087	0.1723	0.0743	0.1444	0.1740	0.0532	0.2094	0.0049	0.0931	0.0270	0.0085	0.0012	0.0131
	1.5	0.716	0.674	11.80	12.54	0.0827	0.1229	0.0854	0.0102	0.1653	0.0860	0.1290	0.2000	0.0391	0.2320	0.0031	0.0953	0.0261	0.0099	0.0008	0.0137
	2.0	0.759	0.661	12.33	14.15	0.0772	0.1321	0.0848	0.0113	0.1601	0.0951	0.1178	0.2191	0.0298	0.2476	0.0021	0.0969	0.0257	0.0109	0.0005	0.0141
0.4	0.4	0.555	0.701	10.02	7.93	0.1040	0.0884	0.0875	0.0067	0.1830	0.0572	0.1686	0.1348	0.0795	0.1661	0.0098	0.0854	0.0282	0.0065	0.0049	0.0188
	0.6	0.615	0.674	10.57	9.64	0.0979	0.0978	0.0869	0.0078	0.1776	0.0663	0.1569	0.1540	0.0688	0.1815	0.0079	0.0878	0.0275	0.0076	0.0041	0.0198
	1.0	0.717	0.637	11.55	13.00	0.0879	0.1144	0.0857	0.0099	0.1680	0.0833	0.1367	0.1888	0.0523	0.2069	0.0054	0.0913	0.0265	0.0095	0.0030	0.0214
	1.5	0.813	0.608	12.59	16.84	0.0784	0.1313	0.0845	0.0123	0.1582	0.1017	0.1165	0.2257	0.0379	0.2305	0.0036	0.0940	0.0254	0.0116	0.0021	0.0228
	2.0	0.885	0.589	13.42	20.17	0.0713	0.1445	0.0835	0.0142	0.1503	0.1171	0.1009	0.2556	0.0281	0.2474	0.0025	0.0957	0.0245	0.0134	0.0016	0.0238
0.5	0.4	0.563	0.670	10.11	8.51	0.1031	0.0875	0.0874	0.0069	0.1820	0.0580	0.1663	0.1344	0.0785	0.1623	0.0100	0.0845	0.0280	0.0067	0.0090	0.0258
	0.6	0.633	0.633	10.72	10.72	0.0969	0.0969	0.0867	0.0081	0.1761	0.0630	0.1538	0.1538	0.0680	0.1761	0.0081	0.0867	0.0274	0.0078	0.0078	0.0274
	1.0	0.757	0.581	11.84	15.45	0.0865	0.1140	0.0853	0.0107	0.1655	0.0880	0.1324	0.1908	0.0523	0.1991	0.0057	0.0899	0.0262	0.0100	0.0060	0.0300
	1.5	0.889	0.540	13.11	21.61	0.0765	0.1326	0.0838	0.0138	0.1538	0.1120	0.1106	0.2326	0.0387	0.2212	0.0039	0.0926	0.0248	0.0127	0.0044	0.0325
	2.0	0.997	0.513	14.23	27.69	0.0686	0.1485	0.0825	0.0168	0.1438	0.1341	0.0929	0.2689	0.0295	0.2377	0.0028	0.0943	0.0237	0.0153	0.0034	0.0344

Straight Haunches—Constant Width

TABLE 37

$a_A = 0.1$ $r_A = 1.0$ a_B = variable r_B = variable

Right Haunch		Carry-over Factors		Stiffness Factors		Unif. Load F.E.M. Coef. × wL^2		Concentrated Load F.E.M.—Coef. × PL, b										Haunch Load at Left F.E.M. Coef. × $W_A L^2$		Right F.E.M. Coef. × $W_B L^2$	
a_B	r_B	C_{AB}	C_{BA}	k_{AB}	k_{BA}	M_{AB}	M_{BA}	0.1 M_{AB}	0.1 M_{BA}	0.3 M_{AB}	0.3 M_{BA}	0.5 M_{AB}	0.5 M_{BA}	0.7 M_{AB}	0.7 M_{BA}	0.9 M_{AB}	0.9 M_{BA}	M_{AB}	M_{BA}	M_{AB}	M_{BA}
0.1	0.4	0.548	0.591	5.37	4.98	0.0969	0.0847	0.0938	0.0032	0.1780	0.0538	0.1472	0.1271	0.0679	0.1596	0.0067	0.0881	0.0016	0.0000	0.0000	0.0016
	0.6	0.565	0.590	5.44	5.14	0.0951	0.0880	0.0937	0.0034	0.1767	0.0562	0.1442	0.1325	0.0643	0.1660	0.0053	0.0905	0.0016	0.0000	0.0000	0.0016
	1.0	0.588	0.588	5.54	5.54	0.0925	0.0925	0.0936	0.0036	0.1749	0.0594	0.1400	0.1400	0.0594	0.1749	0.0036	0.0936	0.0016	0.0000	0.0000	0.0016
	1.5	0.605	0.586	5.62	5.80	0.0906	0.0960	0.0935	0.0037	0.1735	0.0620	0.1368	0.1458	0.0557	0.1816	0.0024	0.0957	0.0016	0.0000	0.0000	0.0016
	2.0	0.615	0.585	5.67	5.97	0.0894	0.0982	0.0934	0.0038	0.1726	0.0636	0.1348	0.1494	0.0534	0.1858	0.0017	0.0970	0.0016	0.0000	0.0000	0.0017
0.2	0.4	0.597	0.579	5.56	5.74	0.0934	0.0918	0.0936	0.0036	0.1748	0.0602	0.1403	0.1409	0.0610	0.1735	0.0064	0.0885	0.0016	0.0000	0.0004	0.0059
	0.6	0.633	0.573	5.71	6.31	0.0899	0.0982	0.0934	0.0040	0.1721	0.0654	0.1342	0.1524	0.0545	0.1858	0.0049	0.0911	0.0016	0.0000	0.0003	0.0061
	1.0	0.685	0.566	5.95	7.19	0.0850	0.1076	0.0931	0.0045	0.1680	0.0732	0.1253	0.1697	0.0450	0.2037	0.0031	0.0944	0.0016	0.0000	0.0002	0.0063
	1.5	0.726	0.560	6.14	7.96	0.0810	0.1154	0.0929	0.0049	0.1646	0.0799	0.1178	0.1842	0.0373	0.2184	0.0018	0.0966	0.0016	0.0000	0.0001	0.0064
	2.0	0.752	0.557	6.28	8.49	0.0784	0.1206	0.0928	0.0052	0.1624	0.0844	0.1129	0.1940	0.0323	0.2279	0.0012	0.0978	0.0016	0.0000	0.0001	0.0065
0.3	0.4	0.638	0.561	5.69	6.48	0.0916	0.0955	0.0934	0.0039	0.1727	0.0651	0.1361	0.1502	0.0582	0.1785	0.0066	0.0878	0.0016	0.0000	0.0015	0.0121
	0.6	0.694	0.550	5.92	7.47	0.0872	0.1042	0.0932	0.0045	0.1687	0.0731	0.1277	0.1671	0.0501	0.1938	0.0051	0.0903	0.0016	0.0000	0.0011	0.0127
	1.0	0.779	0.535	6.31	9.18	0.0803	0.1181	0.0928	0.0054	0.1622	0.0864	0.1143	0.1951	0.0378	0.2175	0.0033	0.0937	0.0016	0.0000	0.0008	0.0133
	1.5	0.853	0.524	6.67	10.85	0.0743	0.1307	0.0924	0.0062	0.1564	0.0991	0.1020	0.2209	0.0275	0.2380	0.0020	0.0960	0.0016	0.0000	0.0005	0.0139
	2.0	0.903	0.516	6.93	12.12	0.0701	0.1396	0.0921	0.0069	0.1521	0.1085	0.0933	0.2400	0.0208	0.2543	0.0014	0.0973	0.0016	0.0000	0.0004	0.0142
0.4	0.4	0.668	0.540	5.78	7.15	0.0909	0.0965	0.0933	0.0042	0.1714	0.0682	0.1340	0.1545	0.0580	0.1766	0.0069	0.0867	0.0016	0.0000	0.0035	0.0194
	0.6	0.742	0.523	6.07	8.61	0.0860	0.1063	0.0930	0.0049	0.1666	0.0785	0.1242	0.1749	0.0499	0.1918	0.0056	0.0890	0.0016	0.0000	0.0029	0.0206
	1.0	0.864	0.500	6.60	11.41	0.0780	0.1233	0.0925	0.0062	0.1581	0.0974	0.1075	0.2113	0.0375	0.2165	0.0037	0.0923	0.0016	0.0000	0.0022	0.0220
	1.5	0.979	0.481	7.15	14.53	0.0704	0.1401	0.0919	0.0075	0.1496	0.1174	0.0911	0.2487	0.0269	0.2387	0.0024	0.0948	0.0016	0.0000	0.0015	0.0233
	2.0	1.063	0.469	7.58	17.17	0.0649	0.1530	0.0914	0.0086	0.1428	0.1336	0.0786	0.2782	0.0198	0.2542	0.0017	0.0964	0.0016	0.0000	0.0011	0.0242
0.5	0.4	0.686	0.519	5.83	7.72	0.0904	0.0957	0.0933	0.0043	0.1706	0.0695	0.1326	0.1541	0.0579	0.1727	0.0071	0.0858	0.0016	0.0000	0.0066	0.0270
	0.6	0.774	0.495	6.17	9.65	0.0854	0.1056	0.0929	0.0052	0.1653	0.0812	0.1223	0.1751	0.0501	0.1864	0.0058	0.0879	0.0016	0.0000	0.0058	0.0285
	1.0	0.931	0.462	6.80	13.70	0.0771	0.1235	0.0922	0.0068	0.1556	0.1041	0.1045	0.2143	0.0384	0.2090	0.0041	0.0910	0.0016	0.0000	0.0044	0.0311
	1.5	1.092	0.437	7.52	18.82	0.0689	0.1427	0.0915	0.0087	0.1450	0.1310	0.0864	0.2576	0.0282	0.2304	0.0028	0.0935	0.0016	0.0000	0.0033	0.0335
	2.0	1.219	0.420	8.15	23.66	0.0625	0.1587	0.0907	0.0107	0.1358	0.1554	0.0720	0.2941	0.0215	0.2458	0.0020	0.0951	0.0016	0.0001	0.0025	0.0353

TABLE 38

		$a_A = 0.2$		a_B = variable							$r_A = 1.0$					r_B = variable			
0.1	0.4	0.528	0.689	6.92	5.31	0.1126	0.0774	0.0946	0.0028	0.2066	0.0405	0.1776	0.1130	0.0833	0.1525	0.0083	0.0874	0.0063	0.0002	0.0000	0.0016
	0.6	0.544	0.687	7.03	5.57	0.1105	0.0806	0.0945	0.0029	0.2054	0.0423	0.1743	0.1181	0.0790	0.1590	0.0066	0.0890	0.0063	0.0002	0.0000	0.0016
	1.0	0.566	0.685	7.19	5.95	0.1076	0.0850	0.0944	0.0031	0.2037	0.0450	0.1697	0.1253	0.0732	0.1680	0.0045	0.0931	0.0063	0.0002	0.0000	0.0016
	1.5	0.582	0.683	7.31	6.24	0.1055	0.0883	0.0943	0.0032	0.2024	0.0470	0.1661	0.1308	0.0688	0.1749	0.0029	0.0954	0.0063	0.0002	0.0000	0.0016
	2.0	0.593	0.681	7.39	6.43	0.1041	0.0905	0.0942	0.0033	0.2016	0.0483	0.1639	0.1343	0.0660	0.1792	0.0021	0.0967	0.0063	0.0002	0.0000	0.0017
0.2	0.4	0.575	0.674	7.20	6.15	0.1087	0.0840	0.0944	0.0031	0.2037	0.0455	0.1701	0.1259	0.0752	0.1661	0.0079	0.0877	0.0063	0.0002	0.0005	0.0058
	0.6	0.609	0.667	7.44	6.80	0.1049	0.0901	0.0942	0.0034	0.2011	0.0497	0.1635	0.1367	0.0673	0.1787	0.0062	0.0904	0.0063	0.0002	0.0004	0.0060
	1.0	0.659	0.659	7.81	7.81	0.0993	0.0993	0.0939	0.0039	0.1973	0.0561	0.1533	0.1533	0.0561	0.1973	0.0039	0.0939	0.0062	0.0003	0.0003	0.0062
	1.5	0.698	0.652	8.12	8.70	0.0947	0.1069	0.0937	0.0043	0.1940	0.0616	0.1449	0.1675	0.0468	0.2127	0.0023	0.0963	0.0062	0.0004	0.0002	0.0064
	2.0	0.724	0.647	8.34	9.32	0.0917	0.1119	0.0935	0.0045	0.1918	0.0653	0.1393	0.1771	0.0407	0.2230	0.0015	0.0976	0.0062	0.0004	0.0001	0.0065
0.3	0.4	0.614	0.653	7.41	6.96	0.1068	0.0873	0.0942	0.0034	0.2018	0.0493	0.1656	0.1344	0.0722	0.1711	0.0081	0.0870	0.0062	0.0003	0.0019	0.0119
	0.6	0.666	0.640	7.77	8.09	0.1019	0.0954	0.0940	0.0038	0.1980	0.0558	0.1564	0.1503	0.0627	0.1868	0.0065	0.0895	0.0062	0.0003	0.0015	0.0125
	1.0	0.748	0.622	8.37	10.06	0.0942	0.1089	0.0935	0.0047	0.1919	0.0668	0.1411	0.1771	0.0480	0.2118	0.0042	0.0931	0.0062	0.0004	0.0011	0.0132
	1.5	0.818	0.609	8.95	12.03	0.0873	0.1215	0.0931	0.0056	0.1860	0.0774	0.1271	0.2028	0.0353	0.2341	0.0026	0.0956	0.0061	0.0005	0.0007	0.0138
	2.0	0.866	0.600	9.38	13.55	0.0825	0.1299	0.0927	0.0061	0.1818	0.0854	0.1170	0.2218	0.0268	0.2494	0.0017	0.0971	0.0061	0.0005	0.0005	0.0142
0.4	0.4	0.641	0.629	7.54	7.69	0.1061	0.0879	0.0941	0.0036	0.2006	0.0517	0.1634	0.1381	0.0719	0.1689	0.0086	0.0858	0.0062	0.0003	0.0044	0.0190
	0.6	0.711	0.609	7.99	9.34	0.1008	0.0971	0.0938	0.0042	0.1960	0.0601	0.1526	0.1573	0.0624	0.1841	0.0070	0.0881	0.0062	0.0003	0.0036	0.0200
	1.0	0.827	0.581	8.82	12.56	0.0919	0.1131	0.0932	0.0054	0.1879	0.0756	0.1338	0.1923	0.0476	0.2092	0.0048	0.0916	0.0062	0.0004	0.0027	0.0215
	1.5	0.936	0.559	9.71	16.24	0.0833	0.1293	0.0925	0.0068	0.1794	0.0925	0.1149	0.2291	0.0346	0.2324	0.0032	0.0942	0.0061	0.0005	0.0019	0.0229
	2.0	1.015	0.545	10.43	19.43	0.0769	0.1420	0.0920	0.0079	0.1726	0.1066	0.1002	0.2588	0.0257	0.2489	0.0022	0.0959	0.0061	0.0006	0.0014	0.0239
0.5	0.4	0.657	0.604	7.62	8.28	0.1057	0.0870	0.0941	0.0037	0.1998	0.0527	0.1618	0.1375	0.0717	0.1649	0.0089	0.0849	0.0062	0.0003	0.0082	0.0261
	0.6	0.740	0.576	8.13	10.43	0.1002	0.0961	0.0937	0.0045	0.1948	0.0621	0.1504	0.1572	0.0626	0.1785	0.0073	0.0870	0.0062	0.0004	0.0072	0.0276
	1.0	0.887	0.538	9.12	15.04	0.0910	0.1127	0.0930	0.0060	0.1855	0.0809	0.1305	0.1944	0.0486	0.2012	0.0052	0.0901	0.0061	0.0005	0.0056	0.0302
	1.5	1.038	0.508	10.28	21.01	0.0819	0.1309	0.0921	0.0079	0.1750	0.1037	0.1097	0.2366	0.0364	0.2230	0.0036	0.0928	0.0060	0.0006	0.0042	0.0327
	2.0	1.157	0.488	11.34	26.88	0.0745	0.1464	0.0913	0.0096	0.1657	0.1248	0.0926	0.2732	0.0279	0.2393	0.0026	0.0945	0.0060	0.0007	0.0032	0.0345

Straight Haunches — Constant Width

$a_A = 0.3$ $r_A = 1.0$ a_B = variable r_B = variable

TABLE 39

| Right Haunch | | Carry-over Factors | | Stiffness Factors | | Unif. Load F.E.M. Coef. × wL^2 | | Concentrated Load F.E.M.—Coef. × PL | | | | | | | | | | Haunch Load at | | | |
| | | | | | | | | b=0.1 | | b=0.3 | | b=0.5 | | b=0.7 | | b=0.9 | | Left (Coef. × $W_A L^2$) | | Right (Coef. × $W_B L^2$) | |
a_B	r_B	C_{AB}	C_{BA}	k_{AB}	k_{BA}	M_{AB}	M_{BA}	M_{AB}	M_{BA}	M_{AB}	M_{BA}	M_{AB}	M_{BA}	M_{AB}	M_{BA}	M_{AB}	M_{BA}	M_{AB}	M_{BA}	M_{AB}	M_{BA}
0.1	0.4	0.499	0.784	8.79	5.60	0.1237	0.0728	0.0940	0.0030	0.2216	0.0337	0.2036	0.1025	0.0981	0.1466	0.0100	0.0867	0.0134	0.0007	0.0001	0.0016
	0.6	0.515	0.782	8.95	5.89	0.1213	0.0759	0.0938	0.0032	0.2203	0.0355	0.2000	0.1074	0.0931	0.1532	0.0079	0.0893	0.0134	0.0008	0.0001	0.0016
	1.0	0.535	0.779	9.18	6.31	0.1181	0.0803	0.0937	0.0033	0.2175	0.0378	0.1951	0.1143	0.0864	0.1622	0.0054	0.0928	0.0133	0.0008	0.0000	0.0016
	1.5	0.551	0.777	9.35	6.64	0.1157	0.0836	0.0935	0.0035	0.2173	0.0396	0.1910	0.1196	0.0813	0.1693	0.0035	0.0952	0.0133	0.0009	0.0000	0.0016
	2.0	0.561	0.775	9.46	6.85	0.1141	0.0857	0.0935	0.0037	0.2162	0.0411	0.1885	0.1230	0.0781	0.1737	0.0025	0.0966	0.0133	0.0009	0.0000	0.0017
0.2	0.4	0.543	0.766	9.19	6.52	0.1194	0.0791	0.0935	0.0034	0.2185	0.0384	0.1955	0.1147	0.0889	0.1601	0.0096	0.0870	0.0133	0.0008	0.0006	0.0058
	0.6	0.576	0.758	9.53	7.24	0.1152	0.0851	0.0934	0.0038	0.2158	0.0422	0.1883	0.1250	0.0798	0.1729	0.0075	0.0898	0.0133	0.0009	0.0005	0.0060
	1.0	0.622	0.748	10.06	8.37	0.1089	0.0942	0.0931	0.0042	0.2118	0.0480	0.1771	0.1411	0.0668	0.1919	0.0047	0.0935	0.0132	0.0011	0.0004	0.0062
	1.5	0.660	0.740	10.52	9.38	0.1037	0.1018	0.0927	0.0047	0.2085	0.0530	0.1678	0.1550	0.0559	0.2078	0.0028	0.0961	0.0130	0.0012	0.0002	0.0064
	2.0	0.684	0.734	10.83	10.09	0.1002	0.1069	0.0924	0.0050	0.2062	0.0565	0.1614	0.1645	0.0487	0.2185	0.0019	0.0974	0.0129	0.0013	0.0001	0.0065
0.3	0.4	0.579	0.741	9.47	7.40	0.1175	0.0822	0.0934	0.0037	0.2164	0.0419	0.1909	0.1225	0.0856	0.1649	0.0100	0.0861	0.0133	0.0009	0.0022	0.0118
	0.6	0.629	0.726	9.98	8.64	0.1120	0.0902	0.0931	0.0042	0.2126	0.0477	0.1808	0.1379	0.0747	0.1807	0.0080	0.0888	0.0132	0.0010	0.0018	0.0124
	1.0	0.705	0.705	10.85	10.85	0.1034	0.1034	0.0924	0.0052	0.2063	0.0577	0.1640	0.1640	0.0577	0.2063	0.0052	0.0924	0.0131	0.0013	0.0013	0.0131
	1.5	0.771	0.689	11.70	13.10	0.0956	0.1157	0.0917	0.0062	0.2002	0.0675	0.1483	0.1892	0.0428	0.2294	0.0033	0.0953	0.0129	0.0015	0.0008	0.0137
	2.0	0.817	0.678	12.33	14.85	0.0901	0.1246	0.0913	0.0069	0.1957	0.0750	0.1368	0.2080	0.0326	0.2455	0.0022	0.0968	0.0128	0.0017	0.0006	0.0141
0.4	0.4	0.604	0.713	9.64	8.16	0.1167	0.0826	0.0933	0.0040	0.2153	0.0440	0.1883	0.1260	0.0851	0.1626	0.0104	0.0849	0.0133	0.0009	0.0052	0.0186
	0.6	0.669	0.689	10.28	9.97	0.1109	0.0915	0.0930	0.0047	0.2107	0.0515	0.1766	0.1444	0.0743	0.1779	0.0084	0.0874	0.0132	0.0011	0.0044	0.0196
	1.0	0.777	0.657	11.46	13.55	0.1010	0.1071	0.0922	0.0058	0.2022	0.0655	0.1560	0.1784	0.0572	0.2033	0.0059	0.0910	0.0130	0.0015	0.0033	0.0212
	1.5	0.878	0.631	12.74	17.72	0.0914	0.1232	0.0910	0.0075	0.1933	0.0811	0.1349	0.2148	0.0420	0.2272	0.0039	0.0938	0.0128	0.0019	0.0024	0.0227
	2.0	0.952	0.614	13.80	21.39	0.0841	0.1360	0.0904	0.0089	0.1861	0.0948	0.1182	0.2448	0.0315	0.2444	0.0026	0.0955	0.0126	0.0022	0.0017	0.0237
0.5	0.4	0.616	0.686	9.75	8.76	0.1161	0.0818	0.0932	0.0041	0.2144	0.0449	0.1864	0.1255	0.0846	0.1587	0.0107	0.0840	0.0133	0.0010	0.0097	0.0254
	0.6	0.692	0.653	10.46	11.09	0.1101	0.0905	0.0931	0.0049	0.2094	0.0532	0.1740	0.1444	0.0743	0.1723	0.0087	0.0863	0.0131	0.0012	0.0085	0.0270
	1.0	0.827	0.607	11.85	16.13	0.0999	0.1056	0.0920	0.0064	0.1997	0.0699	0.1521	0.1803	0.0579	0.1952	0.0063	0.0894	0.0129	0.0016	0.0067	0.0295
	1.5	0.966	0.572	13.49	22.79	0.0896	0.1246	0.0905	0.0086	0.1889	0.0907	0.1289	0.2219	0.0439	0.2173	0.0044	0.0923	0.0126	0.0022	0.0051	0.0320
	2.0	1.076	0.548	14.99	29.43	0.0814	0.1401	0.0898	0.0106	0.1790	0.1116	0.1095	0.2587	0.0339	0.2342	0.0031	0.0940	0.0124	0.0026	0.0039	0.0339

TABLE 40

$a_A = 0.4$ a_B = variable $r_A = 1.0$ r_B = variable

0.1	0.4	0.466	0.870	10.90	5.83	0.1295	0.0705	0.0927	0.0033	0.2198	0.0335	0.2207	0.0961	0.1104	0.1423	0.0113	0.0862	0.0222	0.0019	0.0001	0.0016
	0.6	0.480	0.868	11.11	6.15	0.1268	0.0736	0.0925	0.0035	0.2184	0.0352	0.2168	0.1008	0.1049	0.1489	0.0091	0.0889	0.0221	0.0020	0.0001	0.0016
	1.0	0.500	0.864	11.41	6.60	0.1233	0.0780	0.0923	0.0037	0.2165	0.0375	0.2113	0.1075	0.0974	0.1581	0.0062	0.0925	0.0220	0.0022	0.0000	0.0016
	1.5	0.514	0.861	11.65	6.95	0.1206	0.0814	0.0922	0.0039	0.2149	0.0394	0.2071	0.1127	0.0916	0.1653	0.0041	0.0950	0.0219	0.0023	0.0000	0.0016
	2.0	0.524	0.859	11.79	7.18	0.1188	0.0835	0.0921	0.0041	0.2140	0.0406	0.2044	0.1160	0.0880	0.1698	0.0029	0.0964	0.0219	0.0024	0.0000	0.0017
0.2	0.4	0.507	0.849	11.41	6.81	0.1248	0.0767	0.0923	0.0038	0.2165	0.0379	0.2121	0.1078	0.1004	0.1558	0.0110	0.0865	0.0221	0.0022	0.0007	0.0058
	0.6	0.537	0.840	11.87	7.59	0.1201	0.0828	0.0920	0.0042	0.2136	0.0417	0.2042	0.1180	0.0904	0.1685	0.0086	0.0894	0.0218	0.0024	0.0006	0.0060
	1.0	0.581	0.827	12.56	8.82	0.1131	0.0919	0.0916	0.0048	0.2092	0.0476	0.1923	0.1338	0.0756	0.1879	0.0054	0.0932	0.0215	0.0027	0.0004	0.0062
	1.5	0.616	0.817	13.17	9.92	0.1073	0.0996	0.0912	0.0053	0.2054	0.0528	0.1821	0.1475	0.0633	0.2043	0.0033	0.0958	0.0213	0.0030	0.0002	0.0064
	2.0	0.639	0.811	13.58	10.70	0.1035	0.1048	0.0909	0.0057	0.2027	0.0564	0.1751	0.1570	0.0551	0.2153	0.0022	0.0972	0.0212	0.0032	0.0002	0.0064
0.3	0.4	0.539	0.820	11.76	7.73	0.1227	0.0796	0.0921	0.0042	0.2144	0.0412	0.2071	0.1154	0.0967	0.1605	0.0113	0.0856	0.0219	0.0024	0.0025	0.0116
	0.6	0.585	0.801	12.42	9.06	0.1168	0.0876	0.0917	0.0048	0.2103	0.0470	0.1962	0.1304	0.0847	0.1763	0.0091	0.0884	0.0216	0.0027	0.0021	0.0121
	1.0	0.657	0.777	13.55	11.46	0.1071	0.1010	0.0910	0.0059	0.2033	0.0572	0.1784	0.1560	0.0655	0.2022	0.0058	0.0922	0.0212	0.0033	0.0015	0.0130
	1.5	0.719	0.757	14.65	13.90	0.0985	0.1134	0.0902	0.0070	0.1965	0.0673	0.1614	0.1811	0.0488	0.2259	0.0037	0.0950	0.0208	0.0039	0.0010	0.0136
	2.0	0.761	0.744	15.47	15.83	0.0924	0.1226	0.0898	0.0077	0.1913	0.0752	0.1486	0.2004	0.0372	0.2427	0.0025	0.0966	0.0205	0.0044	0.0007	0.0140
0.4	0.4	0.560	0.787	11.96	8.51	0.1219	0.0801	0.0920	0.0044	0.2133	0.0432	0.2046	0.1187	0.0960	0.1581	0.0119	0.0843	0.0218	0.0025	0.0059	0.0183
	0.6	0.620	0.759	12.77	10.43	0.1155	0.0889	0.0914	0.0052	0.2083	0.0507	0.1921	0.1366	0.0840	0.1734	0.0096	0.0868	0.0215	0.0029	0.0050	0.0193
	1.0	0.720	0.720	14.26	14.26	0.1046	0.1046	0.0905	0.0067	0.1991	0.0649	0.1700	0.1700	0.0649	0.1991	0.0067	0.0905	0.0210	0.0038	0.0038	0.0210
	1.5	0.814	0.689	15.88	18.77	0.0940	0.1209	0.0894	0.0084	0.1893	0.0808	0.1472	0.2063	0.0479	0.2235	0.0045	0.0934	0.0204	0.0047	0.0027	0.0224
	2.0	0.883	0.669	17.23	22.76	0.0859	0.1340	0.0886	0.0099	0.1813	0.0945	0.1290	0.2365	0.0360	0.2414	0.0031	0.0952	0.0200	0.0055	0.0020	0.0235
0.5	0.4	0.569	0.755	12.10	9.11	0.1211	0.0793	0.0919	0.0045	0.2124	0.0440	0.2022	0.1184	0.0950	0.1544	0.0121	0.0834	0.0217	0.0025	0.0108	0.0249
	0.6	0.637	0.717	13.00	11.55	0.1144	0.0879	0.0913	0.0054	0.2069	0.0523	0.1888	0.1367	0.0833	0.1680	0.0099	0.0857	0.0214	0.0030	0.0095	0.0265
	1.0	0.760	0.663	14.72	16.87	0.1033	0.1039	0.0902	0.0073	0.1966	0.0692	0.1653	0.1721	0.0652	0.1911	0.0071	0.0890	0.0208	0.0041	0.0075	0.0291
	1.5	0.887	0.620	16.73	23.95	0.0921	0.1219	0.0889	0.0096	0.1848	0.0901	0.1404	0.2132	0.0492	0.2138	0.0050	0.0918	0.0201	0.0053	0.0057	0.0316
	2.0	0.989	0.591	18.56	31.05	0.0831	0.1376	0.0877	0.0118	0.1743	0.1099	0.1196	0.2500	0.0380	0.2311	0.0037	0.0937	0.0195	0.0065	0.0044	0.0336

Straight Haunches — Constant Width

TABLE 41

Notes: $a_A = 0.5$, a_B = variable, $r_A = 1.0$, r_B = variable

Right Haunch a_B	r_B	Carry-over Factors C_{AB}	C_{BA}	Stiffness Factors k_{AB}	k_{BA}	Unif. Load F.E.M. Coef. × wL^2 M_{AB}	M_{BA}	Conc. Load b=0.1 M_{AB}	M_{BA}	b=0.3 M_{AB}	M_{BA}	b=0.5 M_{AB}	M_{BA}	b=0.7 M_{AB}	M_{BA}	b=0.9 M_{AB}	M_{BA}	Haunch Load Left Coef. × $W_A L^2$ M_{AB}	M_{BA}	Right Coef. × $W_B L^2$ M_{AB}	M_{BA}
0.1	0.4	0.430	0.938	13.08	5.99	0.1302	0.0695	0.0914	0.0036	0.2127	0.0341	0.2243	0.0932	0.1181	0.1397	0.0125	0.0859	0.0315	0.0039	0.0001	0.0016
	0.6	0.444	0.935	13.34	6.33	0.1273	0.0727	0.0912	0.0038	0.2112	0.0359	0.2201	0.0979	0.1122	0.1463	0.0100	0.0886	0.0311	0.0041	0.0001	0.0016
	1.0	0.462	0.931	13.70	6.80	0.1235	0.0771	0.0910	0.0041	0.2090	0.0384	0.2143	0.1045	0.1041	0.1556	0.0068	0.0922	0.0311	0.0044	0.0000	0.0016
	1.5	0.476	0.928	13.98	7.18	0.1205	0.0805	0.0908	0.0043	0.2073	0.0403	0.2098	0.1097	0.0979	0.1628	0.0045	0.0948	0.0309	0.0046	0.0000	0.0016
	2.0	0.485	0.925	14.16	7.42	0.1187	0.0826	0.0907	0.0044	0.2062	0.0416	0.2070	0.1130	0.0939	0.1673	0.0032	0.0963	0.0308	0.0048	0.0000	0.0016
0.2	0.4	0.468	0.913	13.67	7.01	0.1253	0.0757	0.0910	0.0041	0.2092	0.0387	0.2154	0.1047	0.1075	0.1531	0.0121	0.0861	0.0311	0.0044	0.0008	0.0057
	0.6	0.497	0.902	14.21	7.82	0.1203	0.0818	0.0907	0.0045	0.2061	0.0426	0.2061	0.1148	0.0969	0.1659	0.0094	0.0891	0.0308	0.0049	0.0007	0.0059
	1.0	0.538	0.887	15.04	9.12	0.1127	0.0910	0.0901	0.0052	0.2012	0.0486	0.1944	0.1305	0.0809	0.1855	0.0060	0.0930	0.0302	0.0056	0.0005	0.0061
	1.5	0.571	0.875	15.76	10.29	0.1065	0.0989	0.0897	0.0058	0.1969	0.0540	0.1836	0.1442	0.0677	0.2021	0.0037	0.0956	0.0302	0.0062	0.0003	0.0063
	2.0	0.593	0.867	16.25	11.11	0.1023	0.1041	0.0894	0.0062	0.1941	0.0580	0.1762	0.1537	0.0569	0.2133	0.0024	0.0971	0.0294	0.0066	0.0002	0.0064
0.3	0.4	0.497	0.878	14.05	7.95	0.1232	0.0785	0.0908	0.0045	0.2071	0.0420	0.2104	0.1121	0.1034	0.1577	0.0124	0.0853	0.0309	0.0048	0.0028	0.0115
	0.6	0.540	0.857	14.82	9.34	0.1164	0.0862	0.0903	0.0051	0.2027	0.0478	0.1991	0.1268	0.0906	0.1736	0.0098	0.0881	0.0304	0.0055	0.0023	0.0121
	1.0	0.607	0.827	16.13	11.85	0.1066	0.0999	0.0894	0.0063	0.1952	0.0579	0.1803	0.1521	0.0699	0.1997	0.0064	0.0920	0.0295	0.0067	0.0016	0.0129
	1.5	0.666	0.804	17.41	14.43	0.0974	0.1125	0.0889	0.0072	0.1878	0.0684	0.1626	0.1773	0.0520	0.2237	0.0041	0.0948	0.0287	0.0079	0.0011	0.0136
	2.0	0.707	0.788	18.36	16.47	0.0908	0.1218	0.0883	0.0081	0.1824	0.0766	0.1494	0.1963	0.0399	0.2408	0.0027	0.0965	0.0282	0.0087	0.0007	0.0140
0.4	0.4	0.515	0.840	14.27	8.74	0.1222	0.0789	0.0906	0.0047	0.2059	0.0437	0.2078	0.1151	0.1025	0.1553	0.0129	0.0840	0.0307	0.0050	0.0063	0.0181
	0.6	0.570	0.806	15.19	10.73	0.1154	0.0876	0.0900	0.0055	0.2011	0.0511	0.1948	0.1327	0.0896	0.1707	0.0105	0.0865	0.0302	0.0059	0.0054	0.0191
	1.0	0.663	0.760	16.87	14.72	0.1039	0.1033	0.0890	0.0071	0.1911	0.0652	0.1721	0.1653	0.0692	0.1966	0.0073	0.0902	0.0291	0.0075	0.0041	0.0208
	1.5	0.752	0.723	18.69	19.44	0.0929	0.1196	0.0881	0.0086	0.1810	0.0810	0.1487	0.2015	0.0510	0.2212	0.0049	0.0931	0.0280	0.0093	0.0029	0.0223
	2.0	0.819	0.699	20.19	23.66	0.0846	0.1326	0.0872	0.0101	0.1727	0.0946	0.1301	0.2309	0.0384	0.2394	0.0034	0.0950	0.0271	0.0108	0.0021	0.0234
0.5	0.4	0.519	0.804	14.44	9.33	0.1210	0.0780	0.0905	0.0048	0.2049	0.0442	0.2047	0.1147	0.1009	0.1518	0.0131	0.0830	0.0305	0.0053	0.0116	0.0246
	0.6	0.581	0.757	15.45	11.84	0.1140	0.0865	0.0899	0.0057	0.1991	0.0523	0.1908	0.1324	0.0880	0.1655	0.0107	0.0853	0.0300	0.0060	0.0100	0.0262
	1.0	0.692	0.692	17.34	15.45	0.1023	0.1023	0.0887	0.0076	0.1886	0.0686	0.1667	0.1667	0.0686	0.1886	0.0076	0.0887	0.0288	0.0078	0.0078	0.0288
	1.5	0.811	0.640	19.50	17.34	0.0908	0.1197	0.0873	0.0100	0.1769	0.0886	0.1416	0.2065	0.0516	0.2113	0.0053	0.0915	0.0275	0.0101	0.0059	0.0313
	2.0	0.910	0.605	21.45	32.23	0.0817	0.1349	0.0861	0.0122	0.1666	0.1076	0.1208	0.2421	0.0398	0.2286	0.0039	0.0934	0.0263	0.0123	0.0046	0.0333

TABLE 42

$\alpha_A = 0.1$ · α_B = variable · $r_A = 1.5$ · r_B = variable

0.1	0.4	0.547	0.608	5.61	5.04	0.1005	0.0828	0.0959	0.0021	0.1846	0.0504	0.1531	0.1241	0.0708	0.1582	0.0070	0.0880	0.0017	0.0000	0.0001	0.0016
	0.6	0.564	0.607	5.69	5.28	0.0986	0.0861	0.0958	0.0022	0.1833	0.0526	0.1500	0.1294	0.0670	0.1646	0.0055	0.0904	0.0016	0.0000	0.0000	0.0016
	1.0	0.586	0.605	5.80	5.62	0.0960	0.0906	0.0957	0.0024	0.1816	0.0557	0.1458	0.1368	0.0620	0.1735	0.0037	0.0935	0.0016	0.0000	0.0000	0.0016
	1.5	0.603	0.603	5.89	5.89	0.0941	0.0941	0.0957	0.0025	0.1802	0.0581	0.1425	0.1425	0.0581	0.1802	0.0025	0.0957	0.0016	0.0000	0.0000	0.0016
	2.0	0.614	0.602	5.94	6.06	0.0928	0.0962	0.0956	0.0025	0.1793	0.0596	0.1405	0.1462	0.0557	0.1844	0.0017	0.0969	0.0016	0.0000	0.0000	0.0017
0.2	0.4	0.596	0.596	5.81	5.81	0.0968	0.0898	0.0957	0.0024	0.1815	0.0564	0.1461	0.1377	0.0636	0.1718	0.0067	0.0883	0.0017	0.0000	0.0004	0.0059
	0.6	0.631	0.590	5.98	6.40	0.0934	0.0961	0.0956	0.0026	0.1789	0.0613	0.1399	0.1490	0.0569	0.1841	0.0051	0.0909	0.0016	0.0000	0.0003	0.0061
	1.0	0.683	0.582	6.24	7.31	0.0883	0.1055	0.0954	0.0029	0.1749	0.0688	0.1308	0.1661	0.0470	0.2024	0.0032	0.0943	0.0016	0.0000	0.0002	0.0063
	1.5	0.724	0.577	6.46	8.10	0.0843	0.1132	0.0953	0.0032	0.1716	0.0751	0.1232	0.1806	0.0390	0.2174	0.0019	0.0965	0.0016	0.0000	0.0001	0.0064
	2.0	0.750	0.573	6.60	8.65	0.0816	0.1183	0.0952	0.0034	0.1693	0.0794	0.1181	0.1903	0.0339	0.2272	0.0013	0.0977	0.0016	0.0000	0.0001	0.0065
0.3	0.4	0.636	0.577	5.96	6.57	0.0951	0.0934	0.0957	0.0026	0.1794	0.0610	0.1419	0.1468	0.0607	0.1771	0.0069	0.0876	0.0017	0.0000	0.0016	0.0121
	0.6	0.691	0.566	6.22	7.59	0.0906	0.1019	0.0955	0.0030	0.1756	0.0686	0.1333	0.1634	0.0524	0.1925	0.0054	0.0900	0.0016	0.0000	0.0012	0.0127
	1.0	0.777	0.551	6.64	9.35	0.0836	0.1157	0.0952	0.0035	0.1693	0.0813	0.1196	0.1910	0.0396	0.2173	0.0035	0.0935	0.0016	0.0000	0.0009	0.0133
	1.5	0.850	0.539	7.03	11.09	0.0775	0.1281	0.0950	0.0041	0.1635	0.0934	0.1071	0.2169	0.0290	0.2387	0.0022	0.0958	0.0016	0.0000	0.0006	0.0139
	2.0	0.900	0.531	7.32	12.41	0.0732	0.1369	0.0947	0.0046	0.1591	0.1024	0.0980	0.2359	0.0218	0.2532	0.0015	0.0972	0.0016	0.0000	0.0004	0.0142
0.4	0.4	0.666	0.556	6.06	7.26	0.0944	0.0943	0.0956	0.0028	0.1782	0.0639	0.1397	0.1509	0.0606	0.1750	0.0072	0.0865	0.0016	0.0000	0.0037	0.0193
	0.6	0.740	0.539	6.38	8.76	0.0895	0.1039	0.0953	0.0032	0.1735	0.0737	0.1298	0.1710	0.0522	0.1902	0.0058	0.0889	0.0016	0.0000	0.0031	0.0205
	1.0	0.861	0.514	6.95	11.65	0.0814	0.1206	0.0950	0.0041	0.1653	0.0916	0.1127	0.2071	0.0394	0.2149	0.0039	0.0922	0.0016	0.0000	0.0023	0.0219
	1.5	0.976	0.496	7.56	14.88	0.0737	0.1371	0.0946	0.0050	0.1568	0.1107	0.0959	0.2443	0.0284	0.2374	0.0026	0.0947	0.0016	0.0000	0.0016	0.0232
	2.0	1.059	0.483	8.05	17.65	0.0680	0.1498	0.0942	0.0058	0.1501	0.1263	0.0829	0.2739	0.0209	0.2531	0.0018	0.0963	0.0016	0.0000	0.0011	0.0241
0.5	0.4	0.684	0.534	6.12	7.83	0.0939	0.0935	0.0955	0.0029	0.1774	0.0651	0.1383	0.1504	0.0604	0.1711	0.0074	0.0856	0.0016	0.0000	0.0069	0.0268
	0.6	0.772	0.510	6.48	9.81	0.0889	0.1031	0.0953	0.0034	0.1723	0.0761	0.1279	0.1711	0.0525	0.1847	0.0061	0.0877	0.0016	0.0000	0.0060	0.0284
	1.0	0.928	0.476	7.18	13.98	0.0805	0.1205	0.0948	0.0045	0.1628	0.0979	0.1097	0.2098	0.0403	0.2073	0.0043	0.0908	0.0016	0.0000	0.0046	0.0309
	1.5	1.088	0.450	7.98	19.29	0.0722	0.1393	0.0943	0.0058	0.1523	0.1236	0.0910	0.2528	0.0298	0.2287	0.0030	0.0933	0.0016	0.0000	0.0034	0.0333
	2.0	1.215	0.433	8.69	24.39	0.0656	0.1551	0.0938	0.0071	0.1432	0.1468	0.0760	0.2894	0.0226	0.2445	0.0021	0.0950	0.0016	0.0000	0.0026	0.0351

Straight Haunches—Constant Width

TABLE 43

$a_A = 0.2$ a_B = variable $r_A = 1.5$ r_B = variable

| Right Haunch | | Carry-over Factors | | Stiffness Factors | | Unif. Load F.E.M. Coef. × vL^2 | | Concentrated Load F.E.M.—Coef. × PL | | | | | | | | | | Haunch Load at Left F.E.M. Coef. × $W_A L^2$ | | Haunch Load at Right F.E.M. Coef. × $W_B L^2$ | |
| | | | | | | | | b=0.1 | | b=0.3 | | b=0.5 | | b=0.7 | | b=0.9 | | | | | |
a_B	r_B	C_{AB}	C_{BA}	k_{AB}	k_{BA}	M_{AB}	M_{BA}	M_{AB}	M_{BA}	M_{AB}	M_{BA}	M_{AB}	M_{BA}	M_{AB}	M_{BA}	M_{AB}	M_{BA}	M_{AB}	M_{BA}	M_{AB}	M_{BA}
0.1	0.4	0.523	0.730	7.63	5.46	0.1205	0.0736	0.0967	0.0016	0.2212	0.0335	0.1924	0.1060	0.0906	0.1491	0.0090	0.0870	0.0064	0.0001	0.0001	0.0016
	0.6	0.539	0.728	7.77	5.75	0.1184	0.0767	0.0967	0.0017	0.2201	0.0351	0.1889	0.1109	0.0861	0.1556	0.0072	0.0896	0.0064	0.0001	0.0001	0.0016
	1.0	0.560	0.726	7.96	6.14	0.1154	0.0810	0.0966	0.0018	0.2186	0.0373	0.1842	0.1178	0.0799	0.1646	0.0049	0.0929	0.0064	0.0001	0.0000	0.0016
	1.5	0.577	0.724	8.10	6.46	0.1132	0.0843	0.0965	0.0019	0.2174	0.0390	0.1806	0.1232	0.0751	0.1716	0.0032	0.0953	0.0064	0.0001	0.0000	0.0016
	2.0	0.587	0.722	8.19	6.66	0.1118	0.0863	0.0965	0.0019	0.2166	0.0402	0.1782	0.1265	0.0721	0.1760	0.0023	0.0966	0.0064	0.0001	0.0000	0.0017
0.2	0.4	0.569	0.714	7.97	6.35	0.1166	0.0799	0.0966	0.0019	0.2186	0.0377	0.1847	0.1183	0.0821	0.1626	0.0088	0.0873	0.0064	0.0001	0.0006	0.0058
	0.6	0.603	0.707	8.26	7.04	0.1127	0.0858	0.0965	0.0021	0.2163	0.0413	0.1778	0.1288	0.0736	0.1752	0.0068	0.0901	0.0064	0.0001	0.0005	0.0060
	1.0	0.652	0.698	8.70	8.12	0.1069	0.0947	0.0963	0.0023	0.2127	0.0468	0.1675	0.1449	0.0616	0.1940	0.0043	0.0937	0.0064	0.0002	0.0004	0.0062
	1.5	0.691	0.691	9.08	9.08	0.1021	0.1021	0.0962	0.0025	0.2097	0.0515	0.1587	0.1587	0.0515	0.2097	0.0025	0.0962	0.0064	0.0002	0.0002	0.0064
	2.0	0.716	0.686	9.34	9.75	0.0990	0.1071	0.0960	0.0028	0.2077	0.0547	0.1528	0.1681	0.0449	0.2202	0.0017	0.0975	0.0064	0.0002	0.0001	0.0065
0.3	0.4	0.607	0.692	8.21	7.21	0.1148	0.0829	0.0965	0.0021	0.2168	0.0409	0.1801	0.1263	0.0789	0.1674	0.0091	0.0866	0.0064	0.0002	0.0020	0.0118
	0.6	0.659	0.678	8.65	8.40	0.1098	0.0907	0.0964	0.0024	0.2135	0.0464	0.1706	0.1418	0.0688	0.1831	0.0072	0.0892	0.0064	0.0002	0.0017	0.0123
	1.0	0.740	0.660	9.38	10.52	0.1018	0.1037	0.0961	0.0028	0.2078	0.0559	0.1550	0.1678	0.0530	0.2085	0.0047	0.0927	0.0064	0.0002	0.0012	0.0130
	1.5	0.809	0.645	10.09	12.66	0.0947	0.1156	0.0958	0.0033	0.2024	0.0651	0.1403	0.1928	0.0393	0.2311	0.0029	0.0950	0.0063	0.0003	0.0008	0.0137
	2.0	0.857	0.636	10.62	14.32	0.0897	0.1242	0.0955	0.0038	0.1985	0.0720	0.1296	0.2119	0.0299	0.2469	0.0020	0.0968	0.0063	0.0003	0.0005	0.0141
0.4	0.4	0.634	0.667	8.37	7.96	0.1141	0.0833	0.0964	0.0022	0.2158	0.0429	0.1779	0.1297	0.0787	0.1650	0.0095	0.0853	0.0064	0.0002	0.0048	0.0188
	0.6	0.703	0.645	8.91	9.71	0.1087	0.0920	0.0962	0.0026	0.2117	0.0500	0.1669	0.1482	0.0686	0.1802	0.0077	0.0877	0.0064	0.0002	0.0041	0.0197
	1.0	0.817	0.616	9.92	13.17	0.0996	0.1073	0.0958	0.0033	0.2043	0.0633	0.1475	0.1821	0.0528	0.2054	0.0053	0.0912	0.0064	0.0003	0.0030	0.0213
	1.5	0.924	0.593	11.02	17.18	0.0908	0.1229	0.0954	0.0042	0.1964	0.0780	0.1278	0.2182	0.0387	0.2289	0.0036	0.0936	0.0063	0.0003	0.0022	0.0228
	2.0	1.003	0.578	11.93	20.70	0.0842	0.1353	0.0950	0.0049	0.1900	0.0904	0.1121	0.2479	0.0290	0.2459	0.0025	0.0956	0.0063	0.0004	0.0016	0.0238
0.5	0.4	0.649	0.641	8.46	8.57	0.1137	0.0823	0.0964	0.0022	0.2151	0.0437	0.1763	0.1290	0.0765	0.1610	0.0097	0.0843	0.0064	0.0002	0.0090	0.0257
	0.6	0.731	0.612	9.08	10.84	0.1081	0.0908	0.0961	0.0027	0.2106	0.0516	0.1647	0.1476	0.0688	0.1744	0.0080	0.0865	0.0064	0.0002	0.0079	0.0272
	1.0	0.875	0.571	10.29	15.76	0.0989	0.1065	0.0956	0.0037	0.2021	0.0677	0.1442	0.1836	0.0540	0.1969	0.0058	0.0897	0.0063	0.0003	0.0062	0.0297
	1.5	1.023	0.539	11.73	22.25	0.0895	0.1237	0.0951	0.0048	0.1924	0.0874	0.1225	0.2247	0.0408	0.2189	0.0041	0.0923	0.0063	0.0004	0.0047	0.0322
	2.0	1.141	0.519	13.06	28.73	0.0820	0.1385	0.0945	0.0060	0.1836	0.1060	0.1044	0.2609	0.0316	0.2355	0.0030	0.0941	0.0062	0.0005	0.0037	0.0341

TABLE 44

$a_A = 0.3$ $a_B =$ variable $r_A = 1.5$ $r_B =$ variable

a_A																					
0.1	0.4	0.489	0.858	10.34	5.88	0.1365	0.0671	0.0962	0.0019	0.2426	0.0246	0.2299	0.0910	0.1119	0.1407	0.0114	0.0861	0.0139	0.0005	0.0001	0.0016
	0.6	0.504	0.856	10.55	6.21	0.1341	0.0701	0.0960	0.0020	0.2416	0.0266	0.2260	0.0956	0.1066	0.1472	0.0091	0.0888	0.0139	0.0005	0.0001	0.0016
	1.0	0.524	0.853	10.85	6.67	0.1307	0.0743	0.0960	0.0020	0.2380	0.0275	0.2209	0.1020	0.0991	0.1564	0.0062	0.0924	0.0139	0.0005	0.0000	0.0016
	1.5	0.539	0.850	11.09	7.03	0.1281	0.0775	0.0958	0.0022	0.2387	0.0290	0.2169	0.1071	0.0934	0.1635	0.0041	0.0950	0.0139	0.0006	0.0000	0.0016
	2.0	0.549	0.848	11.24	7.27	0.1265	0.0795	0.0958	0.0022	0.2377	0.0300	0.2143	0.1101	0.0898	0.1679	0.0029	0.0964	0.0139	0.0006	0.0000	0.0016
0.2	0.4	0.532	0.838	10.86	6.89	0.1322	0.0729	0.0958	0.0022	0.2399	0.0282	0.2217	0.1022	0.1021	0.1540	0.0111	0.0863	0.0138	0.0006	0.0007	0.0057
	0.6	0.563	0.830	11.32	7.68	0.1278	0.0787	0.0957	0.0023	0.2376	0.0308	0.2141	0.1120	0.0919	0.1668	0.0086	0.0892	0.0138	0.0006	0.0006	0.0059
	1.0	0.609	0.818	12.03	8.95	0.1211	0.0873	0.0956	0.0026	0.2341	0.0353	0.2028	0.1271	0.0774	0.1860	0.0056	0.0931	0.0138	0.0007	0.0005	0.0061
	1.5	0.645	0.809	12.66	10.09	0.1156	0.0947	0.0950	0.0029	0.2311	0.0393	0.1928	0.1403	0.0651	0.2024	0.0033	0.0958	0.0137	0.0008	0.0003	0.0063
	2.0	0.669	0.803	13.08	10.90	0.1120	0.0997	0.0949	0.0032	0.2292	0.0420	0.1862	0.1494	0.0569	0.2135	0.0022	0.0972	0.0137	0.0009	0.0002	0.0065
0.3	0.4	0.566	0.811	11.23	7.83	0.1303	0.0755	0.0958	0.0024	0.2380	0.0306	0.2170	0.1093	0.0985	0.1584	0.0115	0.0854	0.0138	0.0006	0.0026	0.0116
	0.6	0.614	0.794	11.91	9.21	0.1247	0.0831	0.0956	0.0027	0.2348	0.0350	0.2066	0.1236	0.0865	0.1742	0.0092	0.0881	0.0138	0.0007	0.0021	0.0122
	1.0	0.689	0.771	13.10	11.70	0.1157	0.0956	0.0953	0.0033	0.2294	0.0428	0.1892	0.1483	0.0675	0.2002	0.0062	0.0917	0.0137	0.0008	0.0015	0.0129
	1.5	0.753	0.753	14.27	14.27	0.1074	0.1074	0.0945	0.0039	0.2241	0.0506	0.1725	0.1725	0.0506	0.2241	0.0039	0.0945	0.0136	0.0010	0.0010	0.0136
	2.0	0.797	0.741	15.16	16.30	0.1015	0.1160	0.0943	0.0045	0.2200	0.0566	0.1601	0.1910	0.0389	0.2410	0.0027	0.0963	0.0135	0.0011	0.0007	0.0140
0.4	0.4	0.589	0.781	11.45	8.64	0.1297	0.0757	0.0958	0.0025	0.2370	0.0321	0.2146	0.1123	0.0981	0.1558	0.0120	0.0841	0.0138	0.0006	0.0060	0.0181
	0.6	0.652	0.755	12.30	10.63	0.1236	0.0839	0.0955	0.0030	0.2332	0.0378	0.2026	0.1294	0.0862	0.1710	0.0098	0.0866	0.0138	0.0008	0.0052	0.0191
	1.0	0.757	0.719	13.90	14.65	0.1134	0.0985	0.0950	0.0037	0.2259	0.0488	0.1811	0.1614	0.0673	0.1965	0.0070	0.0902	0.0136	0.0010	0.0039	0.0208
	1.5	0.855	0.690	15.69	19.44	0.1034	0.1139	0.0941	0.0049	0.2183	0.0613	0.1587	0.1965	0.0501	0.2209	0.0047	0.0932	0.0135	0.0012	0.0028	0.0223
	2.0	0.927	0.672	17.21	23.75	0.0955	0.1262	0.0938	0.0058	0.2116	0.0724	0.1405	0.2261	0.0381	0.2389	0.0033	0.0951	0.0134	0.0014	0.0021	0.0234
0.5	0.4	0.600	0.752	11.59	9.26	0.1290	0.0748	0.0958	0.0025	0.2362	0.0328	0.2125	0.1118	0.0976	0.1520	0.0123	0.0829	0.0138	0.0006	0.0112	0.0246
	0.6	0.674	0.716	12.54	11.80	0.1229	0.0827	0.0953	0.0031	0.2320	0.0391	0.2000	0.1290	0.0860	0.1653	0.0102	0.0854	0.0137	0.0008	0.0099	0.0261
	1.0	0.804	0.666	14.43	17.41	0.1125	0.0974	0.0948	0.0041	0.2237	0.0520	0.1773	0.1626	0.0684	0.1878	0.0072	0.0889	0.0136	0.0011	0.0079	0.0287
	1.5	0.937	0.627	16.72	24.99	0.1019	0.1140	0.0938	0.0055	0.2145	0.0685	0.1526	0.2022	0.0526	0.2101	0.0053	0.0916	0.0134	0.0014	0.0060	0.0312
	2.0	1.043	0.601	18.88	32.75	0.0933	0.1285	0.0930	0.0070	0.2053	0.0858	0.1317	0.2381	0.0412	0.2274	0.0039	0.0934	0.0129	0.0017	0.0048	0.0331

Straight Haunches — Constant Width

Figure labels: bL, P, $r_A h_c$, W_A, h_c, W_B, $r_B h_c$, $a_A L$, L, $a_B L$, A, B

TABLE 45

$a_A = 0.4$ a_B = variable $r_A = 1.5$ r_B = variable

Right Haunch a_B	r_B	Carry-over C_{AB}	C_{BA}	Stiffness k_{AB}	k_{BA}	Unif. Load M_{AB}	M_{BA}	$b{=}0.1$ M_{AB}	M_{BA}	$b{=}0.3$ M_{AB}	M_{BA}	$b{=}0.5$ M_{AB}	M_{BA}	$b{=}0.7$ M_{AB}	M_{BA}	$b{=}0.9$ M_{AB}	M_{BA}	Left M_{AB}	Left M_{BA}	Right M_{AB}	Right M_{BA}
0.1	0.4	0.443	0.986	13.77	6.26	0.1468	0.0633	0.0951	0.0022	0.2416	0.0238	0.2583	0.0808	0.1322	0.1337	0.0138	0.0853	0.0235	0.0013	0.0001	0.0016
	0.6	0.463	0.983	14.09	6.63	0.1439	0.0663	0.0950	0.0023	0.2404	0.0251	0.2543	0.0851	0.1260	0.1403	0.0110	0.0881	0.0234	0.0014	0.0001	0.0016
	1.0	0.481	0.979	14.53	7.15	0.1401	0.0704	0.0948	0.0024	0.2387	0.0269	0.2487	0.0911	0.1174	0.1496	0.0075	0.0919	0.0233	0.0015	0.0000	0.0016
	1.5	0.496	0.976	14.88	7.56	0.1371	0.0737	0.0947	0.0026	0.2374	0.0284	0.2443	0.0959	0.1107	0.1563	0.0050	0.0946	0.0232	0.0016	0.0000	0.0016
	2.0	0.505	0.973	15.11	7.83	0.1352	0.0757	0.0946	0.0027	0.2365	0.0293	0.2415	0.0989	0.1065	0.1614	0.0035	0.0961	0.0232	0.0017	0.0000	0.0016
0.2	0.4	0.488	0.961	14.52	7.37	0.1420	0.0690	0.0948	0.0025	0.2388	0.0271	0.2496	0.0912	0.1211	0.1468	0.0134	0.0854	0.0234	0.0015	0.0009	0.0057
	0.6	0.517	0.951	15.20	8.26	0.1369	0.0746	0.0946	0.0027	0.2353	0.0300	0.2416	0.1005	0.1097	0.1597	0.0105	0.0885	0.0232	0.0017	0.0007	0.0059
	1.0	0.559	0.936	16.24	9.71	0.1293	0.0833	0.0942	0.0032	0.2324	0.0346	0.2291	0.1149	0.0925	0.1794	0.0068	0.0925	0.0229	0.0019	0.0005	0.0061
	1.5	0.593	0.924	17.18	11.02	0.1229	0.0908	0.0939	0.0036	0.2289	0.0387	0.2182	0.1278	0.0780	0.1964	0.0042	0.0954	0.0228	0.0022	0.0003	0.0063
	2.0	0.615	0.917	17.82	11.96	0.1187	0.0959	0.0937	0.0038	0.2265	0.0416	0.2108	0.1367	0.0683	0.2079	0.0027	0.0969	0.0227	0.0023	0.0002	0.0064
0.3	0.4	0.518	0.928	15.02	8.38	0.1400	0.0714	0.0947	0.0027	0.2370	0.0295	0.2446	0.0978	0.1170	0.1510	0.0139	0.0843	0.0233	0.0017	0.0031	0.0114
	0.6	0.562	0.907	16.00	9.92	0.1338	0.0789	0.0944	0.0031	0.2334	0.0340	0.2337	0.1113	0.1032	0.1668	0.0111	0.0871	0.0230	0.0020	0.0026	0.0119
	1.0	0.631	0.878	17.72	12.74	0.1232	0.0914	0.0938	0.0039	0.2272	0.0420	0.2148	0.1349	0.0811	0.1933	0.0075	0.0910	0.0227	0.0024	0.0019	0.0128
	1.5	0.690	0.855	19.44	15.69	0.1139	0.1034	0.0932	0.0047	0.2209	0.0501	0.1965	0.1587	0.0613	0.2183	0.0049	0.0941	0.0223	0.0028	0.0012	0.0135
	2.0	0.731	0.841	20.80	18.10	0.1069	0.1123	0.0928	0.0053	0.2161	0.0566	0.1826	0.1773	0.0473	0.2362	0.0032	0.0959	0.0220	0.0031	0.0009	0.0139
0.4	0.4	0.537	0.891	15.30	9.22	0.1392	0.0715	0.0946	0.0029	0.2361	0.0310	0.2422	0.1005	0.1164	0.1484	0.0145	0.0831	0.0232	0.0018	0.0072	0.0177
	0.6	0.594	0.859	16.50	11.41	0.1325	0.0795	0.0942	0.0034	0.2317	0.0367	0.2295	0.1165	0.1027	0.1635	0.0119	0.0857	0.0229	0.0021	0.0062	0.0187
	1.0	0.689	0.814	18.77	15.88	0.1209	0.0940	0.0934	0.0045	0.2235	0.0479	0.2063	0.1472	0.0808	0.1893	0.0084	0.0894	0.0224	0.0027	0.0047	0.0204
	1.5	0.779	0.779	21.31	21.31	0.1094	0.1094	0.0925	0.0057	0.2145	0.0608	0.1816	0.1816	0.0608	0.2145	0.0057	0.0925	0.0220	0.0034	0.0034	0.0220
	2.0	0.845	0.756	23.49	26.27	0.1004	0.1221	0.0918	0.0068	0.2068	0.0722	0.1613	0.2112	0.0465	0.2334	0.0041	0.0945	0.0216	0.0041	0.0026	0.0231
0.5	0.4	0.544	0.857	15.52	9.85	0.1382	0.0707	0.0945	0.0029	0.2353	0.0316	0.2394	0.1002	0.1151	0.1448	0.0148	0.0821	0.0231	0.0018	0.0131	0.0238
	0.6	0.608	0.813	16.84	12.59	0.1313	0.0784	0.0940	0.0036	0.2305	0.0379	0.2257	0.1165	0.1017	0.1582	0.0123	0.0845	0.0228	0.0021	0.0116	0.0254
	1.0	0.723	0.752	18.69	18.69	0.1196	0.0929	0.0931	0.0049	0.2212	0.0510	0.2015	0.1487	0.0810	0.1810	0.0086	0.0881	0.0223	0.0029	0.0093	0.0280
	1.5	0.842	0.703	22.57	27.05	0.1076	0.1094	0.0921	0.0065	0.2104	0.0679	0.1742	0.1873	0.0625	0.2039	0.0064	0.0908	0.0218	0.0038	0.0072	0.0305
	2.0	0.939	0.670	25.51	35.71	0.0978	0.1241	0.0911	0.0082	0.2005	0.0843	0.1511	0.2229	0.0491	0.2218	0.0048	0.0928	0.0211	0.0048	0.0057	0.0325

Unif. Load F.E.M. = Coef. × wL^2; Concentrated Load F.E.M. = Coef. × PL; Haunch Load at Left = Coef. × $W_A L^2$; Haunch Load at Right = Coef. × $W_B L^2$.

TABLE 46

	$a_A = 0.5$				a_B = variable						$r_A = 1.5$					r_B = variable			
0.1 0.4	0.406	1.101	17.79	6.56	0.1502	0.0616	0.0939	0.0025	0.2338	0.0249	0.2680	0.0762	0.1476	0.1289	0.0159	0.0846	0.0339	0.0029	0.0001	0.0016
0.6	0.419	1.098	18.22	6.96	0.1470	0.0647	0.0937	0.0026	0.2324	0.0263	0.2637	0.0804	0.1407	0.1356	0.0128	0.0876	0.0337	0.0030	0.0001	0.0016
1.0	0.437	1.092	18.82	7.52	0.1427	0.0689	0.0935	0.0028	0.2304	0.0282	0.2576	0.0864	0.1310	0.1450	0.0087	0.0915	0.0335	0.0033	0.0000	0.0016
1.5	0.450	1.088	19.29	7.98	0.1393	0.0722	0.0933	0.0030	0.2287	0.0298	0.2528	0.0910	0.1236	0.1523	0.0058	0.0943	0.0333	0.0034	0.0000	0.0016
2.0	0.458	1.085	19.59	8.27	0.1372	0.0743	0.0932	0.0030	0.2277	0.0308	0.2497	0.0941	0.1188	0.1569	0.0041	0.0959	0.0332	0.0035	0.0000	0.0016
0.2 0.4	0.442	1.070	18.75	7.74	0.1450	0.0672	0.0935	0.0028	0.2306	0.0284	0.2589	0.0863	0.1355	0.1420	0.0155	0.0848	0.0335	0.0033	0.0010	0.0056
0.6	0.469	1.056	19.63	8.71	0.1394	0.0730	0.0933	0.0031	0.2277	0.0315	0.2502	0.0953	0.1229	0.1549	0.0122	0.0879	0.0332	0.0036	0.0008	0.0058
1.0	0.508	1.038	21.01	10.28	0.1309	0.0819	0.0923	0.0035	0.2230	0.0364	0.2356	0.1097	0.1037	0.1750	0.0079	0.0921	0.0327	0.0042	0.0006	0.0060
1.5	0.539	1.023	22.25	11.73	0.1237	0.0895	0.0923	0.0041	0.2189	0.0408	0.2247	0.1225	0.0874	0.1924	0.0048	0.0951	0.0322	0.0047	0.0004	0.0062
2.0	0.560	1.014	23.10	12.76	0.1189	0.0947	0.0921	0.0044	0.2161	0.0440	0.2165	0.1315	0.0764	0.2042	0.0032	0.0967	0.0319	0.0050	0.0002	0.0064
0.3 0.4	0.468	1.028	19.33	8.80	0.1429	0.0695	0.0934	0.0030	0.2287	0.0308	0.2539	0.0926	0.1307	0.1462	0.0160	0.0836	0.0333	0.0036	0.0035	0.0112
0.6	0.508	1.002	20.59	10.45	0.1359	0.0770	0.0930	0.0035	0.2246	0.0355	0.2420	0.1056	0.1153	0.1620	0.0129	0.0866	0.0329	0.0041	0.0029	0.0118
1.0	0.572	0.966	22.79	13.49	0.1246	0.0896	0.0923	0.0044	0.2173	0.0439	0.2219	0.1289	0.0907	0.1889	0.0086	0.0905	0.0320	0.0051	0.0022	0.0126
1.5	0.627	0.937	24.99	16.72	0.1140	0.1019	0.0916	0.0053	0.2101	0.0526	0.2022	0.1526	0.0685	0.2145	0.0055	0.0938	0.0312	0.0060	0.0014	0.0134
2.0	0.665	0.918	26.67	19.33	0.1062	0.1111	0.0910	0.0061	0.2045	0.0594	0.1872	0.1712	0.0528	0.2332	0.0038	0.0955	0.0306	0.0067	0.0010	0.0138
0.4 0.4	0.483	0.984	19.67	9.65	0.1419	0.0696	0.0932	0.0032	0.2277	0.0321	0.2512	0.0950	0.1297	0.1436	0.0166	0.0824	0.0332	0.0037	0.0081	0.0174
0.6	0.534	0.943	21.16	11.96	0.1345	0.0775	0.0927	0.0038	0.2228	0.0379	0.2376	0.1105	0.1145	0.1587	0.0136	0.0850	0.0327	0.0044	0.0070	0.0184
1.0	0.620	0.887	23.95	16.73	0.1219	0.0921	0.0918	0.0050	0.2138	0.0492	0.2132	0.1404	0.0901	0.1848	0.0096	0.0889	0.0316	0.0057	0.0053	0.0201
1.5	0.703	0.842	27.05	22.57	0.1094	0.1076	0.0908	0.0064	0.2039	0.0625	0.1873	0.1742	0.0679	0.2104	0.0065	0.0921	0.0305	0.0072	0.0038	0.0218
2.0	0.766	0.813	29.84	28.18	0.0997	0.1204	0.0899	0.0077	0.1955	0.0741	0.1659	0.2034	0.0519	0.2299	0.0047	0.0941	0.0296	0.0085	0.0029	0.0229
0.5 0.4	0.484	0.944	19.98	10.25	0.1403	0.0688	0.0931	0.0033	0.2266	0.0325	0.2473	0.0948	0.1272	0.1403	0.0168	0.0815	0.0331	0.0038	0.0145	0.0233
0.6	0.540	0.889	21.61	13.11	0.1326	0.0765	0.0926	0.0039	0.2212	0.0387	0.2326	0.1106	0.1120	0.1538	0.0138	0.0838	0.0325	0.0044	0.0127	0.0248
1.0	0.640	0.811	24.72	19.50	0.1197	0.0908	0.0915	0.0053	0.2113	0.0516	0.2065	0.1416	0.0886	0.1769	0.0100	0.0873	0.0313	0.0059	0.0101	0.0275
1.5	0.748	0.748	28.32	28.32	0.1070	0.1070	0.0903	0.0071	0.1999	0.0679	0.1786	0.1786	0.0679	0.1999	0.0071	0.0903	0.0301	0.0078	0.0078	0.0301
2.0	0.838	0.705	31.64	37.58	0.0967	0.1213	0.0892	0.0088	0.1899	0.0838	0.1551	0.2128	0.0533	0.2180	0.0053	0.0924	0.0291	0.0094	0.0061	0.0321

Straight Haunches — Constant Width

TABLE 47

$a_A = 0.1$ $r_A = 2.0$ a_B = variable r_B = variable

Right Haunch		Carry-over Factors		Stiffness Factors		Unif. Load F.E.M. Coef. × wL^2		Concentrated Load F.E.M.—Coef. × PL										Haunch Load at			
								b=0.1		b=0.3		b=0.5		b=0.7		b=0.9		Left (×W_AL^2)		Right (×W_BL^2)	
a_B	r_B	C_{AB}	C_{BA}	k_{AB}	k_{BA}	M_{AB}	M_{BA}	M_{AB}	M_{BA}	M_{AB}	M_{BA}	M_{AB}	M_{BA}	M_{AB}	M_{BA}	M_{AB}	M_{BA}	M_{AB}	M_{BA}	M_{AB}	M_{BA}
0.1	0.4	0.546	0.619	5.77	5.08	0.1027	0.0817	0.0971	0.0015	0.1888	0.0483	0.1569	0.1221	0.0725	0.1573	0.0071	0.0879	0.0017	0.0000	0.0001	0.0016
	0.6	0.563	0.618	5.85	5.33	0.1008	0.0850	0.0970	0.0016	0.1875	0.0504	0.1537	0.1274	0.0687	0.1637	0.0057	0.0903	0.0017	0.0000	0.0001	0.0016
	1.0	0.585	0.615	5.97	5.67	0.0982	0.0894	0.0970	0.0017	0.1858	0.0534	0.1494	0.1348	0.0636	0.1726	0.0038	0.0934	0.0017	0.0000	0.0000	0.0016
	1.5	0.602	0.614	6.06	5.94	0.0962	0.0928	0.0969	0.0017	0.1844	0.0557	0.1462	0.1405	0.0596	0.1793	0.0025	0.0956	0.0017	0.0000	0.0000	0.0016
	2.0	0.613	0.613	6.11	6.11	0.0950	0.0950	0.0969	0.0018	0.1836	0.0572	0.1441	0.1441	0.0572	0.1836	0.0018	0.0969	0.0017	0.0000	0.0000	0.0017
0.2	0.4	0.595	0.606	5.98	5.87	0.0990	0.0886	0.0970	0.0017	0.1857	0.0541	0.1497	0.1356	0.0653	0.1709	0.0068	0.0882	0.0017	0.0000	0.0004	0.0059
	0.6	0.630	0.600	6.16	6.46	0.0956	0.0948	0.0969	0.0019	0.1831	0.0588	0.1435	0.1468	0.0584	0.1832	0.0053	0.0909	0.0017	0.0000	0.0003	0.0061
	1.0	0.681	0.593	6.43	7.39	0.0905	0.1041	0.0967	0.0021	0.1792	0.0660	0.1343	0.1639	0.0483	0.2016	0.0033	0.0942	0.0017	0.0000	0.0002	0.0063
	1.5	0.722	0.587	6.66	8.19	0.0863	0.1118	0.0956	0.0023	0.1760	0.0721	0.1265	0.1782	0.0402	0.2166	0.0019	0.0965	0.0017	0.0000	0.0001	0.0064
	2.0	0.749	0.583	6.81	8.75	0.0836	0.1168	0.0966	0.0024	0.1738	0.0763	0.1214	0.1879	0.0349	0.2265	0.0013	0.0977	0.0017	0.0000	0.0001	0.0065
0.3	0.4	0.635	0.587	6.14	6.63	0.0973	0.0921	0.0969	0.0019	0.1837	0.0585	0.1454	0.1446	0.0624	0.1760	0.0070	0.0876	0.0017	0.0000	0.0016	0.0121
	0.6	0.690	0.576	6.40	7.67	0.0928	0.1005	0.0968	0.0021	0.1799	0.0658	0.1368	0.1611	0.0540	0.1916	0.0057	0.0900	0.0017	0.0000	0.0012	0.0127
	1.0	0.775	0.561	6.85	9.46	0.0857	0.1141	0.0956	0.0025	0.1737	0.0781	0.1230	0.1885	0.0411	0.2162	0.0037	0.0935	0.0017	0.0000	0.0009	0.0133
	1.5	0.848	0.549	7.27	11.24	0.0795	0.1265	0.0964	0.0029	0.1679	0.0898	0.1101	0.2143	0.0300	0.2377	0.0022	0.0958	0.0016	0.0000	0.0006	0.0139
	2.0	0.898	0.540	7.57	12.59	0.0752	0.1352	0.0962	0.0032	0.1637	0.0985	0.1010	0.2333	0.0226	0.2524	0.0015	0.0972	0.0016	0.0000	0.0004	0.0142
0.4	0.4	0.665	0.556	6.23	7.32	0.0966	0.0929	0.0969	0.0020	0.1825	0.0612	0.1433	0.1487	0.0622	0.1740	0.0074	0.0864	0.0017	0.0000	0.0038	0.0193
	0.6	0.738	0.548	6.57	8.85	0.0917	0.1024	0.0967	0.0023	0.1779	0.0706	0.1333	0.1686	0.0537	0.1892	0.0060	0.0887	0.0017	0.0000	0.0032	0.0205
	1.0	0.859	0.524	7.18	11.79	0.0835	0.1188	0.0964	0.0029	0.1698	0.0880	0.1160	0.2044	0.0406	0.2140	0.0041	0.0921	0.0017	0.0000	0.0024	0.0219
	1.5	0.973	0.505	7.83	15.11	0.0757	0.1352	0.0961	0.0035	0.1614	0.1065	0.0999	0.2415	0.0293	0.2365	0.0027	0.0946	0.0016	0.0000	0.0017	0.0232
	2.0	1.057	0.492	8.35	17.93	0.0700	0.1479	0.0959	0.0041	0.1547	0.1217	0.0857	0.2711	0.0216	0.2524	0.0018	0.0962	0.0016	0.0000	0.0012	0.0241
0.5	0.4	0.683	0.544	6.30	7.90	0.0962	0.0921	0.0968	0.0020	0.1818	0.0623	0.1420	0.1481	0.0621	0.1700	0.0076	0.0855	0.0017	0.0000	0.0071	0.0267
	0.6	0.770	0.519	6.68	9.91	0.0911	0.1015	0.0966	0.0024	0.1767	0.0729	0.1314	0.1686	0.0540	0.1836	0.0062	0.0876	0.0017	0.0000	0.0062	0.0283
	1.0	0.925	0.485	7.42	14.16	0.0826	0.1187	0.0963	0.0032	0.1673	0.0939	0.1130	0.2070	0.0416	0.2062	0.0044	0.0907	0.0016	0.0000	0.0048	0.0308
	1.5	1.085	0.458	8.27	19.59	0.0743	0.1372	0.0959	0.0041	0.1569	0.1188	0.0941	0.2497	0.0308	0.2277	0.0030	0.0932	0.0016	0.0000	0.0035	0.0332
	2.0	1.212	0.441	9.04	24.83	0.0677	0.1527	0.0956	0.0050	0.1480	0.1414	0.0788	0.2863	0.0234	0.2436	0.0022	0.0949	0.0016	0.0000	0.0027	0.0350

TABLE 48

		$a_A = 0.2$				a_B = variable								$r_A = 2.0$					r_B = variable		
0.1	0.4	0.519	0.757	8.12	5.57	0.1258	0.0709	0.0979	0.0011	0.2307	0.0290	0.2022	0.1014	0.0956	0.1468	0.0095	0.0868	0.0065	0.0001	0.0001	0.0016
	0.6	0.535	0.755	8.28	5.86	0.1236	0.0742	0.0978	0.0011	0.2297	0.0304	0.1983	0.1052	0.0909	0.1533	0.0076	0.0394	0.0065	0.0001	0.0001	0.0016
	1.0	0.557	0.752	8.49	6.28	0.1206	0.0784	0.0978	0.0012	0.2283	0.0323	0.1940	0.1129	0.0844	0.1624	0.0052	0.0928	0.0065	0.0001	0.0000	0.0016
	1.5	0.573	0.750	8.65	6.60	0.1183	0.0816	0.0977	0.0013	0.2272	0.0339	0.1903	0.1181	0.0794	0.1693	0.0034	0.0952	0.0055	0.0001	0.0000	0.0016
	2.0	0.583	0.749	8.75	6.81	0.1168	0.0836	0.0977	0.0013	0.2265	0.0349	0.1879	0.1214	0.0763	0.1738	0.0024	0.0966	0.0065	0.0001	0.0000	0.0017
0.2	0.4	0.565	0.741	8.50	6.49	0.1218	0.0772	0.0978	0.0012	0.2283	0.0327	0.1945	0.1133	0.0867	0.1602	0.0092	0.0871	0.0065	0.0006	0.0001	0.0058
	0.6	0.599	0.734	8.83	7.21	0.1178	0.0830	0.0977	0.0013	0.2252	0.0358	0.1876	0.1235	0.0779	0.1729	0.0072	0.0899	0.0065	0.0005	0.0001	0.0060
	1.0	0.647	0.724	9.32	8.34	0.1119	0.0917	0.0976	0.0015	0.2230	0.0407	0.1771	0.1393	0.0653	0.1918	0.0045	0.0935	0.0065	0.0004	0.0001	0.0062
	1.5	0.686	0.716	9.75	9.34	0.1071	0.0990	0.0975	0.0017	0.2202	0.0449	0.1681	0.1528	0.0547	0.2077	0.0028	0.0990	0.0065	0.0002	0.0001	0.0064
	2.0	0.711	0.711	10.05	10.05	0.1039	0.1039	0.0974	0.0018	0.2184	0.0478	0.1621	0.1621	0.0478	0.2184	0.0018	0.0974	0.0065	0.0001	0.0001	0.0065
0.3	0.4	0.603	0.717	8.77	7.37	0.1200	0.0800	0.0978	0.0013	0.2267	0.0355	0.1900	0.1210	0.0835	0.1649	0.0096	0.0862	0.0065	0.0021	0.0001	0.0118
	0.6	0.654	0.703	9.26	8.61	0.1150	0.0876	0.0976	0.0015	0.2237	0.0403	0.1804	0.1359	0.0730	0.1807	0.0077	0.0888	0.0065	0.0018	0.0001	0.0122
	1.0	0.734	0.684	10.09	10.83	0.1069	0.1002	0.0974	0.0019	0.2185	0.0487	0.1645	0.1614	0.0565	0.2062	0.0050	0.0924	0.0065	0.0013	0.0001	0.0129
	1.5	0.803	0.669	10.90	13.08	0.0997	0.1120	0.0972	0.0022	0.2135	0.0569	0.1494	0.1862	0.0420	0.2292	0.0032	0.0949	0.0065	0.0009	0.0002	0.0137
	2.0	0.850	0.659	11.51	14.85	0.0945	0.1204	0.0970	0.0025	0.2098	0.0632	0.1384	0.2049	0.0321	0.2453	0.0022	0.0968	0.0065	0.0006	0.0002	0.0141
0.4	0.4	0.629	0.692	8.94	8.14	0.1195	0.0803	0.0977	0.0014	0.2258	0.0372	0.1878	0.1242	0.0833	0.1624	0.0101	0.0850	0.0065	0.0051	0.0001	0.0186
	0.6	0.698	0.669	9.56	9.96	0.1140	0.0885	0.0975	0.0017	0.2221	0.0434	0.1767	0.1420	0.0729	0.1775	0.0082	0.0874	0.0065	0.0044	0.0001	0.0196
	1.0	0.811	0.639	10.70	13.58	0.1048	0.1035	0.0972	0.0022	0.2153	0.0551	0.1570	0.1751	0.0564	0.2027	0.0057	0.0909	0.0065	0.0032	0.0002	0.0212
	1.5	0.917	0.615	11.96	17.82	0.0959	0.1187	0.0969	0.0027	0.2079	0.0633	0.1367	0.2108	0.0416	0.2265	0.0038	0.0937	0.0064	0.0023	0.0002	0.0227
	2.0	0.994	0.600	13.01	21.58	0.0891	0.1308	0.0967	0.0032	0.2019	0.0795	0.1205	0.2402	0.0313	0.2438	0.0027	0.0954	0.0064	0.0017	0.0002	0.0237
0.5	0.4	0.644	0.665	9.05	8.76	0.1189	0.0792	0.0977	0.0015	0.2252	0.0378	0.1861	0.1234	0.0731	0.1583	0.0103	0.0840	0.0065	0.0095	0.0001	0.0253
	0.6	0.724	0.635	9.74	11.11	0.1134	0.0874	0.0975	0.0018	0.2211	0.0447	0.1745	0.1414	0.0731	0.1716	0.0085	0.0862	0.0065	0.0083	0.0001	0.0269
	1.0	0.867	0.593	11.11	16.25	0.1041	0.1023	0.0971	0.0024	0.2133	0.0589	0.1537	0.1762	0.0530	0.1941	0.0062	0.0894	0.0064	0.0066	0.0002	0.0294
	1.5	1.014	0.560	12.76	23.10	0.0947	0.1189	0.0967	0.0032	0.2042	0.0764	0.1315	0.2165	0.0440	0.2161	0.0044	0.0921	0.0064	0.0050	0.0002	0.0319
	2.0	1.130	0.539	14.31	30.02	0.0872	0.1332	0.0964	0.0040	0.1961	0.0931	0.1128	0.2524	0.0342	0.2328	0.0033	0.0939	0.0064	0.0040	0.0002	0.0337

Straight Haunches—Constant Width

$a_A = 0.3$ a_B = variable $r_A = 2.0$ r_B = variable

TABLE 49

Right Haunch a_B	r_B	Carry-over Factors		Stiffness Factors		Unif. Load F.E.M. Coef. × wL^2		Concentrated Load F.E.M.—Coef. × PL										Haunch Load at Left F.E.M. Coef. × $W_A L^2$		Haunch Load at Right F.E.M. Coef. × $W_B L^2$	
								b=0.1		b=0.3		b=0.5		b=0.7		b=0.9					
		C_{AB}	C_{BA}	k_{AB}	k_{BA}	M_{AB}	M_{BA}	M_{AB}	M_{BA}	M_{AB}	M_{BA}	M_{AB}	M_{BA}	M_{AB}	M_{BA}	M_{AB}	M_{BA}	M_{AB}	M_{BA}	M_{AB}	M_{BA}
0.1	0.4	0.481	0.909	11.50	6.09	0.1455	0.0632	0.0976	0.0013	0.2567	0.0180	0.2487	0.0831	0.1363	0.1222	0.0125	0.0855	0.0143	0.0003	0.0001	0.0016
	0.6	0.496	0.907	11.76	6.44	0.1430	0.0661	0.0973	0.0013	0.2558	0.0190	0.2451	0.0874	0.1429	0.1165	0.0100	0.0884	0.0143	0.0004	0.0001	0.0016
	1.0	0.516	0.903	12.12	6.93	0.1396	0.0701	0.0973	0.0014	0.2543	0.0208	0.2400	0.0933	0.1521	0.1085	0.0069	0.0921	0.0142	0.0004	0.0000	0.0016
	1.5	0.531	0.900	12.41	7.32	0.1369	0.0732	0.0972	0.0015	0.2532	0.0218	0.2359	0.0980	0.1591	0.1024	0.0046	0.0947	0.0142	0.0004	0.0000	0.0016
	2.0	0.540	0.898	12.59	7.57	0.1352	0.0752	0.0972	0.0015	0.2524	0.0226	0.2333	0.1010	0.1637	0.0985	0.0032	0.0962	0.0142	0.0004	0.0000	0.0016
0.2	0.4	0.524	0.888	12.13	7.15	0.1412	0.0687	0.0972	0.0014	0.2543	0.0214	0.2406	0.0934	0.1495	0.1117	0.0122	0.0858	0.0142	0.0004	0.0008	0.0057
	0.6	0.555	0.879	12.69	8.01	0.1367	0.0741	0.0972	0.0016	0.2524	0.0230	0.2333	0.1026	0.1624	0.1010	0.0096	0.0887	0.0142	0.0004	0.0007	0.0059
	1.0	0.600	0.866	13.55	9.38	0.1299	0.0825	0.0971	0.0017	0.2494	0.0258	0.2218	0.1170	0.1818	0.0854	0.0061	0.0927	0.0142	0.0005	0.0005	0.0061
	1.5	0.636	0.857	14.32	10.62	0.1242	0.0897	0.0968	0.0020	0.2469	0.0299	0.2119	0.1296	0.1985	0.0720	0.0038	0.0955	0.0141	0.0005	0.0003	0.0063
	2.0	0.659	0.850	14.85	11.51	0.1204	0.0945	0.0968	0.0022	0.2453	0.0321	0.2049	0.1384	0.2098	0.0632	0.0025	0.0970	0.0141	0.0006	0.0002	0.0065
0.3	0.4	0.557	0.859	12.57	8.15	0.1394	0.0709	0.0972	0.0016	0.2527	0.0232	0.2360	0.0998	0.1537	0.1080	0.0127	0.0843	0.0142	0.0004	0.0028	0.0115
	0.6	0.605	0.841	13.40	9.63	0.1338	0.0780	0.0971	0.0018	0.2500	0.0265	0.2257	0.1133	0.1695	0.0954	0.0102	0.0875	0.0142	0.0005	0.0023	0.0120
	1.0	0.678	0.817	14.85	12.33	0.1246	0.0901	0.0968	0.0022	0.2455	0.0326	0.2080	0.1368	0.1957	0.0750	0.0069	0.0913	0.0141	0.0006	0.0017	0.0128
	1.5	0.741	0.797	16.30	15.16	0.1160	0.1015	0.0963	0.0027	0.2410	0.0389	0.1910	0.1601	0.2200	0.0566	0.0045	0.0943	0.0140	0.0007	0.0011	0.0135
	2.0	0.785	0.785	17.42	17.42	0.1099	0.1099	0.0962	0.0031	0.2375	0.0438	0.1781	0.1781	0.2375	0.0438	0.0031	0.0962	0.0139	0.0008	0.0008	0.0139
0.4	0.4	0.580	0.827	12.83	8.99	0.1389	0.0709	0.0972	0.0017	0.2519	0.0242	0.2338	0.1026	0.1508	0.1077	0.0133	0.0834	0.0142	0.0004	0.0066	0.0179
	0.6	0.642	0.800	13.86	11.12	0.1329	0.0786	0.0970	0.0019	0.2487	0.0286	0.2220	0.1183	0.1659	0.0952	0.0108	0.0860	0.0141	0.0005	0.0058	0.0189
	1.0	0.744	0.761	15.83	15.47	0.1226	0.0924	0.0966	0.0025	0.2427	0.0372	0.2004	0.1486	0.1913	0.0752	0.0077	0.0898	0.0140	0.0007	0.0044	0.0205
	1.5	0.841	0.731	18.10	20.80	0.1123	0.1069	0.0959	0.0032	0.2362	0.0473	0.1773	0.1826	0.2161	0.0566	0.0053	0.0928	0.0139	0.0009	0.0031	0.0220
	2.0	0.911	0.712	20.00	25.60	0.1043	0.1188	0.0957	0.0040	0.2303	0.0564	0.1583	0.2115	0.2346	0.0434	0.0038	0.0948	0.0138	0.0010	0.0024	0.0231
0.5	0.4	0.590	0.797	13.00	9.63	0.1382	0.0699	0.0972	0.0017	0.2512	0.0248	0.2316	0.1020	0.1468	0.1071	0.0136	0.0824	0.0142	0.0004	0.0123	0.0241
	0.6	0.661	0.759	14.15	12.33	0.1321	0.0772	0.0969	0.0021	0.2476	0.0298	0.2191	0.1178	0.1601	0.0951	0.0113	0.0848	0.0141	0.0005	0.0109	0.0257
	1.0	0.788	0.707	16.47	18.36	0.1218	0.0908	0.0965	0.0027	0.2408	0.0399	0.1963	0.1494	0.1824	0.0766	0.0081	0.0883	0.0140	0.0007	0.0087	0.0282
	1.5	0.918	0.665	19.33	26.67	0.1111	0.1062	0.0955	0.0038	0.2332	0.0528	0.1712	0.1872	0.2045	0.0594	0.0061	0.0910	0.0138	0.0010	0.0067	0.0306
	2.0	1.022	0.638	22.09	35.37	0.1024	0.1199	0.0951	0.0049	0.2249	0.0671	0.1495	0.2221	0.2220	0.0471	0.0046	0.0929	0.0136	0.0012	0.0054	0.0325

TABLE 50

		$\alpha_A = 0.4$				α_B = variable				$r_A = 2.0$							r_B = variable				
0.1	0.4	0.437	1.071	16.17	6.60	0.1599	0.0581	0.0966	0.0015	0.2566	0.0174	0.2876	0.0693	0.1497	0.1269	0.0157	0.0845	0.0243	0.0010	0.0001	0.0016
	0.6	0.451	1.068	16.59	7.01	0.1570	0.0609	0.0965	0.0016	0.2556	0.0184	0.2837	0.0732	0.1430	0.1335	0.0127	0.0875	0.0243	0.0010	0.0001	0.0016
	1.0	0.469	1.063	17.17	7.58	0.1530	0.0649	0.0964	0.0017	0.2542	0.0198	0.2782	0.0786	0.1336	0.1428	0.0086	0.0914	0.0242	0.0011	0.0000	0.0016
	1.5	0.483	1.059	17.65	8.05	0.1498	0.0680	0.0963	0.0018	0.2531	0.0209	0.2739	0.0829	0.1263	0.1501	0.0058	0.0942	0.0241	0.0011	0.0000	0.0016
	2.0	0.492	1.057	17.93	8.35	0.1479	0.0700	0.0962	0.0018	0.2524	0.0216	0.2711	0.0857	0.1217	0.1547	0.0041	0.0959	0.0241	0.0012	0.0000	0.0016
0.2	0.4	0.475	1.044	17.15	7.81	0.1551	0.0632	0.0964	0.0017	0.2544	0.0199	0.2792	0.0785	0.1379	0.1398	0.0154	0.0846	0.0242	0.0010	0.0010	0.0057
	0.6	0.504	1.032	18.03	8.81	0.1500	0.0686	0.0962	0.0019	0.2522	0.0221	0.2713	0.0869	0.1255	0.1526	0.0122	0.0877	0.0241	0.0012	0.0008	0.0059
	1.0	0.545	1.015	19.43	10.43	0.1420	0.0769	0.0959	0.0022	0.2489	0.0257	0.2588	0.1002	0.1066	0.1726	0.0079	0.0920	0.0239	0.0014	0.0006	0.0051
	1.5	0.578	1.003	20.70	11.93	0.1353	0.0842	0.0956	0.0025	0.2459	0.0290	0.2479	0.1121	0.0904	0.1900	0.0049	0.0950	0.0238	0.0016	0.0004	0.0063
	2.0	0.600	0.994	21.58	13.01	0.1308	0.0891	0.0954	0.0027	0.2438	0.0313	0.2402	0.1205	0.0795	0.2019	0.0032	0.0967	0.0237	0.0017	0.0002	0.0064
0.3	0.4	0.504	1.007	17.77	8.91	0.1533	0.0652	0.0963	0.0019	0.2529	0.0218	0.2745	0.0842	0.1338	0.1437	0.0160	0.0835	0.0241	0.0012	0.0035	0.0112
	0.6	0.547	0.984	19.07	10.61	0.1468	0.0721	0.0960	0.0021	0.2493	0.0252	0.2637	0.0963	0.1190	0.1595	0.0129	0.0863	0.0239	0.0014	0.0030	0.0117
	1.0	0.614	0.952	21.39	13.80	0.1360	0.0841	0.0955	0.0026	0.2444	0.0315	0.2448	0.1182	0.0948	0.1861	0.0083	0.0904	0.0237	0.0017	0.0022	0.0126
	1.5	0.672	0.927	23.75	17.21	0.1262	0.0955	0.0951	0.0033	0.2389	0.0381	0.2261	0.1405	0.0724	0.2116	0.0058	0.0938	0.0234	0.0021	0.0014	0.0134
	2.0	0.712	0.911	25.60	20.00	0.1188	0.1043	0.0948	0.0038	0.2346	0.0434	0.2115	0.1583	0.0564	0.2303	0.0040	0.0957	0.0231	0.0024	0.0010	0.0138
0.4	0.4	0.522	0.968	18.15	9.79	0.1525	0.0652	0.0962	0.0020	0.2521	0.0228	0.2722	0.0865	0.1330	0.1408	0.0167	0.0821	0.0241	0.0013	0.0082	0.0172
	0.6	0.577	0.932	19.72	12.21	0.1458	0.0723	0.0950	0.0022	0.2487	0.0269	0.2597	0.1007	0.1181	0.1557	0.0137	0.0848	0.0239	0.0015	0.0072	0.0182
	1.0	0.669	0.883	22.76	17.23	0.1340	0.0859	0.0952	0.0031	0.2414	0.0360	0.2365	0.1290	0.0945	0.1813	0.0099	0.0886	0.0235	0.0020	0.0055	0.0200
	1.5	0.756	0.845	26.27	23.49	0.1221	0.1004	0.0945	0.0041	0.2334	0.0465	0.2112	0.1613	0.0772	0.2068	0.0068	0.0918	0.0231	0.0026	0.0041	0.0216
	2.0	0.820	0.820	29.36	29.36	0.1126	0.1126	0.0939	0.0049	0.2264	0.0559	0.1897	0.1897	0.0559	0.2264	0.0049	0.0939	0.0227	0.0031	0.0031	0.0227
0.5	0.4	0.528	0.933	18.43	10.43	0.1515	0.0643	0.0961	0.0020	0.2514	0.0232	0.2692	0.0863	0.1315	0.1373	0.0170	0.0811	0.0240	0.0013	0.0150	0.0230
	0.6	0.589	0.885	19.72	13.42	0.1445	0.0713	0.0957	0.0025	0.2474	0.0281	0.2556	0.1009	0.1171	0.1503	0.0142	0.0835	0.0238	0.0016	0.0134	0.0245
	1.0	0.699	0.819	23.66	20.19	0.1326	0.0846	0.0950	0.0034	0.2394	0.0384	0.2309	0.1301	0.0946	0.1727	0.0101	0.0872	0.0234	0.0021	0.0108	0.0271
	1.5	0.813	0.766	28.18	29.84	0.1204	0.0997	0.0941	0.0047	0.2299	0.0519	0.2034	0.1659	0.0741	0.1955	0.0077	0.0899	0.0229	0.0029	0.0085	0.0296
	2.0	0.905	0.730	32.10	39.81	0.1103	0.1134	0.0933	0.0060	0.2208	0.0655	0.1793	0.1997	0.0593	0.2136	0.0058	0.0919	0.0225	0.0035	0.0068	0.0316

Straight Haunches—Constant Width

TABLE 51

$a_A = 0.5$, $r_A = 2.0$; a_B = variable, r_B = variable

Right Haunch a_B	r_B	Carry-over C_{AB}	C_{BA}	Stiffness k_{AB}	k_{BA}	Unif. Load M_{AB}	M_{BA}	0.1 M_{AB}	M_{BA}	0.3 M_{AB}	M_{BA}	0.5 M_{AB}	M_{BA}	0.7 M_{AB}	M_{BA}	0.9 M_{AB}	M_{BA}	Left M_{AB}	M_{BA}	Right M_{AB}	M_{BA}
0.1	0.4	0.390	1.230	22.23	7.05	0.1667	0.0555	0.0954	0.0017	0.2491	0.0186	0.3046	0.0628	0.1737	0.1199	0.0190	0.0836	0.0357	0.0022	0.0001	0.0016
	0.6	0.403	1.226	22.85	7.51	0.1633	0.0584	0.0953	0.0019	0.2478	0.0197	0.3003	0.0665	0.1661	0.1265	0.0154	0.0867	0.0355	0.0023	0.0001	0.0016
	1.0	0.420	1.219	23.66	8.15	0.1587	0.0625	0.0951	0.0020	0.2458	0.0215	0.2941	0.0720	0.1554	0.1358	0.0107	0.0907	0.0353	0.0025	0.0000	0.0016
	1.5	0.433	1.215	24.39	8.69	0.1551	0.0656	0.0950	0.0021	0.2445	0.0226	0.2894	0.0760	0.1468	0.1432	0.0071	0.0938	0.0351	0.0026	0.0000	0.0016
	2.0	0.441	1.212	24.83	9.04	0.1527	0.0677	0.0949	0.0022	0.2436	0.0234	0.2863	0.0788	0.1414	0.1480	0.0050	0.0956	0.0350	0.0027	0.0000	0.0016
0.2	0.4	0.424	1.194	23.57	8.37	0.1614	0.0606	0.0952	0.0020	0.2463	0.0213	0.2957	0.0716	0.1606	0.1325	0.0187	0.0836	0.0353	0.0025	0.0013	0.0056
	0.6	0.450	1.179	24.85	9.49	0.1555	0.0660	0.0949	0.0023	0.2436	0.0238	0.2870	0.0796	0.1466	0.1454	0.0148	0.0869	0.0350	0.0028	0.0010	0.0058
	1.0	0.488	1.157	26.88	11.34	0.1464	0.0745	0.0945	0.0026	0.2393	0.0279	0.2732	0.0926	0.1248	0.1657	0.0096	0.0913	0.0345	0.0032	0.0007	0.0060
	1.5	0.519	1.141	28.73	13.06	0.1385	0.0820	0.0941	0.0030	0.2355	0.0316	0.2609	0.1044	0.1060	0.1836	0.0060	0.0945	0.0341	0.0037	0.0005	0.0062
	2.0	0.539	1.130	30.02	14.31	0.1332	0.0872	0.0939	0.0033	0.2328	0.0342	0.2524	0.1128	0.0931	0.1961	0.0040	0.0964	0.0337	0.0040	0.0003	0.0064
0.3	0.4	0.449	1.147	24.37	9.54	0.1594	0.0625	0.0950	0.0022	0.2447	0.0232	0.2908	0.0769	0.1561	0.1362	0.0193	0.0825	0.0352	0.0027	0.0042	0.0110
	0.6	0.488	1.117	26.18	11.43	0.1521	0.0694	0.0946	0.0026	0.2409	0.0270	0.2791	0.0886	0.1393	0.1520	0.0156	0.0854	0.0347	0.0031	0.0036	0.0115
	1.0	0.548	1.076	29.43	14.99	0.1401	0.0814	0.0940	0.0031	0.2342	0.0339	0.2587	0.1095	0.1116	0.1790	0.0106	0.0898	0.0339	0.0039	0.0026	0.0124
	1.5	0.601	1.043	32.75	18.88	0.1285	0.0933	0.0934	0.0039	0.2274	0.0412	0.2381	0.1317	0.0858	0.2053	0.0070	0.0930	0.0331	0.0048	0.0018	0.0132
	2.0	0.638	1.022	35.37	22.09	0.1199	0.1024	0.0929	0.0046	0.2220	0.0471	0.2221	0.1495	0.0671	0.2249	0.0049	0.0951	0.0325	0.0054	0.0013	0.0137
0.4	0.4	0.462	1.099	24.84	10.44	0.1584	0.0624	0.0949	0.0023	0.2437	0.0242	0.2882	0.0789	0.1542	0.1336	0.0200	0.0810	0.0350	0.0028	0.0096	0.0167
	0.6	0.510	1.053	26.98	13.06	0.1507	0.0697	0.0945	0.0027	0.2394	0.0288	0.2748	0.0927	0.1373	0.1484	0.0165	0.0837	0.0345	0.0033	0.0084	0.0178
	1.0	0.591	0.989	31.05	18.56	0.1376	0.0831	0.0937	0.0037	0.2311	0.0380	0.2500	0.1196	0.1099	0.1743	0.0118	0.0877	0.0336	0.0044	0.0065	0.0195
	1.5	0.670	0.939	35.71	25.51	0.1241	0.0978	0.0928	0.0048	0.2218	0.0491	0.2229	0.1511	0.0843	0.2005	0.0082	0.0911	0.0325	0.0057	0.0048	0.0211
	2.0	0.730	0.905	39.81	32.10	0.1134	0.1103	0.0919	0.0058	0.2136	0.0593	0.1997	0.1793	0.0655	0.2208	0.0060	0.0933	0.0316	0.0068	0.0036	0.0224
0.5	0.4	0.462	1.058	25.34	11.05	0.1566	0.0617	0.0949	0.0023	0.2426	0.0245	0.2839	0.0790	0.1511	0.1306	0.0203	0.0801	0.0348	0.0029	0.0173	0.0222
	0.6	0.513	0.997	27.69	14.23	0.1485	0.0686	0.0943	0.0028	0.2377	0.0295	0.2689	0.0929	0.1341	0.1438	0.0168	0.0825	0.0344	0.0034	0.0153	0.0237
	1.0	0.605	0.910	32.23	21.45	0.1349	0.0817	0.0934	0.0039	0.2286	0.0398	0.2421	0.1208	0.1076	0.1666	0.0122	0.0861	0.0333	0.0046	0.0123	0.0263
	1.5	0.705	0.838	37.58	31.64	0.1213	0.0967	0.0924	0.0053	0.2180	0.0533	0.2128	0.1551	0.0838	0.1899	0.0088	0.0892	0.0321	0.0061	0.0096	0.0289
	2.0	0.789	0.789	42.61	42.61	0.1103	0.1103	0.0914	0.0067	0.2083	0.0667	0.1875	0.1875	0.0667	0.2083	0.0067	0.0914	0.0310	0.0075	0.0075	0.0310

TABLE 52

		$a_A = 0$		a_B = variable								$r_A = 0$				r_B = variable			
0.1	0.4	0.556	0.496	4.14	4.64	0.0780	0.0946	0.0103	0.1426	0.0724	0.1164	0.1432	0.0534	0.1672	0.0052	0.0889	0.0000	0.0000	0.0016
	0.6	0.573	0.495	4.19	4.85	0.0763	0.0981	0.0108	0.1412	0.0754	0.1137	0.1490	0.0505	0.1735	0.0042	0.0911	0.0000	0.0000	0.0016
	1.0	0.596	0.493	4.25	5.14	0.0741	0.1029	0.0114	0.1393	0.0795	0.1100	0.1568	0.0464	0.1822	0.0028	0.0940	0.0000	0.0000	0.0016
	1.5	0.613	0.492	4.30	5.36	0.0724	0.1065	0.0118	0.1378	0.0826	0.1072	0.1629	0.0434	0.1887	0.0018	0.0960	0.0000	0.0000	0.0016
	2.0	0.624	0.491	4.33	5.50	0.0714	0.1083	0.0121	0.1369	0.0846	0.1055	0.1667	0.0415	0.1928	0.0013	0.0972	0.0000	0.0000	0.0016
0.2	0.4	0.606	0.486	4.26	5.31	0.0747	0.1025	0.0116	0.1391	0.0806	0.1102	0.1581	0.0476	0.1809	0.0050	0.0893	0.0000	0.0003	0.0059
	0.6	0.642	0.481	4.35	5.81	0.0717	0.1093	0.0125	0.1363	0.0871	0.1049	0.1701	0.0423	0.1929	0.0038	0.0917	0.0000	0.0003	0.0061
	1.0	0.694	0.475	4.49	6.57	0.0673	0.1192	0.0140	0.1321	0.0968	0.0971	0.1881	0.0346	0.2105	0.0023	0.0948	0.0000	0.0002	0.0063
	1.5	0.736	0.470	4.61	7.22	0.0638	0.1274	0.0152	0.1287	0.1049	0.0908	0.2030	0.0285	0.2247	0.0014	0.0969	0.0000	0.0001	0.0064
	2.0	0.764	0.467	4.68	7.66	0.0616	0.1327	0.0164	0.1264	0.1104	0.0866	0.2129	0.0246	0.2339	0.0009	0.0980	0.0000	0.0001	0.0065
0.3	0.4	0.648	0.470	4.34	5.98	0.0730	0.1069	0.0127	0.1368	0.0870	0.1064	0.1684	0.0453	0.1865	0.0051	0.0887	0.0000	0.0012	0.0123
	0.6	0.704	0.461	4.48	6.84	0.0690	0.1162	0.0141	0.1327	0.0970	0.0990	0.1862	0.0387	0.2017	0.0039	0.0911	0.0000	0.0009	0.0128
	1.0	0.791	0.449	4.71	8.29	0.0630	0.1311	0.0166	0.1262	0.1134	0.0871	0.2150	0.0289	0.2252	0.0024	0.0943	0.0000	0.0006	0.0135
	1.5	0.866	0.439	4.91	9.68	0.0577	0.1442	0.0190	0.1203	0.1286	0.0771	0.2412	0.0208	0.2452	0.0015	0.0965	0.0000	0.0004	0.0140
	2.0	0.918	0.433	5.06	10.72	0.0542	0.1534	0.0210	0.1161	0.1397	0.0700	0.2539	0.0155	0.2585	0.0010	0.0977	0.0000	0.0003	0.0143
0.4	0.4	0.679	0.453	4.39	6.59	0.0722	0.1084	0.0133	0.1355	0.0911	0.1044	0.1734	0.0449	0.1849	0.0053	0.0877	0.0000	0.0027	0.0199
	0.6	0.754	0.438	4.57	7.86	0.0678	0.1192	0.0153	0.1305	0.1041	0.0958	0.1950	0.0383	0.2001	0.0042	0.0900	0.0000	0.0023	0.0209
	1.0	0.879	0.418	4.87	10.24	0.0607	0.1376	0.0190	0.1219	0.1273	0.0815	0.2327	0.0283	0.2241	0.0028	0.0931	0.0000	0.0016	0.0224
	1.5	0.996	0.403	5.18	12.82	0.0541	0.1554	0.0228	0.1134	0.1513	0.0679	0.2704	0.0199	0.2453	0.0018	0.0954	0.0000	0.0011	0.0237
	2.0	1.082	0.392	5.42	14.94	0.0494	0.1688	0.0258	0.1070	0.1702	0.0578	0.2993	0.0144	0.2597	0.0012	0.0968	0.0000	0.0009	0.0244
0.5	0.4	0.697	0.434	4.43	7.12	0.0718	0.1079	0.0137	0.1346	0.0930	0.1032	0.1733	0.0448	0.1812	0.0055	0.0869	0.0000	0.0051	0.0280
	0.6	0.788	0.413	4.62	8.81	0.0672	0.1191	0.0161	0.1291	0.1079	0.0941	0.1958	0.0384	0.1950	0.0044	0.0890	0.0000	0.0044	0.0295
	1.0	0.948	0.385	4.99	12.28	0.0597	0.1390	0.0208	0.1192	0.1364	0.0788	0.2371	0.0288	0.2175	0.0030	0.0919	0.0000	0.0033	0.0321
	1.5	1.114	0.363	5.39	16.52	0.0524	0.1599	0.0263	0.1087	0.1688	0.0636	0.2812	0.0207	0.2382	0.0020	0.0943	0.0000	0.0024	0.0344
	2.0	1.245	0.349	5.73	20.42	0.0468	0.1770	0.0311	0.1001	0.1969	0.0519	0.3174	0.0153	0.2529	0.0014	0.0958	0.0000	0.0017	0.0365
0.75	0.4	0.691	0.393	4.56	8.02	0.0692	0.1041	0.0139	0.1297	0.0915	0.0972	0.1648	0.0430	0.1737	0.0054	0.0856	0.0000	0.0143	0.0462
	0.6	0.788	0.359	4.80	10.55	0.0641	0.1134	0.0165	0.1227	0.1058	0.0871	0.1824	0.0369	0.1837	0.0045	0.0871	0.0000	0.0126	0.0491
	1.0	0.982	0.311	5.25	16.60	0.0562	0.1302	0.0222	0.1108	0.1343	0.0717	0.2137	0.0282	0.2002	0.0032	0.0894	0.0000	0.0101	0.0540
	1.5	1.225	0.272	5.76	26.92	0.0491	0.1490	0.0298	0.0986	0.1694	0.0580	0.2471	0.0212	0.2160	0.0022	0.0915	0.0000	0.0081	0.0589
	2.0	1.461	0.247	6.24	36.95	0.0437	0.1659	0.0380	0.0886	0.2037	0.0481	0.2756	0.0167	0.2281	0.0017	0.0928	0.0000	0.0066	0.0629
1.00	0.4	0.642	0.388	5.17	8.57	0.0675	0.1011	0.0139	0.1243	0.0885	0.0953	0.1583	0.0434	0.1689	0.0055	0.0850	0.0000	0.0256	0.0586
	0.6	0.709	0.350	5.74	11.63	0.0618	0.1086	0.0168	0.1154	0.1001	0.0850	0.1717	0.0375	0.1766	0.0048	0.0858	0.0000	0.0230	0.0621
	1.0	0.834	0.294	6.86	19.46	0.0529	0.1216	0.0224	0.1005	0.1221	0.0691	0.1951	0.0289	0.1893	0.0035	0.0877	0.0000	0.0190	0.0680
	1.5	0.981	0.247	8.23	32.69	0.0450	0.1352	0.0296	0.0860	0.1475	0.0555	0.2184	0.0221	0.2010	0.0026	0.0893	0.0000	0.0156	0.0738
	2.0	1.119	0.214	9.57	50.13	0.0392	0.1466	0.0370	0.0752	0.1682	0.0460	0.2371	0.0176	0.2097	0.0020	0.0905	0.0000	0.0131	0.0786

TABLE 53. Taper in Two Directions

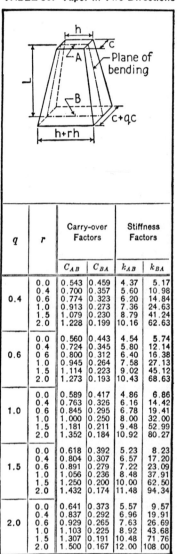

q	r	Carry-over Factors		Stiffness Factors	
		C_{AB}	C_{BA}	k_{AB}	k_{BA}
0.4	0.0	0.543	0.459	4.37	5.17
	0.4	0.700	0.357	5.60	10.98
	0.6	0.774	0.323	6.20	14.84
	1.0	0.913	0.273	7.36	24.63
	1.5	1.079	0.230	8.79	41.24
	2.0	1.228	0.199	10.16	62.63
0.6	0.0	0.560	0.443	4.54	5.74
	0.4	0.724	0.345	5.80	12.14
	0 6	0.800	0.312	6.40	16.38
	1.0	0.945	0.264	7.58	27.13
	1.5	1.114	0.223	9.02	45.12
	2.0	1.273	0.193	10.43	68.63
1.0	0.0	0.589	0.417	4.86	6.86
	0.4	0.763	0.326	6.16	14.42
	0 6	0.845	0.295	6.78	19.41
	1.0	1.000	0.250	8.00	32.00
	1.5	1.181	0.211	9.48	52.99
	2.0	1.352	0.184	10.92	80.27
1.5	0.0	0.618	0.392	5.23	8.23
	0.4	0.804	0.307	6.57	17.20
	0.6	0.891	0.279	7.22	23.09
	1.0	1.056	0.236	8.48	37.91
	1.5	1.250	0.200	10.00	62.50
	2.0	1.432	0.174	11.48	94.34
2.0	0.0	0.641	0.373	5.57	9.57
	0.4	0.837	0.292	6.96	19.91
	0.6	0.929	0.265	7.63	26.69
	1.0	1.103	0.225	8.92	43.68
	1.5	1.307	0.191	10.48	71.76
	2.0	1.500	0.167	12.00	108.00

TABLE 54. Symmetrical Straight Haunches — Constant Depth

a	q	Carry-over Factors C	Stiffness Factors k	Unif. Load F.E.M. Coef. × uL^2 M	Concentrated Load F.E.M.—Coef. × PL, b									
					0.1		0.3		0.5		0.7		0.9	
					M_{AB}	M_{BA}	M_{AB}	M_{BA}	M_{AB}	M_{BA}	M_{AB}	M_{BA}	M_{AB}	M_{BA}
0.1	0.4	0.520	4.30	0.0855	0.0838	0.0080	0.1530	0.0627	0.1285	0.1285	0.0627	0.1530	0.0080	0.0838
	0.6	0.528	4.42	0.0864	0.0849	0.0076	0.1554	0.0626	0.1299	0.1299	0.0626	0.1554	0.0076	0.0849
	1.0	0.540	4.63	0.0876	0.0866	0.0069	0.1591	0.0622	0.1320	0.1320	0.0622	0.1591	0.0069	0.0866
	1.5	0.551	4.83	0.0888	0.0882	0.0062	0.1628	0.0618	0.1339	0.1339	0.0618	0.1682	0.0062	0.0882
	2.0	0.560	5.00	0.0898	0.0894	0.0056	0.1656	0.0613	0.1354	0.1354	0.0613	0.1656	0.0056	0.0894
0.2	0.4	0.532	4.57	0.0868	0.0838	0.0082	0.1562	0.0632	0.1311	0.1311	0.0632	0.1562	0.0082	0.0838
	0.6	0.545	4.82	0.0882	0.0848	0.0079	0.1600	0.0631	0.1335	0.1335	0.0631	0.1600	0.0079	0.0848
	1.0	0.566	5.25	0.0904	0.0864	0.0074	0.1662	0.0628	0.1373	0.1373	0.0628	0.1662	0.0074	0.0864
	1.5	0.586	5.73	0.0924	0.0879	0.0068	0.1725	0.0621	0.1410	0.1410	0.0621	0.1725	0.0068	0.0879
	2.0	0.604	6.14	0.0940	0.0890	0.0063	0.1776	0.0614	0.1439	0.1439	0.0614	0.1776	0.0063	0.0890
0.3	0.4	0.536	4.77	0.0874	0.0833	0.0086	0.1569	0.0641	0.1326	0.1326	0.0641	0.1569	0.0086	0.0833
	0.6	0.553	5.14	0.0890	0.0841	0.0084	0.1609	0.0644	0.1356	0.1356	0.0644	0.1609	0.0084	0.0841
	1.0	0.578	5.82	0.0916	0.0854	0.0081	0.1676	0.0647	0.1407	0.1407	0.0647	0.1676	0.0081	0.0854
	1.5	0.604	6.58	0.0941	0.0867	0.0076	0.1745	0.0646	0.1456	0.1456	0.0646	0.1745	0.0076	0.0867
	2.0	0.625	7.25	0.0961	0.0876	0.0075	0.1801	0.0643	0.1496	0.1496	0.0643	0.1801	0.0075	0.0876

TABLE 55. Straight Haunch at One End — Constant Depth

a	q	Carry-over Factors C_{AB}	C_{BA}	Stiffness Factors k_{AB}	k_{BA}	Unif. Load F.E.M. Coef. $\times wL^2$ M_{AB}	M_{BA}	Conc. Load b=0.1 M_{AB}	M_{BA}	b=0.3 M_{AB}	M_{BA}	b=0.5 M_{AB}	M_{BA}	b=0.7 M_{AB}	M_{BA}	b=0.9 M_{AB}	M_{BA}
0.1	0.4	0.499	0.522	4.24	4.06	0.0876	0.0813	0.0840	0.0075	0.1547	0.0594	0.1319	0.1217	0.0665	0.1453	0.0095	0.0808
	0.6	0.498	0.530	4.35	4.08	0.0893	0.0805	0.0852	0.0070	0.1576	0.0580	0.1346	0.1205	0.0679	0.1447	0.0097	0.0807
	1.0	0.497	0.544	4.49	4.11	0.0920	0.0792	0.0870	0.0061	0.1625	0.0557	0.1389	0.1184	0.0702	0.1436	0.0100	0.0805
	1.5	0.496	0.556	4.64	4.14	0.0945	0.0780	0.0886	0.0053	0.1671	0.0535	0.1431	0.1164	0.0724	0.1426	0.0104	0.0804
	2.0	0.495	0.566	4.76	4.17	0.0965	0.0771	0.0899	0.0047	0.1707	0.0518	0.1464	0.1149	0.0741	0.1418	0.0106	0.0802
0.2	0.4	0.494	0.538	4.46	4.09	0.0901	0.0802	0.0841	0.0075	0.1590	0.0575	0.1366	0.1197	0.0692	0.1442	0.0099	0.0806
	0.6	0.492	0.554	4.65	4.13	0.0928	0.0790	0.0853	0.0069	0.1639	0.0553	0.1414	0.1176	0.0717	0.1431	0.0103	0.0804
	1.0	0.489	0.580	4.97	4.19	0.0974	0.0769	0.0871	0.0060	0.1720	0.0517	0.1494	0.1140	0.0760	0.1412	0.0108	0.0801
	1.5	0.485	0.605	5.31	4.25	0.1020	0.0749	0.0888	0.0052	0.1801	0.0480	0.1576	0.1105	0.0804	0.1393	0.0116	0.0799
	2.0	0.482	0.625	5.58	4.31	0.1057	0.0733	0.0900	0.0046	0.1866	0.0452	0.1642	0.1076	0.0839	0.1377	0.0120	0.0796
0.3	0.4	0.488	0.551	4.64	4.11	0.0912	0.0798	0.0837	0.0075	0.1603	0.0569	0.1393	0.1187	0.0709	0.1436	0.0102	0.0805
	0.6	0.484	0.572	4.92	4.16	0.0945	0.0784	0.0848	0.0071	0.1658	0.0544	0.1454	0.1161	0.0742	0.1422	0.0107	0.0803
	1.0	0.477	0.608	5.41	4.24	0.1001	0.0759	0.0863	0.0062	0.1751	0.0503	0.1559	0.1117	0.0801	0.1397	0.0116	0.0799
	1.5	0.470	0.645	5.95	4.33	0.1059	0.0734	0.0878	0.0055	0.1845	0.0461	0.1670	0.1070	0.0863	0.1372	0.0125	0.0795
	2.0	0.464	0.675	6.41	4.40	0.1108	0.0714	0.0890	0.0049	0.1923	0.0428	0.1763	0.1032	0.0916	0.1350	0.0133	0.0792

TABLE 57. Prismatic Member Having $I = \infty$ at One End

Note:

All carry-over factors are negative
and all stiffness factors are positive.

α	Carry-over Factors		Stiffness Factors		Unif. Load F.E.M. Coef. $\times wL^2$	
	C_{AB}	C_{BA}	k_{AB}	k_{BA}	M_{AB}	M_{BA}
0.05	0.496	0.579	4.91	4.21	0.1002	0.0752
0.10	0.486	0.667	6.09	4.44	0.1175	0.0675
0.15	0.471	0.765	7.64	4.71	0.1352	0.0602
0.20	0.452	0.875	9.69	5.00	0.1533	0.0533
0.25	0.429	1.000	12.44	5.33	0.1719	0.0469

TABLE 56. Prismatic Member Having $I = \infty$ at Both Ends

α	Carry-over Factors	Stiffness Factors	Unif. Load F.E.M. Coef. $\times wL^2$	Concentrated Load F.E.M.—Coef. $\times PL$										
				b										
				0.1		0.2		0.3		0.4		0.5		
	C	k	M	M_{AB}	M_{BA}	M_{AB}	M_{BA}	M_{AB}	M_{BA}	M_{AB}	M_{BA}	M_{AB}	M_{BA}
0.05	0.575	5.23	0.0913	0.0940	0.0030	0.1505	0.0245	0.1711	0.0595	0.1640	0.0999	0.1375	0.1375
0.10	0.648	7.11	0.0983	0.1000	0.0000	0.1722	0.0152	0.1968	0.0532	0.1856	0.1019	0.1500	0.1500
0.15	0.719	10.17	0.1046	0.1000	0.0000	0.1909	0.0056	0.2247	0.0431	0.2095	0.1013	0.1625	0.1625
0.20	0.786	15.56	0.1100	0.1000	0.0000	0.2000	0.0000	0.2546	0.0286	0.2369	0.0964	0.1750	0.1750
0.25	0.846	26.00	0.1146	0.1000	0.0000	0.2000	0.0000	0.2830	0.0118	0.2699	0.0851	0.1875	0.1875

TABLE 58 . Integrals for Members Having Parabolic Haunches and Constant Width

Int. No.	General Integrals I_z Arbitrary	General Integrals $I_z = I_c\left[1+r\left(1-\frac{x}{aL}\right)^2\right]^3$	Transformed Integrals $y = 1 - \frac{x}{aL}$	Evaluated Integrals
1	$L\displaystyle\int_{x_1}^{x_2}\frac{dx}{I_z}$	$\dfrac{L}{I_c}\displaystyle\int_{x_1}^{x_2}\frac{dx}{\left[1+r\left(1-\frac{x}{aL}\right)^2\right]^3}$	$-\dfrac{aL^2}{I_c}\displaystyle\int_{y_1}^{y_2}\frac{dy}{(1+ry^2)^3}$	$-\dfrac{aL^2}{8I_c}\left[\dfrac{2y+3y(1+ry^2)}{(1+ry^2)^2}+\dfrac{3}{\sqrt{r}}\tan^{-1}\sqrt{r}\times y\right]_{y_1}^{y_2}$
1a	$L\displaystyle\int_{a_BL}^{2a_BL}\frac{dx}{I_z}$	$\dfrac{L}{I_c}\displaystyle\int_{a_BL}^{2a_BL}\frac{dx}{\left[1+r\left(1-\frac{x}{a_BL}\right)^2\right]^3}$	$-\dfrac{a_BL^2}{I_c}\displaystyle\int_0^{-1}\frac{dy}{(1+ry^2)^3}$	$-\dfrac{a_BL^2}{8I_c}\left[\dfrac{5+3r}{(1+r)^2}+\dfrac{3}{\sqrt{r}}\tan^{-1}\sqrt{r}\right]$
2	$L\displaystyle\int_{x_1}^{x_2}\frac{xdx}{I_z}$	$\dfrac{L}{I_c}\displaystyle\int_{x_1}^{x_2}\frac{xdx}{\left[1+r\left(1-\frac{x}{aL}\right)^2\right]^3}$	$\dfrac{a^2L^3}{I_c}\displaystyle\int_{y_1}^{y_2}\frac{(y-1)dy}{(1+ry^2)^3}$	$-\dfrac{a^2L^3}{8rI_c}\left[\dfrac{3r^2y^3+5ry+2}{(1+ry^2)^2}+3\sqrt{r}\tan^{-1}\sqrt{r}\times y\right]_{y_1}^{y_2}$
2a	$L\displaystyle\int_0^{aL}\frac{xdx}{I_z}$	$\dfrac{L}{I_c}\displaystyle\int_0^{aL}\frac{xdx}{\left[1+r\left(1-\frac{x}{aL}\right)^2\right]^3}$	$\dfrac{a^2L^3}{I_c}\displaystyle\int_1^0\frac{(y-1)dy}{(1+ry^2)^3}$	$\dfrac{a^2L^3}{8rI_c}\left[\dfrac{r}{r+1}+3\sqrt{r}\tan^{-1}\sqrt{r}\right]$
2b	$L\displaystyle\int_{a_AL}^{(1-a_B)L}\frac{xdx}{I_z}$	When $I_z=I_c$ $\dfrac{L}{I_c}\displaystyle\int_{a_AL}^{(1-a_B)L}xdx$		$\dfrac{L^3}{2I_c}\left[(1-a_B)^2-a_A^2\right]$
2c	$L\displaystyle\int_{a_BL}^{2a_BL}\frac{xdx}{I_z}$	$\dfrac{L}{I_c}\displaystyle\int_{a_BL}^{2a_BL}\frac{xdx}{\left[1+r\left(1-\frac{x}{a_BL}\right)^2\right]^3}$	$\dfrac{a_B^2L^3}{I_c}\displaystyle\int_0^{-1}\frac{(y-1)dy}{(1+ry^2)^3}$	$\dfrac{a_B^2L^3}{8rI_c}\left[\dfrac{5r^2+9r}{(r+1)^2}+3\sqrt{r}\tan^{-1}\sqrt{r}\right]$
3	$\displaystyle\int_{x_1}^{x_2}\frac{x^2dx}{I_z}$	$\dfrac{1}{I_c}\displaystyle\int_{x_1}^{x_2}\frac{x^2dx}{\left[1+r\left(1-\frac{x}{L}\right)^2\right]^3}$	$-\dfrac{a^3L^3}{I_c}\displaystyle\int_{y_1}^{y_2}\frac{(y-1)^2dy}{(1+ry^2)^3}$	$-\dfrac{a^3L^3}{8r^2I_c}\left[\dfrac{(3r^3+r^2)y^3+(5r^2-r)y+4r}{(1+ry^2)^2}+\sqrt{r}(3r+1)\tan^{-1}\sqrt{r}\times y\right]_{y_1}^{y_2}$

3a	$\displaystyle\int_0^{aL}\frac{x^2\,dx}{I_x}$	$\displaystyle\frac{1}{I_c}\int_0^{aL}\frac{x^2\,dx}{\left[1+r\left(1-\frac{x}{aL}\right)^2\right]^3}$	$\displaystyle-\frac{a^3L^3}{I_c}\int_1^0\frac{(y-1)^2\,dy}{(1+ry^2)^3}$	$\displaystyle\frac{a^3L^3}{8r^2I_c}\left[-r+\sqrt{r}\,(3r+1)\tan^{-1}\sqrt{r}\right]$
3b	$\displaystyle\int_{a_AL}^{(1-a_B)L}\frac{x^2\,dx}{I_x}$	When $I_x=I_c$ $\displaystyle\frac{1}{I_c}\int_{a_AL}^{(1-a_B)L}x^2\,dx$		$\displaystyle\frac{L^3}{3I_c}\left[(1-a_B)^3-a_A^3\right]$
3c	$\displaystyle\int_{a_BL}^{2a_BL}\frac{x^2\,dx}{I_x}$	$\displaystyle\frac{1}{I_c}\int_{a_BL}^{2a_BL}\frac{x^2\,dx}{\left[1+r\left(1-\frac{x}{a_BL}\right)^2\right]^3}$	$\displaystyle-\frac{a_B^3L^3}{I_c}\int_0^{-1}\frac{(y-1)^2\,dy}{(1+ry^2)^3}$	$\displaystyle\frac{a_B^3L^3}{8r^2I_c}\left[\frac{7r^3+14r^2-r}{(r+1)^2}+\sqrt{r}\,(3r+1)\tan^{-1}\sqrt{r}\right]$
4	$\displaystyle\int_{x_1}^{x_2}\frac{x^3\,dx}{I_x}$	$\displaystyle\frac{1}{I_c}\int_{x_1}^{x_2}\frac{x^3\,dx}{\left[1+r\left(1-\frac{x}{aL}\right)^2\right]^3}$	$\displaystyle\frac{a^4L^4}{I_c}\int_{y_1}^{y_2}\frac{(y-1)^3\,dy}{(1+ry^2)^3}$	$\displaystyle-\frac{a^4L^4}{8r^2I_c}\left[\frac{(3r^3+3r^2)y^3+4r^2+(5r^2-3r)y+2(3r+1)}{(1+ry^2)^2}+3\sqrt{r}\,(r+1)\tan^{-1}\sqrt{r}\times y\right]_{y_1}^{y_2}$
4a	$\displaystyle\int_0^{aL}\frac{x^3\,dx}{I_x}$	$\displaystyle\frac{1}{I_c}\int_0^{aL}\frac{x^3\,dx}{\left[1+r\left(1-\frac{x}{aL}\right)^2\right]^3}$	$\displaystyle\frac{a^4L^4}{I_c}\int_1^0\frac{(y-1)^3\,dy}{(1+ry^2)^3}$	$\displaystyle\frac{a^4L^4}{8r^2I_c}\left[-3r+3\sqrt{r}\,(r+1)\tan^{-1}\sqrt{r}\right]$
4b	$\displaystyle\int_{a_AL}^{(1-a_B)L}\frac{x^3\,dx}{I_x}$	When $I_x=I_c$ $\displaystyle\frac{1}{I_c}\int_{a_AL}^{(1-a_B)L}x^3\,dx$		$\displaystyle\frac{L^4}{4I_c}\left[(1-a_B)^4-a_A^4\right]$
4c	$\displaystyle\int_{a_BL}^{2a_BL}\frac{x^3\,dx}{I_x}$	$\displaystyle\frac{1}{I_c}\int_{a_BL}^{2a_BL}\frac{x^3\,dx}{\left[1+r\left(1-\frac{x}{a_BL}\right)^2\right]^3}$	$\displaystyle\frac{a_B^4L^4}{I_c}\int_0^{-1}\frac{(y-1)^3\,dy}{(1+ry^2)^3}$	$\displaystyle\frac{a_B^4L^4}{8r^2I_c}\left[\frac{9r^3+22r^2-3r}{(1+r)^2}+3\sqrt{r}\,(r+1)\tan^{-1}\sqrt{r}\right]$

TABLE 59

Integrals for Members Having Straight Haunches and Constant Width

Int. No.	General Integrals		Transformed Integrals $y = 1 - \dfrac{x}{aL}$	Evaluated Integrals
	I_x Arbitrary	$I_x = I_c\left[1+r\left(1-\dfrac{x}{aL}\right)\right]^3$		
1	$L\displaystyle\int_{x_1}^{x_2}\frac{dx}{I_x}$	$\dfrac{L}{I_c}\displaystyle\int_{x_1}^{x_2}\frac{dx}{\left[1+r\left(1-\dfrac{x}{aL}\right)\right]^3}$	$-\dfrac{aL^2}{I_c}\displaystyle\int_{y_1}^{y_2}\frac{dy}{(1+ry)^3}$	$\dfrac{aL^2}{rI_c}\left[\dfrac{1}{2(1+ry)^2}\right]_{y_1}^{y_2}$
1a	$L\displaystyle\int_{0}^{aL}\frac{dx}{I_x}$	$\dfrac{L}{I_c}\displaystyle\int_{0}^{aL}\frac{dx}{\left[1+r\left(1-\dfrac{x}{aL}\right)\right]^3}$	$-\dfrac{aL^2}{I_c}\displaystyle\int_{1}^{0}\frac{dy}{(1+ry)^3}$	$\dfrac{aL^2}{2I_c}\left[\dfrac{2+r}{(1+r)^2}\right]$
2	$L\displaystyle\int_{x_1}^{x_2}\frac{x\,dx}{I_x}$	$\dfrac{L}{I_c}\displaystyle\int_{x_1}^{x_2}\frac{x\,dx}{\left[1+r\left(1-\dfrac{x}{aL}\right)\right]^3}$	$\dfrac{a^2L^3}{I_c}\displaystyle\int_{y_1}^{y_2}\frac{(y-1)\,dy}{(1+ry)^3}$	$\dfrac{a^2L^3}{r^2I_c}\left[\dfrac{1+r}{2(1+ry)^2}-\dfrac{1}{1+ry}\right]_{y_1}^{y_2}$
2a	$L\displaystyle\int_{0}^{aL}\frac{x\,dx}{I_x}$	$\dfrac{L}{I_c}\displaystyle\int_{0}^{aL}\frac{x\,dx}{\left[1+r\left(1-\dfrac{x}{aL}\right)\right]^3}$	$\dfrac{a^2L^3}{I_c}\displaystyle\int_{1}^{0}\frac{(y-1)\,dy}{(1+ry)^3}$	$\dfrac{a^2L^3}{2I_c}\left[\dfrac{1}{1+r}\right]$
2b	$L\displaystyle\int_{a_AL}^{(1-a_B)L}\frac{x\,dx}{I_x}$	When $I_x=I_c$ $\dfrac{L}{I_c}\displaystyle\int_{a_AL}^{(1-a_B)L}x\,dx$		$\dfrac{L^3}{2I_c}\left[(1-a_B)^2-a_A^2\right]$

3	$\displaystyle\int_{x_1}^{x_2} \frac{x^2 dx}{I_x}$	$\displaystyle\frac{1}{I_c}\int_{x_1}^{x_2} \frac{x^2 dx}{\left[1+r\left(1-\frac{x}{\alpha L}\right)\right]^3}$	$\displaystyle-\frac{\alpha^3 L^3}{I_c}\int_{y_1}^{y_2} \frac{(y-1)^2 dy}{(1+ry)^3}$	$\displaystyle-\frac{\alpha^3 L^3}{r^3 I_c}\left[\frac{(1+r)^2}{2(1+ry)^2}+\frac{2(1+r)}{1+ry}+\log(1+ry)\right]_{y_1}^{y_2}$
3a	$\displaystyle\int_0^{\alpha L} \frac{x^2 dx}{I_x}$	$\displaystyle\frac{1}{I_c}\int_0^{\alpha L} \frac{x^2 dx}{\left[1+r\left(1-\frac{x}{\alpha L}\right)\right]^3}$	$\displaystyle-\frac{\alpha^3 L^3}{I_c}\int_1^0 \frac{(y-1)^2 dy}{(1+ry)^3}$	$\displaystyle-\frac{\alpha^3 L^3}{r^3 I_c}\left[\frac{r(2-r)}{2}-\log(1+r)\right]$
3b	$\displaystyle\int_{\alpha_A L}^{(1-\alpha_B)L} \frac{x^2 dx}{I_x}$	When $I_x=I_c$ $\displaystyle\frac{1}{I_c}\int_{\alpha_A L}^{(1-\alpha_B)L} x^2 dx$		$\displaystyle\frac{L^3}{3 I_c}\left[(1-\alpha_B)^3-\alpha_A^3\right]$
4	$\displaystyle\int_{x_1}^{x_2} \frac{x^3 dx}{I_x}$	$\displaystyle\frac{1}{I_c}\int_{x_1}^{x_2} \frac{x^3 dx}{\left[1+r\left(1-\frac{x}{\alpha L}\right)\right]^3}$	$\displaystyle\frac{\alpha^4 L^4}{I_c}\int_{y_1}^{y_2} \frac{(y-1)^3 dy}{(1+ry)^3}$	$\displaystyle\frac{\alpha^4 L^4}{r^4 I_c}\left[\frac{(1+r)^3}{2(1+ry)^2}-\frac{3(1+r)^2}{1+ry}+(1+ry)-3(1+r)\log(1+ry)\right]_{y_1}^{y_2}$
4a	$\displaystyle\int_0^{\alpha L} \frac{x^3 dx}{I_x}$	$\displaystyle\frac{1}{I_c}\int_0^{\alpha L} \frac{x^3 dx}{\left[1+r\left(1-\frac{x}{\alpha L}\right)\right]^3}$	$\displaystyle\frac{\alpha^4 L^4}{I_c}\int_1^0 \frac{(y-1)^3 dy}{(1+ry)^3}$	$\displaystyle\frac{\alpha^4 L^4}{r^4 I_c}\left[\frac{r(r^2-3r-6)}{2}+3(1+r)\log(1+r)\right]$
4b	$\displaystyle\int_{\alpha_A L}^{(1-\alpha_B)L} \frac{x^3 dx}{I_x}$	When $I_x=I_c$ $\displaystyle\frac{1}{I_c}\int_{\alpha_A L}^{(1-\alpha_B)L} x^3 dx$		$\displaystyle\frac{L^4}{4 I_c}\left[(1-\alpha_B)^4-\alpha_A^4\right]$

TABLE 60

Integrals for Members Having Straight Haunches and Constant Depth

Int. No.	General Integrals		Transformed Integrals $y = 1 - \frac{x}{\alpha L}$	Evaluated Integrals
	I_x Arbitrary	$I_x = I_c\left[1 + q\left(1 - \frac{x}{\alpha L}\right)\right]$		
1	$L \displaystyle\int_{x_1}^{x_2} \frac{dx}{I_x}$	$\dfrac{L}{I_c} \displaystyle\int_{x_1}^{x_2} \dfrac{dx}{\left[1 + q\left(1 - \frac{x}{\alpha L}\right)\right]}$	$-\dfrac{\alpha L^2}{I_c}\displaystyle\int_{y_1}^{y_2}\dfrac{dy}{1+qy}$	$-\dfrac{\alpha L^2}{qI_c}\left[\log(1+qy)\right]_{y_1}^{y_2}$
1a	$L \displaystyle\int_0^{\alpha L} \frac{dx}{I_x}$	$\dfrac{L}{I_c} \displaystyle\int_0^{\alpha L} \dfrac{dx}{\left[1 + q\left(1 - \frac{x}{\alpha L}\right)\right]}$	$-\dfrac{\alpha L^2}{I_c}\displaystyle\int_1^0\dfrac{dy}{1+qy}$	$\dfrac{\alpha L^2}{qI_c}\left[\log(1+q)\right]$
2	$L \displaystyle\int_{x_1}^{x_2} \frac{x\,dx}{I_x}$	$\dfrac{L}{I_c} \displaystyle\int_{x_1}^{x_2} \dfrac{x\,dx}{\left[1 + q\left(1 - \frac{x}{\alpha L}\right)\right]}$	$\dfrac{\alpha^2 L^3}{I_c}\displaystyle\int_{y_1}^{y_2}\dfrac{(y-1)dy}{1+qy}$	$\dfrac{\alpha^2 L^3}{q^2 I_c}\left[(1+qy)-(1+q)\log(1+qy)\right]_{y_1}^{y_2}$
2a	$L \displaystyle\int_0^{\alpha L} \frac{x\,dx}{I_x}$	$\dfrac{L}{I_c} \displaystyle\int_0^{\alpha L} \dfrac{x\,dx}{\left[1 + q\left(1 - \frac{x}{\alpha L}\right)\right]}$	$\dfrac{\alpha^2 L^3}{I_c}\displaystyle\int_1^0\dfrac{(y-1)dy}{1+qy}$	$-\dfrac{\alpha^2 L^3}{q^2 I_c}\left[q-(1+q)\log(1+q)\right]$
2b	$L \displaystyle\int_{\alpha_A L}^{(1-\alpha_B)L} \frac{x\,dx}{I_x}$	When $I_x = I_c$ $\dfrac{L}{I_c} \displaystyle\int_{\alpha_A L}^{(1-\alpha_B)L} x\,dx$		$\dfrac{L^3}{2I_c}\left[(1-\alpha_B)^2 - \alpha_A^2\right]$

3	$\displaystyle\int_{x_1}^{x_2} \frac{x^2 dx}{I_x}$	$\displaystyle\frac{1}{I_c}\int_{x_1}^{x_2} \frac{x^2 dx}{\left[1+q\left(1-\frac{x}{aL}\right)\right]}$	$\displaystyle-\frac{a^3 L^3}{I_c}\int_{y_1}^{y_2} \frac{(y-1)^2 dy}{1+qy}$	$\displaystyle-\frac{a^3 L^3}{q^3 I_c}\left[\frac{1}{2}(1+qy)^2 - 2(1+q)(1+qy) + (1+q)^2 \log(1+qy)\right]_{y_1}^{y_2}$
3a	$\displaystyle\int_0^{aL} \frac{x^2 dx}{I_x}$	$\displaystyle\frac{1}{I_c}\int_0^{aL} \frac{x^2 dx}{\left[1+q\left(1-\frac{x}{aL}\right)\right]}$	$\displaystyle-\frac{a^3 L^3}{I_c}\int_1^0 \frac{(y-1)^2 dy}{1+qy}$	$\displaystyle-\frac{a^3 L^3}{q^3 I_c}\left[\frac{q}{2}(2+3q) - (1+q)^2 \log(1+q)\right]$
3b	$\displaystyle\int_{a_AL}^{(1-a_B)L} \frac{x^2 dx}{I_x}$	when $I_x = I_c$ $\displaystyle\frac{1}{I_c}\int_{a_AL}^{(1-a_B)L} x^2 dx$		$\displaystyle\frac{L^3}{3I_c}\left[(1-a_B)^3 - a_A^3\right]$
4	$\displaystyle\int_{x_1}^{x_2} \frac{x^3 dx}{i_x}$	$\displaystyle\frac{1}{I_c}\int_{x_1}^{x_2} \frac{x^3 dx}{\left[1+q\left(1-\frac{x}{aL}\right)\right]}$	$\displaystyle\frac{a^4 L^4}{I_c}\int_{y_1}^{y_2} \frac{(y-1)^3 dy}{1+qy}$	$\displaystyle\frac{a^4 L^4}{q^4 I_c}\left[\frac{1}{3}(1+qy)^3 - \frac{3}{2}(1+q)(1+qy)^2 + 3(1+q)^2(1+qy) - (1+q)^3 \log(1+qy)\right]_{y_1}^{y_2}$
4a	$\displaystyle\int_0^{aL} \frac{x^3 dx}{I_x}$	$\displaystyle\frac{1}{I_c}\int_0^{aL} \frac{x^3 dx}{\left[1+q\left(1-\frac{x}{aL}\right)\right]}$	$\displaystyle\frac{a^4 L^4}{I_c}\int_1^0 \frac{(y-1)^3 dy}{1+qy}$	$\displaystyle-\frac{a^4 L^4}{q^4 I_c}\left[\frac{q}{6}(6+15q+11q^2) - (1+q)^3 \log(1+q)\right]$
4b	$\displaystyle\int_{a_AL}^{(1-a_B)L} \frac{x^3 dx}{I_x}$	when $I_x = I_c$ $\displaystyle\frac{1}{I_c}\int_{a_AL}^{(1-a_B)L} x^3 dx$		$\displaystyle\frac{L^4}{4I_c}\left[(1-a_B)^4 - a_A^4\right]$

TABLE 61
Integrals for Members Tapered in Two Directions

Int. No.	General Integrals — I_x Arbitrary	General Integrals — $I_x = I_c\left(1+r\frac{x}{L}\right)^3\left(1+q\frac{x}{L}\right)$	Transformed Integrals $y=\frac{x}{L}$	Evaluated Integrals
1a	$L\displaystyle\int_0^L \frac{dx}{I_x}$	$\dfrac{L}{I_c}\displaystyle\int_0^L \dfrac{dx}{\left(1+r\frac{x}{L}\right)^3\left(1+q\frac{x}{L}\right)}$	When $r\neq q$ $\dfrac{L^2}{I_c}\displaystyle\int_0^1 \dfrac{dy}{(1+ry)^3(1+qy)}$	$\dfrac{L^2}{I_c}\left[\dfrac{r}{r-q}\dfrac{2+r}{2(1+r)^2}\dfrac{1}{1+r}-\dfrac{rq}{(r-q)^2}\dfrac{1}{1+r}+\dfrac{rq^2}{(r-q)^3}\dfrac{\log(1+r)}{r}-\dfrac{q^3}{(r-q)^3}\dfrac{\log(1+q)}{q}\right]$
2a	$L\displaystyle\int_0^L \frac{x\,dx}{I_x}$	$\dfrac{L}{I_c}\displaystyle\int_0^L \dfrac{x\,dx}{\left(1+r\frac{x}{L}\right)^3\left(1+q\frac{x}{L}\right)}$	When $r\neq q$ $\dfrac{L^3}{I_c}\displaystyle\int_0^1 \dfrac{y\,dy}{(1+ry)^3(1+qy)}$	$\dfrac{L^3}{I_c}\left[-\dfrac{1}{r-q}\dfrac{2+r}{2(1+r)^2}+\dfrac{r}{(r-q)^2}\dfrac{1}{1+r}-\dfrac{rq}{(r-q)^3}\dfrac{\log(1+r)}{r}+\dfrac{q^2}{(r-q)^3}\dfrac{\log(1+q)}{q}\right]$
3a	$L\displaystyle\int_0^L \frac{x^2\,dx}{I_x}$	$\dfrac{1}{I_c}\displaystyle\int_0^L \dfrac{x^2\,dx}{\left(1+r\frac{x}{L}\right)^3\left(1+q\frac{x}{L}\right)}$	When $r\neq q$ $\dfrac{L^3}{I_c}\displaystyle\int_0^1 \dfrac{y^2\,dy}{(1+ry)^3(1+qy)}$	$\dfrac{L^3}{I_c}\left[\dfrac{1}{r(r-q)}\dfrac{2+r}{2(1+r)^2}-\dfrac{2r-q}{r(r-q)^2}\dfrac{1}{1+r}+\dfrac{r}{(r-q)^3}\dfrac{\log(1+r)}{r}-\dfrac{q}{(r-q)^3}\dfrac{\log(1+q)}{q}\right]$
1b	$L\displaystyle\int_0^L \frac{dx}{I_x}$	$\dfrac{L}{I_c}\displaystyle\int_0^L \dfrac{dx}{\left(1+r\frac{x}{L}\right)^3\left(1+q\frac{x}{L}\right)}$	When $r=q$ $\dfrac{L^2}{I_c}\displaystyle\int_0^1 \dfrac{dy}{(1+ry)^4}$	$\dfrac{L^2}{I_c}\left[\dfrac{3+3r+r^2}{3(1+r)^3}\right]$
2b	$L\displaystyle\int_0^L \frac{x\,dx}{I_x}$	$\dfrac{L}{I_c}\displaystyle\int_0^L \dfrac{x\,dx}{\left(1+r\frac{x}{L}\right)^3\left(1+q\frac{x}{L}\right)}$	When $r=q$ $\dfrac{L^3}{I_c}\displaystyle\int_0^1 \dfrac{y\,dy}{(1+ry)^4}$	$\dfrac{L^3}{I_c}\left[\dfrac{3+r}{6(1+r)^3}\right]$
3b	$L\displaystyle\int_0^L \frac{x^2\,dx}{I_x}$	$\dfrac{1}{I_c}\displaystyle\int_0^L \dfrac{x^2\,dx}{\left(1+r\frac{x}{L}\right)^3\left(1+q\frac{x}{L}\right)}$	When $r=q$ $\dfrac{L^3}{I_c}\displaystyle\int_0^1 \dfrac{y^2\,dy}{(1+ry)^4}$	$\dfrac{L^3}{I_c}\left[\dfrac{1}{3(1+r)^3}\right]$

B

FLEXURE FORMULAS

Because all the methods of statically indeterminate structural analysis for beams, frames, arches, and rings make use of the ordinary flexure formulas, it is important for the structural engineer to be cognizant of the assumptions made in the development of the formulas. Only then can he appreciate the significance of the analysis of a beam or a rigid frame. The derivation presented here emphasizes the significance of the following assumptions.

1. The loads acting upon the beam can be resolved into moments acting in a principal plane of the cross-section.
2. A plane section before bending remains plane after bending.
3. The beam is straight and remains nearly so after bending.
4. The beam does not twist.
5. The material is elastic.
6. The material is homogeneous (properties are everywhere the same).
7. The beam is in a state of static equilibrium.
8. The beam is prismatic.

Consider any short segment of a prismatic beam as shown in Fig. B–1A. Two plane sections AB and CD are shown parallel to each other and separated by an infinitesimal distance ds. The loads are resolved into moments acting at each end in a principal plane, yy (assumption 1). Under the action of the moment the beam bends and plane DC rotates with respect to AB into position EF, which causes strains ϵ_c and ϵ_y to occur c and y (any variable distance) from the neutral axis. If plane CD remains plane after it rotates to position FE (assumption 2), we have

$$\frac{\epsilon_y}{\epsilon_c} = \frac{y}{c}$$

Unit strain e is defined as deformation ϵ, divided by original length. If the beam was originally straight (assumption 3), the original length of all fibers in section $ABCD$ was ds, so we have

$$e = \frac{\epsilon}{ds} \qquad \text{or} \qquad \epsilon = e\,ds$$

$$\frac{y}{c} = \frac{e_y\,ds}{e_c\,ds}$$

521

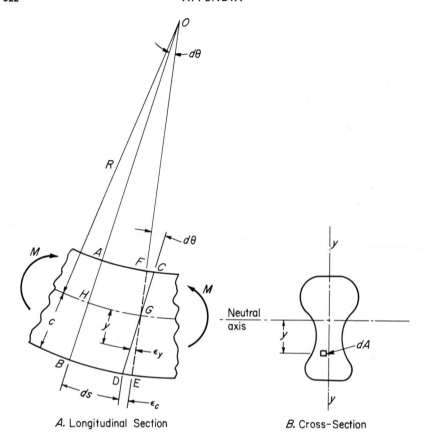

A. Longitudinal Section *B.* Cross-Section

Fig. B–I. Flexure.

But if the beam were to twist (violating assumption 4), the strains would also vary with distance from the yy axis which would invalidate the above equation. If the material is elastic (assumption 5), we have

$$e_y = \frac{s_y}{E_y} \qquad \text{and} \qquad e_c = \frac{s_c}{E_c}$$

where E is Young's modulus of elasticity.

$$\frac{y}{c} = \frac{e_y}{e_c} = \frac{s_y E_c}{s_c E_y}$$

If the material is also homogeneous (assumption 6), we have

$$E_y = E_c$$

So

$$s_y = \frac{s_c}{c} y \tag{B–1}$$

Since stress equals force divided by area, we have

$$s_y = \frac{dF}{dA} \qquad \text{or} \qquad dF = s_y \, dA$$

If the loads can be resolved into nothing but moment (assumption 1 again), the total force acting upon the cross-section (Fig. B–1B) is zero provided the beam is in equilibrium (assumption 7):

$$F = 0 = \int_0^F dF = \int_0^A s_y \, dA$$

Substituting Eq. B–1 for s_y gives

$$\int_0^A \frac{s_c}{c} y \, dA = 0$$

But if the beam is prismatic (assumption 8), s_c and c are constant over length ds, so s_c/c can be placed before the integral sign:

$$\frac{s_c}{c} \int_0^A y \, dA = 0$$

Since s_c/c cannot be zero, $\int_0^A y \, dA$ must be zero, which means the neutral axis coincides with the centroid and is, therefore, one of the principal planes of the cross-section. (This, by way of emphasis, can be true only when the external moments act in the plane of the other principal axis.)

Since moment equals force times distance, we have

$$dM = y \, dF = y s_y \, dA = \frac{s_c}{c} y^2 \, dA$$

Again, if the beam is in static equilibrium, the external moments minus the internal moments equal zero:

$$M - \frac{s_c}{c} \int_0^A y^2 \, dA = 0$$

The term $\int_0^A y^2 \, dA$ is called the moment of inertia.

$$M = \frac{s_c}{c} I = \frac{s_y}{y} I \qquad\qquad \text{(B–2)}$$

In Fig. B–1A, triangle OGH is similar to triangle GDE, so that

$$\frac{ds}{R} = \frac{\epsilon_c}{c} = \frac{e_c \, ds}{c} = \frac{s_c \, ds}{E \, c}$$

Substitution of Eq. B–2 gives

$$\frac{1}{R} = \frac{s_c}{Ec} = \frac{Mc}{IEc} = \frac{M}{EI} \qquad\qquad \text{(B–3)}$$

Since $d\theta$ is a small angle, we have

$$d\theta = \frac{ds}{R} = \frac{M}{EI}\,ds \qquad\qquad\qquad \text{(B–4)}$$

Assumption 1 is rarely satisfied in practice because there are usually transverse loads which cause shear. But unless the depth of the beam is at least one-quarter of its span length, the error is small. Assumption 2 can be verified experimentally. It is usually true except near joints or near points of application of concentrated loads. Assumption 3 is often violated, but the errors are small unless the curvature is great. For example, the stresses computed by the flexure formula are within 10 percent of the true stress if the radius of curvature is not less than five times the depth of the beam, and if the radius of curvature is 50 times the depth, the error is only 1 percent. Assumption 4 is usually true since structures are sufficiently braced by purlins, girts, or by other bracing to prevent twisting. Assumption 5 is reasonable for short-term loads, because at the low stresses permitted in bridges and buildings, nearly all structural materials—steel, concrete, masonry, and wood—are essentially elastic. Some materials, such as concrete creep at fairly low stress, so that over a long period of time considerable readjustment of stress may take place. This may or may not prove beneficial to the structure in a structural sense. Assumption 6 is reasonable for steel and even for wood, but it is often a poor approximation when applied to reinforced concrete, which develops minute cracks and has unbalanced reinforcement to invalidate the assumption. Consequently the deflection of concrete beams is proportional to load only at very low stresses. However, if the concrete is prestressed so that the fibers remain in compression, the assumption is reasonable. Assumption 7 holds true for slowly applied loads, but errors are likely to be serious for vibratory and blast loadings. Assumption 8 is frequently violated. If the taper is slight, the error is not great, but considerable error results within joints and where the beam is sharply tapered.

PROBLEMS

PART 1

Chapter 1

1–1. Find the reactions in terms of horizontal and vertical components.

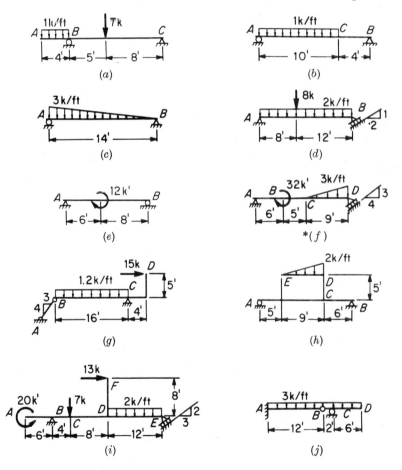

(a)

(b)

(c)

(d)

(e)

*(f)

(g)

(h)

(i)

(j)

*Answers are given for problems marked with an asterisk; see pages 585–593.

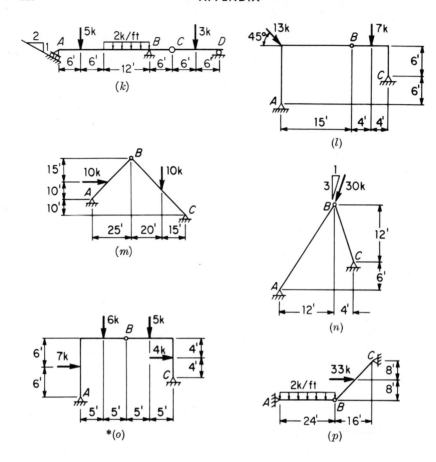

(k)

(l)

(m)

(n)

*(o)

(p)

1-2. Find the forces in all the indicated members.

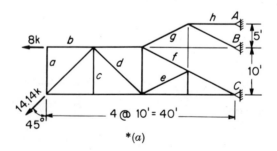

*(a)

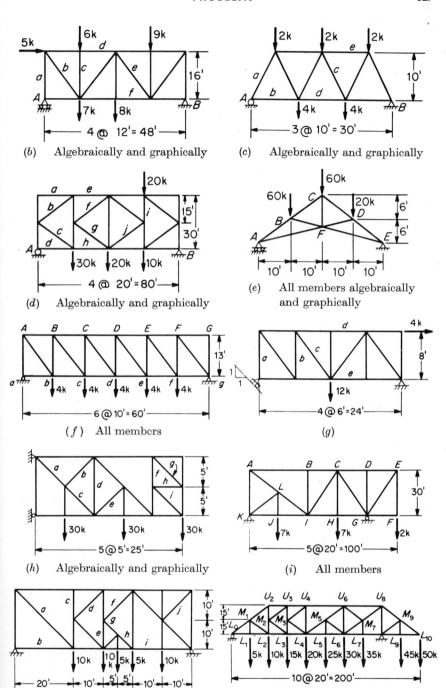

(b)   Algebraically and graphically

(c)   Algebraically and graphically

(d)   Algebraically and graphically

(e)   All members algebraically
       and graphically

(f)   All members

(g)

(h)   Algebraically and graphically

(i)   All members

*(j)

(k)   All members

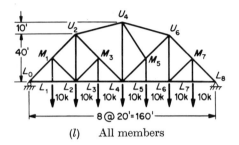

(l)   All members

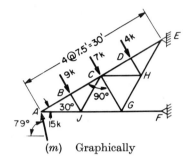

(m)   Graphically

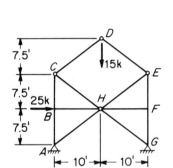

(n)   All members

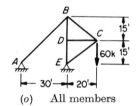

(o)   All members

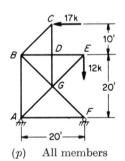

(p)   All members

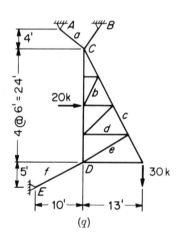

(q)

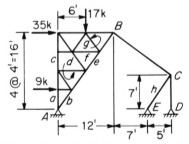

*(r)   Analytically and graphically

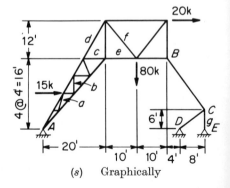

(s)   Graphically

1-3. Is each structure statically determinate or indeterminate, stable or unstable?

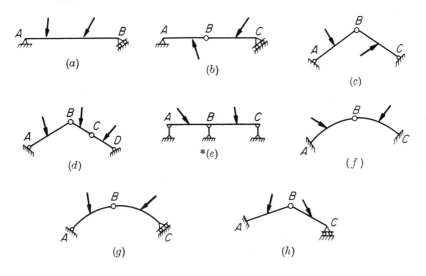

(a)

(b)

(c)

(d)

*(e)

(f)

(g)

(h)

Chapter 2

2-1. Draw the load diagram, shear diagram, moment diagram, and the approximate elastic curve. Calculate the maximum and minimum ordinates for the shear and moment diagrams.

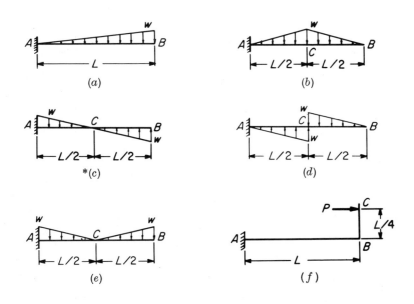

(a)

(b)

*(c)

(d)

(e)

(f)

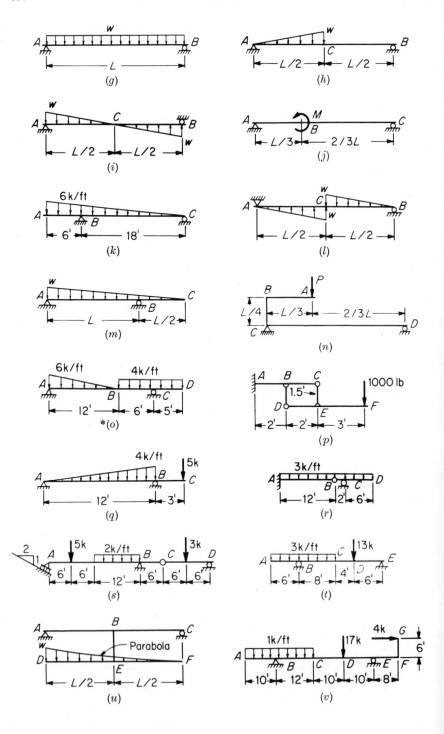

(g)

(h)

(i)

(j)

(k)

(l)

(m)

(n)

*(o)

(p)

(q)

(r)

(s)

(t)

(u)

(v)

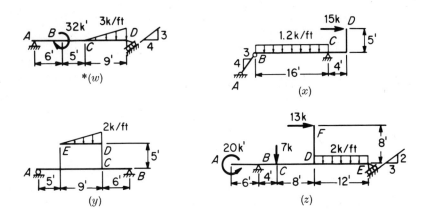

(w)   (x)

(y)   (z)

2-2. Draw moment diagrams in cantilever parts from the left. Add the parts to obtain the total moment diagrams.

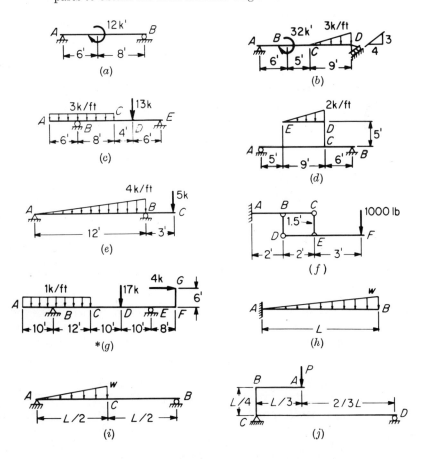

(a)

(b)

(c)

(d)

(e)

(f)

(g)

(h)

(i)

(j)

2-3. Draw moment diagrams in cantilever parts from the right. Add the parts to obtain the total moment diagrams.

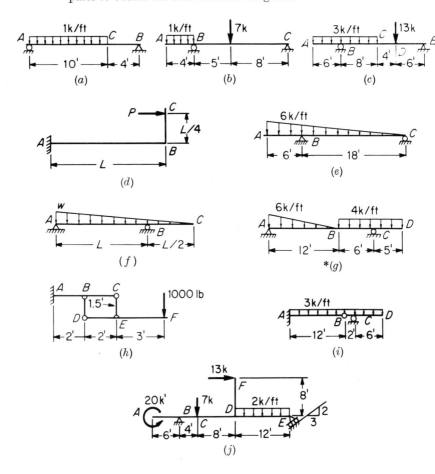

2-4. Draw moment diagrams in cantilever parts from the left to the middle and from the right to the middle. Add the parts to obtain the total moment diagrams. What is the advantage of this construction?

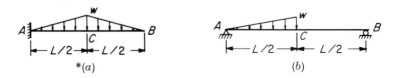

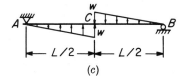

(c)

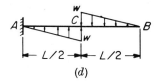

(d)

2-5. Draw the moment diagrams in cantilever parts.

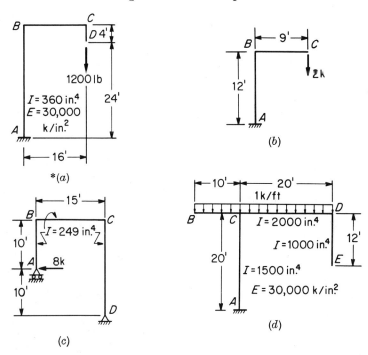

*(a)

(b)

(c)

(d)

2-6. Replace redundant reactions by letter symbols (V for vertical force, H for horizontal force, and M for moment). Draw moment diagrams by cantilever parts from right or left or in any combination to yield the simplest diagrams.

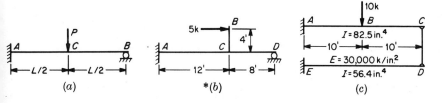

(a)

*(b)

(c)

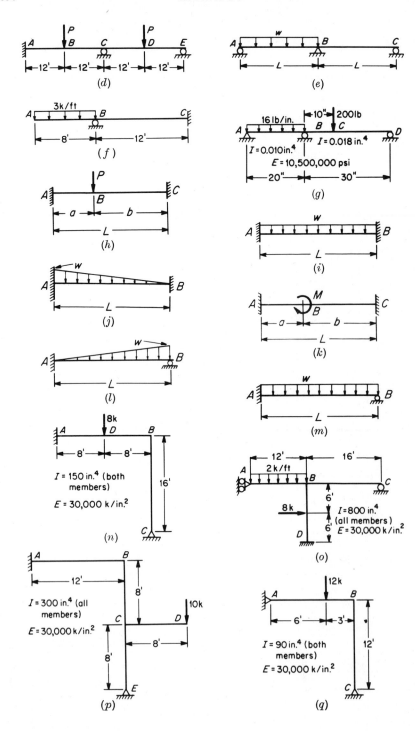

(d)

(e)

(f)

(g)

(h)

(i)

(j)

(k)

(l)

(m)

(n)

(o)

(p)

(q)

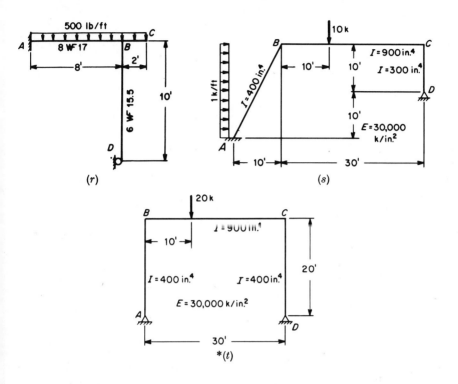

(r)

(s)

*(t)

2-7. Using the moment diagram shown, reconstruct the structure, its loads, and its type of supports.

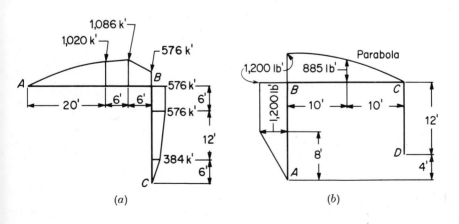

(a)

(b)

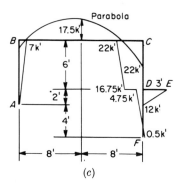

(c)

2-8. Write the moment equations in terms of a variable x, measured from the left end of the beam.

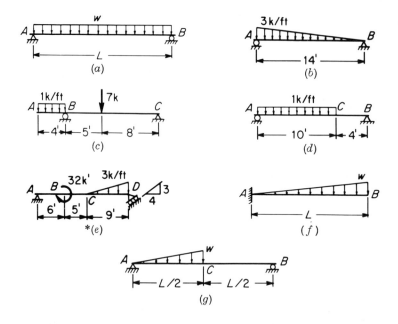

2-9. Write the moment equations in terms of a variable distance x, measured from the right end of the beam.

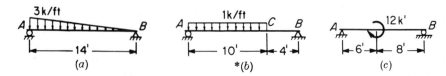

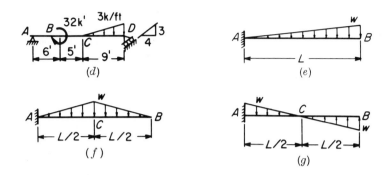

(d)

(e)

(f)

(g)

2–10. Write the moment equations for the portion of the beam between the two supports in terms of x measured from the right support.

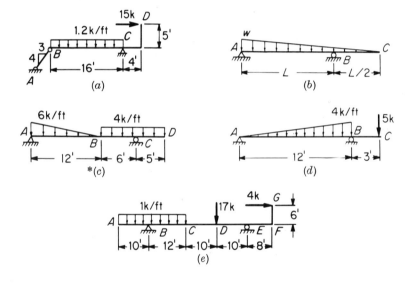

(a)

(b)

(c)

(d)

(e)

2–11. Replace redundant reactions by letter symbols (V for vertical force and M for moment). Write moment equations in terms of a variable distance x, measured from the right end of the beam.

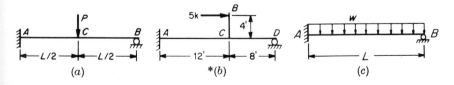

(a)

*(b)

(c)

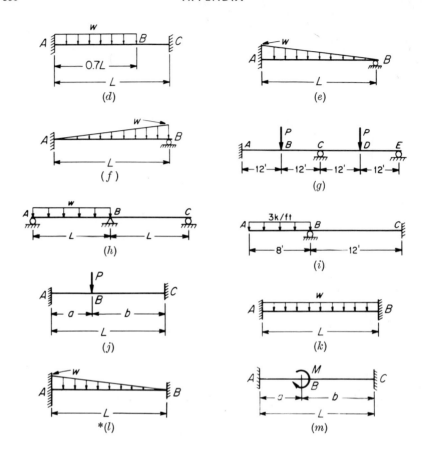

2-12. Draw the moment diagrams by simple beam parts.

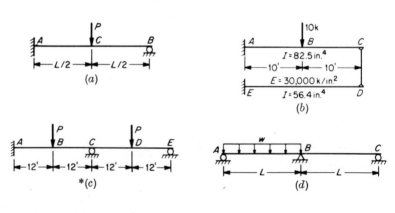

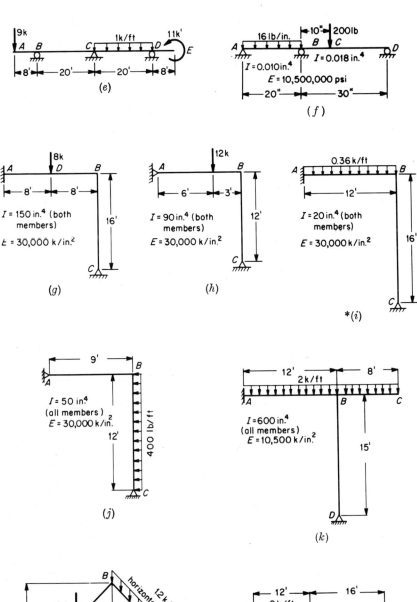

(e)

(f)

(g)

(h)

*(i)

(j)

(k)

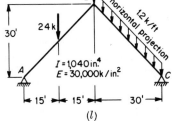

(l)

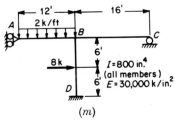

(m)

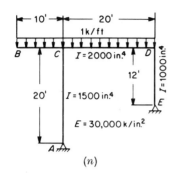

(n)

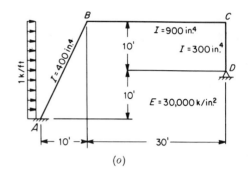

(o)

Chapter 3

3–1. Find the areas and centroids of the total moment diagrams.

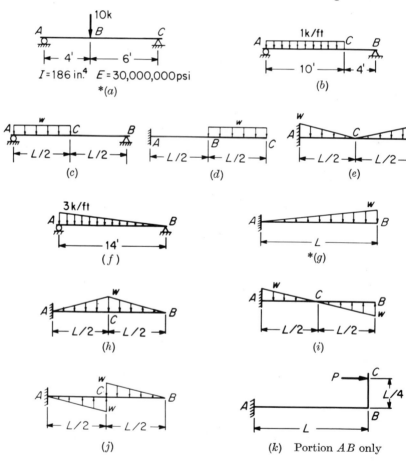

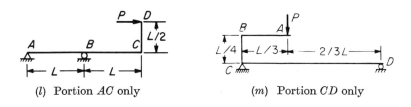

(l) Portion AC only   (m) Portion CD only

PART II

Chapter 4

4-1. Find the indicated deflections and rotations by the integral moment area method.

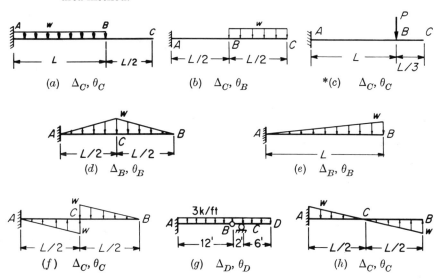

(a) Δ_C, θ_C (b) Δ_C, θ_B *(c) Δ_C, θ_C

(d) Δ_B, θ_B (e) Δ_B, θ_B

(f) Δ_C, θ_C (g) Δ_D, θ_D (h) Δ_C, θ_C

4-2. Find the indicated deflections and rotations by the integral moment area method.

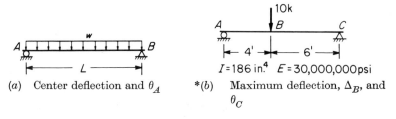

$I = 186$ in.^{4} $E = 30,000,000$ psi

(a) Center deflection and θ_A *(b) Maximum deflection, Δ_B, and θ_C

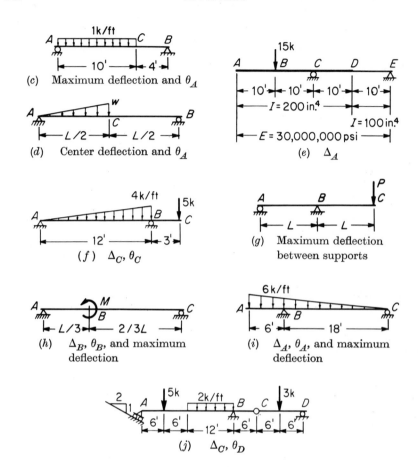

(c)   Maximum deflection and θ_A

(d)   Center deflection and θ_A

(e) Δ_A

(f) Δ_C, θ_C

(g)   Maximum deflection between supports

(h) Δ_B, θ_B, and maximum deflection

(i) Δ_A, θ_A, and maximum deflection

(j) Δ_C, θ_D

4–3. Work Prob. 4–1 by graphical moment area.

4–4. Work Prob. 4–2 by graphical moment area.

Chapter 5

5–1. Determine the reactions and draw the total shear and moment diagrams for the beams shown. Use graphical moment area.

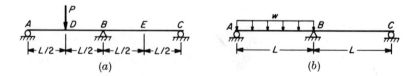

(a)

(b)

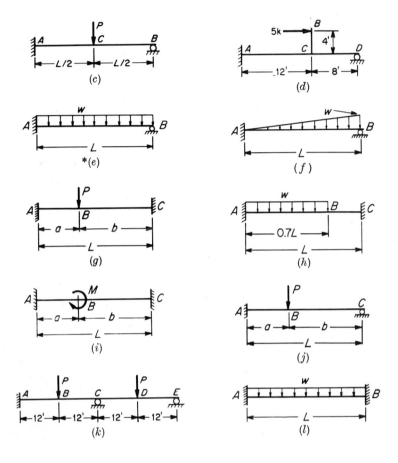

5-2. Determine the indicated deflections and rotations for the beams of Prob. 5-1.

(a) Deflection at load

(b) Deflection at mid-span of BC and θ_B

(c) Δ_C, θ_B

(d) θ_D, Δ_C

*(e) Center deflection and θ_B

(f) Mid-span deflection and θ_B

(g) Maximum deflection

(h) Δ_B and maximum deflection

(i) Δ_B, θ_B

(j) Δ_B, θ_C

(k) Deflection at load points and maximum deflection

(l) Maximum deflection and slope

Chapter 6

6-1. Compute all the reactions of the rigid frames shown, and draw the total moment diagrams.

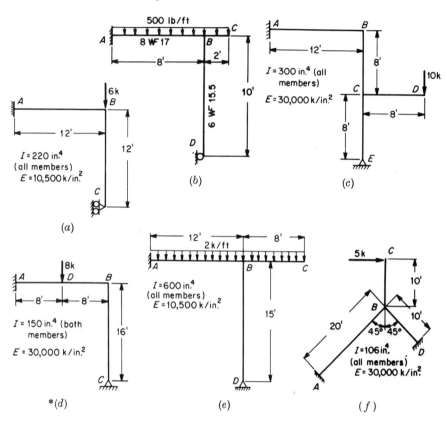

(a)

(b)

(c)

*(d)

(e)

(f)

6-2. Compute the reactions of the rigid frames shown. Draw the total moment diagrams. Sketch the approximate elastic curves.

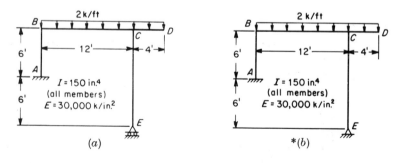

(a)

*(b)

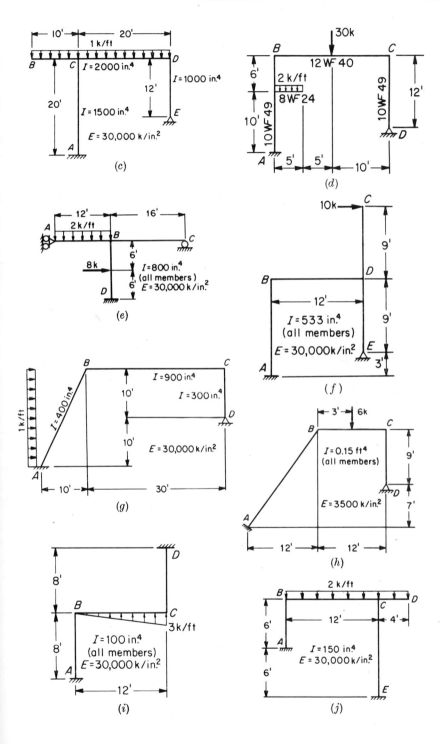

6–3. Compute the indicated deflections and rotations.

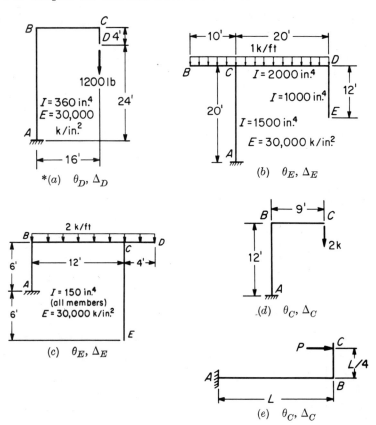

*(a) θ_D, Δ_D

(b) θ_E, Δ_E

(c) θ_E, Δ_E

(d) θ_C, Δ_C

(e) θ_C, Δ_C

6–4. Compute the indicated deflections and rotations.

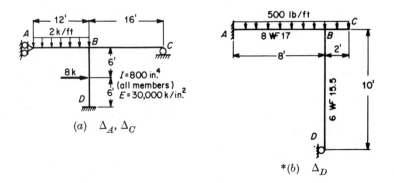

(a) Δ_A, Δ_C

*(b) Δ_D

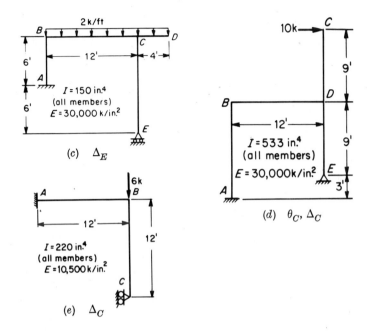

(c) Δ_E

(d) θ_C, Δ_C

(e) Δ_C

6–5. Compute the reactions of the two-hinged rigid frames shown. Draw the total moment diagrams. Sketch the approximate elastic curves.

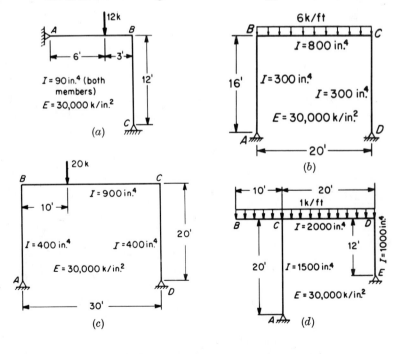

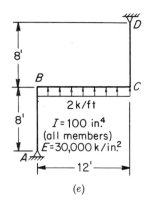

2 k/ft

$I = 100$ in.^{4}
(all members)
$E = 30,000$ k/in.^{2}

12'

(e)

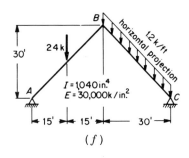

30'

24 k

$I = 1040$ in.^{4}
$E = 30,000$ k/in.^{2}

12 k/ft horizontal projection

15'   15'   30'

(f)

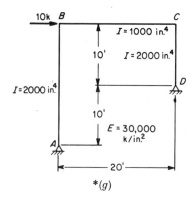

10k B   C

$I = 1000$ in.^{4}

$I = 2000$ in.^{4}

$I = 2000$ in.^{4}

D

10'

10'

$E = 30,000$ k/in.^{2}

20'

*(g)

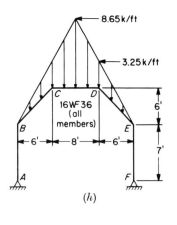

8.65 k/ft

3.25 k/ft

16 WF 36
(all members)

6'   8'   6'

6'

7'

(h)

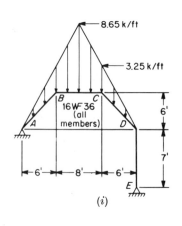

8.65 k/ft

3.25 k/ft

16 WF 36
(all members)

6'   8'   6'

6'

7'

(i)

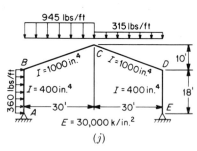

945 lbs/ft

315 lbs/ft

360 lbs/ft

B $I = 1000$ in.^{4} C $I = 1000$ in.^{4} D

$I = 400$ in.^{4} $I = 400$ in.^{4}

30'   30'

A   E

10'

18'

$E = 30,000$ k/in.^{2}

(j)

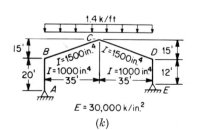

1.4 k/ft

C

15'

20'

B $I = 1500$ in.^{4} $I = 1500$ in.^{4} D

$I = 1000$ in.^{4} $I = 1000$ in.^{4}

35'   35'

A   E

15'

12'

$E = 30,000$ k/in.^{2}

(k)

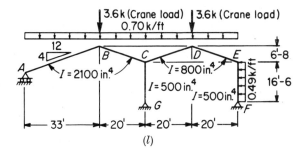

3.6k (Crane load)   3.6k (Crane load)
0.70 k/ft

$I = 2100$ in.^{4}

$I = 800$ in.^{4}

$I = 500$ in.^{4}

$I = 500$ in.^{4}

0.49 k/ft

12
4

A
B
C
D
E

G

F

6-8

16'-6

33'   20'   20'   20'

(l)

6–6. Compute the moments in the structures.

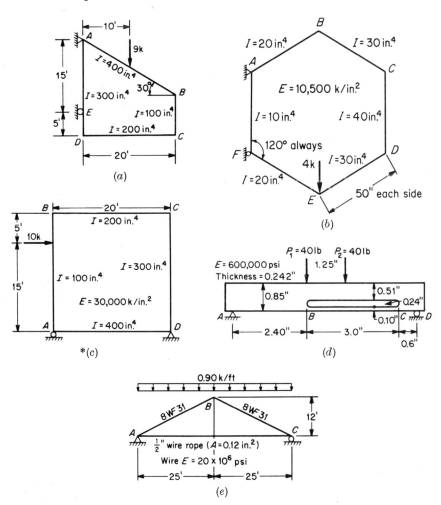

10'
9k
15'
$I = 400$ in.^{4}
$I = 300$ in.^{4}
30°
$I = 100$ in.^{4}
$I = 200$ in.^{4}
5'
E
A
B
D
C
20'

(a)

B
$I = 20$ in.^{4} $I = 30$ in.^{4}
A
C
$E = 10,500$ k/in.^{2}
$I = 10$ in.^{4} $I = 40$ in.^{4}
120° always
F
$I = 30$ in.^{4}
D
4k
$I = 20$ in.^{4}
E
50" each side

(b)

B   20'   C
$I = 200$ in.^{4}
5'
10k
$I = 300$ in.^{4}
$I = 100$ in.^{4}
15'
$E = 30,000$ k/in.^{2}
A
$I = 400$ in.^{4}
D

*(c)

$P_1 = 40$ lb $P_2 = 40$ lb
1.25"
$E = 600,000$ psi
Thickness = 0.242"
0.85"
0.51"
A
B
0.24"
C
D
0.10"
2.40"   3.0"
0.6"

(d)

0.90 k/ft
8WF31
B
8WF31
12'
A
C
$\frac{1}{2}$" wire rope ($A = 0.12$ in.^{2})
Wire $E = 20 \times 10^6$ psi
25'   25'

(e)

6–7. Using the summation procedure of moment area, compute the live-load reactions and draw the total live-load moment diagrams for the structures.

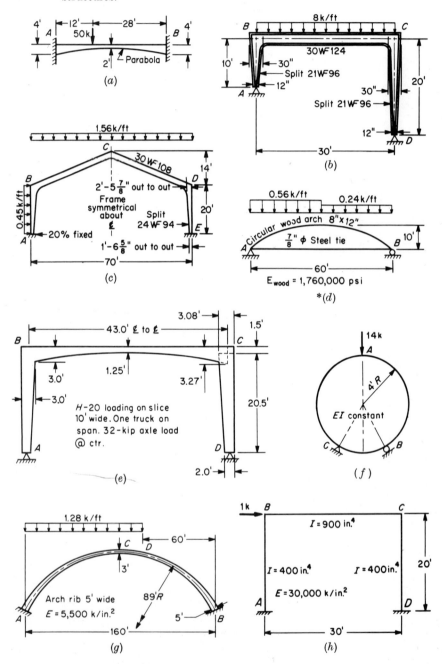

(a)

(b)

(c)

0.56 k/ft   0.24 k/ft

Circular wood arch 8"x12"

$\frac{7}{8}$" φ Steel tie

60'

$E_{wood} = 1,760,000$ psi

*(d)

(e)

(f)

(g)

(h)

6-8. Work Prob. 6-7 by constructing cardboard models of the *M/EI* diagrams. Weigh the cardboard to determine areas and balance to find the centroids.

6-9. Using integral moment area, find the reactions and the moments in the structures.

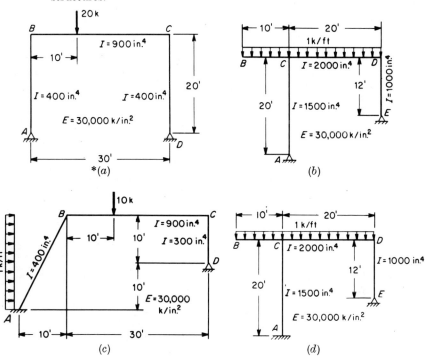

*(a)

(b)

(c)

(d)

PART III

Chapter 7

7-1. Compute the indicated deflection due to the indicated causes.

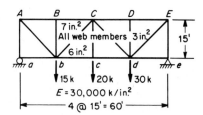

(a) Deflection at point *C* due to fabricating each tension member $\frac{3}{16}$ in. short.

(b)   Deflection at point C (Prob. 7–1a) due to top chord heated 20° F more than rest of truss. Coefficient of expansion is 0.0000065 per °F.

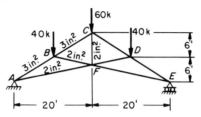

(c)   Deflection at point F due to top chord heated 20° F more than rest of truss. Coefficient of expansion = 0.0000065 per °F.

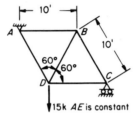

*(d)   Member BD shortens 1 in. Find movement of point C.

7–2.   Compute the indicated deflections due to the action of the loads shown. Assume $E = 30,000,000$ psi except as noted.

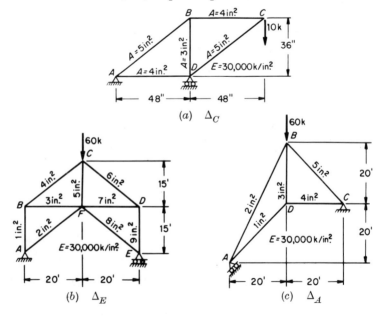

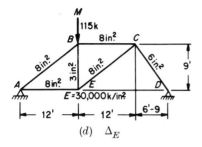

(d) Δ_E

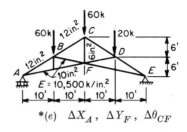

*(e) ΔX_A, ΔY_F, $\Delta\theta_{CF}$

7-3. Compute the force in each member.

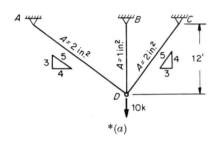

*(a)

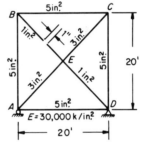

(b)   Note member BD is shortened 1 in.

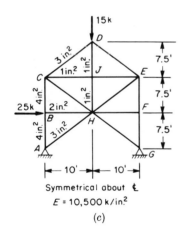

Symmetrical about ℄
$E = 10,500$ k/in.²
(c)

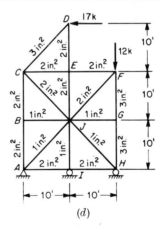

(d)

7-4. For Prob. 7-3, compute the indicated deflection of the indicated point. Assume $E = 30,000,000$ psi except as noted.

*(a) Δ_D (b) Δ_C (c) Δ_D (d) Δ_F

Chapter 8

8–1. Evaluate the deflection and rotation at the free end of the beam by integral virtual work.

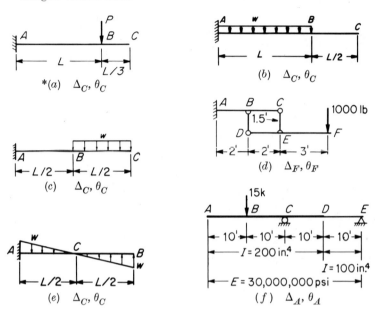

*(a) Δ_C, θ_C

(b) Δ_C, θ_C

(c) Δ_C, θ_C

(d) Δ_F, θ_F

(e) Δ_C, θ_C

(f) Δ_A, θ_A

8–2. Evaluate the central deflection between supports by integral virtual work.

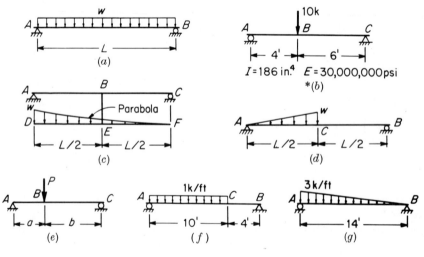

(a)

$I = 186$ in.^{4} $E = 30,000,000$ psi
*(b)

(c)

(d)

(e)

(f)

(g)

8–3. For Prob. 8–2, evaluate the maximum deflection between supports by integral virtual work.

8-4. Find the reactions and draw the shear and moment diagrams for the beams shown. Use integral virtual work.

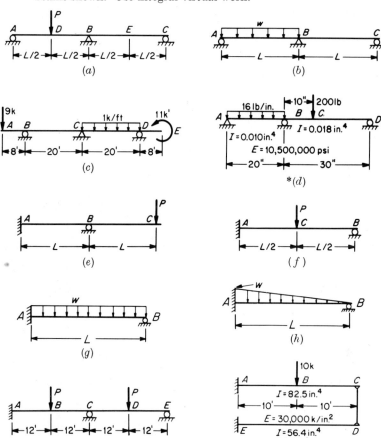

8-5. Using integral virtual work, determine the indicated deflections and rotations for the beams of Prob. 8-4.

(a) Deflection at point of load

(b) θ_B, Deflection at mid-point of AB

(c) θ_E, Δ_A

*(d) Δ_C

(e) Positive Δ_{max} negative Δ_{max}

(f) Δ_C, θ_B

(g) θ_{max}, Δ_{max}

(h) θ_B, $\Delta_{mid-span}$

(i) Δ_D, θ_C

(j) θ_C, θ_D, Δ_D

8–6. Work Prob. 8–1 by semi-graphical virtual work.

8–7. Work Prob. 8–2 by semi-graphical virtual work.

8–8. For Prob. 8–2 evaluate the maximum deflection between supports using semi-graphical virtual work.

8–9. Work Prob. 8–4 using semi-graphical virtual work.

8–10. Compute the central deflections between supports and the rotation at the right-hand support for the beams of Prob. 8–4.

Chapter 9

9–1. Compute all the reactions for the rigid frames shown.

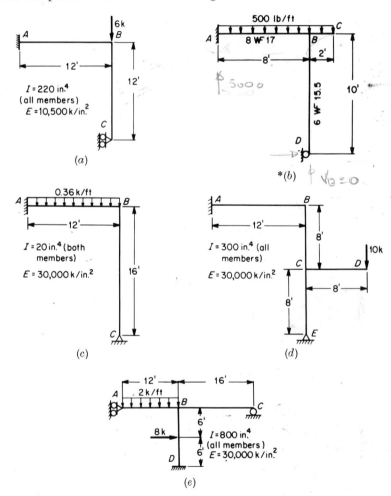

(a)

*(b)

(c)

(d)

(e)

9-2. Compute the indicated deflections and rotations. Draw the approximate elastic curves.

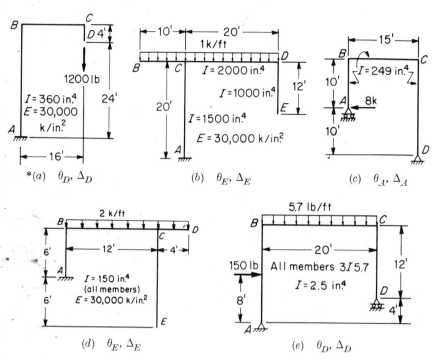

*(a) θ_D, Δ_D

(b) θ_E, Δ_E

(c) θ_A, Δ_A

(d) θ_E, Δ_E

(e) θ_D, Δ_D

9-3. For Prob. 9-1, compute the indicated deflections and rotations, and draw the approximate elastic curves.

(a) Δ_C, θ_B *(b) Δ_D (c) θ_B and deflection at mid-point of AB

(d) θ_C, Δ_C (e) Δ_A, θ_C

9-4. Compute the reactions of the rigid frames. Draw the total moment diagrams. Sketch the approximate elastic curves.

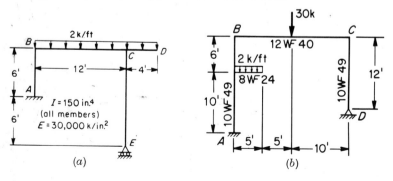

(a)

(b)

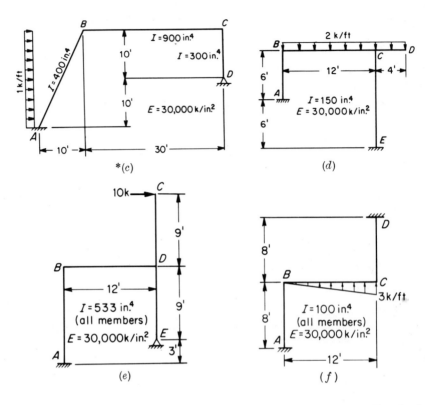

*(c)

(d)

(e)

(f)

9–5. Find the reactions. Draw the total moment diagrams. Sketch the approximate elastic curve.

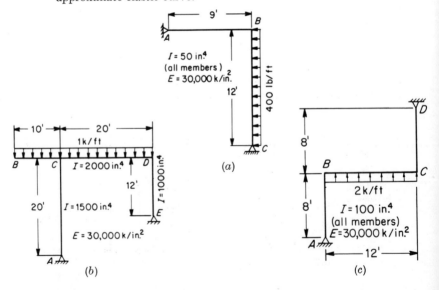

(a)

(b)

(c)

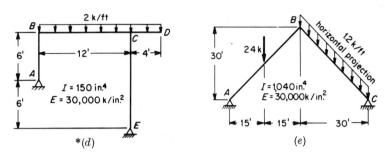

*(d)   (e)

Chapter 10

10-1. Select any non-prismatic beam in Appendix A and compute the moment for a uniform load, the stiffness, and the carry-over factor for each end, using integral virtual work. Compare your answer with the tabulated values.

10-2. Using the summation procedure, compute the reactions and draw the total moment diagrams for the structures shown.

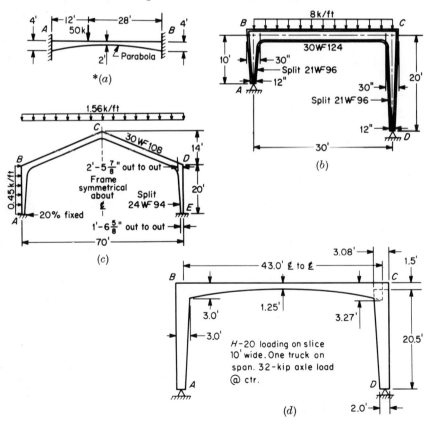

10–3. Compute the moments in the structure.

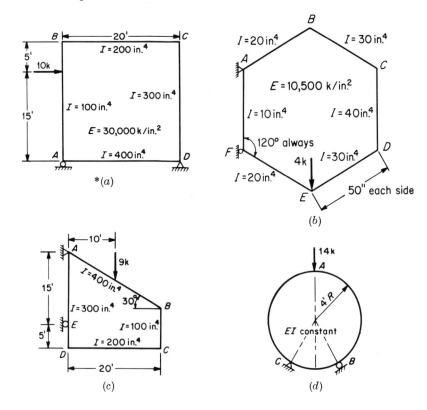

(a)

(b)

(c)   *(d)*

Chapter 11

11–1.*(a) Compute the relative effect of shear and flexure upon the deflection in a simply supported beam $2\frac{5}{8}$ in. wide by $5\frac{1}{2}$ in. deep by 30 in. long loaded with a concentrated load of 1800 lb, 12 in. from one support.

(b) A round steel bar 2 in. in diameter projects from a rigid wall for a distance of 12 in. (on the centerline), and then is sharply bent at 90° extending horizontally 6 in. from the point of bend. A vertical load of 12,000 lb is applied at the extreme end of the bent bar. Compute the maximum deflection.

(c) Two horizontal pipes 12 in. I.D. by $12\frac{1}{2}$ in. O.D. are each rigidly fixed to an external support at one end and firmly welded to each other in a 90°-joint at the other end. Each pipe is 8 ft long. Compute the deflection caused by a 12-ton load applied vertically at the joint.

(d) Assume the load in part (c) to be applied to one of the two pipes at a point 3 ft from the juncture. Compute the deflection at the load and at the joint.

11-2. Determine the bending moments in the beam (or arch) and the tension in the tie.

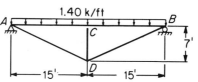

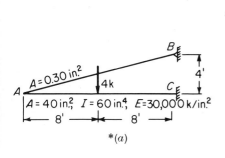

$A = 0.30\ \text{in.}^2$

4k

$A = 40\ \text{in.}^2,\ I = 60\ \text{in.}^4,\ E = 30,000\ \text{k/in.}^2$

8' — 8'

(a)

$AB: 2\text{-}12\ [25,\ A = 14.64\ \text{in.}^2,\ I = 287\ \text{in.}^4$
$CD: 2\text{-}6\ [10.5,\ A = 6.1\ \text{in.}^2,\ I = 30.2\ \text{in.}^4$
$AD,\ DB: 2\ \text{bars } 3 \times \tfrac{1}{2},\ A = 3.0\ \text{in.}^2,\ I = 0$

(b)

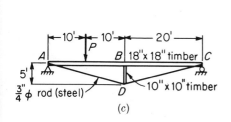

18"x 18" timber

$\tfrac{3}{4}$" ϕ rod (steel)

10"x 10" timber

(c)

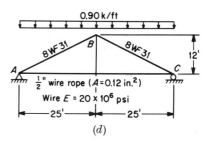

0.90 k/ft

8 WF 31

$\tfrac{1}{2}$" wire rope (A = 0.12 in.²)

Wire E = 20 × 10⁶ psi

25' — 25'

(d)

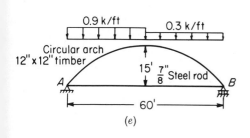

0.9 k/ft

0.3 k/ft

Circular arch
12"x 12" timber

15' 7/8" Steel rod

60'

(e)

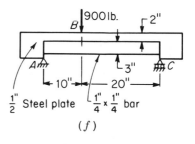

900 lb.

2"

$\tfrac{1}{2}$" Steel plate

3"

10" — 20"

$\tfrac{1}{4}$" × $\tfrac{1}{4}$" bar

(f)

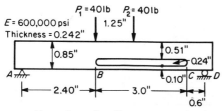

$P_1 = 40\ \text{lb}$ $P_2 = 40\ \text{lb}$

E = 600,000 psi
Thickness = 0.242"

1.25"

0.85"

0.51"

0.24"

0.10"

2.40" — 3.0"

0.6"

(g) Assume there is no bending moment in the tie *BC*.

PART IV

Chapter 12

12–1. Determine the moments at the joints, find the reactions, and draw the moment diagrams in simple beam parts.

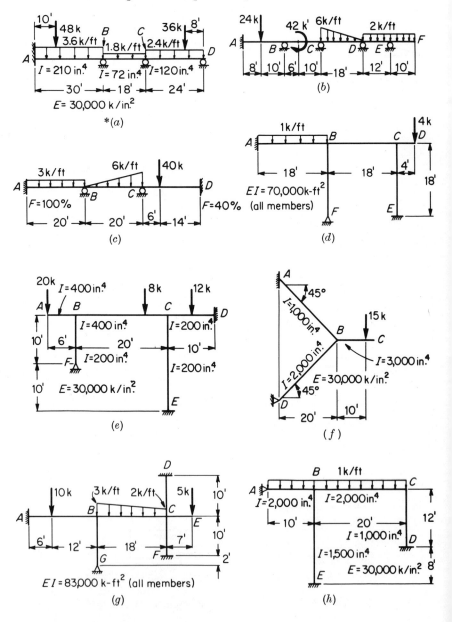

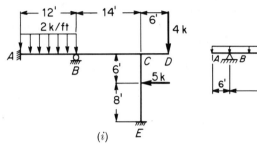

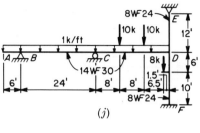

(i)

(j)

Chapter 13

13–1. Compute the moments caused by the indicated action.

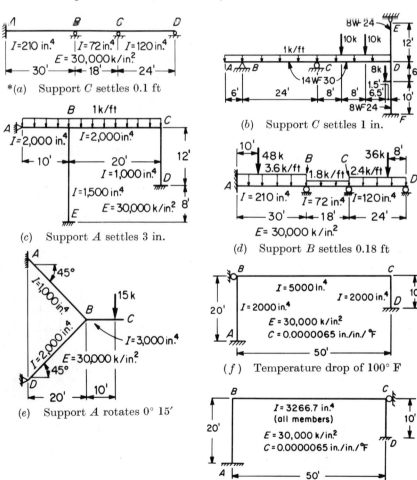

(a) Support C settles 0.1 ft

(b) Support C settles 1 in.

(c) Support A settles 3 in.

(d) Support B settles 0.18 ft

(e) Support A rotates 0° 15′

(f) Temperature drop of 100° F

(g) Temperature rise of 40° F

13–2. Compute the fixed-end moments, the stiffness at each end, and the carry-over factors, using moment distribution and temporary supports.

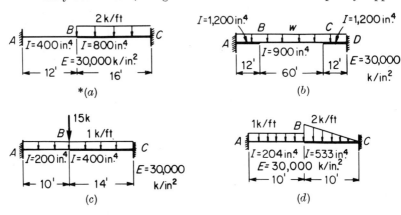

(a)   *(b)*   *(c)*   *(d)*

13–3. Compute the moments at the joints and the reactions. Draw the moment diagrams. Determine the angle of rotation of each joint and sketch the elastic curve.

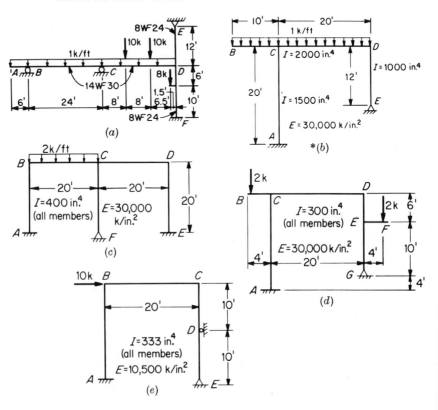

(a)   *(b)*   *(c)*   *(d)*   *(e)*

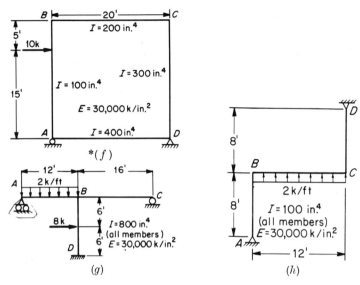

(f)

(g)

(h)

Chapter 14

14–1. Compute the moments at the joints and the reactions. Draw the moment diagrams.

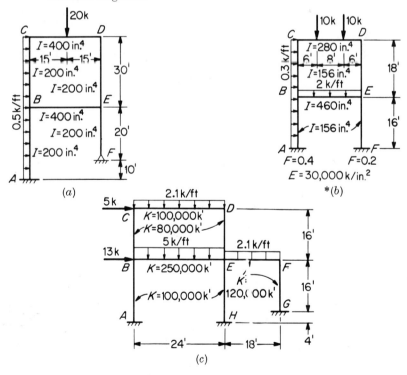

(a)

(b)

(c)

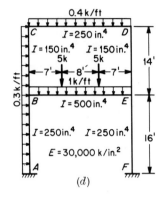

(d)

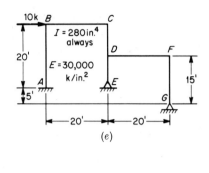

(e)

14–2. Find the shear in each column in terms of F where $F = 1/R$. R equals shear in a fixed-ended prismatic beam with a relative end deflection of unity. EI is the same for all columns.

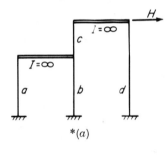

*(a)

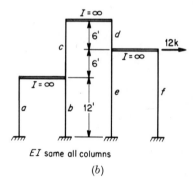

EI same all columns

(b)

14–3. Find the moments at each joint, find the reactions, and draw the moment diagrams in simple beam parts.

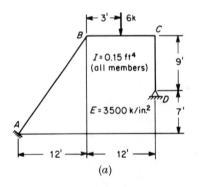

(a)

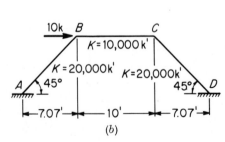

(b)

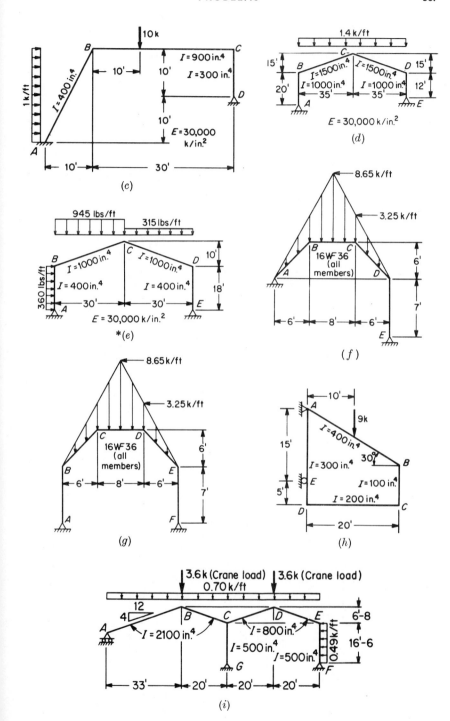

(c)

(d)

*(e)

(f)

(g)

(h)

(i)

Chapter 15

15-1. Make static and elastic checks of your answers for problems of Chapters 12, 13, and 14.

15-2. Making whatever assumptions appear most reasonable, find the moments at each joint, draw the moment diagrams in parts, and perform static and elastic checks.

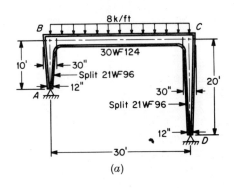

(a)

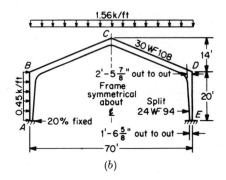

(b)

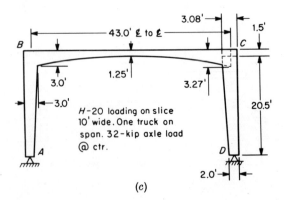

(c)

Chapter 16

16–1. Making those assumptions which appear most reasonable, find the moments at each joint, draw the moment diagrams in parts, and make the static and elastic checks.

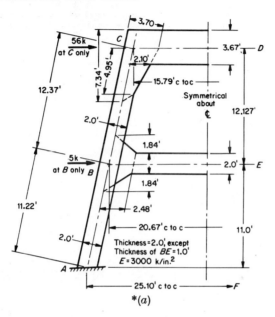

(a)

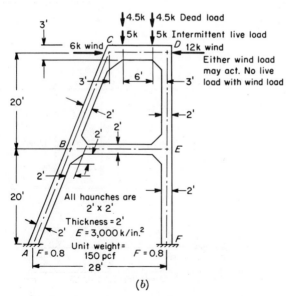

(b)

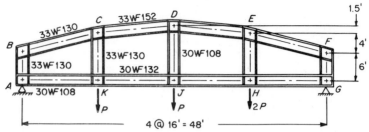

(c) Find the value of P that will produce a maximum flexural stress of 14,000 psi.

16–2. Analyze the trussed structures for the indicated quantities.

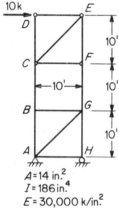

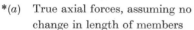

*(a) True axial forces, assuming no change in length of members

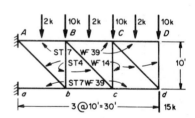

(b) End moments

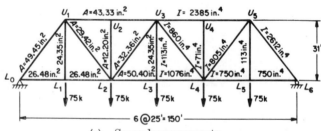

(c) Secondary moments

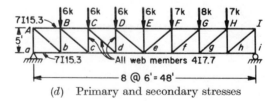

(d) Primary and secondary stresses

16–3. Draw the total moment diagram for each column due to each load separately: (1) crane loads; (2) wind load; (3) the combination which yields maximum moment.

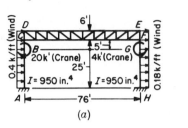

(a)

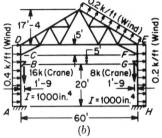

(b)

16–4. Analyze the building frames by the K-percentage method. Compare a second approximation with a first approximation.

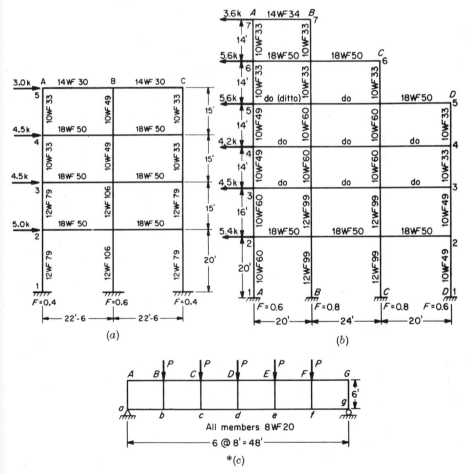

(a)

(b)

*(c)

16–5. Determine the maximum (and minimum, where applicable) design moments at the faces of supports and at mid-span, the design shears, and the points of inflection for the beams shown. Refer to *Continuity of Concrete Building Frames* by the Portland Cement Association, Chicago, Illinois, for the theory and practical application of short-cut methods.

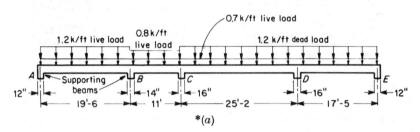

(a)

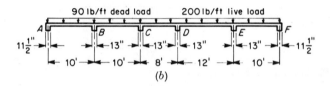

(b)

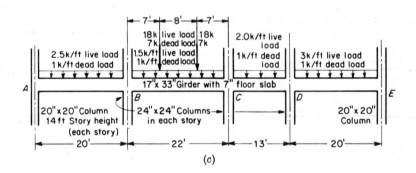

(c)

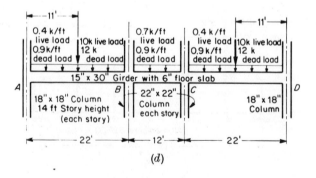

(d)

PART V

Chapter 17

17–1. Find the deflection of the panel points by Williot diagrams.

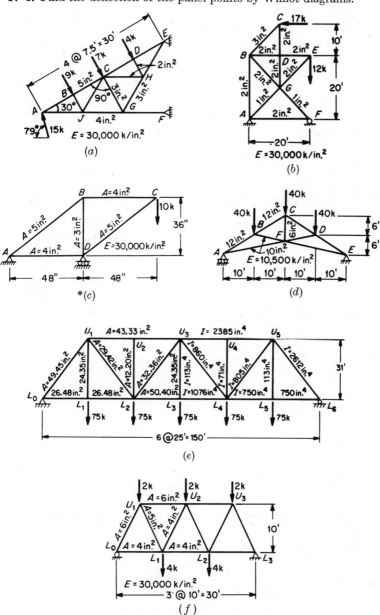

17–2. Find the deflection of the panel points by Williot-Mohr diagrams.

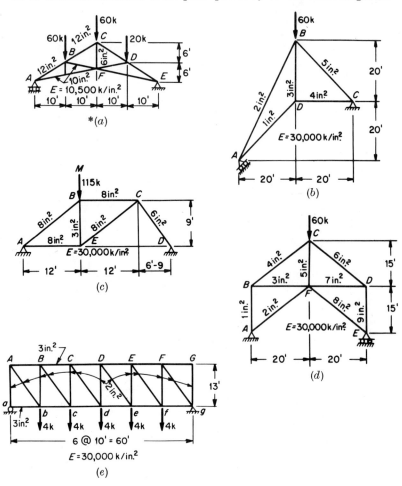

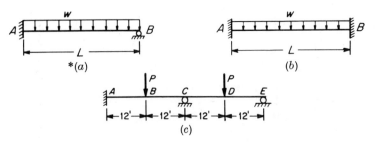

Chapter 18

18–1. Use the method of consistent deflections and either moment area or virtual work to obtain the reactions of the structure shown.

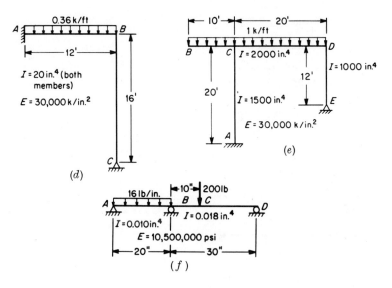

(d)

(e)

(f)

Chapter 19

19-1. Find the indicated deflections by means of double integration.

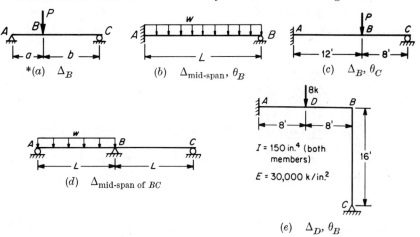

*(a) Δ_B

(b) $\Delta_{\text{mid-span}}$, θ_B

(c) Δ_B, θ_C

(d) $\Delta_{\text{mid-span of } BC}$

(e) Δ_D, θ_B

Chapter 20

20-1. Determine the indicated deflections (and where necessary, find the reactions) by the method of elastic weights.

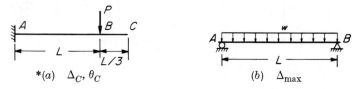

*(a) Δ_C, θ_C

(b) Δ_{max}

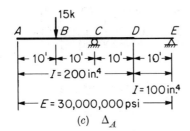

(c) Δ_A

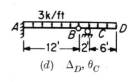

(d) Δ_D, θ_C

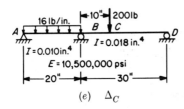

(e) Δ_C

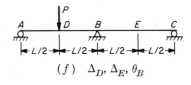

(f) $\Delta_D, \Delta_E, \theta_B$

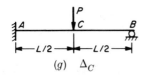

(g) Δ_C

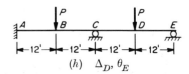

(h) Δ_D, θ_E

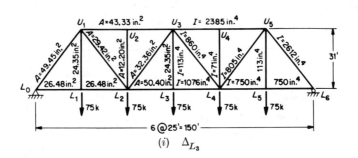

(i) Δ_{L_3}

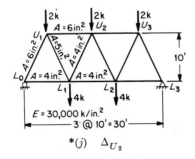

*(j) Δ_{U_2}

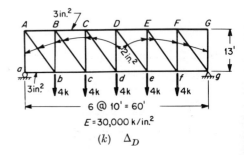

(k) Δ_D

Chapter 21

21-1. Use the elastic center method to determine the redundant reactions.

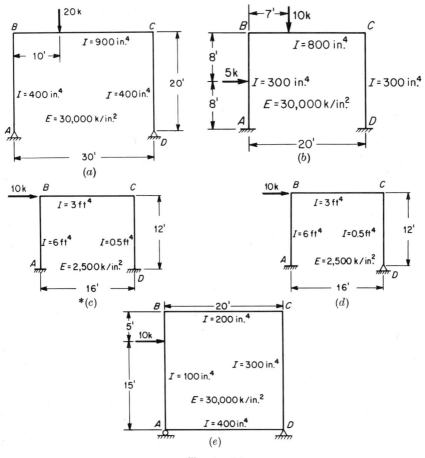

(a)

(b)

*(c)

(d)

(e)

Chapter 22

22-1. Find the redundant reactions by means of the column analogy.

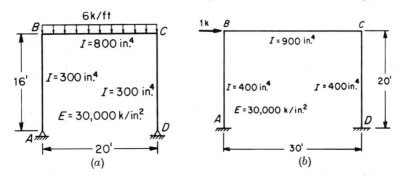

(a)

(b)

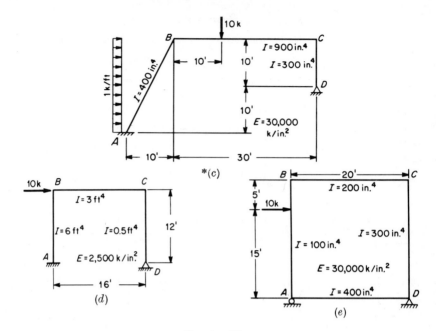

(c)

(d)

(e)

Chapter 23

23–1. Determine the moments at each joint by means of the slope deflection equations.

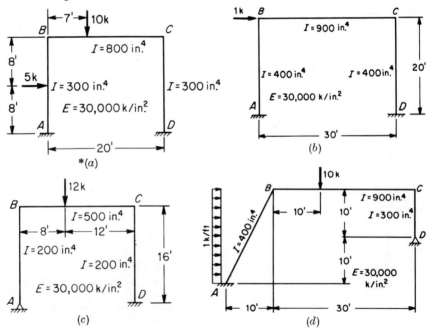

(a)

(b)

(c)

(d)

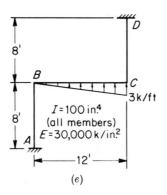

(e)

Chapter 24

24-1. Find the indicated deflections by means of Castigliano's theorems.

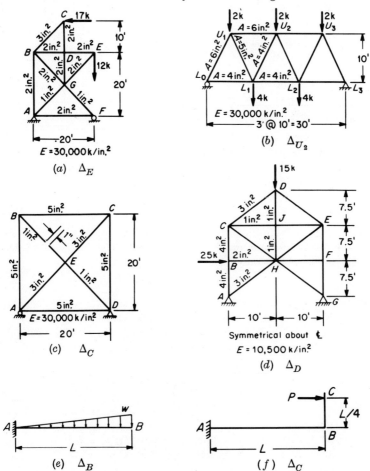

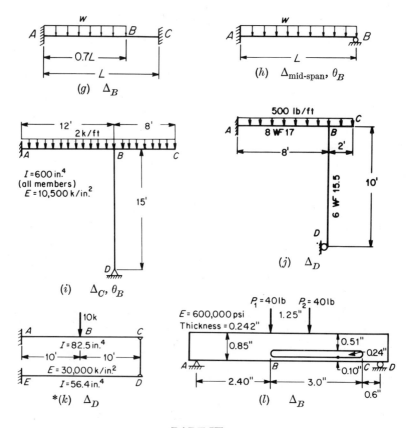

(g) Δ_B

(h) $\Delta_{\text{mid-span}}$, θ_B

$I = 600$ in.^{4}
(all members)
$E = 10,500$ k/in.^{2}

(i) Δ_C, θ_B

500 lb/ft

8 WF 17

6 WF 15.5

(j) Δ_D

10k

$I = 82.5$ in.^{4}

$E = 30,000$ k/in.^{2}

$I = 56.4$ in.^{4}

*(k) Δ_D

$E = 600,000$ psi
Thickness = 0.242"

$P_1 = 40$ lb $P_2 = 40$ lb

(l) Δ_B

PART VI

Wide variations in facilities and objectives would appear to make an extensive list of definite problems impractical. The following problems are intended as suggestions only.

Chapter 25

25–1. (a) Use a wire spline to obtain influence lines for each reaction (including the moment reaction at A) of the beam shown.

(b) Using these influence lines, determine the reactions caused by the loads shown and draw the shear and moment diagrams.

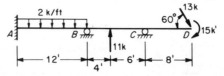

(c) Use the influence lines from part (a) to construct influence lines for shear and moment 8 ft from point A, and shear and moment 15 ft from point D.

(d) Obtain the influence lines required in part (c) by means of a deformeter (Beggs, Eney, Sanks, or Tse types of deformeters are suitable).

(e) Using this beam and any weight, prove Maxwell's law experimentally.

(f) Calibrate rubber bands (or coil springs, which are better), and use them to produce the loads shown acting on the beam. Draw the elastic curve to a suitable scale assuming the beam to be a steel 18 W 50 section with a moment of inertia of 801 in.[4]

*(g) Check all of the reactions by analytical methods.

(h) Check the center deflections and the deflection at point D by analytical methods.

25–2. (a) Construct a wire model of a single-story rigid frame.

(b) Obtain influence lines for each reaction experimentally.

(c) Using these influence lines, determine the reactions caused by load.

(d) Draw the shear and moment diagrams, using the results of part (c).

(e) Check the reactions, the moments, and the shears by analytical methods.

(f) Draw the elastic curve due to load, using the loaded model as an aid.

(g) Compute analytically the deflections at the joints and at the mid-span of each member.

25–3. (a) Construct a model of the arched, rigid frame in the figure.

(b) Obtain influence lines for the reactions considering them to be: (i) 100 percent fixed, (ii) 33 percent fixed, and then (iii) pinned (or 0 percent fixed).

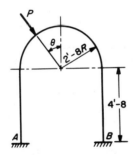

*(c) Plot graphs of θ versus vertical reaction, and determine the position of the load P that will cause the greatest reactions for each condition of fixity. θ varies from 0° to 90°.

(d) Sketch the elastic curves for P acting at $\theta = 45°$ for (i), (ii), and (iii).

25–4. Construct a wire model of a circular prismatic arch with pin-connected supports. Select any convenient span, rise (the rise should fall within 15 to 30 percent of the span), and uniform snow load which acts on the left half only. Keep a record of the time required to:

*(a) Use the model for obtaining the horizontal reaction.

(b) Use your choice of any analytical method for computing the horizontal reaction.

(c) What are your conclusions regarding the relative ease, speed, and accuracy?

25–5. Repeat Prob. 25–2, using a two-story rigid frame and a deformeter to obtain shear, thrust, and moment at some point in the upper story.

25–6. The horseshoe conduit is subjected to two separate load conditions: one vertical and one horizontal as shown.

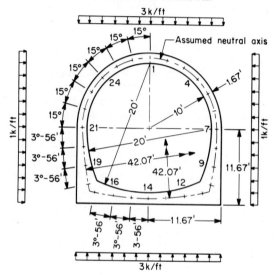

(a) Make a model of plastic, cardboard, or wire.

(b) Cut the model at station 21, insert a deformeter, and obtain horizontal and vertical components of influence lines for moment, thrust, and shear.

*(c) Plot the moment, thrust, and shear diagrams from the influence lines for (i) the vertical loads; (ii) the horizontal loads.

Chapter 26

26–1. A prismatic beam rests upon an elastic foundation. Select the span, moment of inertia, modulus of foundation reaction, a concentrated load, and its point of application. Design a wire model. Use a "slicing" factor to produce a suitable stiffness. Use calibrated rubber bands (or better, coil springs) in opposing pairs to furnish the proper support.

(a) Load the model and obtain the elastic curve.

(b) Determine the maximum moment.

(c) Outline completely an analytical method for obtaining the elastic curve and the maximum moment.

(d) Compare the two methods.

26–2. (*a*) Make a preliminary design of main cables, suspenders, and stiffening elements for a rudimentary suspension bridge to support either pedestrians, or livestock, or single vehicles, and to fit any given set of imposed hypothetical conditions.

(*b*) Select a suitable linear reduction scale and design a model. Select suitable materials and compute model sizes and loads.

(*c*) Construct the model and use it to determine (i) maximum force in the main cable; (ii) maximum deflection; (iii) maximum stress in the stiffening elements; (iv) frequency of vibration for any one load condition.

Chapter 27

27–1. Construct analytically the influence lines required in Probs. 25–1(*a*) and (*c*).

27–2. Construct analytically the influence lines required in Prob. 25–2(*b*).

ANSWERS TO SELECTED PROBLEMS

1-1. (f) $V_A = 0.42$ kip U, $H_A = 9.8$ kips R, $V_D = 13.08$ kips U,
        $H_D = 9.8$ kips L

      (o) $V_A = 3.66$ kips U, $H_A = 2.95$ kips L, $V_C = 7.34$ kips U,
        $H_C = 8.05$ kips L

1-2. (a) $a = 0$, $b = 8$ kips T, $c = 0$, $d = 14.14$ kips C, $e = 0$,
        $f = 4.47$ kips T, $g = 26.9$ kips T, $h = 48$ kips T

      (j) $a = 24.2$ kips T, $b = 0$, $c = 0$, $d = 5$ kips C, $e = 8.95$ kips T,
        $f = 3.82$ kips T, $g = 3.82$ kips C, $h = 7.35$ kips C,
        $i = 17.9$ kips T, $j = 7.07$ kips T

      (r) $a = 17.6$ kips C, $b = 26.8$ kips T, $c = 11.6$ kips C, $d = 3.75$
        kips T, $e = 15.6$ kips T, $f = 12.6$ kips T, $g = 10.5$ kips C,
        $h = 48.1$ kips T

1-3. (e)   Indeterminate but unstable.

2-1. Partial answers:
      (c) $V_{\max} = -wL/4$ at C, $M_C = +wL^2/12$, $M_A = +wL^2/6$
      (o) $V_A = +29.2$ kips, $V_B = -6.8$ kips, $V_{CA} = -30.8$ kips,
        $M_{\max} = +87$ kip-ft, $M_C = -50$ kip-ft
      (w) $V_A = +0.42$ kip, $V_D = -13.08$ kips, $M_{BC} = +34.52$ kip-ft,
        $M_{\max} = 37.06$ kip-ft at 1.59 ft right of C

2-2. (g)

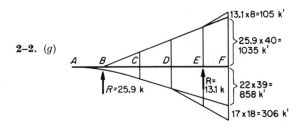

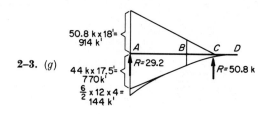

2-3. (g)

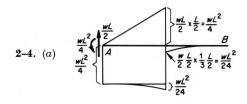

2-4. (a)

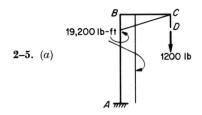

2-5. (a)

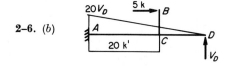

2-6. (b)

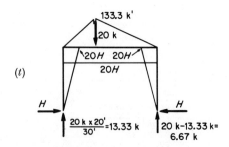

(t)

2-8. (e) From A to B $M = 0.42x$

                B to C $M = 0.42x + 32$

                C to D $M = -0.0556x^3 + 1.833x^2 - 19.747x + 105.94$

2-9. (b) From B to C $\quad M = 3.57x$

C to A $\quad M = 3.57x - (1\text{ kip/ft})\dfrac{(x-4)^2}{2}$

2-10. (c) From C to B $\quad M = -2x^2 + 30.8x - 50$

B to A $\quad M = -\dfrac{x^3}{12} + \dfrac{3x^2}{2} - 2.2x + 40$

2-11. (b) From D to C $\quad M = Vx$

C to A $\quad M = Vx - 20$

(l) $\quad M = Vx - M_B - \dfrac{wx^3}{6L}$

2-12. (c)

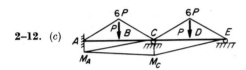

(i)

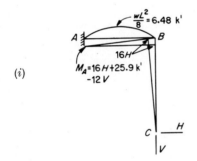

3-1. (a) Area $= 120$ kip-ft^2; centroid at 4.667 ft from A

(g) Area $= \dfrac{wL^3}{8}$; centroid at $\frac{2}{5}L$ from A

4-1. (c) $\Delta_C = \dfrac{PL^3}{2EI}$, $\quad \Delta\theta_C = \dfrac{PL^2}{2EI}$

4-2. (b) $\Delta\theta_C = \dfrac{56}{EI}$, $\quad \Delta_B = \dfrac{192}{EI}$, $\quad \Delta_{\max} = \dfrac{198}{EI}$

4-3. (c) $\Delta_C = \dfrac{PL^3}{2EI}$, $\quad \Delta\theta_C = \dfrac{PL^2}{2EI}$

4-4. (b) $\Delta\theta_C = \dfrac{56}{EI}$, $\quad \Delta_B = \dfrac{192}{EI}$, $\quad \Delta_{\max} = \dfrac{198}{EI}$

5-1. (e) Partial answer: $V_A = \dfrac{5}{8}\,wL$, $M_A = -\dfrac{wL^2}{8}$,

$$V_B = -\dfrac{3}{8}\,wL,$$

$$+M_{\max} = \dfrac{9}{128}\,wL^2 \text{ at } \dfrac{5}{8}\,L \text{ from } A$$

5-2. (e) $\Delta_{\text{ctr}} = \dfrac{wL^4}{192EI}$, $\Delta\theta_B = \dfrac{wL^3}{48EI}$

6-1. (d) Partial answer: $H_C = 0.43$ kip L, $V_C = 3.1$ kips U,
$M_A = -20.6$ kip-ft.

6-2. (b) Partial answer: $H_E = 0.7$ kip L, $V_E = 21.1$ kips U

6-3. (a) $\Delta X_D = 0.76$ in. R, $\Delta Y_D = 1.64$ in. D,
$\Delta\theta_D = 0.0092$ radian CW

6-4. (b) $\Delta X_D = 0$, $\Delta Y_D = 0.28$ in. D

6-5. (g) $H_A = 2.45$ kips L, $V_A = 6.25$ kips D, $H_D = 7.55$ kips L,
$V_D = 6.25$ kips U

6-6. (c) $M_A = 45$ kip-ft, $M_B = 13$ kip-ft, $M_C = 38$ kip-ft, $M_D = 54$ kip-ft

6-7. (d) $V_A = 14.4$ kips U, $V_B = 9.6$ kips U, $H_A = H_B = $ tie
force $= 17.6$ kips T (neglecting tie rod strain). $H = 17.4$ kips
(including tie rod strain)

6-8. (d) See 6–7d

6-9. (a) $H_A = 1.67$ kips R, $V_A = 13.33$ kips U, $V_B = 6.67$,
$H_B = 1.67$ kips L

7-1. (d) $\Delta X_C = 0.67$ in. R

7-2. (e) $\Delta X_A = 1.81$ in. L, $\Delta Y_F = 2.38$ in. D, $\Delta\theta_{CF} = 0.0010$
radian CCW

7-3. (a) $AD = 3.54$ kips T, $BD = 4.11$ kips T, $CD = 4.71$ kips T

7-4. (a) $\Delta X_D = 0.002$ in. R, $\Delta Y_D = 0.020$ in. D

8-1. (a) $\Delta Y_C = \dfrac{PL^3}{2EI}$, $\Delta\theta_C = \dfrac{PL^2}{2EI}$

8-2. (b) $\Delta_{\text{ctr}} = 0.061$ in. D

8-3. (b) $\Delta_{\max} = 0.0611$ in. D, at 5.29 ft from C

8-4. (d) Partial answer: $V_D = 35.4$ lb U

8-5. (d) $\Delta Y_C = 0.20$ in. D

8-6. (a) $\Delta Y_C = \dfrac{PL^3}{2EI}$, $\quad \Delta\theta_C = \dfrac{PL^2}{2EI}$

8-7. (b) $\Delta_{\text{ctr}} = 0.061$ in. D

8-8. (b) $\Delta_{\max} = 0.0611$ in. D at 5.29 ft from C

8-9. (d) Partial answer: $V_D = 35.3$ lb. U

8-10. (d) Partial answer: $\Delta_{\text{ctr } AB} = 0.094$ in. D, $\quad \Delta_{\text{ctr } BD} = 0.228$ in. D
$$\Delta\theta_D = 0.022 \text{ radian CCW}$$

9-1. (b) Partial answer: $H_D = 0.58$ kip R, $\quad V_D = 0$

9-2. (a) $\Delta X_D = 0.75$ in. R, $\quad \Delta Y_D = 1.65$ in. D,
$\Delta\theta_E = 0.0092$ radian CW

9-3. (b) $\Delta_D = 0.28$ in. D

9-4. (c) $V_D = 1.99$ kips U, $\quad H_D = 4.23$ kips L

9-5. (d) $V_E = 21.8$ kips U, $\quad H_E = 0.99$ kip L

10-2. (a) $M_A = 391$ kip-ft, $\quad M_B = 126$ kip-ft

10-3. (a) $M_A = 45$ kip-ft, $M_B = 13$ kip-ft, $M_C = 38$ kip-ft,
$M_D = 54$ kip-ft

11-1. (a) $\dfrac{\Delta_{\text{shear}}}{\Delta_{\text{flexure}}} = \dfrac{1}{28.5}\dfrac{E}{G}$

11-2. (a) $M_C = -16.6$ kip-ft, tie tension $= 3.96$ kips

12-1. (a) Partial answer: $M_A = 614$ kip-ft, $\quad V_A = 102.6$ kips,
$M_B = 115$ kip-ft, $\quad V_B = 68.0$ kips
$M_C = 143$ kip-ft, $\quad V_C = 64.6$ kips
$M_D = 0$, $\quad V_D = 52.8$ kips

13-1. (a) $M_A = 9$ kip-ft, $M_B = 17$ kip-ft, $M_C = 18$ kip-ft, $M_D = 0$

13-2. (a) $M_{AC} = -44$ kip-ft, $M_{CA} = +111$ kip-ft, $K_{CA} = 22{,}030$ kip-ft,
$C_{AC} = 0.645$

13-3. (b) Partial answer: $M_A = 6$ kip-ft, $M_{CD} = 53$ kip-ft
$M_D = 6$ kip-ft, $M_E = 0$

(f) See Prob. 6-6(c)

14-1. (b) Partial answer: $M_{AB} = 30$ kip-ft CCW $M_{BA} = 19$ kip-ft CCW,
$M_{BC} = 8$ kip-ft CW, $\quad M_{CB} = 19$ kip-ft CW,
$M_{DE} = 39$ kip-ft CCW, $M_{ED} = 37$ kip-ft CCW,
$M_{EF} = 58$ kip-ft CCW, $M_{FE} = 17$ kip-ft CCW

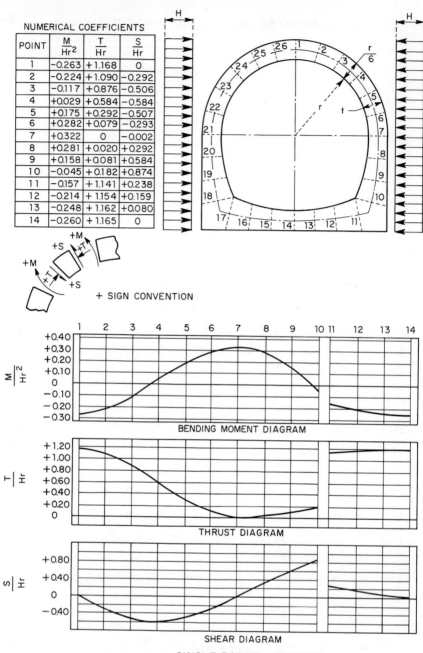

NUMERICAL COEFFICIENTS

POINT	$\dfrac{M}{Hr^2}$	$\dfrac{T}{Hr}$	$\dfrac{S}{Hr}$
1	−0.263	+1.168	0
2	−0.224	+1.090	−0.292
3	−0.117	+0.876	−0.506
4	+0.029	+0.584	−0.584
5	+0.175	+0.292	−0.507
6	+0.282	+0.079	−0.293
7	+0.322	0	−0.002
8	+0.281	+0.020	+0.292
9	+0.158	+0.081	+0.584
10	−0.045	+0.182	+0.874
11	−0.157	+1.141	+0.238
12	−0.214	+1.154	+0.159
13	−0.248	+1.162	+0.080
14	−0.260	+1.165	0

+ SIGN CONVENTION

BENDING MOMENT DIAGRAM

THRUST DIAGRAM

SHEAR DIAGRAM

SINGLE BARREL CONDUIT
BEGGS DEFORMETER STRESS ANALYSIS
COEFFICIENTS FOR MOMENT, THRUST, AND SHEAR
SHAPE A $t = \dfrac{r}{6}$
UNIFORM LATERAL LOAD−BOTH SIDES

Courtesy of the U. S. Bureau of Reclamation.

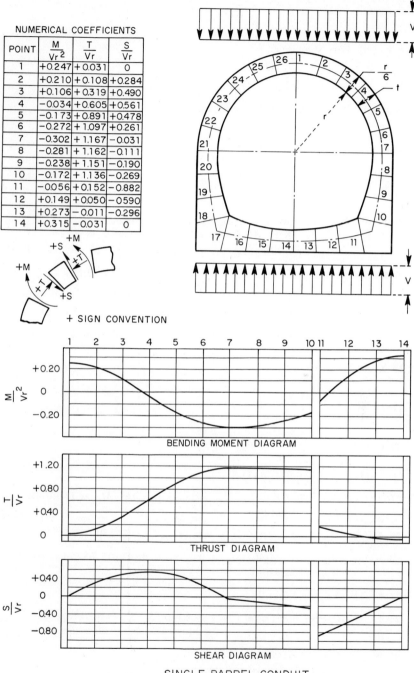

NUMERICAL COEFFICIENTS

POINT	$\dfrac{M}{Vr^2}$	$\dfrac{T}{Vr}$	$\dfrac{S}{Vr}$
1	+0.247	+0.031	0
2	+0.210	+0.108	+0.284
3	+0.106	+0.319	+0.490
4	−0.034	+0.605	+0.561
5	−0.173	+0.891	+0.478
6	−0.272	+1.097	+0.261
7	−0.302	+1.167	−0.031
8	−0.281	+1.162	−0.111
9	−0.238	+1.151	−0.190
10	−0.172	+1.136	−0.269
11	−0.056	+0.152	−0.882
12	+0.149	+0.050	−0.590
13	+0.273	−0.011	−0.296
14	+0.315	−0.031	0

+ SIGN CONVENTION

BENDING MOMENT DIAGRAM

THRUST DIAGRAM

SHEAR DIAGRAM

SINGLE BARREL CONDUIT
BEGGS DEFORMETER STRESS ANALYSIS
COEFFICIENTS FOR MOMENT, THRUST, AND SHEAR
SHAPE A $t = \dfrac{r}{6}$
UNIFORM VERTICAL LOAD − UNIFORM FOUNDATION REACTION

Courtesy of the U. S. Bureau of Reclamation.

14–2. (*a*)   Partial answer:

$$H_D = H \, \frac{1/F_d}{1/F_{abc} + 1/F_d} \quad \text{where} \quad F_{abc} = \frac{1}{1/F_a + 1/F_b} + F_c$$

14–3. (*e*)   Partial answer: $M_B = 86$ kip-ft, $M_C = 87$ kip-ft,
$M_D = 145$ kip-ft

16–1. (*a*) $M_{AB} = 158$ kip-ft, $M_{BA} = 86$ kip-ft, $M_{BC} = 50$ kip-ft,
$M_{BE} = 136$ kip-ft, $M_{CB} = 222$ kip-ft

16–2. (*a*)   Partial answer: $DE = 12.07$ kips C, $EF = 14.19$ kips C,
$AG = 18.27$ kips T, $AH = 1.21$ kips C

16–4. (*c*)   Partial answers (in P-ft) to first approximation:
$M_{AB} = -5.3P, M_{BA} = -4.8P, M_{CB} = -3.7P, M_{DC} = -1.5P,$
$M_{ab} = -5.1P, \ M_{ba} = -4.9P, \ M_{cb} = -3.5P, \ M_{dc} = -1.5P$

16–5. (*a*)   Partial answer: $M_{AB} = +5$ kip-ft, $M_{BA} = -52$ kip-ft,
$M_{BC} = -57$ kip-ft, $M_{\text{ctr } AB} = +57$ kip-ft

17–1. (*c*)   Partial answer: $\Delta X_C = 0.011$ in. R, $\Delta Y_C = 0.034$ in. D

17–2. (*a*)   Partial answer: $\Delta X_A = 1.8$ in. L, $\Delta Y_F = 2.4$ in. D

18–1. (*a*) $V_A = \dfrac{5}{8} wL, \quad M_A = \dfrac{wL^2}{8}, \quad V_B = \dfrac{3}{8} wL$

19–1. (*a*) $\Delta_B = \dfrac{Pa^2b^2}{3EIL}$

20–1. (*a*) $\Delta_C = \dfrac{PL^3}{2EI}, \qquad \Delta\theta_C = \dfrac{PL^2}{2EI}$

   (*j*) $\Delta U_2 = 0.024$ in. D

21–1. (*c*) $M_A = 70.5$ kip-ft, $M_B = 28.5$ kip-ft D, $M_C = 11$ kip-ft,
$M_D = 10$ kip-ft

22–1. (*c*) $M_A = 80$ kip-ft, $M_B = 9$ kip-ft, $M_C = 75$ kip-ft

23–1. (*a*) $M_A = 16.5$ kip-ft, $M_B = 9.5$ kip-ft, $M_C = 17.7$ kip-ft,
$M_D = 15.2$ kip-ft

24–1. (*k*) $\Delta Y_D = 3.5$ in. D

25–1. (*g*)   Partial answer: $M_A = -49.6$ kip-ft, $V_A = 18.4$ kips U,
$V_B = 14.2$ kips D, $V_C = 20.1$ kips U

25–3. (*c*)   Partial answer:
Maximum pinned reactions:
$V_A = 0.84P$ D   at $\theta = 90°$, $V_B = 1.02P$ U   at $\theta = 58°$
$H_A = 0.61P$ L   at $\theta = 90°$, $H_B = 0.42P$ L   at $\theta = 68°$

Maximum fixed reactions:

$V_A = 0.50P$ U at $\theta = 0°$, $V_B = 0.55P$ U at $\theta = 21°$
$H_A = 0.70P$ L at $\theta = 90°$, $H_B = 0.39P$ L at $\theta = 56°$
$M_A = 23.5P$ in.   at $\theta = 90°$, $M_B = 16.8P$ in.   at $\theta = 63°$

25–4. Refer to J. Michalos, "Direct Design of Two-Hinged Arches of Constant Section," *Civil Engineering* (January, 1956), pp. 65–68; or to J. Michalos, *Theory of Structural Analysis and Design* (New York: The Ronald Press Company, 1958), Chap. 6.

25–6. See pages 590-591.

INDEX